SERPENTINE
AND ITS VEGETATION

SERPENTINE AND ITS VEGETATION

A Multidisciplinary Approach

by

Robert Richard Brooks, Ph.D.

Ecology, Phytogeography & Physiology Series
VOLUME 1
Theodore R. Dudley, Ph.D., General Editor

DIOSCORIDES PRESS
Portland, Oregon

ISBN 0-931146-04-6
Printed in Hong Kong

DIOSCORIDES PRESS
9999 SW Wilshire
Portland, Oregon 97225

CONTENTS

Chapter 21
NEW ZEALAND

PREFACE

My first introduction to serpentine and serpentine vegetation was in the middle 1960s when I visited the "Mineral Belt" in South Island of New Zealand and was immediately struck by the sharp vegetation boundary between ultramafites and sediments. It was as if the area had been partially ravaged by fire, with the stunted serpentine vegetation contrasting with the luxuriant forest of the limestone. That first impression remains with me to this day and has endowed me with an abiding interest in serpentine and its vegetation, an interest which has resulted in the appearance of this book.

At the time of my first visit to a serpentine area, the only general source material was a 1958 paper (in German) by W. Krause (who is still active today) entitled "Andere Bodenspezialisten." It was not until 1975 that the next review appeared, a paper in English by J. Proctor and S. R. J. Woodell entitled "The ecology of serpentine soils." Finally another German publication appeared in 1982, a paper by H. Kinzel with the title "Serpentin-Pflanzen."

Despite the appearance of the above reviews which might have been expected to stimulate interest in the field, it is indeed surprising that no book on the subject of serpentine ecology and floras has yet appeared. It was to redress this deficiency that I began this present work with the aim of presenting to a very wide spectrum of readers, a broad overview, in English, of the entire field. By means of an extensive bibliography of about 900 citations it is intended that those who wish to study the subject more deeply may do so by referring to the appropriate references.

Somewhat naively, I had originally imagined that it would be possible to cover the entire field in a book of quite modest proportions, but it immediately became obvious that such was not to be the case. Nearly 1000 references were uncovered, and I was also overwhelmed by the volume of illustrative material, primarily colour slides, which friends and colleagues in New Zealand and overseas kindly donated to me. To write a book on serpentine and its environment is an endless task because of the continual discovery of fresh material, so that finally ceasing the research, required a certain degree of self-discipline. When I began to assemble the data therefore, I was conscious that some of the newest material would have to be omitted, but am reasonably satisfied that no important reference predating 1985 has been omitted.

This work would not have been possible without the kind assistance of a large number of people in a number of countries, who supplied documents and information and donated illustrative material. My warmest thanks are therefore extended to the following, designated by countries: Austria (K. H. Rechinger), Britain (A. J. M. Baker, J. Dransfield, J. Proctor and D. R. Slingsby), Canada (P. Dearden and T. R. Moore), Corsica (M. Conrad), Germany (W. Krause, D. Johannes and F. Sasse), Greece (D. Balalonas), Holland (M. M. J. van Balgooy and A. de Vogel), Italy (R. Gabbrielli, M. Guido, C. Montanari and O. Vergnano Gambi), Japan (N. Doi, K. Ishizuka, S. Nosaka and The National Trust of Japan), New Caledonia (T. Jaffré), New Zealand (L. Homer, W. G. Lee, L. F. Molloy, J. Rhodes, M. J. B. Sedborough, R. D. Reeves and the late W. R. Lauder), South Africa (K. Balkwill), Spain (F. F. Guitian Ojea), United States (A. R. Kruckeberg, D. Ela, T. Nelson, Mary Gamble and R. B. Walker), and Zimbabwe (A. I. Robertson and M. D. Prendergast). Thanks are also due to Mrs J. M. Trow for most of the line drawings which accompany this book and to the many colleagues who reviewed the text.

A number of individuals, institutions, private companies and funding organisations which helped in providing finance, logistic support in the field or the provision of laboratory facilities, also deserve my thanks. They include: R. D. Batt of Massey University; T. R. Dudley of the U.S. National Arboretum; R. M. McFarlane of San Francisco; L. E. Smythe of the University of New South Wales; Australian Selection Pty. and Western Mining Corporation of Western Australia; Lime and Marble Ltd. of New Zealand; T. Jaffré of O.R.S.T.O.M., Nouméa, New Caledonia; and the Mineral Resources Subcommittee of the New Zealand University Grants Committee.

I would also like to thank many of my former students such as: W. J. Kersten, J. Lee, G. L. Lyon, M. T. Lyons, R. S. Morrison, J. S. Nielsen, C. C. Radford, B. C. Severne, S. Shaw and E. D. Wither for their hard work in the field and in the laboratory, and for producing many excellent theses on the subject of serpentine and its ecology, which have allowed me to enhance my knowledge of this subject.

It is only when a list of acknowledgements is prepared that an author becomes fully aware of the extent of his dependence on others and I thank all those who have helped me in this work either directly or indirectly.

My final word is this: the aim of this book is to reach a wide spectrum of scientists and laymen by above all simplicity of presentation while at the same time providing adequate citations for deeper study. To what extent I have achieved this aim, only time will tell, but if I have succeeded in contributing in any measure to a stimulation of interest in the subject of serpentine and its vegetation, then I will be well satisfied.

R. R. Brooks

Palmerston North, New Zealand
September, 1985

PART ONE

SERPENTINE ECOLOGY

Chapter 1
GENERAL INTRODUCTION

From the Arctic tundra to the tropical rainforest, ultramafic rocks support a highly unusual flora distinguishable from its surroundings both in physiognomy and in species composition. The most common effect of this rock type upon the vegetation is to produce a xeromorphic impoverished flora, poor in species and individuals. Sometimes these differences are so pronounced that the geology can be mapped from the air from the vegetation patterns alone.

Ultramafic rocks have been recognised from their floral cover for several hundred years, well before the edaphic reasons for the development of such vegetation had been established. We find for example in Tuscany, the 16th century botanist A. Caesalpino recognising in 1583 the presence of an "alyson" (*Alyssum bertolonii*) growing over "black stones" of the Upper Tiber Valley, and Sir Joseph Banks in 1770 recording an ochre-coloured mountain on the west coast of South Island, New Zealand during his voyage with Captain Cook. This mountain was aptly named "Red Mountain" and is shown in Plate 1.1a.

In far-off Japan, scientists and local people had long recognised the unusual flora which covered Mt Hayachine in northern Honshu and many other ultramafic massifs in Hokkaido. Mt Hayachine is shown in Plate 1.1b where it lies to the left of the granite mass of Mt Yakushi and is characterised not only by the reddish brown colour of the serpentine, but also by the much lower tree line. The serpentine flora of Mt Hayachine was studied in the period 1868–1879 by the eminent Russian botanist C. J. Maximowicz using plants collected by C. Sukawa in 1868. The serpentine massifs of Red Mountain and Mt Hayachine represent two very good examples of vegetational discontinuities across a boundary involving ultramafic and non-ultramafic rocks.

Before beginning a study of the ecology of ultramafites and of their floras, a very important point must first be established. The term "serpentine" *sensu stricto* refers specifically to the minerals antigorite and chrysotile (asbestos) which have the general formula $(Mg_3Si_2O_5(OH)_4$. These minerals are derived from the "serpentinization" of ultramafic rocks. There is, however, a tendency for some workers to classify all ultramafic rocks under the general heading of serpentine; and the problem is further compounded by the insistance of botanists of always referring to ultramafic floras as "serpentine floras", whether the soils are derived from serpentinized rocks or not. Although the term "ultramafic flora" is certainly more accurate, it is used mainly by specialists, so that to attempt to re-educate the broad masses of non-specialist scientists or laymen would be a painful and tedious process. Mindful of the old adage: "If you can't beat them, join them," I have therefore decided to use in this book the terms *serpentine* as well as *ultramafic* to describe the floras and sometimes use the former appellation to describe ultramafic rocks in general. When the mineral serpentine is specifically intended to be described, this will be evident from the context of the book.

Although ultramafic rocks occupy only a very small part of the land surface of the earth (<1%), they have an importance which far outweighs this small extent. They are, for example, hosts for asbestos and the important minerals of nickel, cobalt and chromium, and are so infertile that few areas can be used for agriculture. Their unusual and highly-specialised floras have been for many years targets for botanists, plant physiologists, phytochemists, plant geographers and scientists from many other disciplines whose roles will be uncovered in the following pages of this book.

Because of the multitude of topics covered in this work, it has been divided into two parts. Part I may be considered loosely as "The ecology of serpentine" including such diverse subjects as: the nature, composition and distribution of ultramafic rocks; the serpentine factor (reasons for the infertility of serpentine soils); plant evolution; animals and serpentine; the phytochemistry of serpentinophytes; and the floras of kimberlites and carbonatites.

Part II of this book is a guided tour of serpentine floras of the world and is introduced separately in Chapter 10 so that nothing more will be said about this second section at this stage.

One of the greatest problems facing the English-speaking student of serpentine and its floras is that only about 70% of the literature is in the English language. Table 1.1 is a breakdown of some 900 "serpentine" papers among the various languages of these publications and shows that in descending order, the main languages are: English (70.9%), German (7.9%), French (6.6%) and Italian (4.1%). If, however, a specific region such as southern Europe is chosen, the pattern is very different and gives the following order: German (28.9%), Italian (19.0%), English (17.5%), Spanish (8.4%), French (6.9%), and Czech (6.8%). Most students of the subject can presumably cope to some extent with English, German, French or Italian, but the problem presented by Russian, or perhaps Serbo-Croat is usually of a very different order.

A knowledge of a few foreign languages is clearly a *sine qua non* for the proper understanding of the serpentine floras of some parts of the world. A good example is the use of the German language for papers on plant sociology, a subject not taught in many English-speaking countries. Even Japanese papers on the subject tend to be written in German or at least have a German abstract. The problem of language has been addressed in this book only to the extent that it is written in the English language. It is intended primarily as a review of the entire field with an emphasis on simplicity to afford the maximum advantage to a multidisciplinary readership. The literature review is meant for those who want to study a certain region or subject more deeply but then the student is on his own, with only the language barrier to surmount.

As implied above, the purpose of this book is to bring together in a single volume in the English language, elements of many scientific disciplines recorded in many different languages and involving such diverse topics as: botany, zoology, geology, geochemistry, biogeography, phytochemistry, ecology, plant physiology, and phytosociology. The lack of a broad overview is one of the continuing problems in today's scientific world. The saying that: "An expert is someone who knows more and more about less and less, until he finally knows everything about nothing," is rather more than just a facetious comment. It has a certain ring of truth about it. In no field is interdisciplinary co-operation more necessary than in the study of serpentine and its vegetation. Yet we hesitate to stray from the confines of our own discipline and are unaware of what others are doing. To break down these artificial barriers is the ultimate purpose of this book, and I will be well satisfied if this aim can be achieved, however modestly.

TABLE 1.1   The Languages of Papers Concerned with Serpentine Ecology and Floristics

Language	Number of papers	Percentage of total
English	641	70.9
German	71	7.9
French	60	6.6
Italian	37	4.1
Russian	26	2.9
Spanish	19	2.1
Japanese	14	1.5
Czech	11	1.2
Serbo-Croat	6	0.6
Polish	5	0.5
Portuguese	5	0.5
Finnish	5	0.5
Norwegian	5	0.5
Hungarian	2	0.2
Swedish	1	0.1
Dutch	1	0.1

Chapter 2
THE NATURE, OCCURRENCE, AND COMPOSITION OF ULTRAMAFIC ROCKS

2.1 INTRODUCTION

The term "serpentine" is but one of a bewildering array of names which loosely describe a particular class of rock giving rise to the so-called "serpentine soils" which support "serpentine floras." The origin of the term "serpentine" as applied to rocks and minerals has been discussed by Faust and Fahey (1962). In its narrowest sense it applies only to the serpentine group of minerals (including antigorite and chrysotile) which have the general formula $Mg_3Si_2O_5(OH)_4$ and which are important constituents of weathered "ultramafic rocks." Rocks which are rich in serpentine minerals derived from the alteration of previously existing olivines and pyroxenes are known as "serpentinites." The definition of these and other terms is given in Table 2.1. For a fuller discussion of nomenclature the two fundamental textbooks on the subject (Wyllie, 1967 and Coleman, 1977) are invaluable reference sources.

A somewhat more specific definition of serpentine rocks is afforded by the terms "ultramafic" or "ultrabasic". The former implies >70% ferromagnesian minerals, whereas the latter refers to rocks containing <45% silica. These two terms are nevertheless confusing, particularly as rocks such as anorthite (43.2% SiO_2), nephelinite (42.3% SiO_2), and limestone (zero SiO_2) are ultrabasic but obviously not ultramafic. The term ultramafic is clearly preferable and though there have been moves to remove "ultrabasic" from the literature, its use still persists, particularly in Europe. In this book, however, the term ultramafic will be used where appropriate. Because the term "serpentine" is too well established to be removed from the geological vocabulary, it will be used in this book as a synonym for "ultramafic" or "ultramafite". Where it is intended to refer to the mineral, this will be obvious from the context.

TABLE 2.1 The Nomenclature of "Serpentine" Rock Types

Term	Minerals or rocks described
Serpentine	Antigorite and/or chrysotile minerals ($Mg_3Si_2O_5(OH_4)$)
Serpentinite	Rock composed of serpentine minerals.
Ultramafic rock	Rock containing high concentrations of magnesium (ma) and iron (f) hence the term ultramafic. Contains >70% mafic minerals.
Ultrabasic rock	Rocks with <45% silica.
Ophiolite	Originally serpentinite but later modified (see text) to include ultramafic rock assemblages some of whose constituents are not necessarily ultramafites.
Ultramafites	Ultramafic rocks.

2.2 ULTRAMAFIC ROCK ASSOCIATIONS

Wyllie (1967) has listed 9 ultramafic rock associations. An abbreviated version of these (Coleman, 1977) is given below:

1. Layered gabbro-norite-peridotite associations in major intrusions such as at Stillwater, Great Dyke, Bushveld, Muskox and Skaergaard.

2. Ultramafic rocks in differentiated basic sills such as at Skye.

3. Concentrically-zoned dunite-peridotite associations such as at Duke Island, Alaska and The Urals.

4. Alpine-type peridotite-serpentinite associations (ophiolites) such as in Papua, Newfoundland, Cyprus and Oman.

5. Minor associates of batholithic complexes such as at Sierra Nevada.

6. Alkalic ultramafic rocks in ring complexes such as at Magnet Cove, and The Kola Peninsula.

7. Kimberlites such as in South Africa and Arizona.

8. Ultramafic lavas such as in Canada, Western Australia and South Africa.

9. Ultramafic nodules such as in alkaline basalt from places such as Hawaii and Arizona.

The above classification clearly distinguishes the alpine-type peridotite-serpentine associations (ophiolites) from all others. The term "ophiolite" was originally used to refer to the rock type serpentinite (Brongniart, 1827). Ophiolites are the subject of an excellent book (Coleman, 1977) which is at the same time a useful reference for ultramafic rocks in general. The appellation ophiolite was later used by Steinmann (1927) to include an entire association of consanguineous rocks known as the "Steinmann Trinity" (Fig. 2.1), some of which are not ultramafic in nature at all. He described the magmatic evolution of the rock suite as follows:

First the main body of the ultrabasic mass solidifies as peridotite, then follows the gabbro (the 'eufotide' of the Italians) and associated pyroxenitic dikes (now represented by nephrite and carcaro) and finally diabase-spilite with variolitic border zones (the 'gabbro rosso' and 'verde' of the Italians) after which come copper-bearing metalliferous veins that cut the gabbro, diabase-spilite, and the sedimentary wall rocks. The densest and volatile-poor components are thus the first to solidify, but this is not merely to be explained by gravity separation as has been assumed by Staub (1922) for the alpine serpentines. If it were, the still fluid rest-magma from which feldspathic rocks crystallized must always overlie the serpentines, whereas they actually break through from below. Much more likely, we are dealing with a differentiation independent of gravity stratification, with the lighter masses always remaining in deeper magma pockets. The second differentiation process followed in the same way, with the diabase-spilite and the mineralizing fluids remaining at depth while the gabbro rose. The relative abundance of fugitive constituents in the latest member of the series is emphasized by the filling of the spilite pillow interstices and varioles with secondary minerals, quartz in the copper veins and the steatitization of the wall rocks as well as certain phenomena of contact metamorphism associated with the spilite.

The distribution of the ophiolitic belts throughout the world is shown in Fig. 2.2. These belts are closely associated with tectonic plate boundaries.

In the collection of papers edited by Wyllie (1967), a mantle origin was favoured for most ultramafic rocks. Later, other workers (Coleman, 1971; Dewey and Bird, 1971; Davies, 1971; Moores and Vine, 1971; Church, 1972) suggested that fragments of the oceanic lithosphere had been thrust over or into (obducted) continental margins at consuming plate

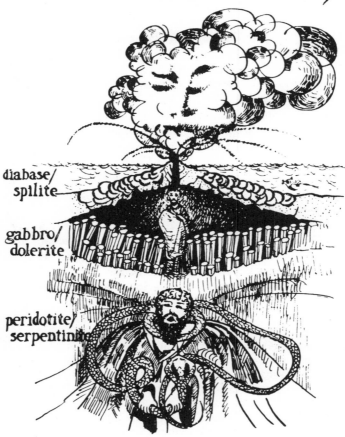

Fig. 2.1   The Steinmann Trinity depicting the nature of ophiolites.
Source: Coleman (1977). After a cartoon by E. den Tex.

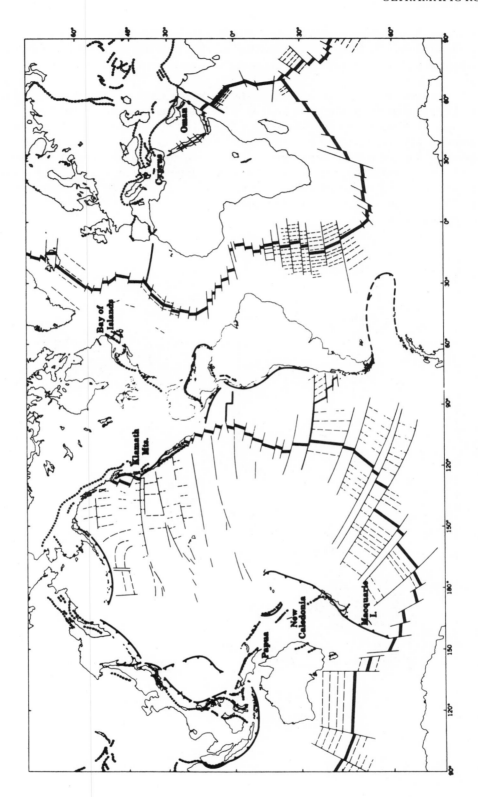

Fig. 2.2 The distribution of ophiolitic belts throughout the world.
Source: Coleman (1977).

margins. This is obvious from Fig. 2.2, and a further illustration is provided by the New Zealand Ophiolitic Belt (Fig. 2.3) situated exclusively along the New Zealand Alpine Fault which is a plate boundary where the two plates have been mutually displaced by some 450 km.

In spite of the progress made in recent years, there is still not complete unanimity concerning the definition of ophiolites. This task has been attempted by the Geological Society of America Penrose Conference (Anon, 1972), as reported by Coleman (1977). An ophiolite was here defined as a distinctive assemblage of mafic to ultramafic rocks comprised of (bottom to top): ultramafic complex—gabbroic complex—mafic sheeted dike complex—mafic volcanic complex. Associated rock types include: 1. an overlying sedimentary section typically including ribbon cherts, thin shale interbeds and minor limestones; 2. podiform bodies of chromite generally associated with dunite; 3. sodic felsic intrusive and extrusive rocks.

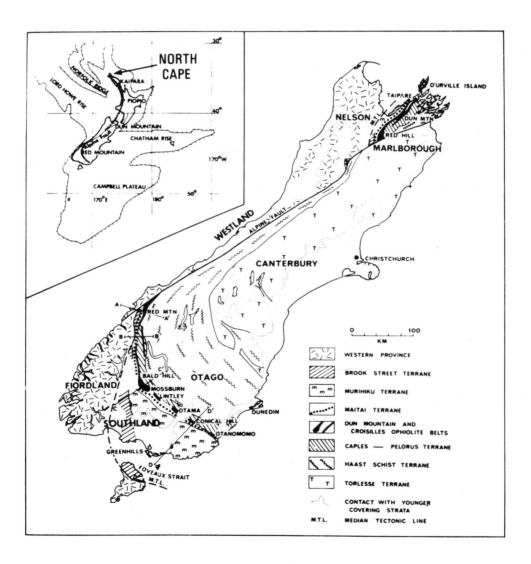

Fig. 2.3   The New Zealand ophiolitic belt.
Source: Coombs et al. (1976)

2.3 THE MINERALOGY AND MAJOR ELEMENT COMPOSITION OF ULTRAMAFIC ROCKS

Ultramafic rocks are composed essentially of the minerals olivine, clinopyroxene, orthopyroxene, amphibole, biotite and serpentine. Each of the ultramafic minerals is represented by a monomineralic ultramafic rock such as dunite (olivine), pyroxenite (pyroxene), hornblendite (amphibole), and biotitite (biotite). Peridotites are olivine-rich rocks containing pyroxene but little or no felspar.

Den Tex (1969) has suggested that peridotites be divided into non-orogenic (stratiform) and alpine types. The latter were to be subdivided into "true" alpine peridotites and orogenic "root zone" types. In the broadest sense, ultramafic rocks are sometimes described as ophiolites though it should never be forgotten that the latter term also embraces non-ultramafic rock types within gabbroic, mafic sheeted and mafic volcanic complexes, and it must also be remembered that ultramafites embrace rocks other than ophiolites. Coleman (1977) has used the term "metamorphic peridotites" (the "harzburgite" subtype of Nicolas and Jackson, 1972) to describe the ultramafites found at the basal parts of the ophiolitic sequences.

The modal proportions (vol %) of minerals in ultramafic rock types in metamorphic peridotites are shown in Fig. 2.4 which clearly shows the restricted range of composition of these peridotites and compares them with the so-called "metamorphic lherzolites." In the

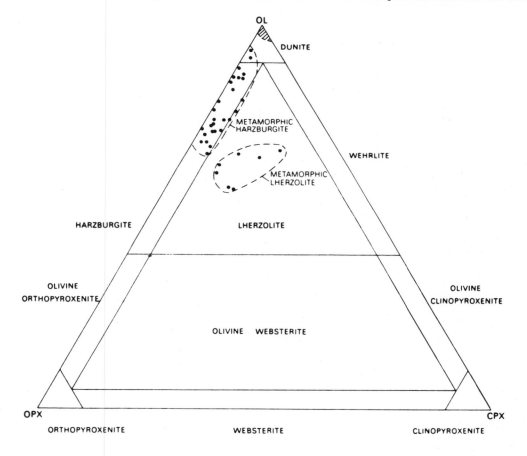

Fig. 2.4 Modal proportions of olivine, orthopyroxene and clinopyroxene in harzburgites and dunites from ophiolitic metamorphic peridotites.
Source: Coleman (1977).

progression from dunite to harzburgite, the amounts of orthopyroxene and clinopyroxene lie separately in the same range, but the latter mineral never seems to constitute >5% and orthopyroxene does not exceed 30%. The metamorphic lherzolites correspond with the orogenic root zone peridotites of Den Tex (1969) (see above) and consist almost entirely of ultramafic material with higher concentrations of aluminium, calcium and alkali metals compared with harzburgite subtypes associated with ophiolites.

Olivines from metamorphic peridotites have a very consistent MgO/(MgO + FeO) ratio when major element compositions are normalized after removal of water and carbon dioxide. Table 2.2 compares the major element composition of dunites, harzburgites and lherzolites. Values from other rock types are also given for comparison. Normalization after loss of water and carbon dioxide compensates for the different degrees of serpentinization which may have occurred in the ultramafic rocks listed.

Certain trends in Table 2.2 are immediately obvious. The first of these is the much higher concentrations of total iron, magnesium, cobalt, chromium and nickel compared with non-ultramafic rocks. The second trend is the low concentrations of aluminium, calcium, potassium and sodium in ultramafites.

TABLE 2.2   The Chemical Composition (major elements) of Ultramafic and Other Rock Types

Component	A	B	C	D	E	F	G	H
SiO_2	35.80	41.10	56.00	44.62	40.49	70.18	48.24	79.66
Al_2O_3	0.15	0.10	2.05	3.66	0.65	14.47	17.88	5.78
FeO	4.80	5.55	2.00	7.58	4.84	1.78	5.95	0.30
Fe_2O_3	2.80	1.70	2.94	0.59	6.01	1.57	3.16	1.58
MgO	44.30	44.33	34.92	38.98	37.36	0.88	7.51	1.67
MnO	0.10	0.10	0.19	0.13	0.22	0.12	0.13	0.01
CaO	0.16	0.20	0.60	3.31	0.74	1.99	10.99	6.52
Na_2O	0.05	0.09	0.03	0.26	0.15	3.48	2.55	0.45
K_2O	0.03	0.02	0.03	0.01	0.10	4.11	0.89	1.32
TiO_2	0.10	0.10	0.06	0.14	0.65	0.30	0.97	0.25
NiO	0.38	0.32	0.15	0.27	0.30	0.005	0.02	0.001
Cr_2O_3	0.27	0.27	0.60	0.33	0.50	0.005	0.01	0.001
CoO	0.03	0.03	0.03	0.02	0.02	0.005	0.01	0.002
H_2O	10.60	4.70	0.05	*	8.18	0.84	1.45	2.33
Total (%)	99.57	98.60	99.65	100.00	100.20	99.74	99.76	99.67

A —Dunite, New Caledonia (Trescases, 1975)
B —Harzburgite, New Caledonia (Guillon, 1975)
C —Pyroxenite, New Caledonia (Guillon, 1975)
D —Lherzolite, Serrania de Ronda (Dickey, 1970)
E —Av. ultramafic rocks (Krause, 1958)
F —Av. granites (Krause, 1958)
G —Av. granites (Krause, 1958)
H—Av. sandstones (Krause, 1958)
* —normalized to water-free and carbonate-free basis

2.4 SERPENTINIZATION OF ULTRAMAFIC ROCKS

The process of serpentinization involves the conversion of a peridotite to serpentine mainly by hydration of primary igneous minerals. Examples of such processes are shown below (Coleman, 1977):

$$2Mg_2SiO_4 + 3H_2O = Mg_3Si_2O_5(OH)_4 + Mg(OH)_2 \qquad \ldots \ldots \ldots (2.1)$$
olivine $\qquad\qquad$ serpentine $\qquad$ brucite

$$2Mg_2SiO_4 + 2H_2O = Mg_3Si_2O_5(OH)_4 + MgO \qquad \ldots \ldots \ldots (2.2)$$
olivine $\qquad\qquad$ serpentine $\qquad$ must be removed

$$3MgSiO_4 + 4H_2O + SiO_2 = 2Mg_3Si_2O_5(OH)_4 \qquad \ldots \ldots \ldots (2.3)$$
serpentine

From equations 2.2 and 2.3 it will be noted that olivine is converted to serpentine only by removal of MgO or addition of silica. If the excess MgO is converted to brucite (equation 2.1), then dunite can be converted to serpentine only by addition of water. Serpentine minerals typically contain 12–13.5% water.

Conversion of peridotite to serpentine is a metasomatic process in which there is change of composition of the rock involved. Experimental evidence (Wenner and Taylor, 1974) indicates that most serpentinization occurs at temperatures between 100–300°C. Apart from the introduction of water, another chemical change which occurs during serpentinization is the partial oxidation of iron to magnetite. This is taken into account when using the ratio MgO/(MgO + FeO) to classify ultramafic rocks. The ratio is 0.86 for dunites, 0.85 for harzburgites and 0.84 for lherzolites.

The Fe^{3+}/Fe^{2+} ratio in serpentines reflects changes in the alteration of iron during serpentinization since the original FeO content of dunites, harzburgites and lherzolites is about the same. During serpentinization, the partition of iron among serpentine, brucite, magnetite and awaruite depends on the availability of oxygen.

2.5 TRACE ELEMENTS IN ULTRAMAFIC ROCKS

A knowledge of trace element abundances in ultramafic rocks is an essential prerequisite to an appreciation of the role that these elements play in plant nutrition, and by inference, in controlling the type of vegetation that can be supported by serpentine-derived soils. Until the 1960s it was not easy to obtain reliable data for trace element concentrations in the various rock types for want of analytical methods with sufficient speed, sensitivity and precision to carry out the very large number of reliable analyses required for the compilation of such data. In the past two decades however, the rapid development of techniques such as atomic absorption spectrometry, x-ray fluorescence spectrometry and more recently plasma emission spectrometry (ICP) has rendered possible this important task. Table 2.3 lists trace elements in ultramafic and non-ultramafic rock types.

As a general rule, the siderophile (iron-loving) elements such as cobalt, chromium, iron and nickel are strongly enriched in ultramafites relative to other rock types, whereas plant nutrients such as calcium, nitrogen, phosphorus and potassium have much lower relative abundances. This is of course of great significance for the nature of the vegetation cover of ultramafic rocks and will be discussed further in chapter 4.

The relatively high concentrations of cobalt and nickel in ultramafic rocks are largely because the ionic radii (0.072 and 0.069 nm respectively) of their divalent states are very close to that of Mg^{2+} (0.072 nm) so that ionic substitution into magnesium-rich minerals such as olivine and pyroxene which are dominant in ultramafic rocks readily occurs. Chromium is enriched in ultramafic rocks because Cr^{3+} (r = 0.064 nm) readily substitutes in Fe^{3+} (r = 0.067 nm) minerals.

TABLE 2.3 Trace Elements (μg/g) in Ultramafic and other Rock Types

Element	Igneous Rocks			Sedimentary Rocks		
	Ultramafites	Basalts	Granites	Shales	Sandstones	Carbonates
Antimony	0.1	0.2	0.2	1.5	0.01	0.2
Arsenic	1.0	2.0	1.7	13	1.0	1.0
Barium	0.4	0.03	0.06	0.06	10	10
Beryllium	0.1	1.0	2.5	3.0	0.1	0.1
Bismuth	—	0.007	0.01	—	—	—
Boron	3	5	9	100	35	20
Cadmium	0.1	0.2	0.13	0.3	0.01	0.04
Cerium	0.1	48	85	59	92	12
Cesium	0.1	1.1	3.0	5.0	0.1	0.1
Chromium	1600	170	13	90	35	11
Cobalt	150	48	4	19	0.3	0.1
Copper	10	87	20	45	1.0	4.0
Erbium	0.1	2.1	3.8	2.5	4.0	0.5
Europium	0.1	0.8	1.5	1.0	1.6	0.2
Gadolinium	0.1	5.3	9.5	6.4	10	1.3
Gallium	1.5	17	17	19	12	4.0
Germanium	1.5	1.3	1.3	1.6	0.8	0.2
Gold	0.006	0.004	0.004	0.001	0.001	0.001
Hafnium	0.6	2.0	3.1	2.8	3.9	0.3
Holmium	0.1	1.1	1.9	1.2	2.0	0.3
Indium	0.01	0.22	0.13	0.1	0.01	0.01
Lanthanum	0.1	15	50	92	30	1.0
Lead	1.0	6.0	17	20	7.0	9.0
Lithium	0.1	17	32	66	15	5
Lutetium	0.1	0.6	1.2	0.7	1.2	0.2
Manganese	1620	1500	470	850	100	1100
Molybdenum	0.3	1.5	1.2	2.6	0.2	0.4
Neodymium	0.1	20	35	24	37	4.7
Nickel	2000	130	10	68	2.0	20
Niobium	16	19	20	11	0.01	0.3
Nitrogen	6	20	20	—	—	—
Palladium	0.003	0.002	0.001	—	—	—
Phosphorus	220	1100	760	700	170	400
Praseodymium	0.1	4.6	8.3	5.6	8.8	1.1
Rubidium	0.2	30	140	140	60	3
Samarium	0.1	5.3	9.4	6.4	10	1.3
Scandium	15	30	10	13	1.0	1.0
Selenium	0.05	0.05	0.05	0.6	0.05	0.08
Silver	0.06	0.11	0.04	0.07	0.01	0.01
Strontium	1.0	465	270	300	20	610
Tantalum	1.0	1.1	3.9	0.8	0.01	0.01
Terbium	0.1	0.8	1.5	1.0	1.6	0.20
Thallium	0.06	0.2	1.5	1.4	0.8	0.01
Thorium	0.004	4.0	13	12	1.7	1.7
Tin	0.5	1.5	2.8	6.0	0.1	0.1
Tungsten	0.7	0.7	1.7	1.8	1.6	0.6
Uranium	0.001	1.0	3.0	3.7	0.5	2.2
Vanadium	40	250	66	130	20	20
Ytterbium	0.1	2.1	3.8	2.6	4.0	0.5
Yttrium	0.1	21	38	26	40	30
Zinc	50	105	50	95	16	20
Zirconium	45	140	160	160	220	19

Source: Green (1972)

REFERENCES

Anon, 1972. Penrose Field Conference on Ophiolites. *Geotimes,* 17: 24–25.

Brongniart, A., 1827. *Classification et Caractères Minéralogiques des Roches Homogènes et Hétérogènes.* Levrault, Paris.

Church, W. R., 1972. Ophiolite: its definition, origin as ocean crust, and mode of emplacement in orogenic belts with special reference to the Appalachians. Dep. Energy Mines Res. Canada, Pub. 42: 71–85.

Coleman, R. G., 1971. Plate tectonic emplacement of upper mantle peridotites along continental edges. *J. Geophys. Res.,* 76: 1212–1222.

Coleman, R. G., 1977. *Ophiolites.* Springer, New York.

Coombs, D. S., Landis, C. A., Norris, R. J., Sinton, J. M., Borns, D. J. and Craw, D., 1976. The Dun Mountain Ophiolitic Belt New Zealand, its tectonic setting constitution and origin, with special reference to the southern portion. *Am. J. Sci.,* 276: 561–603.

Davies, H. L., 1971. Peridotite-gabbro-basalt complex in eastern Papua: an over-thrust plate of ocean mantle and crust. Australian Bur. Min. Res. Bull., 128: 1–48.

Den Tex, E., 1969. Origin of ultramafic rocks, their tectonic setting and history; a contribution to the discussion of the paper "The origin of ultramafic and ultrabasic rocks," by P. J. Wyllie. *Tectonophysics,* 7: 457–488.

Dewey, J. F. and Bird, J. M., 1971. Origin and emplacement of the ophiolitic suite: Appalachian ophiolites in Newfoundland. *J. Geophys. Res.,* 76: 3179–3206.

Dickey, J. S. Jr., 1975. A hypothesis of origin for podiform chromite deposits. *Geochim. Cosmochim. Acta,* 39; 1061–1074.

Faust, G. T. and Fahey, J. J., 1962. The serpentine group minerals. U.S. Geol. Surv. Prof. Pap., 384-A: 1–91.

Green, J., 1972. Elements: planetary abundances and distribution. In (R. W. Fairbridge, ed.) *Encyclopedia of Geochemistry and Environmental Sciences IVA.* Van Nostrand Reinholt, New York, 268–300.

Guillon, J. H., 1975. Les massifs péridotiques de Nouvelle Calédonie. Mém. ORSTOM (Nouméa), No.76: 1–120.

Krause, W., 1958. Andere Bodenspezialisten. In, *Encyclopedia of Plant Physiology,* Vol. 4. Springer, Berlin, 755–806.

Moores, E. M. and Vine, F. J., 1971. Troodos Massif Cyprus and other ophiolites as oceanic crust: evaluation and implications. Roy. Soc. Lond. Philosoph. Trans., A268: 443–466.

Nicolas, A. and Jackson, E. D., 1972. Repartition en deux provinces des péridotites des chaînes alpines longeant la Méditerannée: implications géotectoniques. Bull. Suiss. Min. Petr., 52: 479–495.

Staub, R., 1922. Uber die Verteilung der Serpentine in den alpinen Ophioliten. Schweiz. Min. Petr. Mitt., 2: 78–199.

Steinmann, G., 1927. Die ophiolithischen Zonen in dem mediterranen Kettengebirge. 14th Int. Geol. Congr. Madrid, 2: 638–667.

Trescases, J. J., 1975. L'évolution géochimique supergène des roches ultrabasiques en zone tropicale. Mém. ORSTOM (Nouméa), No. 78: 1–259.

Wenner, D. B. and Taylor, H. P. Jr., 1973. Oxygen and hydrogen isotope studies of the serpentinization of ultramafic rocks in oceanic environments and continental ophiolitic complexes. *Am. J. Sci.,* 273: 207–239.

Wenner, D. B. and Taylor, H. P. Jr., 1974. D/H and $^{18}O/^{16}O$ studies of serpentinization of ultramafic rocks. *Geochim. Cosmochim. Acta,* 38: 1255–1286.

Wyllie, P. J. (ed.), 1967. *Ultramafic and Related Rocks.* Wiley, New York.

Chapter 3

THE FORMATION AND COMPOSITION OF SERPENTINE SOILS

3.1 INTRODUCTION

Ultramafic rocks weather by various processes and at different rates to produce the well-known "serpentine soils" which in turn support "serpentine floras." As has already been mentioned in Chapter 2, the term "serpentine" as applied to the soils is somewhat inaccurate since the mineral serpentine, though present in these soils, is by no means the only mafic mineral and is not necessarily the major component. The term "serpentine" is, however, so well established that it would be difficult to remove it without causing confusion and consternation among the multitude of scientists of many disciplines who have been used to the term almost from time immemorial.

There appears to be no general agreement as to whether ultramafic rocks are readily weathered or not. According to Goldich (1938) the order of stability of igneous rocks towards weathering is in the reverse order of their precipitation or crystallisation during magmatic differentiation: i.e. the first-formed minerals such as olivine are the least resistant to weathering. Using the Goldich scheme, the resistance to weathering increases in the following order: olivine, augite, hornblende, biotite, potash felspar, muscovite, quartz. Fig. 3.1 shows how primary minerals change to successive secondary minerals through weathering processes. The primary minerals are listed in approximately the order of their ease of weathering (most-easily weathered at the top). Although Goldich's scheme is supported by workers such as Menezes de Sequeira (1969) and Mitchell (1964), other workers such as Krause (1958), Pichi-Sermolli (1948) and Rune (1953) have proposed that mafic minerals are in fact highly resistant to weathering. This apparent contradiction may arise from the fact that field observations indicate widely differing rates of weathering of ultramafic rocks even within the same general area (Proctor and Woodell, 1971, 1975).

In laboratory studies on the rate of weathering of ultramafic rocks, Pédro and Bitar, (1966a, b) showed that well-drained ultramafic rocks weather by two main processes. The first of these involves leaching with water or water containing carbon dioxide. Under such conditions, silica is removed more quickly than magnesium and the latter remains in the weathered material. If acetic acid is used instead of water, magnesium is removed at a faster rate than silica and the process corresponds to podzolization. The relative rates of removal of silica and magnesium depend not only on the nature of the leachate but also on the temperature of the process (Pédro and Delmas, 1971). Similar experiments were carried out by Wildman et al. (1968a) using water containing different amounts of carbon dioxide. Hydrolysis is a third process and is also of paramount importance.

Field observations tend to show that in the weathering process there is usually a loss of magnesium relative to silica and a relative loss of both compared with aluminium and iron oxides (Butler, 1953; Bogatyrev, 1958; Harada, 1953; Kanno et al., 1965; Hoyos de Castro, 1960; Veniale and Van der Marel, 1963; Wildman et al., 1968b). This loss pattern is very similar to that occurring in the process of laterization (see below).

It is well known that the type of soil produced during the weathering process is dependent not only on the nature of the parent material but also on factors summarized by Brooks (1983), i.e.: climate, relief, time, and biological activity. It is not surprising therefore that an extremely diverse range of soils is produced from the weathering of ultramafic rocks, and it is therefore difficult to generalize about the composition of a "typical" serpentine soil. Nevertheless it can be said most of these soils have the following characteristics in common:

1. High concentrations of siderophile elements such as iron, chromium, nickel and cobalt.

2. Low concentrations of plant nutrients such as nitrogen, phosphorus and potassium. The former is of course very low in parent rocks and its presence in soils is mainly due to biological activity. However, since such activity is low in serpentine soils, these substrates have reduced fertility.

3. A low Ca/Mg quotient compared with non-serpentine soils.

4. They tend to have lower clay contents than "normal" soils, and the clay minerals which occur, tend to have a low exchange capacity. All of these characteristics are discussed below.

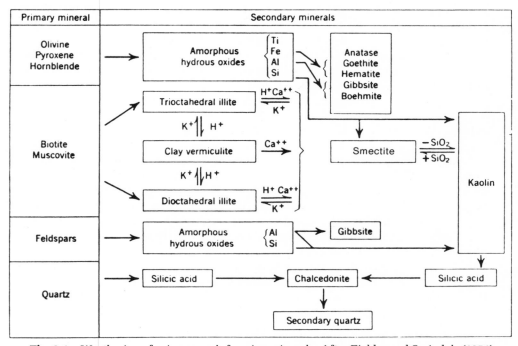

Fig. 3.1   Weathering of primary rock-forming minerals. After Fieldes and Swindale (1954).

3.2 SOME PHYSICAL PROPERTIES OF SERPENTINE SOILS

Many years after its first appearance, the excellent review by Krause (1958) still remains one of the best descriptions of serpentine soils and their effect on vegetation. Krause demonstrated that serpentine soils, which are usually found in mountainous areas, exert a strong microclimatic effect on root systems due to their porous nature which permits excellent soil aeration. The dark colour of the soils also produces greater extremes of temperature due to radiant losses and gains during the diurnal cycle. This dark colour is caused by the high iron content and is not related to a high humus level. The unusually good drainage of these soils results in a moisture deficiency due to their granular texture, even in regions where the rainfall is high. Serpentine soils provide unusual environments for plant growth. An interesting example has been given by Rune (1953), who discovered a typical tundra flora on Mount Albert in the Gaspé Peninsula, Quebec. This was located at least 10° south of the most southerly limit of tundra flora. It seems that the flora was underlain by an impenetrable layer of ultramafic rocks just below the surface of the soil and afforded the same conditions as the permafrost layers of the Canadian Arctic.

The physical characteristics of serpentine soils has also been reviewed by Proctor and Woodell (1975). Although shallow serpentine soils are often very well drained, this is not the case for deep lateritic soils formed from serpentine parent materials in many tropical areas; e.g., Cuba (Bennett and Allison, 1928) and Philippines (Frasche, 1941), where the large mass of soil may contribute to water retention. Even in temperate areas, deep poorly-drained soils can form from ultramafic rocks as has occurred in Portugal (Menezes de Sequeira, 1969), Scotland (Wilson, 1969), and the Soviet Union (Malyuga, 1947).

Another physical problem in serpentine soils is the frequent appearance of stable viscous lumps within the soil which impart a stickiness to the material under wet conditions and dry out to a hard impermeable structure during drought. This feature was ascribed by Bogatyrev (1958) to the presence of excess magnesium in the Albanian soils where the problem was studied. A discussion of the effect of the physical characteristics of serpentine soils upon their fertility will be given in Chapter 4. It must be emphasized that the above properties are not confined to serpentine soils, though they are of course very characteristic of them.

3.3 LATERITIC SOILS

The term "laterite" was originally used by Buchanan (1807) to describe the mantle of ferruginous rocks covering large areas of the Indian Subcontinent. Laterite has a pisolitic (pea-like) appearance and in exposed places a reddish to black-brown scoriaceous appearance. It is soft when quarried, but hardens quite easily to form material suitable for making bricks and indeed is used for that purpose in many tropical countries. Laterite requires four main factors for its formation: an iron-rich parent rock, well-drained terrain, abundant rainfall, and of course time.

Until fairly recently there was little unanimity concerning the classification and definition of laterites, but this problem has been discussed at an international seminar on laterization processes held in India (Krishnaswamy, 1980). In his original definition of laterites Buchanan (1807) said:

What I have called 'indurated clay' is one of the most valuable materials for building. It is diffused in immense masses, without any appearance of stratification and is placed over the granite that forms Malayala. It is full of cavities and pores, and contains a very large quantity of iron in the form of red and yellow ochres. In the mass, while excluded from the air, it is so soft that any iron instrument readily cuts it, and is dug up in square masses with a pick-axe, and immediately cut into the shape wanted with a trowel or with a large knife. It very soon afterwards becomes as hard as brick, and resists the air and water much better than any brick I have seen in India. The most proper English name would be laterite, from lateritis, the appelation that may be given to it in science.

In a more modern definition of laterites, Alexander and Cady (1962) suggested that:

Laterite is a highly-weathered material rich in the secondary oxides of iron, aluminium, or both. It is nearly void of bases and primary silicates, but may contain large amounts of quartz and kaolinite. It is either hard or capable of hardening on exposure to wetting and drying.

The latest classification of laterites is that of Schellmann (1980) who used the following definition:

Laterites are products of intense subaerial rock weathering whose Fe and/or Al content is higher and Si lower than in merely kaolinized parent rocks. They consist predominantly of mineral assemblages of goethite, hematite, aluminium hydroxides, kaolin minerals and quartz.

The same author listed six criteria of lateritic material as follows:

1. Laterites are composed mainly of SiO_2, Al_2O_3, Fe_2O_3, and H_2O and are best characterised by a triangular diagram of the first three components.

2. The major minerals are gibbsite, hematite, goethite, quartz and anatase, plus chromite in the case of laterites weathered from ultramafic rocks.

3. In the early weathering stages, primary silicates are kaolinised and most of the alkali metals and alkaline earths are removed.

4. Three processes occur in the later weathering stages:

(i) Incongruent dissolution of kaolinite with formation of gibbsite. Because only silica is removed, alumina and Fe_2O_3 are concentrated.

(ii) Congruent dissolution of kaolinite by which alumina and silica are simultaneously removed and only Fe_2O_3 is concentrated.

(iii) Dissolution of quartz with concentration of alumina and Fe_2O_3.

5. There are great differences in laterites derived from different rock types. Incongruent dissolution of kaolinite is more pronounced in the laterization of ultramafic, basic and alkali rocks, with less pronounced formation of gibbsite from predominantly acidic rocks.

6. There are pronounced differences in induration of laterites which occurs more readily in laterites derived from acidic rocks. The lateritic weathering products above basic and ultramafic rocks show a much lower tendency towards unduration and crust formation. The ferruginous limonitic laterite of ultramafic rocks is quite soft and usually only forms a crust at the surface.

The removal of silica and increase of the sesquioxide content of lateritic material is largely a function of the pH of the environment. Fig. 3.2 shows the solubility of alumina and silica as a function of pH. From pH 5–9, the solubility of silica increases, whereas that of alumina remains low. Even under tropical conditions, the pH of the soil can be sufficiently

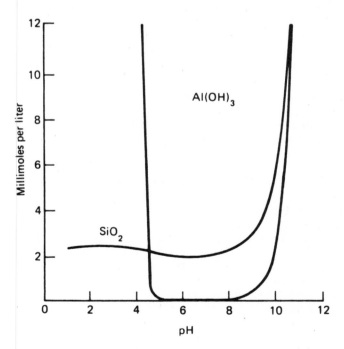

Fig. 3.2   The solubility of amorphous silica and aluminium hydroxide as a function of pH at 25°C. Source: Mason and Moore (1982). Copyright J. Wiley, New York.

high (provided that the parent material is base rich) to cause leaching of significant amounts of silica from the soil profile. In the course of laterization, there is a separation of the siderophiles Fe, Mn, Co, and Ni. The divalent forms of these metals are readily soluble and are easily leached through the soil profile. The high oxidation states are however much less mobile. From the oxidation potentials, it can be seen that the ease of oxidation follows the order Fe>Mn>Co>Ni. Therefore the iron is immediately immobilized at the surface of the soil followed downwards by manganese, cobalt and finally nickel. These four metals are all immobilized as their higher oxides.

Laterites may be formed from a wide variety of rock types from granites to basalts to peridotites and even clays or shales. The composition of some typical laterites derived from ultramafic rocks is shown in Table 3.1. Values for laterites derived from granitic rocks are also included for comparison.

Triangular plots for the system $SiO_2/Al_2O_3/Fe_2O_3$ are shown in Fig. 3.3 for laterites derived from ultramafic and granitic rocks. It is clear from these plots that the criteria for "strong", "moderate" and "weak" laterization depend entirely on the nature of the parent material.

Laterites derived from ultramafic rocks cover large areas of the tropics and are very large sources of low-grade nickel ores. For example, the lateritic nickel ores (garnierite) of New Caledonia account for one third of the world's annual production of this metal. Prominent regions of laterized ultramafic rocks are to be found in Cuba (Kemp, 1916; Vletter, 1955); Guatemala, Colombia and Oregon (Hotz, 1964); New Caledonia (Chetelat, 1947; Routhier, 1952; Trescases, 1975; Jaffré, 1980); Indonesia (Reynolds et al. 1973); Oman, Philippines, New Hebrides and the Solomons (Coleman, 1970). These are usually all developed over partially or completely serpentinized peridotites and show that metamorphic serpentinization is an essential prerequisite for the lateritic weathering process. Fig. 3.4 shows a geochemical scheme for lateritic alteration of peridotite in New Caledonia (Coleman, 1977).

Deposits on serpentinized peridotites such as in Cuba or the Philippines are called nickeliferous ferruginous laterites (Coleman, 1977) and average 40% iron and 1% nickel. Laterites derived from weathered serpentinized peridotites such as in New Caledonia and Oregon are called nickel silicate deposits (Hotz, 1964). These deposits have a relatively low iron content (<35%) and can contain up to 15% nickel silicate (garnierite). The garnierites of New Caledonia contain typically 3.5% nickel (Chetelat, 1947).

TABLE 3.1 The Major Element Composition of Lateritic Crusts Derived from Acidic and Ultramafic Rocks

Locality	%SiO$_2$	%Al$_2$O$_3$	%Fe$_2$O$_3$	%TiO$_2$	%Ig. loss
GRANITIC ROCKS					
Angadipuram, India	18.6	30.1	29.1	1.3	19.1
Kandana, Sri Lanka	41.4	21.5	24.5	1.1	11.0
Yalanbee, W. Australia	20.3	28.5	34.4	1.5	14.4
Porto Platon, Brazil	35.9	19.6	33.4	0.9	10.4
ULTRAMAFIC ROCKS					
Yaté, New Caledonia	0.7	4.3	74.8	0.3	15.1
Ambatovy, Malagasy Rep.	5.1	2.5	76.0	2.0	12.8
Barro Alto, Brazil	4.5	10.6	68.4	0.7	10.6
Mayaguez, Puerto Rico	1.8	10.2	65.0	0.7	15.5
Conacry, Guinea	0.8	11.1	67.7	0.6	14.7

Source: Schellmann (1980)

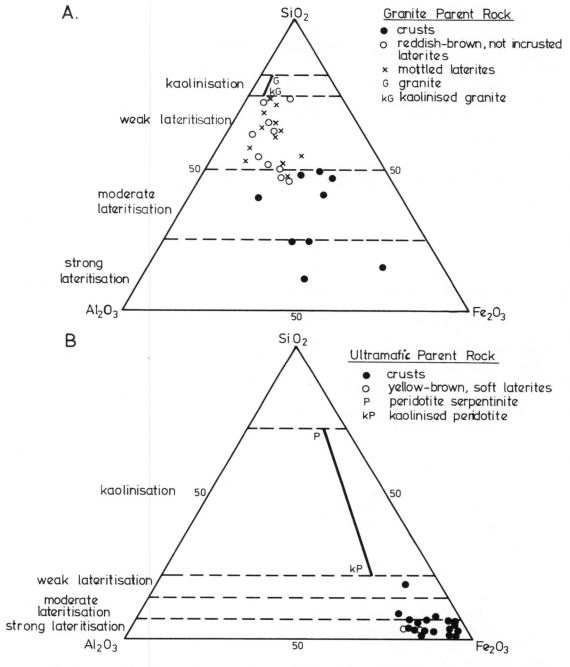

Fig. 3.3 The $SiO_2/Al_2O_3/Fe_2O_3$ system in laterites derived from granites (A) and ultramafites (B). Source: Schellmann (1980).

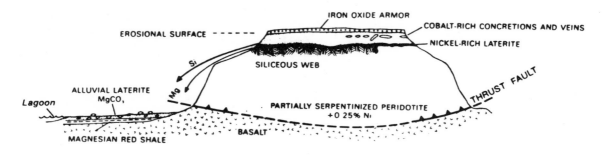

Fig. 3.4   Geochemical scheme of lateritic alteration of peridotites in New Caledonia showing relationships between ferruginous laterite and nickel concentrations. Source: Coleman (1978).

3.4 SIDEROPHILES AND PLANT NUTRIENTS IN SERPENTINE SOILS

The important question of the infertility of serpentine soils will be discussed in the next chapter, but at this stage it will be appropriate to present data for the concentrations in such soils, of elements whose excessive or deficient abundances are reported to affect soil fertility. Data will also be presented for the major constituents of serpentine soils. The plant nutrients are: calcium, magnesium, nitrogen, phosphorus and potassium and the siderophiles are chromium, cobalt and nickel. The abundances of these eight elements in a wide variety of serpentine soils from different parts of the world are summarized in Table 3.2. It will be noted that different types of ultramafic rock can give rise to soils with greatly different chemical compositions. For example calcium ranges from 71 to 17300 μg/g, and chromium from 110 to 37230 μg/g. Despite these enormous concentration differences, the main chemical criteria of serpentine soils: i.e., elevated siderophile and lowered nutrient status, remain intact. Weathered tropical serpentine soils tend to have lower nutrient levels than those from temperate areas and are correspondingly higher in siderophiles. An example of this is the New Caledonian (Boulinda) soils (Jaffré, 1980) compared with those from Shetlands (Slingsby and Brown, 1977).

Just as in the case of the siderophiles listed in Table 3.2, the bulk composition of serpentine soils varies considerably in relation to climatic, geological and other factors, even for soils in the same region derived from similar parent rocks. This is illustrated in Table 3.3 which gives the bulk composition of a number of serpentinic and non-serpentinic soils from temperate and tropical regions of the earth.

The extreme variability of soil composition, mentioned above, is well illustrated by considering the hypermagnesian brown eutrophic soils and their ferruginous companions both derived from ultramafic rocks in New Caledonia. These are shown in the first two columns of Table 3.3. The hypermagnesian brown eutrophic soils are found at the base of ultramafic massifs where they overlay serpentinites or peridotites with varying degrees of serpentinization. They correspond to a stage where pedogenesis is marked by a recombination of silicates of iron and magnesium. They have an argillaceous texture due to the presence of smectites rich in magnesium and iron. Although there is a significant loss of silica, the content of this oxide (30%) is much higher than in the ferruginous soils (1%). The magnesium content is also relatively high (15%). Chromium and nickel are also abundant in these soils, whereas the plant nutrients calcium, phosphorus and potassium have extremely low concentrations.

TABLE 3.2 Concentrations (μg/g) of Plant Nutrients and Siderophile Elements in Serpentine Soils

Country	Location	n	Ca	Co	Cr	Mg	Ni	N	P	K	Ref
Austria	Kraubath	1	1285		480	154000	2000				1
Cuba	Matanzanas	2	1550			43000			<400	825	2
England	Lizard	14	13600	139	2414	69000	2028		144	7112	3
Finland	Lapland	10		140	4000		1200				4
Greece	Chromio	5	1560	176	34846	171000	3563				5
Japan	Horokanai	1			5200		2600				6
New Caledonia	Mts Koghis	72	6900	877	3612	44000	6400		349	446	7
	Pl. Lacs	75	3200	806	8787	6000	5200		187	99	7
	Not known	2	71	194	16800	86000	3888	14000	133	87	8
	Boulinda	6	71	108	37230	3000	4884	1840	106	87	8
Poland	G. Radunia	2		40	600		80				9
	Wzgorze	2		50	1200		160				9
Portugal	Bragança	5	9928	108	2800	112000	2130	3260		3610	10
Scotland	Kilrannoch	6							570		11
		3							413		11
	Aberdeen	1	1090		660	128000	2440				12
	Shetlands	3	1260		1000	141000	2300				12
		2			3500		2800				13
		2			3300		1250				13
	Kilrannoch	2			4000		1250				13
	Shetlands	15	12380	322	10380	158000	5460		108	1493	3
		3	4642	77	1667	150000	2200		443	8300	3
	Aberdeen	4	15890	277	4875	132000	4625		192	5808	3
Spain	La Coruña	6	17300		2323	52000	1711				14
United States	Maryland	2			1900		324				15
Wales	Holyhead	1	7142	70	2700	102000	1700		190	5808	3
Zimbabwe	Gt. Dyke	20		250	110		6600				16
		20		230	2200		6800				16
		20		240	2400		7100				16
		12		73	1200		430				16
		6		200	1900		3500				16
		2		270	480		4600				16
		7			27000		2655	1700			17

1—Shewry and Peterson (1976)
2—Dirven et al. (1976)
3—Slingsby and Brown (1977)
4—Lounamaa (1956)
5—Karataglis et al. (1982)
6—Susuki et al. (1971)
7—Lee et al. (1977)
8—Jaffré (1980)
9—Sarosiek (1964)
10—Menezes de Sequeira
11—Johnston and Proctor (1980)
12—Shewry and Peterson (1975)
13—Proctor (1971)
14—Lopez Lopez and Guitian Ojea (1981)
15—Robinson et al. (1935)
16—Proctor et al. (1980)
17—Soane and Saunder (1959)

A second type of serpentine soil in New Caledonia is the ferruginous highly-weathered lateritic group (sols férralitiques férritiques—Jaffré, 1980) which are composed mainly of oxides and hydroxides of iron and have exceedingly low concentrations of magnesium (0.3%), silica (1%), and the plant nutrients calcium, phosphorus, and potassium. The iron content (75% Fe_2O_3) is very high. These soils have a relatively low pH and poor exchange capacity in all horizons. The highly-weathered lateritic soils of New Caledonia are one extreme of a spectrum which extends to the more fertile serpentine soils of Europe and other regions of the temperate zone.

TABLE 3.3 Bulk composition of the A Horizons of Serpentine and other Soils

Constituent	Ultramafic Soils						Non-ultramafic soils	
	A	B	C	D	E	F	G	H
SiO_2	40.28	66.30	34.00	1.67	38.70	27.60	69.32	95.49
Al_2O_3	2.36	7.17	1.35	3.00	7.61	8.80	11.39	2.12
Fe_2O_3	9.31	6.44	13.70	76.70	14.91	50.30	3.84	0.16
MnO	0.13	0.09	0.22	0.44	0.32	1.10	0.16	0.01
Cr_2O_3	0.29	0.17	0.60	3.61	0.72	—	—	—
NiO	0.25	0.01	0.47	1.23	0.41	—	—	—
CaO	trace	0.20	0.01	0.01	1.13	—	1.61	0.15
MgO	36.42	12.96	15.60	0.38	22.03	1.30	0.92	0.07
K_2O	trace	0.66	0.01	0.01	0.29	0.20	1.80	0.98
Na_2O	0.02	0.53	0.04	0.08	—	0.10	0.14	0.18
P_2O_5	0.02	0.03	0.01	0.01	—	0.10	0.17	0.01
SO_3	0.08	0.13	—	—	—	—	0.14	0.01
CoO	—	—	0.02	0.02	0.02	—	—	—
TiO_2	0.12	0.83	0.04	0.06	0.39	0.10	0.49	0.09
Ignition loss	12.25	5.55	20.40	13.40	12.42	7.40	9.53	0.68
Insoluble res.	—	—	16.40	0.18	—	—	—	—
Total (%)	101.5	101.1	102.9	97.8	99.0	97.0	100.5	100.0

A—Mt Tamalpais, Calif.'(Robinson et al. 1935)
B—Dublin, Maryland (Robinson et al. 1935)
C—Boulinda, New Caledonia (Jaffré, 1980)
D—New Caledonia (Jaffré, 1980)
E—Bragança, Portugal (Menezes de Sequeira, 1969)
F—Matanzanas, Cuba (Dirven et al. 1976)
G—Chernozem over granite, South Dakota (Bear, 1964)
H—Podsol over sandstone, Michigan (Bear, 1964)

3.5 THE GENESIS OF SERPENTINE SOILS

Weathering and soil formation processes occurring on ultramafic rocks differ markedly from those occurring on acidic rocks largely because of the high levels of magnesium and iron and the low levels of silicon and aluminium which occur in ultramafites. Weathering depletes magnesium and silicon relative to iron and aluminium and magnesium is depleted to a greater degree than silicon. Furthermore, the rate of depletion of magnesium and silicon increases with increasing temperature and intensity of leaching and varies with the Mg:Si ratio of the weathering materials (Schellmann, 1964; Hotz, 1964; Wildman et al. 1968b).

In work in New Zealand, Kirkman (1975) showed that ferromagnesian minerals, especially chrysotile and lizardite, have altered to vermiculite. In three profiles the vermiculite contained much interlayer material and altered to chlorite, whereas in the fourth profile, this mineral contained little interlayer material and did not alter to chlorite.

Although the pedogenesis of serpentine soils varies widely according to climatic and other factors, it is appropriate to give details of a scheme proposed by Rabenhorst et al. (1982) for the formation of Maryland soils derived from serpentinite. This type of approach is needed to understand the pedogenesis of these soils, even though it might not be completely applicable in other regions; e.g. the tropics. The work was carried out over four pedons where eluvial and illuvial processes had caused formation of weak to moderately-expressed argillitic horizons. Total nickel and chromium concentrations had maximum values of 18, 900 and 5850 μg/g respectively. Weathering of serpentine minerals tended towards the formation of smectite, which with vermiculite, dominated the fine clay fractions. Often interstratified clay minerals and minerals containing hydroxy-interlayered material were observed. Serpentine, which was absent in the <0.2 μm fraction, occurred with chlorite and vermiculite in the larger size fractions.

A generalized model for pedogenesis of the Maryland serpentine soils is shown in Fig. 3.5 based on work by Rabenhorst et al. (1982). The release and translocation of iron has resulted in a brownish-coloured B horizon. Impeded drainage may cause the iron to become

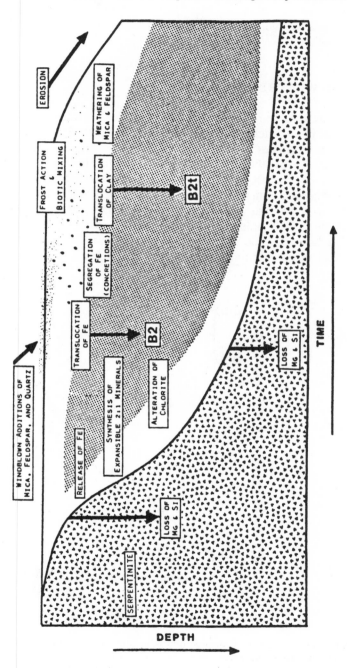

Fig. 3.5 Generalized model of the genesis of a soil derived from serpentinite in Maryland. Source: Rabenhorst et al. (1982). Reproduced from Soil Science Society of America Journal, v.86, 607–616 (1982). By permission of The Soil Science Society of America.

segregated as mottles or concretions. The processes of eluviation and illuviation of clay have produced weakly to moderately expressed argillitic horizons. As a result of denudation, which counteracts the processes of profile development and horizon differentiation, soils occurring on steeper slopes tend to have less strongly expressed B horizons. The magnesium-rich parent material has resulted in the dominance of Mg^{2+} on the exchange complex, causing these soils to have fairly high pH values. The intensity of weathering near the surface has resulted in increased Mg^{2+} saturation and increased pH with depth. Nickel and chromium levels are generally very high but they show considerable variation from one locality to another.

3.6 BIOLOGICAL WEATHERING

A possible stage in pedogenesis is the biological weathering of ultramafic rocks by bacteria and lower plants such as lichens. Lebedeva et al. (1978) studied the role of nitrifying bacteria in the weathering of these rocks. Their experiments were centred around the degradation of serpentinite by *Nitrosospira briensis* and *Nitrobacter winogradskyi* in which 1 g of crushed rock was incubated with 50 ml of nutrient inoculated with the organism concerned. Breakdown of serpentinite was measured by the rate of migration of magnesium ions into the aqueous phase. There was also a correlation with the build-up of nitrite in the system. The results of these experiments are shown in Fig. 3.6. It was concluded that these bacteria as well as other heterotrophic microorganisms participate in the weathering of serpentinized ultramafic rocks, rendering elements mobile for leaching, and formation of the weathering crust.

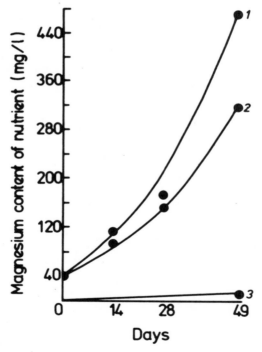

Fig. 3.6 Decomposition of serpentinite as measured by the Mg content in the ambient nutrient in which crushed rock was suspended.
1. Culture of *Nitrosospira briensis* + *Nitrobacter winogradskyi*
2. Culture of *N. briensis* only
3. Sterile control.
Source: Lebedeva et al. (1978).

Lichens as well as bacteria have been shown to decompose ultramafic rocks. Wilson et al. (1981) carried out experiments with the lichen *Lecanora atra* on a substrate of serpentinite. The lichen thallus contains appreciable amounts of oxalic acid secreted by the mycobiont. This reacts with the serpentinite to form an amorphous silica gel retaining the fibrous morphology of the chysotile from which it was derived. It was suggested by these authors that heavy metals are absorbed on to magnesium oxalate dihydrate formed during the decomposition and that this strategy enables the lichen to tolerate high concentrations of phytotoxic elements in the environment.

REFERENCES

Alexander, L. T. and Cady, J. G., 1962. Genesis and hardening of laterites in soils. USDA Tech. Rep., 1282; 1–90.

Bear, F. E., 1964. *Chemistry of the Soil*. Van Nostrand Reinhold, New York.

Bennett, H. H. and Allison, R. U., 1928. *The Soil of Cuba*. Trop. Pl. Res. Found. Bull., Washington.

Bogatyrev, K. P., 1958. Smolnitsa of Albania (in Russ.). *Pochvovedenie*, 14: 358–364.

Brooks, R. R., 1983. *Biological Methods of Prospecting for Minerals*. Wiley, New York.

Buchanan, F., 1807. *A journey from Madras through the countries of Mysore, Canara and Malabar*. East India Co. Lond., 2: 440–441.

Butler, J. R., 1953. The geochemistry and mineralogy of rock weathering. I The Lizard area, Cornwall. *Geochim. Cosmochim. Acta*, 4: 157–178.

Chetelat, E de, 1947. La genèse et l'évolution des gisements de nickel de la Nouvelle Calédonie. Bull. Soc. Géol. France Sér. 5, 17: 105—160.

Coleman, P. J., 1970. Geology of the Solomon and New Hebrides islands as part of the Melanesian re-entrant, Southwest Pacific. *Pac. Sci.*, 24: 289–314.

Coleman, R. G., 1977. *Ophiolites*. Springer, New York.

Dirven, J. M. C., Schulenborgh, J. van and Breemen, N. van, 1976. Weathering of serpentinite in Matanzanas Province, Cuba: mass transfer calculations and irreversible reaction pathways. *Soil Sci. Soc. Am. J.*, 40: 901–907.

Fieldes, M. and Swindale, L. D. 1954. Chemical weathering of silicates in soil formation. *N.Z. J. Sci. Tech.*, 36B: 140–154.

Frasche, D. F., 1941. Origin of the Surigao iron ores. *Econ. Geol.*, 36: 280–305.

Goldich, S. S., 1938. A study in rock weathering. *J. Geol.*, 46: 17–58.

Harada, M., 1953. The weathering of serpentine in Wakasamachi Tottori Prefecture. *J. Sci. Soil Manure*, Tokyo, 23: 137–140.

Hotz, P. E., 1964. Nickeliferous laterites in south-western Oregon and north-western California. *Econ. Geol.*, 59: 355–396.

Hoyos de Castro, A., 1960. La genèse du sol sur roches basiques. Trans. 7th Int. Congr. Soil. Sci., 4: 413–417.

Jaffré, T., 1980. *Etude Ecologique du Peuplement Végétal des Sols Dérivés de Roches Ultrabasiques en Nouvelle Calédonie*. ORSTOM, Paris.

Johnston, W. R. and Proctor, J., 1980. Ecological studies on Meikle Kilrannoch serpentines. *Trans. Bot. Soc. Edinb.*, 43: 207–215.

Kanno, I., Tokudome, S., Arimura, S. and Onikura, Y., 1965. Genesis and characterisation of brown forest soils derived from serpentine in Kyushu, Japan. Part 2. Genesis and characterisatics of brown forest soils. *Soil Sci. Pl. Nutr.*, 11: 141–150.

Karataglis, S., Babalonas, D. and Kabasakalis, B., 1982. The ecology of plant populations growing on serpentine soils II. *Phyton* (Austria), 22: 317–327.

Kemp, J. F., 1916. The Mayari iron-ore deposit, Cuba. *Am. Inst. Mining Eng. Trans.*, 51: 3–30.

Kirkman, J. H., 1975. Clay minerals in soils derived from ultrabasic rocks of southern Westland, New Zealand. *N.Z. J. Geol. Geophys.*, 18: 849–864.

Krause, W., 1958. Andere Bodenspezialisten. In, *Handbuch der Pflanzenphysiologie*, v. 4. Springer, Berlin, 755–806.

Krishnaswamy, V. S., 1980. *Laterisation Processes*. Oxford and IBH Pub. Co., New Delhi.

Lebedeva, E. V., Lyalikova, N. N. and Bugel'skii, Yu.Yu., 1978. Participation of nitrifying bacteria in the weathering of serpentinized ultrabasic rocks (in Russ.). *Mikrobiologiya*, 47: 1101–1107.

Lee, J., Brooks, R. R., Reeves, R. D., Boswell, C. R. and Jaffré, T., 1977. Plant-soil relationships in a New Caledonian serpentine flora. *Pl. Soil*, 46: 675–680.

Lopez Lopez, M. I. and Guitian Ojea, F., 1981. Suelos de la zona humeda española. X Suelos sobre serpentinas. *An. Edaf. Agrobiol.*, 40: 1–10.

Lounamaa, J., 1956. Trace elements in plants growing wild on different rocks in Finland. *Ann. Bot. Soc. Zool.-Bot. Fenn. "Vanamo"*, 29: 1–196.

Malyuga, D. P., 1947. Soils and plants and their significance for the search for ore deposits (in Russ.). *Priroda*, 6: 13–17.

Mason, B. and Moore, C. B., 1982. *Principles of Geochemistry* 4th Ed., Wiley New York.

Menezes de Sequeira, E., 1969. Toxicity and movement of heavy metals in serpentine soils (northeastern Portugal). *Agron. Lusit.*, 30: 115–154.

Mitchell, R. L., 1964. Trace elements in soils. In, *Chemstry of the Soil* (ed. F. E. Bear). Reinhold, New York, 320–368.

Pédro, G. and Bitar, K. E., 1966a. Contribution à l'étude de la genèse des sols hypermagnésiens: recherches expérimentales sur l'alteration chimique des roches ultrabasiques (serpentinites). *Annls. Agron.*, 17: 611–651.

Pédro, G. and Bitar, K. E., 1966b. Sur l'influence du type chimique de la roche mère dans le developpement des phenomènes d'alteration superficielle: Recherches expérimentales sur l'évolution des roches ultrabasiques (serpentinites). *C. R. Acad. Sci. Paris Sér.D*, 263: 313–316.

Pédro, G. and Delmas, A. B., 1971. Sur l'alteration de l'olivine par lessivage à l'eau et la mise en évidence de trois grands domaines d'évolution géochimique. *C. R. Acad. Sci. Paris Sér.D*, 273; 1543–1546.

Pichi-Sermolli, R., 1948. Flore e vegetazione delle serpentine e delle altre ofioliti dell'alta valle del Tevere (Toscana). *Webbia*, 6: 1–380.

Proctor, J., 1971. The plant ecology of serpentine. II Plant response to serpentine soils. *J. Ecol.*, 59: 397–410.

Proctor, J., Burrow, J. and Craig, G. C., 1980. Plant and soil chemical analyses from a range of Zimbabwean serpentine sites. *Kirkia*, 12: 127–139.

Proctor, J. and Woodell, S. R. J., 1971. The plant ecology of serpentine. I Serpentine vegetation of England and Scotland. *J. Ecol.*, 59: 375–395.

Proctor, J. and Woodell, S. R. J., 1975. The ecology of serpentine soils. *Adv. Ecol. Res.*, 9: 255–366.

Rabenhorst, M. C., Foss, J. E. and Fanning, D. S., 1982. Genesis of Maryland soils formed from serpentinite. *Soil Sci. Soc. Am. J.*, 46: 607–616.

Reynolds, C. D., Havryluk, I., Saleh Bastaman, and Soepomo Atmowidjojo. The exploration of nickel laterite deposits in Irian Barat. Geol. Soc. Malaysia Bull., 6: 309–323.

Routhier, P., 1952. Les gisements de fer de la Nouvelle Calédonie. *19th Int. Geol. Congr. Symposium sur les Gisements de Fer du Monde*, 11: 567–587.

Rune, O., 1953. Plant life on serpentines and related rocks in the north of Sweden. *Acta Phytogeogr. Suec.*, 31: 1–139.

Sarosiek, J., 1964. Ecological analysis of some plants growing on serpentine soil in Lower Silesia (in Pol.). *Monographiae Bot.*, 18: 1–105.

Schellmann, W., 1980. Considerations of the definition and classification of laterites. In, (ed. V. S. Krishnaswamy) *Laterisation Processes*. Oxford and IBH Pub. Co., New Delhi, 1–10.

Schellmann, W., 1964. Laterite weathering of serpentinite. *Geol. Jahrb.*, 81: 645–678.

Shewry, P. R. and Peterson, P. J., 1975. Calcium and magnesium in plants and soils from a serpentine area on Unst, Shetland. *J. Appl. Ecol.*, 12: 381–391.

Shewry, P. R. and Peterson, P. J., 1976. Distribution of chromium and nickel in plants and soils from serpentine and other sites. *J. Ecol.*, 64: 195–212.

Slingsby, D. R. and Brown, D. H., 1977. Nickel in British serpentine soils. *J. Ecol.*, 65: 597–618.

Susuki, S., Mizuno, N. and Kimura, K., 1971. Distribution of heavy metals in serpentine soils. *Soil Sci. Pl. Nutr.,* 17: 195–198.

Trescases, J. J., 1975. L'évolution géochimique supergène de roches ultrabasiques en zone tropicale. *Mém. ORSTOM (Nouméa)* No. 78: 1–259.

Veniale, F. and Marel, H. W. van der, 1963. An interstratified saponite-swelling chlorite mineral as a weathering product of lizardite rock from St Margherita Staffora (Pavia Province) Italy. *Beitr. Miner. Petrogr.,* 9: 198–245.

Vletter, R. de, 1955. How Cuban nickel ore was formed—a lesson in laterite genesis. *Eng. Mining J.,* 156: 84–87.

Wildman, W. E., Jackson, M. L. and Whittig, L. D., 1968a. Serpentine rock dissolution as a function of carbon dioxide pressure in aqueous solution. *Am. Miner.,* 53: 1252–1263.

Wildman, W. E., Jackson, M. L. and Whittig, L. D., 1968b. Iron-rich montmorillonite formation in soils derived from serpentinite. *Proc. Soil Sci. Soc. Am.,* 32: 787–794.

Wilson, A. D., 1969. *Pedological Studies on Soils Derived from Serpentinite in North-eastern Scotland.* MSc Thesis, Univ. Aberdeen.

Wilson, M. J., Jones, D. and McHardy, W. J., 1981. The weathering of serpentinite by *Lecanora atra. Lichenologist,* 13: 167–176.

Chapter 4

THE SERPENTINE FACTOR

4.1 INTRODUCTION

The presence of an unusual sparse flora over ultramafic rocks has led to many studies of the reasons for this apparent infertility, dating back as far as the 16th century when Caesalpino (1583) described a plant restricted to the Upper Tiber Valley in Tuscany near Florence. Modern interest in the subject began with the work of Amidei (1841), who described the floristics of serpentine areas near Florence, and with work on the serpentine flora of Serbia by Pancic (1859). These and other early workers soon noticed the paucity of species, dwarfism and xeromorphism of these plants and observed, in addition their chlorotic, narrow and glaucescent leaves, strong sclerenchymatic development, and enlarged root systems. The "serpentine barrens" (as they later became known in the United States) showed a complete cessation of forest growth on climatically-favourable terrain.

The early work on serpentine barrens was concerned primarily with a description of the floristics of some important ultramafic regions in southern and south-eastern Europe and particularly in The Balkans (Markgraf, 1932; Lämmermayr, 1926; Novak, 1928). A good summary of this earlier literature has been given by Krause (1958). Following work on the floristics, the emphasis switched to the discovery of the causes of the infertility of soils derived from ultramafic rocks. The serpentine factor may be defined as the causal factor or factors (chemical or physical) related to the infertility of serpentine soils and to the nature of the vegetation colonising them. The general infertility of serpentine soils may be defined as the "serpentine problem". Many a scientist has claimed to have solved the problem, only to have his claims refuted by fresh evidence from another worker. For example, Hilgard (1906) blamed serpentine soil infertility on the excess of magnesium over calcium in serpentines, whereas Gordon and Lipman (1926) proposed that the control factor was the low levels of plant nutrients in these soils. Nine years later, Robinson et al. (1935) implicated the high concentrations of phytotoxic chromium and nickel, though West (1912) had originally suggested these as causal effects. Although each school of thought has its adherents, it is probable that many factors and combinations of factors are responsible for the infertility of serpentine soils.

Part of the problem in studying the serpentine factor lies in the limitations of experiments designed to elucidate this elusive entity. Most pot trials have been designed to alter one variable while keeping all others constant, so that when a response is obtained to one variable, there is tendency to assume that it alone is the main component of the serpentine factor. Altering several variables simultaneously, which more closely approximates to field conditions, renders interpretation of the data virtually impossible. Among the most comprehensive reviews of the serpentine problem which have appeared in the last 30 years or so, are those of Krause (1958), Proctor and Woodell (1975) and Kinzel (1982). Virtually the entire literature on the subject up to 1979 is covered by these three important papers.

Because of the confusing and often contradictory nature of studies on the serpentine factor, it is very difficult to assess the evidence and conclusions in a logical, orderly manner. However, in this chapter I shall discuss the reasons for the infertility under five main headings: the toxic effects of nickel, chromium and cobalt; the toxicity of excess magnesium; infertility due to the low calcium content of serpentine soils; problems arising from an adverse calcium/magnesium quotient in the substrate; and infertility arising from low levels of plant nutrients in the soils. Before beginning this discussion, however, some consideration must be given to the very important subject of the availability of soil constituents to the plants.

4.2 PLANT-AVAILABLE CONCENTRATIONS OF ELEMENTS IN SERPENTINE SOILS

The infertility of serpentine soils is largely related to their chemical composition, though it must not be forgotten (Chapter 3) that the physical nature of the soil, particularly its well-drained character, is to some extent responsible for the unfavourable response of vegetation. Although infertility is related primarily to chemical factors, it is not necessarily related directly to the total concentrations of elements in the soil. For example, although the chromium content of serpentine soils is usually very high (typically 3000 μg/g), the proportion which is available to plants is so low, that chromium toxicity *per se* does not appear to be as much a problem as other chemical factors.

Some indication of the probable degree of availability of certain metals to plants can be afforded by theoretical consideration of the solubility of their hydroxides at various pH values. Fig. 4.1 gives values for the solubilities (μg/ml) of 4 siderophile (members of the iron family) elements expressed as a function of pH. It is clear that the order of increasing solubility is Fe, Cr, Ni, and Co. At the mean pH of serpentine soils (6.8), the solubility of the metals is such as to give 10^{-10}, 10^{-7}, 5×10^{-4}, and 10^5 μg/ml (ppm) respectively. The pH values required to provide a concentration of 1 μg/ml in solution are 9.2 for cobalt, 9.0 for nickel, 4.5 for chromium and 3.5 for iron. The availability of chromium and iron would clearly be much lower than that of cobalt and nickel. The values in Fig. 4.1 should not be taken too literally as no account has been taken of either the ability of plants to accumulate these elements by chelation with organic ligands or of the mineral form of the elements in the soil. The values do, however, provide a basis for comparison.

The effect of pH on the plant-availability of several nutrients is shown in Fig. 4.2. The thickness of each band is an approximate indication of availability. Several plant nutrients are discussed below.

Nitrogen and sulphur

Compounds containing these elements are water-soluble at almost any pH and are usually available to plants. Most nitrogen is derived from organic material which tends to be low in serpentine soils, due to their low productivity, so that such soils are usually deficient in this element. The same is true to some extent for sulphur.

Phosphorus

Many phosphorus compounds in soils have low solubilities. Even when phosphatic fertilizers are added to the soil, they tend to form only slightly-soluble compounds due to chemical reaction with other soil constituents. However, a pH of 6.5–7.0 gives the optimum availability of phosphorus. At lower pH values, phosphate is precipitated by aluminium and iron, whereas above pH 7.0 insoluble calcium phosphate is formed.

Potassium

Potassium is soluble at all pH values, but is readily removed from soils by sorption processes involving clay minerals. This element is readily leached from acid soils and in alkaline media becomes non-exchangeable.

Calcium and magnesium

These elements are readily available at pH 6.8 (typical for serpentine soils) and there is usually no deficiency of either element except in heavily leached tropical lateritic ultramafic soils where the calcium content can be as low as 70 μg/g (see Table 3.2) and that of magnesium may be greatly reduced. However, magnesium can be antagonistic to uptake of calcium by plants so that deficiency of the latter can sometimes manifest itself for this reason.

Iron, manganese, copper and zinc

All these elements precipitate as hydroxides at high pH values. Deficiencies of these elements can therefore appear in some alkaline serpentine soils. At a low pH, manganese,

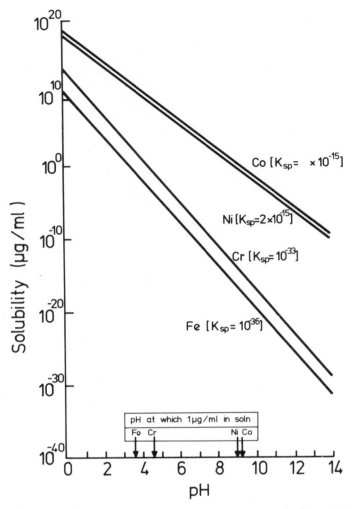

Fig. 4.1. The solubility of the hydroxides of cobalt, nickel, chromium and iron (μg/ml) expressed as a function of pH.

copper and zinc become so soluble that they can be readily leached. However, iron has such a high concentration in serpentine soils that it is never deficient in the soils, even though chlorotic symptoms of iron deficiency can appear in some plants due to antagonistic effects from excessive concentrations of other soil constituents.

Boron

Boron is leached at low and high pH values and is usually deficient in serpentine soils because of the usually low content of boron in the parent rock.

Molybdenum

The solubility of molybdenum is increased at pH values above 6.0. This element is therefore readily leached from serpentine soils and its deficiency can contribute to the general infertility of these soils.

Cobalt, chromium and nickel

There are no reliable data for the plant-availability of cobalt, chromium and nickel as a function of pH beyond the theoretical values for the solubility of their hydroxides at various pH values (Fig. 4.1). This is probably because they have minor importance as plant nutrients and have not been studied as "essential" elements.

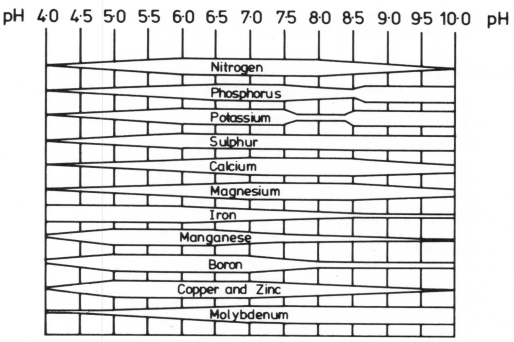

Fig. 4.2.   The plant-availability of nutrients in soils expressed as a function of pH.
Source: Thompson and Troeh (1978). Reproduced by permission of McGraw Hill Book Co.

The important question of the proportion of total elements in soils which is available to plants has occupied the attention of scientists for many years, but even today there is little consensus concerning the procedure which should be adopted to determine this availability. A number of different tests have been proposed to determine plant-available concentrations of plant nutrients in soils. Perhaps the most meaningful is a bioassay procedure such as that proposed by Slingsby and Brown (1977) in which they planted oat (*Avena sativa*) seedlings in each of 5 pots containing the soil samples. The plants were grown, harvested and analysed for the element concerned. Unfortunately bioassay procedures are slow, time-consuming and expensive, so recourse has to be made to simpler procedures. These can involve extracting the soil with solutions containing: 0.5 M acetic acid (Spence, 1957), 0.5 M ammonium nitrate (Soane and Saunder, 1959), 10% w/v disodium-EDTA (Jensen and Lamm, 1961), neutral ammonium acetate (Soane and Saunder, 1959), and 1 M ammonium chloride (White, 1971). It has been suggested (Proctor and Woodell, 1975) that the use of dilute acid results in an over-estimation of plant-available concentrations of soil elements. However, in a thorough survey of nickel and other elements in British serpentine soils, Slingsby and Brown (1977) demonstrated that bioassay data for several elements including nickel, agreed very well with values obtained from acetic acid extracts of the soils.

The literature concerning plant-available quantities of various elements in serpentine soils is extremely confusing for three main reasons: the multiplicity of frequently contradictory data; the very variable basis of reporting the data (e.g. m.eq./100 g soil, μg/100 g soil, μg.atoms/g soil); and finally the bewildering range of different extractants. In an attempt to bring some sort of order into this confusing situation, Table 4.1 presents data from only three sources (Slingsby and Brown, 1977; Jaffré, 1980; Sasse, 1979a) chosen on the basis of the wide geographical range of the soils and the thoroughness of the surveys. This table has

TABLE 4.1 Mean Total and Exchangeable Elemental Concentration (μmol/g) in Serpentine Soils from Europe and New Caledonia

Element	Extractant	La Flotte (France)	La Roche (France)	Tuscany (Italy)	Kraubath (Austria)	Lizard (UK)	Unst (UK)	Pl.Lacs (New Cal.)	Boulinda (New Cal.)
		n = 5	n = 3	n = 3	n = 3	n = 64	n = 43	n = 13	n =10
Ni	Total	15.10	17.60	28.86	23.60	29.81	105.40	89.00	69.60
	Amm. acet.	0.14	0.15	0.19	0.08	—	—	0.15	0.78
	Dil. HCl	1.92	1.44	3.54	2.78	—	—	—	—
	Amm. nitr.	—	—	—	—	0.03	0.13	—	—
	Acetic acid	—	—	—	—	0.21	0.83	—	—
Cr	Total	10.61	14.56	18.53	2.62	42.71	199.00	498.00	121.10
	Amm. acet.	0.02	0.02	0.03	0.01	—	—	0.05	0.1
	Dil. HCl	0.06	0.05	0.18	0.01	—	—	—	—
Co	Total	2.80	1.54	2.39	2.24	2.40	5.75	12.50	7.81
	Amm. acet.	0.01	0.01	0.02	0.01	—	—	—	—
	Dil HCl	0.12	0.08	0.71	0.43	—	—	—	—
Ca	Total	48.12	5.96	154.00	78.00	363.00	176.00	2.50	20.00
	Amm. acet.	12.05	2.85	28.3	26.50	—	—	0.75	9.20
	Amm. nitr.	—	—	—	—	9.50	4.00	—	—
Mg	Total	1002.00	774.00	6123.00	4013.00	2875.00	6583.00	92.00	5958.00
	Amm. acet.	68.00	78.00	86.00	139.00	—	—	1.75	192.00
	Amm. nitr.	—	—	—	—	40.00	27.00	—	—
Ca/Mg	Total	0.05	0.01	0.03	0.02	0.13	0.03	0.03	0.003
	Amm. acet.	0.18	0.04	0.33	0.19	—	—	0.43	0.05
	Amm. nitr.	—	—	—	—	0.24	0.15	—	—
K	Total	17.00	7.50	14.40	182.00	38.30	2.50	2.50	2.50
	Amm. acet.	2.00	1.30	3.60	2.80	—	—	0.30	2.10
	Amm. nitr.	—	—	—	—	0.005	0.002	—	—
Na	Total	12.20	4.65	5.23	8.34	149.00	35.50	8.70	17.40
	Amm. acet.	3.1	2.48	2.65	2.49	—	—	0.30	3.20
	Amm. nitr.	—	—	—	—	19.75	3.42	—	—
Fe	Total	1439.00	1302.00	1310.00	902.00	1544.00	2641.00	8291.00	2053.00
	Amm. acet.	0.16	0.03	0.10	0.09	—	—	—	—
	Amm. nitr.	—	—	—	—	0.02	0.02	—	—
	Acetic acid	—	—	—	—	0.08	0.08	—	—
Mn	Total	48.20	12.71	21.87	22.17	40.00	54.00	125.00	41.10
	Amm. acet.	0.18	0.10	0.20	0.31	—	—	—	—
P	Total	17.70	6.19	3.04	—	4.66	3.50	6.03	—
	NaHCO	—	—	—	—	1.84	1.00	—	—
	Dil. HCl	0.10	0.04	0.13	—	—	—	—	—
pH		6.1	6.2	7.3	6.8	6.0	6.7	5.2	6.8
Ref.		A	A	A	A	B	B	C	C

A—Sasse (1979a)
B —Slingsby and Brown (1977)
C —Jaffré (1980)

standardised all concentration data to the units μmol (= μgatoms)/g soil) which is a compromise between μg/g and meq./100 g. To convert μmol/g to μg/g (= ppm) it is only necessary to multiply by the atomic mass of the element concerned. Table 4.2 lists other sources of data on plant-available concentrations of plant nutrients in serpentine soils and is by no means complete.

TABLE 4.2   References for Papers which Have Data for Exchangeable or Plant-available Elemental Concentrations in Serpentine Soils

Birrell and Wright (1945)	Del Moral (1982)
Dirven et al. (1976)	Duvigneaud (1966)
Ernst (1972)	Fernandez et al. (1965)
Griffin (1965)	Guitian Ojea and Lopez Lopez (1980)
Halstead (1968)	Hunter (1954)
Hunter and Vergnano (1952)	Jaffré (1980)
Johnston and Proctor (1977, 1979, 1980)	Kinzel (1982)
Koenigs et al. (1982a, 1982b)	Krapfenbauer (1960)
Krause (1958)	Krause et al. (1963)
Krause and Ludwig (1957)	Kruckeberg (1967, 1969)
Lee et al. (1977)	Lopez Lopez and Guitian Ojea (1981)
Main (1974)	McMillan (1956)
Menezes de Sequeira (1969)	Mizuno (1979)
Nemec (1951a, 1951b)	Proctor (1970, 1971a, b, 1972)
Proctor et al. (1980)	Proctor and Cottam (1982)
Proctor and Johnston (1977)	Proctor and Woodel (1971, 1975)
Rabenhorst and Foss (1981)	Ragg and Ball (1964)
Robinson et al. (1935)	Sarosiek (1964)
Sasse (1979a)	Shewry and Peterson (1975, 1976)
Slingsby and Brown (1977)	Spence (1957)
Spence and Millar (1963)	Soane and Saunder (1959)
Tassoulas (1970)	Verger (1979)
Vergnano (1953)	Vergnano Gambi et al. (1982)
Walker (1954)	Walker et al. (1955)
Whittaker (1960)	Wild (1974a, b)
Williams (1967)	Wiltshire (1972)
Woodell et al. (1975)	

The data in Table 4.1 show that there is little uniformity in the values obtained, though one or two trends do emerge. It is clear that calcium is usually more available than magnesium so that soil extracts usually contain a higher Ca/Mg value than the original unextracted soil. This counteracts to some extent the adverse Ca/Mg level in serpentine soils which is said to be a primary cause of their infertility. A second trend which emerges from Table 4.1 is the low solubility of chromium compared to nickel. Even though chromium levels in some serpentine soils may exceed nickel concentrations by a substantial margin, the amount of extracted chromium by plants is nearly always negligible. Iron is likewise very insoluble in serpentine soils. Typically only about 0.01% of the total iron is extracted into ammonium acetate solution.

A novel approach to the problem of determining plant availability of constituents of soils from Scotland and Zimbabwe has been suggested by Proctor et al. (1981) who removed soil solutions from water-saturated serpentine soils by centrifuging at 12,000 g. The solutions were analysed for 8 ions (Ni^{2+}, Ca^{2+}, Mg^{2+}, K^+, Na^+, Cl^-, NO_3^- and PO_4^{3-} These workers concluded that calcium concentrations in the soils were adequate for healthy plant growth and that the possibility of calcium deficiency, as a factor in the serpentine problem, should be reconsidered. Their work has shown that nutrient concentrations in serpentine soils are higher than originally believed.

4.3 TOXIC HEAVY METALS AS A SERPENTINE FACTOR

Robinson et al. (1935) suggested that high levels of phytotoxic nickel and chromium in serpentine soils were responsible for their infertility, since high concentrations of these elements were the only common factors in the serpentine soils which they examined. Because of the very extensive literature which now exists on the phytotoxicity of nickel, chromium and cobalt, it is appropriate to consider each element separately

4.3.1 Nickel

Uptake of nickel by plants

Of the three siderophiles, nickel, cobalt and chromium, the first is the most likely to be a major contributor to the serpentine factor because of the very low availability of chromium and the relatively low abundance of cobalt compared to nickel. Although only about 1% of the total nickel in soils is available to plants, this far exceeds the percentage of available chromium.

The nickel content of plants growing over non-serpentinic soils is in the range 0.1 to 5 μg/g in dry matter (Vanselow, 1966; Brooks, 1983). Over serpentine soils this increases to about 20–100 μg/g. The typical range of nickel values to be expected in serpentine plants is given in Fig. 4.3, and refers to western American species from Oregon and California. It will be noted from this figure that there is a discontinuity between about 200 μg/g for *Viola cuneata* and 5000–10000 μg/g for *Thlaspi montanum* var. *montanum* and *T. siskiyouense*. The last two species are a specialised type of plant containing nickel concentrations an order of magnitude higher than those found in most other serpentine plants. Plants of this class (>1000 μg/g Ni) have been termed "hyperaccumulators of nickel" (Brooks et al. 1977) and will be discussed in chapter 8 of this book.

Plant tolerance to nickel

Plants appear to be remarkably tolerant to high nickel concentrations in serpentine soils. In an attempt to determine the extent to which nickel is a contributor to the serpentine factor, Lee et al. (1977), Brooks and Yang (1984) and Yang et al. (1985) analysed serpentine plants in Zimbabwe and New Caledonia and carried out correlation analysis on concentration data for 18 elements. In both surveys, nickel was correlated only with other siderophiles (Fe, Mn, Co and Cr) and had no relationship to plant nutrients. These studies would appear to indicate that nickel is not a major contributor to the serpentine factor which is in contradiction to the findings of Soane and Saunder (1959) who concluded that nickel toxicity was the cause of the acute infertility of Zimbabwean soils which they tested in pot trials using tobacco, maize, and oat seedlings.

There is an appreciable amount of evidence that plants are readily able to develop tolerance to serpentinic environments. This is shown in Fig. 4.4 which gives the results of pot trials in which various *Alyssum* species were grown in soils containing varying concentrations of nickel. Among these species was the non-serpentine-tolerant *A. serpyllifolium* whose relative, the serpentine-endemic subsp. *lusitanicum* (now elevated by Dudley (1986) to full specific rank and named *A. pintodasilvae*), not only has a much higher nickel content (ca. 10,000 μg/g [= 1.0%]) than has its probable parent, but also tolerates a much higher nickel content in the soil (3000 μg/g in a fully plant-available form compared with 300 μg/g).

Pancaro et al. (1981) studied the effects of cobalt, nickel and chromium on the germination of the serpentine-endemic *Alyssum bertolonii* and *A. argenteum* compared with the non-serpentine *A. nebrodense*. The degree of inhibition was in the order: Cr> Ni> Co. Both endemics showed a greater tolerance to all three metals compared with *A. nebrodense*. Work by Gabbrielli et al. (1982) on the tolerance of all three species to nickel alone, using root elongation and protoplasmic resistance of epidermal cells as criteria, showed that the order of decreasing resistance to nickel was: *A. bertolonii, A. argenteum* and *A. nebrodense*.

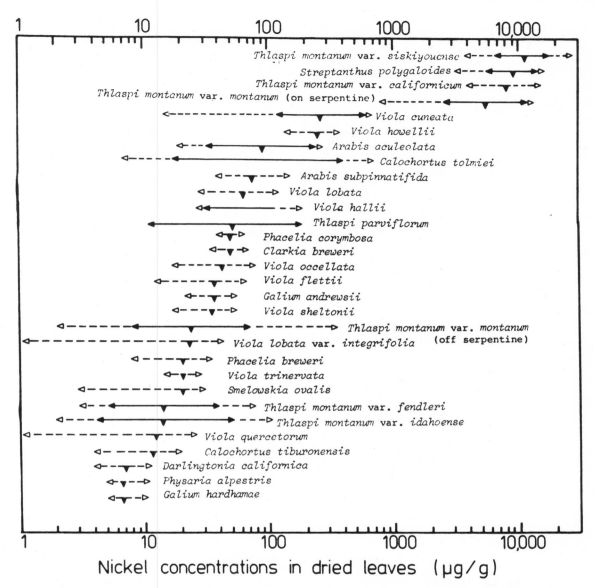

Fig. 4.3.   Representation of means (geometric), standard deviations (continuous lines), and ranges (broken lines) for nickel concentrations in west American plants with serpentine-tolerant representatives.
Source: Reeves et al. (1983).

Perhaps the most extreme example of nickel uptake and tolerance is shown by the New Caledonian tree *Sebertia acuminata* (sève bleue) which contains a blue sap containing 11% nickel as the citrate complex (Jaffré et al. 1976—see also Chapter 8).

A survey of the literature on nickel as an important contributor to the serpentine factor reveals that there is a great deal of contradictory evidence. The positive evidence may be summarized as follows: Sasse (1979a, b) studied serpentine soils and vegetation in ultramafic areas of France, Germany, Austria and Italy. He made the observation that dense and richer vegetation was always associated with lower nickel levels in the soil. Heath and pine forest only occurred when total nickel concentrations in the soils were below 880 µg/g. Whereas these findings may be true for non-endemic vegetation on serpentine, Lee at al. (1975) determined elemental levels in soils supporting endemic and non-endemic plants in a New

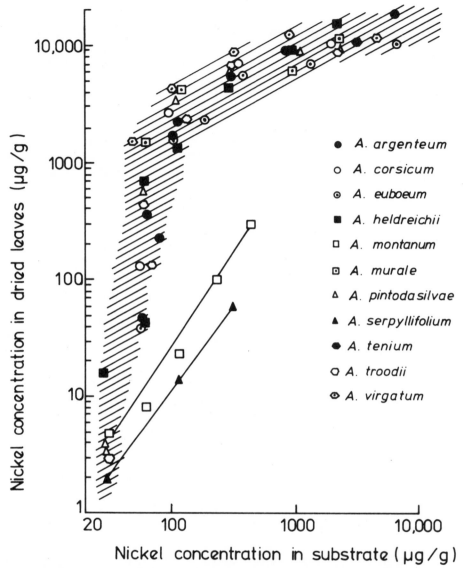

Fig. 4.4.   Nickel concentrations (μg/g) in dried leaves of *Alyssum* species as a function of nickel concentrations (μg/g) measured in the substrate.
Source: Morrison et al. (1980).

Zealand serpentine barren. They found that the endemic species *Pimelea suteri* and *Myosotis monroi* grew over soils with consistently higher nickel levels than the non-endemic species *Cassinia vauvilliersii* and *Leptospermum scoparium*. This is illustrated in Fig. 4.5.

In pot trials on populations of *Linanthus androsaceus* growing on and off serpentines, Woodell et al. (1975) concluded that nickel and chromium toxicity was a contributory factor to the inability of non-adapted strains of these species to colonise ultramafic substrates.

The classical work of Hunter and Vergnano (1952) has frequently been cited as a justification for the statement that nickel is a prime cause of the infertility of serpentine soils. The work was carried out over experimental plots at Whitecairns north of Aberdeen in Scotland. Deficiency symptoms of nickel toxicity disappeared after liming the ground. This was asserted to be evidence for the overriding influence of nickel toxicity upon the crops. Adding lime of course increases the pH and decreases the availability of nickel as was also shown by the work of Mizuno (1968) in Fig. 4.6.

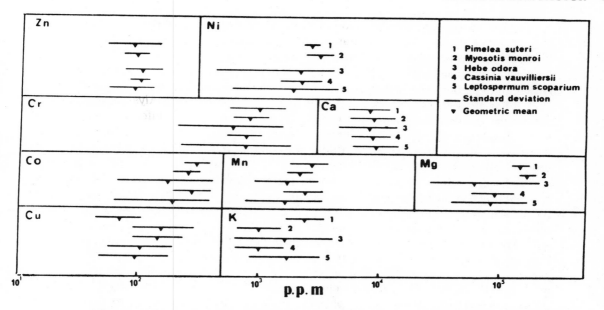

Fig. 4.5. Elemental concentrations in soils supporting serpentine-tolerant plants from the Dun Mountain area, New Zealand.
Source: Lee et al. (1975).

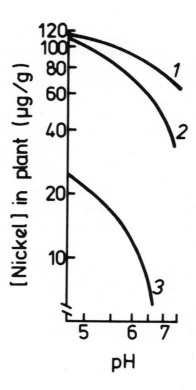

Fig. 4.6. The effect of liming serpentine soils supporting various crops: (1) potato, (2) alfalfa, (3) oats.
Source: Mizuno (1968).

There has already been mention of the work of Proctor et al. (1981) on soil solutions extracted directly from water-saturated serpentine soils. Johnston and Proctor (1981) grew *Festuca rubra* in water cultures containing the same ion concentrations as in the soil solutions of Scottish soils. The observed toxicity symptoms were similar to those observed by growing the plants directly in the soils from which these solutions had been obtained.

It has already been shown how nickel tolerance has evolved in *Alyssum serpyllifolium* subsp. *lusitanicum* in comparison with its probable parent *A. serpyllifolium*. The same has been demonstrated in nickel-tolerant strains of many species not distinguishable morphologically from non-tolerant strains. An example was undertaken by Ernst (1972) who tested the plasmolytic resistance of various strains of *Indigofera dyeri* grown in a graduated series of nickel nitrate solutions. He showed that a population of *I. setiflora* from serpentine at Tipperary Claims in Zimbabwe was resistant to nickel but not to other elements such as copper which were abundant in this ore deposit. This a particularly good indication of selective development of tolerance to a specific element.

The above studies would seem to indicate that nickel toxicity is an important if not overriding component of the serpentine factor. Other workers, however, (e.g., Slingsby and Brown, 1977) do not consider it to be so. At the opposite extreme there are workers who assert that the chemical components of soil play little or no part in controlling the serpentine floras, and that the main factors are physical. For example, Koenigs et al. (1982a) carried out studies on serpentine soils and floras in California using principal components analysis and found no correlation between vegetation and soil chemistry. Similarly, Koenigs et al. (1982b) found no evidence for nickel, chromium or cobalt having a controlling influence on another Californian serpentine stand.

Factors contributing to the phytotoxicity of nickel

Whether or not nickel in serpentine soils exerts a strong toxic effect on plants depends on a number of contributory factors related to other constituents in the soil. The first of these is pH (see above), as it is well known that adding lime to serpentine soils decreases the availability of nickel and decreases the toxicity of the soil (Hunter and Vergnano, 1952; Crooke, 1956; Halstead, 1968; Halstead et al. 1969).

Some workers (Crooke et al. 1954; Mizuno, 1968) consider that the toxicity of nickel is due to iron deficiency caused by competition between these two elements. Even though serpentine soils contain a very high iron content, the proportion of plant-available iron is extremely low (of the order of 0.01%), so that iron deficiency could possibly arise in the presence of high nickel levels in the soil. Because of the greater availability of nickel, soil extracts contain equal amounts of iron and nickel even though the total iron content of the soil is about 100 times greater.

The presence of organic matter in soils can also reduce nickel toxicity by removing this metal as a chelate complex (Crooke, 1956; Halstead, 1969; Halstead et al. 1969). Usually however, particularly in well-leached tropical serpentine soils, the organic content is relatively low in these soils so that nickel is less likely to be complexed by organic matter. There is the further point that serpentine soils being less fertile than other soils support less vegetation to provide the organic matter, hence compounding nickel toxicity.

It has also been observed that nickel toxicity of serpentine soils is apparently reduced in the presence of plant nutrients such as nitrogen, potassium and magnesium (Crooke and Inkson, 1955; Hunter and Vergnano, 1952; Kock, 1956; Crooke et al. 1954). Since serpentine soils are low in many nutrients, nickel toxicity is once again compounded.

4.3.2 Chromium

Uptake of chromium by plants

Apart from nickel, chromium is the major siderophile in serpentine soils which is suspected of having toxic effects on vegetation. The chromium content of non-serpentinic soils is on the order of 100 $\mu g/g$, whereas in serpentine soils values of around 5000 $\mu g/g$ (0.5%) are common; but the range of concentrations is from 1000 to 25,000 $\mu g/g$, with the latter commonly found in heavily-leached tropical serpentine soils such as those of New Caledonia (Jaffré, 1980). The variability of these concentrations is due to the scattered occurrence of chromite, the source of most of the chromium in the soils. Nickel, however, readily substitutes as the Ni^{2+} ion in magnesium minerals because of the similarity of charge and ionic radius of Ni^{2+} and Mg^{2+} and therefore has a more uniform abundance than does chromium.

It has been shown (Table 4.1 and Fig. 4.1) that chromium concentrations in the plant-available form are extremely low in serpentine soils at their mean pH of 6.8. This low solubility is reflected in the very slight uptake of this element by plants. It is my experience that serpentine plants seldom, if ever, have a chromium content exceeding 100 $\mu g/g$. Indeed this low level of uptake can be used to gauge the degree of contamination of plant samples by soil. Brooks and Yang (1984) found a maximum of only 77 $\mu g/g$ chromium in serpentine-endemic plants of the Great Dyke, Zimbabwe. Similarly, Jaffré et al. (1979) found a mean chromium content not exceeding 45 $\mu g/g$ in 17 species (132 specimens) of Geissois from New Caledonia where Lee et al. (1977) found <10 $\mu g/g$ chromium in Homalium guillainii growing over soils containing nearly 1% of this element. These findings apparently contradict work by Lyon et al. 1970, and Wild (1974a), who both reported a very high chromium content in serpentine plants. However in the case of the work by Lyon et al. (1970), we believe that the chromium values may be too high due to unexpected spectral line interference in the emission spectrographic technique used at that time. Wild (1974a) has reported very high chromium concentrations in the Zimbabwean serpentine endemic Sutera fodina (ca. 2400 $\mu g/g$ in dried material). The sample was collected, however, in the vicinity of the Noro chrome mine and I believe that it may have been contaminated by wind-blown dust, since other specimens of the same species from other parts of the Great Dyke (Brooks and Yang, 1984), gave a maximum of only 2 $\mu g/g$ chromium in dried leaves.

Plant tolerance to chromium

There is no record of specific adaptation of plant to chromium-rich soils, although Soane and Saunder (1959) found that maize had a greater tolerance to chromium than had tobacco. Scharrer and Schropp (1935) found that oats (Avena sativa), rye (Secale cereale), wheat (Triticum sp.) and maize (Zea mays) were more resistant to chromium than were barley (Hordeum vulgare), and peas (Pisum sativum).

Factors contributing to chromium toxicity

Chromium can readily exist in both cationic (chromic) and anionic (chromate) forms. Lyon et al. (1969a, b) found that chromium existed in the chromate form when taken up by the serpentine-tolerant Leptospermum scoparium. Scharrer and Schropp (1935) and Hewitt (1953) have suggested that the anionic form of chromium is more phytotoxic than the cationic state. At present, however, very little is known about the form of chromium in serpentine plants.

Proctor (1969, 1971b) has shown that the chromic ion toxicity is reduced by the presence of calcium ions. This ties in with the findings of Lyon et al. (1971) that serpentine-tolerant Leptospermum scoparium has a high calcium content. This may explain its tolerance to serpentine soil.

To conclude, it must be emphasized that there is no real evidence that the chromium in serpentine soils is to any degree responsible for the toxicity of such substrates. I do not believe that chromium is part of the serpentine problem, particularly as the chromic ion concentration in equilibrium with the hydroxide at pH 6.8 is only 10 $\mu g/ml$. It is also noteworthy that there are no reliable records of any floras specifically adapted to chromium-rich soils anywhere on earth, though there are many adapted to nickel and/or cobalt (Brooks, 1983; Brooks and Malaisse, 1985).

4.3.3 Cobalt

Uptake of cobalt by Plants

The cobalt content of non-serpentine soils is around 20 μg/g though serpentine soils can contain 500 μg/g of this element. The mean cobalt content of non-serpentine vegetation is only about 1 μg/g on a dry weight basis. Some plants, however, such as *Nyssa sylvatica* and *N. sinensis* can contain over 500 μg/g even when growing over non-cobaltiferous substrates (Brooks et al. 1977). The above example shows that under certain conditions, cobalt is readily available to plants, particularly as the solubility of the hydroxide is relatively high at pH 6.8.

As the availability of cobalt and nickel to plants is similar, it is not surprising to find hyperaccumulators of cobalt (>1000 μg/g in dry material) as well as hyperaccumulators of nickel (see Chapter 8). Brooks et al. (1980) have listed 15 taxa of cobalt tolerant plants from the Shaban Copper Arc in Zaire which have this hyperaccumulator status (see also Brooks and Malaisse, 1985). One of these plants (*Haumaniastrum robertii*) contained 10,000 μg/g (1.0%) cobalt. Among serpentinophytes, however, no such hyperaccumulators are known. This is probably because of the relatively low (compared to nickel) concentrations of cobalt. Typical cobalt levels in serpentine plants are around 10 μg/g; however, species capable of hyperaccumulating nickel are also capable of accumulating anomalously high concentrations of cobalt. For example, Brooks and Yang (1984) have reported 115 μg/g cobalt in the Zimbabwean *Pearsonia metallifera* which also contained 13,600 μg/g (1.36%) nickel.

Tolerance of plants to cobalt

Pot trials on crop plants by Scharrer and Schropp (1933) showed that in order of decreasing resistance to cobalt were: maize, barley, wheat, rye, oats and peas. Cobalt at high concentrations is certainly phytotoxic as has been shown for cobaltiferous areas of Africa (Brooks and Malaisse, 1985), but there is no evidence that the levels of this element present in serpentine soils are toxic to any degree, and it is unlikely that cobalt is a cause of or contributes appreciably to the serpentine factor.

4.4 CALCIUM AND MAGNESIUM AS SERPENTINE FACTORS

4.4.1 Introduction

The role played by calcium and magnesium in controlling the nature and distribution of serpentine floras is considered by many workers to be the most important component of the serpentine factor. There are three ways in which calcium and/or magnesium levels in serpentine soils can affect the vegetation which can colonise this type of vegetation: (a) the toxicity of magnesium; (b) deficiency of calcium; (c) an unfavourable Ca/Mg quotient in the soil. Each of these will now be discussed.

4.4.2 The Unfavourable Effects of Magnesium

The unfavourable effect of magnesium is considered to be one of the most likely causes of the serpentine problem. This subject has been reviewed thoroughly by Krause (1958) and by Kinzel (1982) and has been known for over 150 years since Davy (1814) showed the deleterious effects of liming soils with dolomite. Part of this toxicity is derived from the very high magnesium content of some soils, which can be as high as 36% MgO (Table 3.3), coupled with the relatively high plant-availability of magnesium minerals. Proctor (1971b) reported up to 4320 μg/ml of magnesium in soil solutions from the Meikle Kilrannoch serpentine outcrop. He used vegetation from the same soil to measure the tolerance of *Agrostis canina* in solutions of varying magnesium content. A comparison was made with an *Agrostis stolonifera* from non-serpentine soil. The results are shown in Fig. 4.7 and clearly show the much greater tolerance to magnesium, of the serpentine *Agrostis canina*.

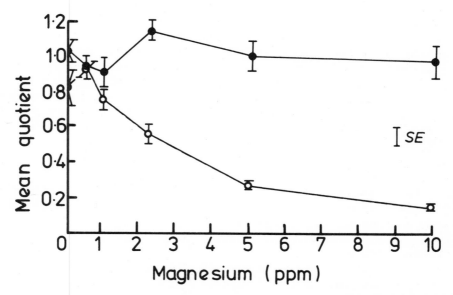

Fig. 4.7. Mean ratio of growth in length of longest adventitious roots in magnesium solutions/growth in distilled water. Solid circles = *Agrostis canina* from Meikle Kilrannoch; open circles = *A. stolonifera* from non-serpentine soil.
Source: Proctor (1971b).

If plants need to develop a specific tolerance to magnesium (as opposed to chromium which appears to be virtually 100% non-available to plants), the magnesium must be clearly phytotoxic, at least at the concentrations encountered. An illustration of this adaptation is the observation that many plants from maritime environments such as *Cochlearia officinalis*, *Silene maritima*, *Herniaria ciliolata*, *Armeria maritima* and *Asparagus officinalis* subsp. *prostratus* (Kruckeberg, 1954; Ferreira, 1963; Proctor, 1971a) are likewise tolerant to serpentine. In both environments an excess of magnesium is encountered and has to be coped with.

As reported by Kinzel (1982), Ferreira (1964) carried out pot trials using a soil deficient in calcium and magnesium, to which were added calcium and magnesium salts in varying proportions and absolute amounts. He then grew calcicolous and basiphilous plants in these media and found that all species grew better when calcium salts were added. Addition of magnesium salts however produced toxic symptoms only in the calcicolous plants such as *Saxifraga aizoides*, *S. oppositifolia* and *Dryas octopetala*, whereas the basiphilous *Lychnis alpina* and *Minuartia verna* thrived under these conditions.

In a well-known experiment by Walker et al. (1955), two species of sunflower, the serpentine-endemic *Helianthus bolanderi* subsp. *exilis* and the common sunflower *H. annuus*, were grown in nutrient solutions containing incremental magnesium concentrations. The marked differences in the tolerance of the two taxa showed that the serpentine-endemic *H. bolanderi* subsp. *exilis* had a marked tolerance to magnesium. Later, Madhok and Walker (1969) showed that the latter grew very well in a solution containing 20 m.eq./L of magnesium, whereas this concentration was lethal to *H. annuus*.

Some mention should also be made of the work of Jørgensen (1974) who studied a serpentine flora at Høle in southwest Norway. The substrate is unusual in that the soil contains high levels of plant nutrients (34% CaO and more than adequate levels of nitrogen, potassium and phosphorus). The magnesium content is 13% MgO. Despite these favourable nutritional factors for plant growth, the Høle area shows the appearance of a typical serpentine barren and furnishes perhaps one of the best known examples of the effect of magnesium alone in controlling a serpentine flora.

The role of magnesium in controlling plant growth on serpentine is further illustrated by the work of Brooks and Yang (1984) on serpentine-endemic plants from the Great Dyke, Zimbabwe. In the plant material there was a highly significant inverse relationship between the concentrations of magnesium and the nutrients boron, iron, manganese, phosphorus and sodium. These findings point to the great importance of antagonism to nutrient uptake caused by high magnesium levels in the soil. Brooks and Yang (1984) considered that high magnesium levels were one of the principal factors in the serpentine problem.

Main (1970) showed that magnesium tolerance was an inherited character by hybridizing serpentine and non-serpentine strains of *Agropyron spicatum*. He found that the hybrids had a magnesium tolerance intermediate between that of the parents.

The toxicity of magnesium is probably due as much to antagonism to other elements as it is to the phytotoxicity of this metal itself. For example, Krapfenbauer (1969) studied the nutrition of forest species on serpentine and showed a marked antagonism to potassium uptake by pine and spruce trees.

4.4.3 Calcium Deficiency

The calcium content of serpentine soils is extremely low (Table 4.1) and in some cases (e.g., New Caledonian lateritic soils) is <100 μg/g. Low calcium concentrations are not, however, the primary cause of serpentine infertility; but the situation is exacerbated by Ca/Mg quotients which are usually very low compared with non-serpentinic soils. If present in large enough concentrations, calcium has the ability to counteract deleterious effects of ions such as Na^+, Mg^{2+}, and H^+ which might otherwise damage vegetation (Wallace et al. 1966; Wyn Jones and Lunt,1967). Deficiency of calcium therefore results in a lowered tolerance to other elements in the soil. Experimental work by Crooks and Inkson (1955), Jowett (1958), Gregory and Bradshaw (1965) and Proctor (1971b) has shown that addition of calcium can greatly reduce the incidence of nickel toxicity symptoms in vegetation.

Gigon (1975) determined which of several factors distinguished the fertility of two different soils. He added carbonate to a serpentine soil and noted the appearance of a calciphilous vegetation in spite of the presence of phytotoxic nickel and chromium. He considered that the serpentine factor was related not to nickel and chromium but to nutrient deficiences and imbalances.

It is clear that serpentine plants are adapted to low calcium levels in the substrate. This was convincingly demonstrated by Main (1981) by use of the serpentine-endemic *Poa curtifolia* (Fig. 4.8) which showed decreasing yields for increasing calcium concentrations in test solutions containing a constant amount of magnesium. Similar findings were made by Walker et al. (1955) using the serpentine-endemic *Helianthus bolanderi* which showed no increase of yield when calcium was added to serpentine soils. In sharp contrast to this, buckwheat and the common sunflower *H. annuus* showed greatly increased yields (Fig. 4.9).

A rather novel approach to studying plant adaptation to low levels of calcium in serpentine soils was that of Willett and Batey (1977) who measured the root phosphatase (an enzyme which enables plants to utilize phosphorus) levels of plants tolerant and intolerant of serpentine. Addition of calcium to serpentine soils in which the plants were growing, increased the phosphatase activity of only the tolerant species: *Festuca rubra, F. pratensis* and *Holcus lanatus* and there was no effect on the non-tolerant *Phleum pratense* and *Lolium perenne*. The same subject was studied by Alexander and Hardy (1981) who found that phosphatase activity in the root systems of the Sitka spruce (*Picea sitchensis*) was inversely related to the phosphorus content of the soil and clearly showed the association between phosphorus levels and the enzyme.

There are many references in the literature to the beneficial effects of addition of calcium to serpentine soils. Workers such as Walker (1954) believe that this indicates

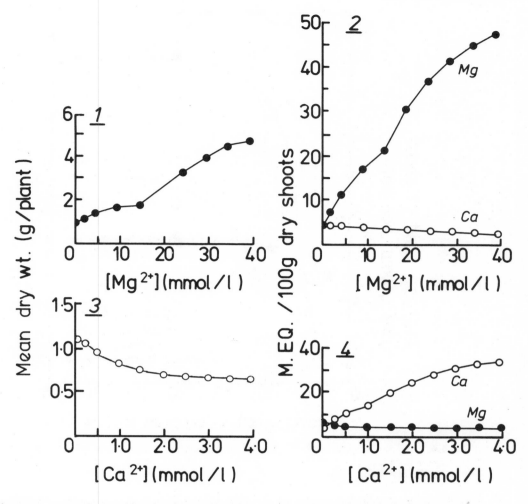

Fig. 4.8.   Mean plant yield and cation content in the shoots of *Poa curtifolia* grown in varying magnesium and calcium levels: (1) yield at increasing magnesium levels, (2) cation content in shoots at increasing magnesium levels, (3) yield at increasing calcium levels, (4) cation content in shoots at increasing calcium levels.
Source: Main (1981).

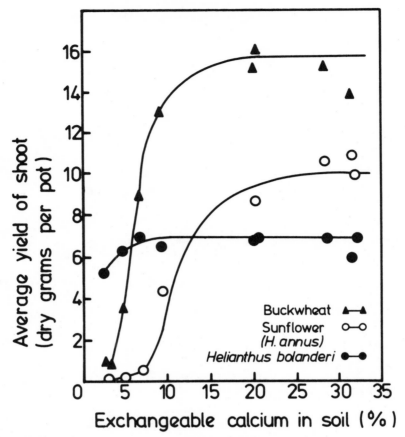

Fig. 4.9. Yields of *Helianthus bolanderi, H. annuus* and buckwheat as affected by % exchangeable calcium in the soil.
Source: Walker et al. (1955).

calcium deficiency as being one of the principal causes of the serpentine problem. This may not however be the case, as it is equally likely that the physiological effects of low calcium concentrations are related to the ability of this element to prevent damage from other metals rather than to calcium deficiency *per se*. It should also be pointed out, as noted by Robinson et al. (1935), that many non-serpentine soils have an equally low, or even lower calcium status without displaying a serpentine-type vegetation.

Important recent work by Robertson (1985) has shown fairly conclusively that for *Zea mays* at least, magnesium and calcium do indeed protect this plant from the toxic effects of nickel. He carried out experiments on maize tillers grown in water cultures containing a constant amount (0.25 mg/L) of nickel and varying amounts (in separate experiments) of calcium and magnesium (0–4096 mg/L). The results of these experiments are shown in Fig. 4.10 and represent the tolerance index (percentage change in length in 48 h of roots compared with 100% for tillers grown in the control solutions) expressed as a function of the concentration of magnesium or calcium. Tolerance rose to maximum at 4 mg/L and 32 mg/L respectively for these two nutrients. Excess of magnesium or calcium produced its own toxic effects at concentrations exceeding 64 and 1000 mg/L respectively. This work gives one of the best indications so far of the beneficial effects of calcium and magnesium in ameliorating the toxicity of nickel.

Despite the work reported above, the role of low calcium levels in serpentine soils remains unclear at present. All that can be said, with any degree of certainty, is that addition of calcium to serpentine soils does indeed increase their fertility.

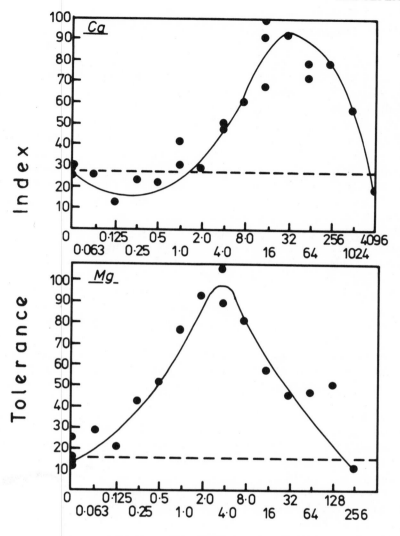

Fig. 4.10 Dose response curves showing the protective effects of magnesium and calcium ions as measured by the growth of roots of *Zea mays* in water cultures containing a constant amount (0.25 mg/L of nickel). Maximum tolerance as measured by the tolerance index (percentage change of length of roots after 48 h compared with controls), was at 4 and 32 mg/L of magnesium and calcium. Source: Robertson (1985).

4.4.4 The Calcium/Magnesium Quotient

An unfavourable Ca/Mg value in serpentine soils has been for many years a suggested reason for their infertility ever since Loew and May (1901) concluded that a soil Ca/Mg quotient greater than unity was necessary for healthy plant growth. Similar conclusions were reached by Lipman (1916), Vlamis and Jenny (1948), Vlamis (1949), Kruckeberg (1954), Walker (1954), Proctor and Woodell (1975), Woodell et al. (1975), and Woolhouse (1983). Other workers such as Sasse (1979a), however, have relegated this factor to second place behind nickel toxicity. Wallace et al. (1977) have shown from experiments on the bush bean (*Phaseolus vulgaris*) grown in serpentine soils, that compensating for calcium deficiency by liming, also increased the magnesium uptake and resulted in higher yields.

The total Ca/Mg quotient as opposed to the exchangeable quotient in soils, differs by a factor of about 50–100 due to the much lower availability of magnesium compared to calcium (see Table 4.1). For example, Shewry and Peterson (1975) found Ca/Mg atom quotients averaging 0.4 and 0.007 respectively for the total and exchangeable values in Shetland serpentine soils, whereas for Aberdeen serpentines the corresponding values were 0.12 and 0.009. This is in sharp contrast with Ca/Mg quotients of about 5 and 1.5 for the total and exchangeable values for non-serpentine soils. Clearly the adverse total Ca/Mg quotient is ameliorated to some extent by the greater solubility of calcium. This is illustrated in Fig. 4.11 which shows the range of extractable Ca/Mg values for serpentine and non-serpentine soils (94 samples). The two populations are entirely separated by a Ca/Mg quotient of 0.70.

Johnston and Proctor (1979) examined serpentine soils from the Lime Hill area of Scotland and noted a very high (for serpentine) Ca/Mg value of 0.7 which accounted for the relatively luxuriant vegetation of this area despite fairly high heavy metal concentrations in the soil.

Ca/Mg atom quotients in plants reflect to some extent the same quotients (total and/or exchangeable) in soils. Data for Ca/Mg values in various families of plants are shown in Table 4.3 which represents 326 species of 18 families with a mean value of 5.29. The data show that there is a tendency for families well represented on serpentine to have lower-than-average Ca/Mg quotients. For example, the Caryophyllaceae have a mean value of only 2.77. Colonisation of serpentine by the Caryophyllaceae has been discussed by Kinzel (1982). According to Patschowsky (1920), Kinzel (1963) and Lew (1974), this family readily secretes oxalate in the vacuoles of individual species. Both calcium and magnesium are very insoluble in the presence of excess oxalate as the solubility products of their oxalates are 1.8×10^{-9} and 8.6×10^{-5} respectively. Therefore the concentrations of both elements in the vacuole solution will be extremely small (0.008 and 240 μg/ml respectively) and although the Ca/Mg atom quotient then reaches the extremely unfavourable value of 2×10^{-5}, this does not appear to be important because of the extremely low concentrations of each ion.

The work of Main (1981) on the serpentine-endemic *Poa curtifolia* has already been discussed in connection with calcium deficiency. The same worker studied the interaction between calcium and magnesium in the metabolism of this taxon. Fig. 4.8 shows the results of experiments in which yield and elemental content were plotted as a function of varying calcium and magnesium concentrations of *Poa curtifolia* seedlings grown in culture solutions. A constant concentration of 0.5 mmol/L of the other ion was used in the experiments with varying concentrations of calcium and magnesium. The yield and magnesium concentrations of plant material increased with the increased magnesium levels, whereas the calcium content decreased to give a Ca/Mg quotient of 0.014 at a magnesium concentration of 40 mmol/L. This was not accompanied by any loss of yield. The calcium content of 2.04 meq./100 g dry tissue is only about half that reported by Johnston (1974) for *Festuca* sp. and by Proctor (1969) for *Agrostis stolonifera*. In the varying calcium experiments of Main (1981) with *Poa curtifolia*, yields actually decreased and the Ca/Mg value reached a

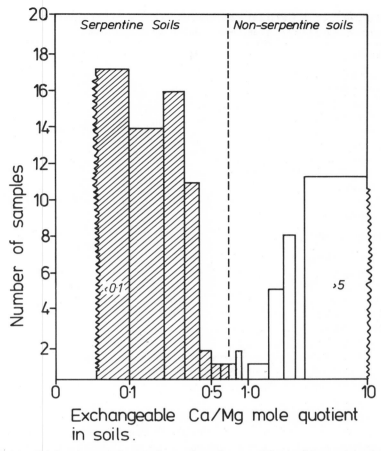

Fig. 4.11   Calcium/magnesium mole quotients in serpentine and non-serpentine soils. After: Krause (1958).

limiting value of 17. This high Ca/Mg quotient was clearly not acceptable to the serpentine-endemic plant because of the decreased yields shown in Fig. 4.8.

4.4.5 Plant Nutrient Deficiencies

The fourth and final factor which may be connected with the serpentine problem is the paucity of plant nutrients in serpentine soils. Levels of nitrogen, phosphorus and potassium are particularly low in these soils though this is partially offset by their optimum availability at pH 6.8 (typical for serpentine soils). One of the earliest references to this aspect of the serpentine problem was by Gordon and Lipman (1926) who regarded nitrogen and phosphorus deficiency as being particularly important. Similar observations concerning these and other nutrients were made by Minguzzi and Vergnano (1953), Walker (1954), Spence and Millar (1963), Sarosiek (1964), Griffin (1965), Rai et al. (1970), Proctor and Woodell (1971), Ferreira and Wormell (1971), Mizuno (1979), and Turitzin (1981).

The low concentrations of available phosphorus in serpentine soils may possibly be related to the high affinity of soluble phosphates to serpentine. This has been demonstrated by Bulusu et al. (1978) who passed phosphate solutions through columns packed with serpentine minerals and found that a cubic metre of serpentine removed about 1.5 kg of phosphate from solution. Many workers have observed that the low nutrient status of serpentine soils is reflected in low levels of these nutrients in serpentine vegetation. For example, Birrell and Wright (1945) reported that the New Caledonian *Araucaria muelleri*

TABLE 4.3 Percentage of Calcium and Magnesium (in dry matter) in the Aerial Parts of Serpentine Plants Classified According to Families

Family	Species	Samples	Ca	Mg	Ca/Mg**
Saccharomycetae	7	7	1.78	2.89	1.04
Chenopodiaceae	11	54	10.68	6.79	2.67
Lycopodiae	3	3	2.19	1.39	2.67
*Caryophyllaceae	8	14	11.13	6.82	2.77
*Ascomycetae	17	17	2.01	1.11	3.07
Basidiomycetae	21	23	2.35	1.17	3.40
*Polypodiaceae	8	8	6.49	3.10	3.56
*Leguminosae (Genisteae)	5	7	4.28	1.71	4.25
*Ericaceae	4	10	3.80	1.41	4.59
Asteraceae	28	45	15.91	5.25	5.15
Cyperaceae	7	7	4.83	1.58	5.20
Mean of 326 species	326	883	10.08	3.24	5.29
Polygonaceae	5	25	16.18	5.00	5.48
Lemnaceae	4	6	8.10	2.31	5.96
Fabaceae (Trifoliae)	25	294	13.73	3.05	7.65
Apiaceae	4	9	23.15	4.45	8.84
Brassicaceae	6	13	15.99	2.60	10.50
Nymphaceae	2	5	18.75	2.06	15.47

* Families with many representatives growing on serpentine soils
** Quotient expressed in terms of moles
Source: Krause (1958).

contained only one sixth as much phosphate as *A. cookii* growing on greywacke. White (1971) analysed about 100 serpentine and non-serpentine plants for nitrogen and found that almost without exception, the former had a lower nitrogen content.

Experiments in which serpentine soils have been artificially fertilized usually result in improved crop yields, though some workers (Blackshaw, 1921; Vlamis, 1949; Johnson et al. 1952; Soane and Saunder, 1959, Proctor, 1971a) have reported no improvement. The main reason for this is that although factors such as high nickel and chromium concentrations and low Ca/Mg quotients are a common feature of most serpentine soils, a low nutrient status is not always universal. For example, Robinson et al. (1935) noted that the calcium, potassium and phosphorus status of most serpentine soils, though low, was no lower than many non-serpentine soils which were farmed successfully. Turitzin (1981) proposed that nutrient deficiency is the main cause of the serpentine problem. His conclusions were based on pot trials with the annual grasses *Bromus mollis* and *Vulpia microstachys*.

Many of the deficiency symptoms found in plants growing on serpentine soils may be due to restriction of nutrient uptake by competition from other ions. For example, Brooks and Yang (1984) studied 20 serpentine-endemic plants from the Great Dyke, Zimbabwe and observed inverse statistical correlations between the magnesium content of these plants and the concentrations of nutrients such as boron, iron, manganese, phosphorus and sodium.

There are several studies (e.g., Proctor 1971a) which have shown that serpentine-tolerant plants have a relatively poor rate of growth when transferred to soils with adequate amounts of plant nutrients. Apart from nitrogen, potassium and phosphorus, there have been some studies on molybdenum deficiency in serpentine soils (Walker, 1948a, b, 1954; Johnson et al. 1952; Mizuno, 1979). Mizuno (1979) showed that symptoms of molybdenum deficiency were reduced when calcium was added to experimental pots containing plants grown in serpentine soils. This improvement was probably due to increased availability of molybdenum at higher pH values (see Fig. 4.2). Conversely, Millikan (1947) showed that addition of molybdenum mitigated heavy metal toxicity in soils.

4.5 GENERAL CONCLUSIONS

The discussion in the preceding pages of this chapter shows that we are hardly any closer today to solving or explaining the serpentine factor, than we were 50 years ago. Although the evidence is still confusing and contradictory, a degree of consensus is starting to emerge as to some aspects of the problem. The first of these is that no single factor is responsible for the infertility of serpentine soils but rather that a combination of factors (including edaphic-biotic, Tadros, 1957), varying from region to region, is in the main responsible.

The high concentrations of nickel, cobalt and chromium in serpentine soils were first thought to be of overriding importance as the controlling factor for serpentine vegetation. But many workers now consider that the chromium and cobalt soil content has little or no influence on the plant cover because of the very low abundance of plant-available chromium and the lower toxicity of cobalt, which in any case has a low concentration relative to chromium and nickel. Nickel toxicity does, however, remain a probable source of some or much of the toxicity of serpentine soils.

The effects of adverse Ca/Mg quotients in serpentine soils continue to occupy the attention of many workers in this field. Calcium *per se* appears to play a key role in reduction or elimination of the toxic effects of magnesium and/or nickel upon the vegetation of serpentine areas. The work of Jørgensen (1974) on the nutrient-rich serpentines of Høle, Norway, highlights the toxicity of excess magnesium levels in soils.

We may perhaps state that the serpentine factor is related primarily to the absolute or relative abundance of the key elements magnesium, nickel and calcium. Although deficiency of plant nutrients in serpentine soils is an obvious reason for infertility, such infertility may arise not so much from absolute concentrations of such elements in the soil, as from antagonism to their uptake by other constituents—primarily nickel and magnesium, whose effects may or may not be ameliorated by the pH and calcium status of the soil. Reduced to its simplest elements, it may be proposed that the serpentine problem is related to concentrations of the above key elements and also to the pH of the soil.

Several workers have suggested that the presence of serpentine plants may be related to some specific nutritional requirement of such taxa—i.e., a genetic factor. The bulk of evidence tends, however, to negate such arguments. For example, Kruckeberg (1954) showed that the serpentine-endemic *Streptanthus glandulosus* var. *pulchellus* grew very well on non-serpentine soil but was quickly overwhelmed by weeds which also flourished in the same medium. The growth of endemic plants on serpentine is probably related to the freedom from competition which these substrates provide, rather than to a specific nutritional requirement. It has also been observed (Morrison, 1980) that plants tolerant of mineralized ground soon succumb to attack from fungi when grown on non-mineralized soils. Fungi are scarce in mineralized soils so that endemic plants never acquire a tolerance to them.

Kinzel (1982) has suggested that serpentine-tolerant families such as the Caryophyllaceae are able to tolerate magnesium by precipitating this element as the oxalate. Another mechanism of tolerance to serpentine is provided by plants such as *Sedum* which is calciotrophic and has a very efficient mechanism for extracting calcium from soils deficient in this element.

The serpentine problem is still not solved after perhaps nearly a century of effort, but some progress has been made in the past 30 years and there seems no doubt that some time, perhaps before the turn of the century, a firm consensus will emerge defining the true nature of the serpentine problem and its solution. When that stage is reached, it will represent the unravelling of what is one of the most important problems in plant physiology today. The solution will depend above all on co-operation between scientists of many disciplines: analytical chemists, biochemists, plant physiologists, botanists, biosystematists and many others.

REFERENCES

Alexander, I. J. and Hardy, K., 1981. Surface phosphatase activity of Sitka spruce mycorrhizas from a serpentine site. *Soil Biol. Biochem.*, 13: 301–305.

Amidei, G., 1841. Specie di plante osservate nei terrani serpentinesi. *Atti Terza Riunione Scienz. It.* Firenze: 523–524.

Birrell, K. S. and Wright, A. C. S. 1945. A serpentine soil in New Caledonia. *N.Z. J. Sci. Technol.*, 27A: 72–76.

Blackshaw, G. N., 1921. Magnesia impregnated soils. *S. Afr. J. Sci.*, 17: 171–178.

Brooks, R. R., 1983. *Biological Methods of Prospecting for Minerals.* Wiley, New York.

Brooks, R. R., Lee, J., Reeves, R. D. and Jaffré, T., 1977. Determination of nickeliferous rocks by analysis of herbarium specimens of indicator plants. *J. Geochem. Explor.*, 7: 49–57.

Brooks, R. R. and Malaisse, F., 1985. *The Heavy Metal Tolerant Flora of South Central Africa—a Multidisciplinary Approach.* Balkema, Rotterdam.

Brooks, R. R., McCleave, J. A. and Schofield, E. K., 1977. Cobalt and nickel uptake by the Nyssaceae. *Taxon*, 26: 197–201.

Brooks, R. R., Reeves, R. D., Morrison, R. S. and Malaisse, F., 1980. Hyperaccumulators of copper and cobalt—a review. *Bull. Soc. Roy. Bot. Belg.*, 113: 166–172.

Brooks, R. R. and Yang, X. H., 1984. Elemental levels and relationships in the endemic serpentine flora of the Great Dyke, Zimbabwe, and their significance as controlling factors for this flora. *Taxon*, 33: 392–399.

Bulusu, K. R., Kulkarn, D. N. and Lutade, S. L., 1978. Phosphate removal by serpentine mineral. *Ind. J. Environ. Hlth.*, 20: 268–271.

Caesalpino, A., 1583. *De Plantis*, Vol. 46. Marescotti, Firenze.

Crooke, W. M., 1956. Effect of soil reaction on uptake of nickel from a serpentine soil. *Soil. Sci.*, 81: 269–276.

Crooke, W. M., Hunter, J. G. and Vergnano, O., 1954. The relation between nickel toxicity and iron supply. *Ann. Appl. Biol.*, 41: 311–324.

Crooke, W. M. and Inkson, R. H. E., 1955. The relation between nickel toxicity and major nutrient supply. *Pl. Soil*, 6: 1–15.

Davy, Sir H., 1814. *Elements of Agricultural Chemistry*, 2nd Ed. London.

Del Moral, R., 1982. Control of vegetation on contrasting substrate herb patterns on serpentine and sandstone. *Am. J. Bot.*, 69: 227–238.

Dirven, J. M. C., Schulenbergh, J. van and Breemen, N van, 1976. Weathering of serpentinite in Matanzas Province, Cuba. Mass transfer calculations and irreversible reaction pathways. *Soil. Sci. Soc. Am. J.*, 40: 901–907.

Dudley, T. R., 1986. A new nickeliphilous species of *Alyssum* (Cruciferae) from Portugal; *Alyssum pintodasilvae*. *Fedd. Rep.* (in press).

Duvigneaud, P., 1966. Note sur la biogéochimie des serpentines du sudouest da la France. *Bull. Soc. Roy. Bot. Belg.*, 99: 271–329.

Ernst, W., 1972. Ecophysiological studies on heavy metal plants in South Central Africa. *Kirkia*, 8: 125–145.

Fernandez, T. C., Taboadila, M. M. and Guitian Ojea, F., 1965. Niquel en los suelos de la provincia de la Coruña. *An. Edafol. Agrobiol.*, 24: 267–293.

Ferreira, R. E. C., 1963. Some distinctions between calciphilous and basiphilous plants. I Field data. *Trans. Proc. Bot. Soc. Edinb.*, 39: 399–413.

Ferreira, R. E. C., 1964. Some distinctions between calciphilous and basiphilous plants. II Experimental data. *Trans. Proc. Bot. Soc. Edinb.*, 39: 512–524.

Ferreira, R. E. C. and Wormell, P., 1971. Fertilizer response of vegetation on ultrabasic terrain on Rhum. *Trans. Proc. Bot. Soc. Edinb.*, 41: 149–154.

Gabbrielli, R., Birtolo, R. and Vergnano Gambi, O., 1982. Evaluation of nickel tolerance in *Alyssum*. *Att. Soc. Tosc. Sci. Nat. Mem. Ser. B*, 88: 143–153.

Gigon, A., 1975. Models for alpine ecosystems on different substrates. 12th Int. Bot. Congr. Leningrad Sec. 8—*Ecol. Bot. Abs.*, 146.

Gordon, A. and Lipman, C. B., 1926. Why are serpentine and other magnesian soils infertile? *Soil Sci.*, 22: 291–302.

Gregory, R. P. G. and Bradshaw, A. D., 1965. Heavy metal tolerance in populations of *Agrostis tenuis* Sibth. and other grasses. *New Phytol.*, 64: 131–143.

Griffin, J. R., 1965. Digger pine seedling response to serpentinite and non-serpentinite soil. *Ecology*, 46: 801–807.

Guitian Ojea, F. and Lopez Lopez, M. I., 1980. Suelos de la zona humeda española. X Suelos sobre serpentinas. *An. Edaf. Agrobiol.*, 39: 403–415.

Halstead, R. L., 1968. Effect of different amendments on yield and composition of oats grown on a soil derived from serpentine material. *Can. J. Soil Sci.*, 48: 301–305.

Halstead, R. L., Finn, B. J. and MacLean, A. J., 1969. Extractability of nickel added to soils and its concentration in plants. *Can. J. Soil Sci.*, 49: 335–342.

Hewitt, E. J., 1953. Metal interrelationships in plant nutrition. I. Effects of some metal toxicities on sugar beet, tomato, oat, potato and marrowstem kale grown in sand culture. *J. Exp. Bot.*, 4: 59–64.

Hilgard, E., 1906. *Soils*. Macmillan, New York.

Hunter, J. G., 1954. Nickel toxicity in a Southern Rhodesian soil. *S. Afr. J. Sci.*, 51, 133–135.

Hunter, J. G. and Vergnano, O., 1952. Nickel toxicity in plants. *Ann. Appl. Biol.*, 39: 279–284.

Jaffré, T., 1980. Etude Ecologique du Peuplement Végétal des Sols Dérivés de Roches Ultrabasiques en Nouvelle Calédonie. *ORSTOM*, Paris.

Jaffré, T., Brooks, R. R., Lee, J., Reeves, R. D., 1976. *Sebertia acuminata* a nickel-accumulating plant from New Caledonia. *Science.* 193: 579–580.

Jaffré, T., Brooks, R. R. and Trow, J. M., 1979. Hyperaccumulation of nickel by *Geissois* species. *Pl. Soil.*, 51: 157–162.

Jensen, H. L. and Lamm, C. G., 1961. On the zinc content of Danish soils. *Acta Agric. Scand.*, 11: 63–81.

Johnson, C. M., Pearson, G. A. and Stout, P. R., 1952. Molybdenum nutrition in crop plants. *Pl. Soil,* 4: 178–196.

Johnston, W. R., 1974. *Mineral Uptake by Plants of Serpentine and Lead Mine Soils.* BA(Hons) Thesis, Univ. Stirling.

Johnston, W. R. and Proctor, J., 1977. Metal concentrations in plants and soils from two British serpentine sites. *Pl. Soil* 46: 275–278.

Johnston, W. R. and Proctor, J., 1979. Ecological studies on the Lime Hill serpentine, Scotland. *Trans. Proc. Bot. Soc. Edinb.*, 43: 145–150.

Johnston, W. R. and Proctor, J., 1980. Ecological studies on Meikle Kilrannoch serpentines. *Trans. Proc. Bot. Soc. Edinb.*, 43: 207–215.

Johnston, W. R. and Proctor, J., 1981. Growth of serpentine and non-serpentine races of *Festuca rubra* in solutions simulating the chemical conditions in a toxic serpentine soil. *J. Ecol.* 69; 855–869.

Jørgensen, P. M., 1974. Flora and vegetation in a magnesium silicate area in Høle, SW-Norway. *Arbok Univ. Bergen Mat. Naturv. Ser.* No. 1: 1–63.

Jowett, D., 1958. Populations of *Agrostis* spp. tolerant of heavy metals. *Nature*, 182: 816.

Kinzel, H., 1963. Zellsaft Analysen zum pflanzlichen Calcium- und Säurestoffwechsel und zum Problem der Kalk- und Silikatpflanzen. *Protoplasma*, 57: 522–555.

Kinzel, H., 1982. Serpentin-Pflanzen. In, *Pflanzenphysiologie und Mineralstoff-wechsel*. Ulmer, Stuttgart.

Kock, P. C. De, 1956. Heavy metal toxicities and iron chlorosis. *Ann. Bot. NS*, 20: 133–141.

Koenigs, R. L., Williams, W. A. and Jones, M. B., 1982a. Principal components analysis of vegetation data. *Hilgardia,* 50: 1–14.

Koenigs, R. L., Williams, W. A., Jones, M. B. and Wallace, A., 1982b. Chemical composition of foliage and soil. *Hilgardia,* 50, 15–26.

Krapfenbauer, A., 1969. Böden auf Dolomit und Serpentin in ihrer Auswirkung auf die Waldernährung., *Cbl. Ges. Forstwesen* 86: 189–219.

Krause, W., 1958. Andere Bodenspezialisten. In, *Handbuch der Pflanzenphysiologie* v.4. Springer, Berlin, 755–806.

Krause, W. and Ludwig, W., 1957. Zum Kenntnis der Flora und Vegetation auf Serpentinstandorten des Balkans. 2. Pflanzengesellschaften und Standorte im Gostovic-Gebiet (Bosnien). *Flora* (Jena), 145: 78–131.

Krause, W., Ludwig, W. and Seidel, F., 1963. Zur Kenntnis der Flora und Vegetation auf Serpentinstandorten des Balkans. 6. Vegetationsstudien in der Umgebung von Mantoudi. *Bot. Jb.,* 82: 337–403.

Kruckeberg, A. R., 1954. Plant species in relation to serpentine soils. *Ecology,* 35: 267–274.

Kruckeberg, A. R., 1967. Ecotypic response to ultramafic soils by some plant species of northwestern United States. *Brittonia,* 19: 133–151.

Kruckeberg, A. R., 1969. Plant life on serpentines and other ferromagnesian rocks in northwestern North America. *Syesis,* 2: 15–114.

Lämmermayr, L., 1926. Materialen zur Systematik und Okologie der Serpentinflora. I Neue Beiträge zur Kenntnis der Flora Steirischer Serpentine. *Sitz. Ber. Ost. Akad. Wiss, Math.—Nat. Kl. Abt.* I, 135: 360–402.

Lee, J., Brooks, R. R., Reeves, R. D. and Boswell, C. R., 1975. Soil factors controlling a New Zealand serpentine flora. *Pl. Soil,* 42: 153–160.

Lee, J., Brooks, R. R., Reeves, R. D., Boswell, C. R. and Jaffré, T., 1977. Plant-soil relationships in a New Caledonian serpentine flora. *Pl. Soil,* 46: 675–680.

Lew, H., 1974. *Vergleichend Physiologische Untersuchungen an Oxalathaltigen Planzen.* Diss. Univ. Wien, Austria.

Lipman, C. B., 1916. A critique of the hypothesis of the lime-magnesia ratio. *Plant World,* 19; 83–105, 119–135.

Loew, O. and May, D. W., 1901. The relation of lime and magnesium to plant growth. Bull. Bur. Pl. Ind. U.S. Dep. Agric., 1: 1–53.

Lopez Lopez, M. I. and Guitian Ojea, F., 1981. Suelos de la zona humeda española. X. Suelos sobre serpentinas. *An. Edaf. Agrobiol.,* 40: 1–10.

Lyon, G. L., Peterson, P. J. and Brooks, R. R., 1969a. Chromium-51 transport in the xylem sap of *Leptospermum scoparium* (manuka). *N.Z. J. Sci.,* 21: 541–545.

Lyon, G. L., Peterson, P. J. and Brooks, R. R., 1969b. Chromium-51 distribution in tissues and extracts of *Leptospermum scoparium. Planta,* 88: 282–287.

Lyon, G. L., Brooks, R. R., Peterson, P. J. and Butler, G. W., 1970. Some trace elements in plants from serpentine soils. *N.Z. J. Sci.,* 13: 133–139.

Lyon, G. L., Brooks, R. R., Peterson, P. J. and Butler, G. W., 1971. Calcium, magnesium and trace elements in a New Zealand serpentine flora. *J. Ecol.,* 59: 421–429.

Madhok, O. P. and Walker, R. B., 1969. Magnesium nutrition of two species of sunflower. *Pl. Physiol.,* 44: 1016–1022.

Main, J. L., 1970. *A Demonstration of Genetic Differentiation of Grass Species to Levels of Calcium and Magnesium.* PhD Thesis, Univ. Washington, Seattle.

Main, J. L., 1974. Different responses to magnesium and calcium by native populations of *Agropyron spicatum. Am. J. Bot.,* 61: 931–937.

Main, J. L., 1981. Magnesium and calcium nutrition of a serpentine endemic grass. *Am. Midl. Nat.,* 105: 196–199.

Markgraf, F., 1932. Pflanzengeographie in Albanien. *Biblioth. Bot.,* 105: 1–132.

McMillan, C., 1956. The edaphic restriction of *Cupressus* and *Pinus* in the coastal ranges of central California. *Ecol. Monogr.,* 26: 177–212.

Menezes de Sequeira, E. M., 1969. Toxicity and movement of heavy metals in serpentine soils (north-eastern Portugal). *Agronom. Lusit.,* 30: 115–154.

Millikan, C. R., 1947. Effect of molybdenum on the severity of toxicity symptoms in flax induced by an excess of either manganese, zinc, copper, nickel or cobalt in the

Plate 1.1 (Above) The ultramafic massif (left) of Mt Hayachine (1913 m) in northern Honshu, Japan. To the right is the granitic Mt Yakushi (1645 m). The timber line is much lower on Mt Hayachine. Photograph by courtesy of the National Trust of Japan. (Below) The ultramafic massif of Red Mountain (1704 m), South Island, New Zealand. The mountain carries a very sparse vegetation cover which reveals the reddish brown colour of the rocks beneath. It was first observed by Sir Joseph Banks in 1770 during Captain Cook's expedition to New Zealand. The snow-capped mountains in the background are in the Mt Aspiring National Park and have a maximum elevation (Mt Aspiring) of 3036 m. Photograph by Lloyd Homer, New Zealand Geological Survey.

Plate 5.1 Asbestos tailings in the Eastern Townships region, Quebec. Photo by T. R. Moore.

nutrient solution. *J. Austral. Inst. Agr. Sci.*, 180: 180–186.

Millikan, C. R., 1948. Antagonism between molybdenum and certain heavy metals in plant nutrients. *Nature,* 161: 528.

Minguzzi, C. and Vergnano, O., 1953. Il contenuto de elementi inorganici delle piante della formazione ofiolitica dell'Impruneta. *Nuov. G. Bot. Ital.*, 60: 287–319.

Mizuno, N., 1968. Interaction between iron and nickel, and copper and nickel, in various plant species. *Nature,* 219: 1271–1272.

Mizuno, N., 1979. Studies on chemical characteristics of serpentine soils and mineral deficiencies and toxicities of crops.

Morrison, R. S., 1980. *Aspects of the accumulation of cobalt, copper and nickel by plants.* PhD Thesis, Massey University, Palmerston North, New Zealand.

Morrison, R. S., Brooks, R. R. and Reeves, R. D., 1980. Nickel uptake by *Alyssum* species. *Pl. Sci. Lett.*, 17: 451–457.

Nemec, A., 1951a. A contribution to the question of stunting growth in pine stands on degraded serpentine soil (in Czech.). *Lesn. Prir.* 30: 214–236.

Nemec, A., 1951b. A study of serpentine forest soil with regard to its chromium content and to the resorption of chromium by a stunted pine stand (in Czech.). *Sborn. Ceskoslov. Akad. Zemed.*, 1951: 395–404.

Novak, F. A., 1928. Quelques remarques relative au problème de la végétation sur les terrains serpentiniques. *Preslia* 6: 42–71.

Pancaro, L., Innamorati, M., Vergnano Gambi, O. and Occhiochiuso, S., 1981. Effeti del cobalto, nichel e cromo sulla germinazione di *Alyssum*, durante il ciclo di post-matarazione e invecchiamento. *G. Bot. Ital.*, 6: 265–284.

Pancic, J., 1859. Die Flora der Serpentinberge in Mittel-Serbien. *Verh. Zool.-Bot. Ges. Wien*, 9: 139–150.

Patschowsky, N. von, 1920. Studien uber Nachweis und Lokalisierung, Verbreitung, und Bedeutung der Oxalsäure in Pflanzenorganismus. *Beih. Bot. Zbl.*, 37: 259–380.

Proctor, J., 1969. *Studies in Serpentine Plant Evolution.* D. Phil Thesis, Oxford Univ.

Proctor, J., 1970. Magnesium as a toxic element. *Nature,* 227: 742–743.

Proctor, J., 1971a. The plant ecology of serpentine. II Plant response to serpentine soils. *J. Ecol.*, 59: 397–410.

Proctor, J., 1971b. The plant ecology of serpentine. III The influence of a high calcium/magnesium ratio and high nickel and chromium levels in some British and Swedish serpentine soils. *J. Ecol.*, 59: 827–842.

Proctor, J., 1972. Studies on available nickel in serpentine soils. Unpublished work cited by Proctor and Woodell (1975).

Proctor, J., Burrow, J. and Craig, G. C., 1980. Plant and soil chemical analyses for a range of Zimbabwean serpentine sites. *Kirkia,* 12: 127–139.

Proctor, J. and Cottam, D. A., 1982. Growth of oats, beet and rape in four serpentine soils. *Trans. Proc. Bot. Soc. Edinb.*, 44: 19–25.

Proctor, J. and Johnston, W. R., 1977. *Lychnis alpina* L. in Britain. *Watsonia*, 11: 199–204.

Proctor, J., Johnston, W. R., Cottam, D. A. and Wilson, A. B., 1981. Field-capacity water extracts from serpentine soil. *Nature,* 294: 245–246.

Proctor, J. and Woodell, S. R. J., 1971. The plant ecology of serpentine. I Serpentine vegetation of England and Scotland. *J. Ecol.*, 59: 375–395.

Proctor, J. and Woodell, S. R. J., 1975. The ecology of serpentine soil. *Adv. Ecol. Res.*, 9: 255–366.

Rabenhorst, M. C. and Foss, J. E., 1981. Soil and geologic mapping over mafic and ultramafic parent material in Maryland. *Soil Sci. Soc. Am. J.*, 45: 1156–1160.

Ragg, J. M. and Ball, D. T., 1964. Soils of the ultrabasic rocks of the island of Rhum. *J. Soil Sci.* 15: 124–133.

Rai, D., Simonsen, G. H. and Youngberg, C. T., 1970. *Serpentine Derived Soils in Watershed and Forest Management.* Dep. Soils Oregon State Univ., Corvallis.

Reeves, R. D., McFarlane, R. M. and Brooks, R. R., 1983. Accumulation of nickel and zinc by western North American genera containing serpentine-tolerant species. *Am. J. Bot.*, 70: 1297–1303.

Robertson, A. I., 1985. The poisoning of roots of Zea mays by nickel ions, and the protection afforded by magnesium and calcium. *New Phytol.,* 100: 173–189.

Robinson, W. O., Edgington, G. and Byers, H. G., 1935. *Chemical studies of infertile soils derived from rocks high in magnesium and generally high in chromium and nickel.* U.S. Dep. Ag. Tech. Bull. No. 471: 1–17.

Sarosiek, J., 1964. Ecological analysis of some plants growing on serpentine soil in Lower Silesia (in Pol.). *Monographiae Bot.,* 18: 1–105.

Sasse, F., 1979a. Untersuchungen an Serpentin Standorten in Frankreich, Italien, Osterreich und der Bundesrepublik Deutschland. I Bodenanalysen. *Flora* (Jena) 168: 379–395.

Sasse, F., 1979b. Untersuchungen an Serpentin Standorten in Frankreich, Italien, Osterreich und der Bundesrepublik Deutschland. II Pflanzenanalysen. *Flora* (Jena), 168: 578–594.

Scharrer, K. and Schropp, W., 1933. Sand und Wasserkulturversuche mit Nickel und Kobalt. *Z. Pfl.ernähr. Düng. Bodenk.,* 31: 94–113.

Scharrer, K. and Schropp, W., 1935. Die Wirkung von Chromi- und Chromat-Ion auf Kulturpflanzen. *Z. Pfl.ernähr. Düng. Bodenk.,* 37: 137–149.

Shewry, P. R. and Peterson, P. J., 1975. Calcium and magnesium in plants and soils from a serpentine area on Unst, Shetland. *J. Appl. Ecol.,* 12: 381–391.

Shewry, P. R. and Peterson, P. J., 1976. Distribution of chromium and nickel in plants and soils from serpentine and other sites. *J. Ecol.,* 64: 195–212.

Slingsby, D. R. and Brown, D. H., 1977. Nickel in British serpentine soils. *J. Ecol.,* 65: 597–618.

Soane, B. D. and Saunder, D. H., 1959. Nickel and chromium toxicity of serpentine soils in Southern Rhodesia. *Soil Sci.,* 88: 322–330.

Spence, D. N. H., 1957. Studies on the vegetation of Shetland. I The serpentine debris vegetation of Unst. *J. Ecol.,* 45: 917–945.

Spence, D. H. N. and Millar, E. A., 1963. An experimental study of the infertility of Shetland serpentine soil. *J. Ecol.,* 51: 333–343.

Tadros, T. M., 1957. Evidence for the presence of an edapho-biotic factor in the problem of serpentine tolerance. *Ecology,* 38: 14–23.

Tassoulas, J. A., 1970. *Comparative Studies of the Composition of Magnesium Soils with Partial Reference to the Heavy Metal (chromium, iron, manganese, nickel) Status.* MSc Thesis, Univ. Abderdeen.

Thompson, L. M. and Troeh, F. R., 1978. *Soils and Soil Fertility.* McGraw-Hill, New York.

Turitzin, S. N., 1981. Natural limits to plant growth in a Californian grassland. *Am. Midl. Nat.,* 107: 95–106.

Vanselow, A. P., 1966. Nickel. In (H. D. Chapman ed.) *Diagnostic Criteria for Plants and Soils.* Univ. Calif. Div. Agr. Sci. 302–309.

Verger, J. P., 1979. Origine du sols sur prasinites et serpentinites sous végétation pionnière en climat alpin (Val d'Aosta). *Doc. Cartogr. Ecol.,* 21: 127–138.

Vergnano, O., 1953. L'azione fisiologica del nichel sulle piante di un terrano serpentinosa. *Nuov. G. Bot. Ital.,* 60: 109–183.

Vergnano Gambi, O., Gabbrrielli, R. and Pancaro, L., 1982. Nickel, chromium, and cobalt in plants from Italian serpentine areas. *Acta Oecol./Oecol. Plant.,* 3: 291–306.

Vlamis, J., 1949. Growth of lettuce and barley as influenced by the degree of calcium saturation of the soil. *Soil Sci.,* 67: 453–466.

Vlamis, J. and Jenny, H., 1948. Calcium deficiency in serpentine soils as revealed by absorbent techniques. *Science* 107: 549–551. 3: 291–306.

Walker, R. B., 1948a. *A Study of Serpentine Soil Infertility with Special Reference to Edaphic Endemism.* PhD Thesis, Univ. Calif., Berkeley.

Walker, R. B., 1948b. Molybdenum deficiency in serpentine barren soils. *Science* 108: 473–475.

Walker, R. B., 1954. Factors affecting plant growth on serpentine soils. *Ecology,* 35: 259–266.

Walker, R. B., Walker, H. M. and Ashworth, P. R., 1955. Calcium-magnesium nutrition with special reference to serpentine soils. *Pl. Physiol.,* 30: 214–221.

Wallace, A., Frolich, E. and Lunt, O. R., 1966. Calcium requirements of higher plants. *Nature*, 209: 634.

Wallace, A., Romney, E. M. and Kinnear, J. E., 1977. Metal interactions in bush bean plants grown in a glasshouse in amended serpentine soils from California. *Commn. Soil Sci. Pl. Analysis*, 8: 727–732.

West, W., 1912. Notes on the flora of Shetland with some ecological observations. *J. Bot. Lond.*, 50: 265–275, 297–306.

White, C. D., 1971. *Vegetation-Soil Chemistry Correlations in Serpentine Ecosystems.* PhD Thesis, Univ. Oregon, Eugene.

Whittaker, R. H., 1960. Vegetation of the Siskiyou Mountains Oregon and California. *Ecol. Monogr.*, 30: 279–338.

Wild, H., 1974a. Indigenous plants and chromium in Rhodesia. *Kirkia*, 9: 233–241.

Wild, H., 1974b. Variations in the serpentine floras of Rhodesia. *Kirkia*, 9: 209–232.

Willett, I. R. and Batey, T., 1977. The effect of metal ions on the root surface phosphatase activity of grasses differing in tolerance to serpentine soil. *Pl. Soil*, 48: 213–221.

Williams, F. C., 1967. Nickel, iron and manganese in the metabolism of the oat plant. *Nature* 214: 628.

Wiltshire, G. H., 1972. Effect of nitrogen source on translocation of nickel in some crop plants and weeds. *Kirkia*, 8: 103–123.

Woodell, S. R. J., Mooney, H. A. and Lewis, H., 1975. The adaptation to serpentine soils in California of the annual species *Linanthus androsaceus* (Polemoniaceae). *Bull. Torrey Bot. Club.*, 102: 232–238.

Woolhouse, H. W., 1983. Toxicity and tolerance in the responses of plant to metals. In (O.L. Lange et al. eds.) *Encyclopedia of Plant Physiology* n.s. Vol 12C. Springer, New York.

Wyn Jones, R. G. and Lunt, O. R., 1967. The function of calcium in plants. *Bot. Rev.*, 33: 407–426.

Yang, X. H., Brooks, R. R., Jaffré, T. and Lee, J., 1985. Elemental levels and relationships in the Flacourtiaceae of New Caledonia and their significance for the evaluation of the serpentine problem. *Pl. Soil*, 87: 281–292.

Chapter 5

SERPENTINE AND AGRICULTURE

5.1 INTRODUCTION

The exploitation of serpentine soils for agriculture has been of interest for several hundred years. In countries such as Britain where ultramafic rocks cover perhaps less than 0.5% of the total land mass (most of this in climatically-unfavourable Scotland and Shetland), the incentive to develop such terrain is not as great as Cuba, New Caledonia and Turkey where 10–35% of the land consists of ultramafic rocks. In this chapter, three main topics will be discussed. The first is the use of serpentine as an additive to agricultural fertilizers. The second is research into ways of making serpentine soils more favourable for growing crops. Finally, consideration will be given to methods of revegetating mine dumps derived from the exploitation of ultramafic rocks for nickel, chromium and asbestos, in order to improve the esthetic appearance of the environment, and at the same time to reduce hazards to human health posed by the presence of asbestos fibres in these waste deposits.

5.2 SERPENTINE AS AN ADDITIVE TO FERTILIZERS

The high magnesium content of serpentine rock makes it an obvious additive for fertilizers designed to be applied to magnesium-deficient soils. The finely-ground rocks can be added to superphosphate to form the so-called "serpentine-superphosphate" developed in New Zealand during World War II when fertilizers were scarce. Serpentine-superphosphate contains about 5–6% of magnesium of which 40–60% is water soluble and hence available to plants (Hogg, 1962; McNaught et al. 1968). It is made by mixing one part of ground serpentine rock with 3 parts of hot, freshly-prepared superphosphate. A proportion of the serpentine remains unchanged while the remainder reacts chemically with the superphosphate to produce a phosphatic compound in which the magnesium is more available than in the original serpentine. Hogg (1962) analysed 25 samples of serpentine-superphosphate and found a mean magnesium content of 5.6% with a range of 3.0–7.0%. The concentrations of trace elements in serpentine-superphosphate are shown in Table 5.1. Despite the beneficial effect of adding magnesium, there is the adverse effect of adding phytotoxic elements such as nickel and chromium which also become more available to plants than in the original serpentine, because of the lower pH of the compound fertilizer. However, this fertilizer also adds a large amount of calcium to the soil, hence raising the adversely low Ca/Mg quotient of ultramafic materials (see Chapter 4).

Serpentine-superphosphate is considered to be an alternative to dolomite as a source of magnesium. Chittenden et al. (1964) considered that a dressing with finely-ground serpentine rock at a rate of 200 kg/ha was about as effective as an equal weight of dolomite. On the other hand McNaught (see During, 1972) reported that dolomite was more effective in raising the magnesium content of pasture than was an equal weight of serpentine rock.

The residual effects of magnesian fertilizers were tested by Hogg and Dorofaeff (1976) in field trials on magnesium-deficient pumice soils in New Zealand. Residual effects were lesser with serpentine than with dolomite containing an equal amount of magnesium. The difference was assumed to be due to leaching. Earlier McNaught et al. (1968) carried out analogous experiments with serpentine-superphosphate, superphosphate and dolomite.

Both magnesian fertilizers appreciably raised exchangeable magnesium levels in the soil and maintained pasture levels of this element above 0.20%. They concluded that 4 parts of serpentine-superphosphate were equivalent to 1.3 parts of dolomite in their effects on plant and soil magnesium levels. McNaught et al. (1973) found however that serpentine superphosphate and other magnesian fertilizers did not improve crop yields in soils of moderate magnesium status.

To summarize, there seems little doubt that freshly-ground serpentine rock or serpentine-superphosphate are useful additives to magnesium-deficient soils. The use of such additives is popular in New Zealand due to a ready availability of the ultramafic source material coupled with extensive areas of magnesium-deficient pumice soils in that country. In other countries where neither ultramafic rocks nor magnesium-deficient soils are common, the use of the above additives is not favoured to the same degree.

TABLE 5.1 Trace Elements in Serpentine Superphosphate Fertilizers

Element	Concentration (%)
Phosphorus	7.0–8.0
Calcium	15.0
Sulphur	7.5–9.0
Magnesium	4.5–5.5
Silicon	5.0–6.0
Iron	0.1–0.8
Aluminium	0.4–0.6
Nickel	0.05–0.07
Cobalt	0.003–0.004
Vanadium	0.0005–0.0030
Chromium	0.01–0.10

Source: During (1972). By courtesy of the New Zealand Government Printing Office who hold the copyright.

5.3 AGRICULTURAL EXPLOITATION OF SERPENTINE SOILS

There has been some mention in Chapter 4 of the use of crop plants for measuring the infertility of serpentine soils, but a clear distinction must be made between the use of crop plants as a diagnosic tool for determining the degree and nature of soil infertility, and their use for determining how serpentine soils may be colonised and developed for agricultural purposes. It is this latter topic which will now be examined.

One of the classical papers on the growing of crops on serpentine soils is the often-quoted work by Hunter and Vergnano (1952). They ascribed the infertility of serpentine primarily to nickel toxicity and performed field experiments with fertilized serpentine soils using untreated soils as controls. Yield data showed that barley was the most tolerant to these soils. Toxicity symptoms (chlorosis and necrosis) in wheat (cv. Fylgia), Italian ryegrass and beans were also slight, but crops such as oats, red clover, potato, turnip, cabbage and kale, were seriously affected by serpentine soils and all showed improvement after liming of the plots. Fodder-type beet was most susceptible to the toxic effects of the soils and no amount of fertilization or liming produced a detectable improvement in yields. The nickel toxicity symptoms of the above crop plants are summarized in Table 5.2.

When the dried matter of the crop plants was analysed for nickel, it was apparent (Table 5.3) that nickel levels decreased in most cases due presumably to decreased availability of this element as the pH was raised from 4.8 to 6.0 after liming. It may be

TABLE 5.2 Nickel Toxicity Symptoms in Crop Plants

Crop	Symptoms
Oat ('Victory'), wheat ('Fylgia'), ryegrass ('Italian')	Leaves chlorotic and necrosis present as longitudinal stripes
Barley ('Ymer')	Similar to oat, but leaf tips normally necrotic. Necrotic areas initially colourless but usually become brown
Clover ('Broad-leaved Red')	Chlorosis in first leaves as fine pattern and whole leaflets occasionally completely necrotic (colourless)
Turnip, yellow ('Balmoral'), swede ('Balmoral')	First leaves chlorotic, older leaves yellow or brownish-yellow. Scattered brown necrosis
Potato ('Kerr's Pink')	Few leaves chlorotic and ultimately yellow with scattered brown necrotic areas
Beet ('Pajbjerg Rex')	Leaves yellowish green with scattered brown necrotic areas
Cabbage ('McEwans Early'), kale ('Thousand-headed')	Leaves chlorotic or yellow with scattered brown necrotic areas

Source: Hunter and Vergnano (1952)

TABLE 5.3 The Nickel Content of Crop Plants Growing on Serpentine Soil with and without Added Lime and Compound Fertilizer

Crop	Plant part	Nickel content of dried material	
		Control	Fertilizer + Lime
Oat	Leaves	42	33
Barley	Leaves	4	2
Wheat	Leaves	4	5
Ryegrass	Leaves	48	40
Clover	Leaves	58	35
Turnip (yellow)	Bulb	99	71
Turnip (swede)	Bulb	73	44
Potato	Tuber	7	7
Bean	Leaves	90	50

Source: Hunter and Vergnano (1952)

significant that the crop plant most resistant to serpentine soil (barley) also had the lowest nickel content in unlimed plots.

The tolerance of crop plants to serpentine has also been determined by Mizuno (1979), who grew several crops in plots containing variable amounts of lime which raised the mean pH of the serpentine soils from 5.0 to 7.0 and reduced the available nickel from 20 to 10 μg/g. A poor tolerance to serpentine soils was shown by oats, alfalfa, azuki bean, kidney bean and cabbage, which all developed necrotic and chlorotic symptoms. Medium resistance was shown by timothy, perennial ryegrass, orchard grass, radish and sugar beet. The maximum resistance was given by potato, maize and rice. These findings are similar to those of Hunter and Vergnano (1952).

Other experiments with crop plants grown on serpentine soils were carried out by Proctor and Cottam (1982) on three serpentine soils from Scotland and one from Sweden. The crops studied were oat (*Avena sativa* cv. Victory), beet (*Beta vulgaris* cv. Maris

Vanguard), and rape (*Brassica napus* cv. Rigo). The soils were treated with NPK, Ca and CaNPK fertilizers and the yields of seedlings of each species were determined. The findings are shown in Table 5.4. There are marked differences in species response, particularly in relation to the application of calcium. From soil analyses and plant yields, the authors concluded that the causes of the acute toxicity were the high magnesium and low calcium status of the soils, particularly in the very toxic Swedish soil.

Serpentine soils may also be improved by addition of organic matter. Halstead (1968) showed that adding organic matter to such soils was as effective as liming in increasing the yield of oat plants (Table 5.5). There was a four-fold increase of yield with either type of addition. The fact that calcium sulphate instead of calcium hydroxide did not increase yield, indicated that increase of soil pH by liming was responsible for the yield increase rather than a more favourable (higher) Ca/Mg quotient. After liming, the nickel content of the soil decreased from 890 to 150 μg/g. The effectiveness of organic matter in improving crop yields was probably because of formation of chelate complexes between nickel and the humic compounds, thus reducing the available proportion of this phytotoxic element. Organic matter was also instrumental in raising the Ca/Mg quotient to a more favourable level.

TABLE 5.4 Yields (g of aerial parts of plant per pot) of Oat, Beet and Rape Plants on Four Serpentine Soils with Different Fertilizer Amendments

Crop	n	Treatment	Greenhill	Towanreef	Keen of Hamar	Kittelfjäll
Oat	8	Control	0.043	0.129	0.234	0.023
		NPK	0.086	0.245	0.286	0.020
		Ca	0.237	0.258	0.196	0.123
		CaNPK	0.930	0.858	0.427	0.280
Beet	8	Control	0.040	0.094	0.063	0.008
		NPK	0.934	0.717	0.639	died
		Ca	0.184	0.153	0.077	0.030
		CaNPK	1.446	1.151	0.693	0.035
Rape	8	Control	died	died	0.019	died
		NPK	died	0.049	0.239	died
		Ca	0.099	0.073	0.037	0.026
		CaNPK	0.600	1.080	0.536	0.056

Source: Proctor and Cottam (1982)

TABLE 5.5 Effect of Different Treatments on the Yield (g per pot of dried aerial parts of plant) and Composition of Oat grown in Serpentine Soils

Treatment	Yield	Ca	Mg	K	Ni	Ca/Mg*
Control	0.07	8400	14400	6000	890	0.4
NPK	0.11	10800	14880	12800	940	0.4
CaSO	0.12	18800	13680	8000	770	0.8
Ca(OH)$_2$	0.34	15200	10800	15200	150	0.8
Organic matter	0.26	12400	11040	17600	260	0.7

Concentrations (μg/g) in dried plant material

*Mole quotient
Source: Halstead (1968). Reproduced from the Canadian Journal of Soil Science.

Another set of classical experiments was carried out by Soane and Saunder (1959). They grew maize, tobacco, oats and lucerne in Zimbabwean serpentine soils both in field and pot trials and obtained a wide range of toxicity symptoms among which were stunting, necrosis, chlorosis and non-germination of seed. Unlike numerous other workers such as Hunter and Vergnano (1952), and Halstead (1968), they found little favourable response to liming and concluded that a major cause of the infertility of these soils was the extremely high chromium and nickel content which could not be reduced to low enough plant-available concentrations to allow for healthy growth of crops.

The effect of various fertilizers on the yield of the bush bean (*Phaseolus vulgaris* cv. Improved Tendergreen) grown in Californian serpentine soils was determined by Wallace et al. (1977). As found by so many other workers for other crops, liming increased yields by about 50%.

It has been reported by Mizuno (1979) that crops showing poor yields when grown in serpentine soil, have low Fe/Ni and Cu/Ni quotients, thus indicating restricted iron and copper uptake due to excess nickel. For each crop studied, there was a specific Fe/Ni value in leaves, below which toxicity symptoms appeared (e.g., 10.0 for rice plants). Molybdenum deficiency was also apparent in several crops grown on serpentine soils, particularly alfalfa. Liming reduced molybdenum-deficiency symptoms by increasing the availability of this element at higher pH values.

An alternative to liming to reduce nickel availability, and hence improve the Fe/Ni and Cu/Ni quotients, has been proposed by Japanese workers such as Takagishi et al. (1973) and Iizuka (1975) who advocated foliar spraying with iron and/or zinc to improve the health of mulberry trees growing on serpentine soil. The heavy necrosis and chlorosis of leaves of this species readily disappeared when these elements were added either to the leaves or to the soils. The results of such experiments by Iizuka (1975) are shown in Fig. 5.1. The same author developed a so-called "T value" which was related to relative metal chelate formation within the plants:

$$T = [Ni] + 0.17[Fe] + 0.38\ [Zn]$$

where the square brackets refer to elemental concentrations (μg/g) in young dried mulberry leaves. For healthy plants containing no chlorotic or necrotic symptoms, T values were relatively constant at approximately 160 units. Deviations from this value were evidenced by plants showing the above toxicity symptoms. This is illustrated in Fig. 5.2. This work is important in that it shows that addition of zinc can also improve the health of plants grown on serpentine soils (see also: Fujiwara et al. 1950; Shiotani, 1939; Tanaka, 1960).

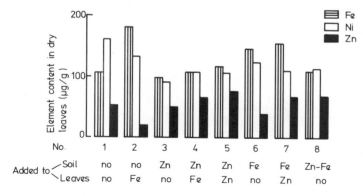

Fig. 5.1 The composition of mulberry leaves as affected by additions of iron and/or zinc to the leaves or to the supporting serpentine soil.
Source: Iizuka (1975).

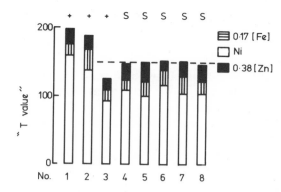

Fig. 5.2   The relationship between "T Values" and stress symptoms in the leaves of mulberry growing on serpentine soil. T = [Ni] + 0.17 [Fe] + 0.38 [Zn]
Source Iizuka (1975).

To summarize the work reported in this section some general conclusions may be made. By far the most efficacious and inexpensive method of improving serpentine soil fertility for exploitation by crops is to top dress with lime. Organic matter is equally efficacious, though there could be problems of supply in many regions of the world. Foliar sprays with iron and/or zinc are also a possibility, though economic conditions might restrict this treatment to smaller-scale horticultural crops rather than to cereals grown on a large scale.

Most of the classical work on development of crops suitable for serpentine soils was carried out about 30 years ago and there are relatively few modern references to this subject. Those which do exist, have been centred around serpentine areas predominantly in northern temperate zones where the problem is not severe because of the limited acreage involved. Further work should be concentrated in tropical areas of the world such as in Philippines and Cuba where population pressures are making exploitation of potential agricultural land an ever more pressing necessity, and where serpentine soils already cover a significant proportion of the total land area. It may also be possible to exploit serpentine terrain by afforestation with trees tolerant to ultramafic soils or by developing more tolerant cultivars of such trees. Possible species for this purpose include various serpentinicolous pines such as *Pinus nigra, P. halepensis,* and *P. pinaster* which are common over serpentine in the Mediterranean region. It is indeed surprising that little or no effort has been devoted to this promising potential field and every effort should be made to consider it further.

5.4 REVEGETATING SERPENTINIC MINE DUMPS AND TAILINGS

The revegetating of mine dumps and tailings derived from ultramafic rocks, is assuming the dimensions of a serious problem in the world today. There are two principal reasons for this. The first is related to the need to render the environment esthetically more attractive and the second, a more serious problem, involves the risk to human health posed by dumps containing carcinogenic asbestos. As detailed by Germine and Puffer (1981), cancer of the lung, pleura, peritoneum, kidney, larynx and gastrointestinal tract as well as several other types of cancer and respiratory ailments have been linked to asbestos exposure in humans (Rohl et al. 1977; Becklake, 1976; Desaulniers et al. 1979; Frank et al. 1979; Hallenbeck and Patel-Mandliak, 1979; Wade et al. 1979; Puffer et al. 1980). Among the areas of concern are the very large asbestos tailings in southeast Quebec, near Thetford in the Gaspé Peninsula where such dumps currently cover about 5.5 km^2 (Moore and Zimmermann, 1977). Streams at the base of the dumps contain up to 2×10^9 asbestos fibres per litre. There is an even greater hazard from wind-blown dust from dumps which have remained virtually unvegetated for the past 60 years.

As reported by Moore and Zimmermann (1977), the asbestos dumps of southeast Quebec (Plate 5.1) have all the unfavourable chemical and physical factors associated with serpentine soils; i.e., low nutrient status, high concentrations of phytotoxic chromium and nickel, and excessive drainage. The few plants found on the dumps are invariably associated with pockets of soil, overburden, or waste rock incorporated into the tailings. These plants are mainly ryegrass (*Lolium perenne*), foxtail barley (*Hordeum jubatum*), bluegrasses (*Poa palustris* and *P. pratensis*), weedy composites (*Sonchus, Lactuca, Leontodon, Taraxacum*), white clover (*Melilotus alba*) and vetch (*Vicia cracca*). A number of small trees such as trembling aspen (*Populus tremuloides*), pin-cherry (*Prunus pensylvanica*) and paper birch (*Betula papyrifera*) are also to be found. Locally prominent are: goldenrod (*Solidago canadensis*) and New England aster (*Aster novaeangliae*). The balsam poplar (*Populus balsamifera*) and willows (*Salix* spp.) are found in damp places.

Moore and Zimmermann (1977) prepared nine experimental plots (4m × 4m) to study ways of vegetating the asbestos dumps. Standard agricultural fertilizer (ammonium nitrate—potassium sulphate—sulphur) was added at rates of 0, 0.1, 0.25, 0.5 and 1.0 kg/m^2. Other supplementary treatments were also added including 1 kg/m^2 of aluminium sulphate which lowered the pH of the dumps from 9.0 to 8.5. The plots were seeded with common agricultural grasses and legumes at a rate of 20 g/m^2. Only plots with at least 1 kg/m^2 of fertilizer had a 90% ground cover at the end of the first growing season. Deficiency symptoms did appear however in many of these plants at the end of the second season. The most successful grass colonisers of the mine dumps were *Lolium perenne, Poa pratensis, Elymus junceus* and *Bromus inermis*. The most successful legumes were *Medicago sativa, Trifolium hybridum* and *Melilotus alba*. Only *E. junceus* produced roots over 10 cm deep into the substrate. The rate of inorganic fertilizing for adequate plant growth in the first 3 years was about 10 times that required for normal agricultural dressings. Furthermore, adequate vegetation cover could only be achieved with organic amendments such as sawdust, dairy manure and sewage sludge. Costs in 1977 were about $CAN 3000–3500 per hectare and will be about $CAN 5000–6000 today. Plate 5.2a shows the reclamation of asbestos tailings in the Eastern Townships region of Quebec. The steep slopes were treated with sawdust and fertilizer and now have a thick grassy cover.

It can be seen that reclamation of serpentine waste is an extremely expensive business and that only governmental pressure and legislation is likely to force mining companies to initiate such work. There is the further problem that many of the tailings are in regions where mining activities have long since ceased, so that responsibility for reclamation frequently devolves on local authorities with limited financial resources.

With the relative decline of the Canadian asbestos mining industry of southeast Quebec, the centre of gravity of such activities has moved to South Africa and Zimbabwe. In the latter country, extensive chrome and asbestos mining (and to a lesser extent nickel mining) is being carried out on and near the Great Dyke, a large ultramafic body extending along almost the entire length of the country. Concern about the environmental consequences of these mining activities led to the formation of a research school dedicated to this matter, led by the late Hiram Wild at the University of Rhodesia (as it then was). The procedure which Wild and his co-workers adopted was to try to colonise dumps derived from ultramafic rocks, with serpentine-endemic and serpentine-tolerant grasses (Wild, 1965). Among these were: *Aristida* spp., *Loudetia flavida, L. simplex, Andropogon gayanus* and *Themeda triandra* (Wild and Wiltshire, 1971a, b; Wild and Hill, 1979).

Hill (1977) has reported extensive trials on revegetating serpentine wastes at the Trojan nickel mine in Zimbabwe. Experiments involved the testing of a number of species of shrubs and trees grown in plots with various fertilizer treatments. These are detailed in Table 5.6.

TABLE 5.6 Mean Biomass Yields (kg of fresh material per plant) in Revegetation Trials on Serpentinic Wastes at the Trojan Nickel Mine, Zimbabwe

Species	n	Age (months)	Fertilizer treatment			
			1	2	3	4
TREES						
Acacia saligna	128	15	0.72	3.05	2.93	2.80
Casuarina glauca	32	15	0.38	1.04	0.68	0.64
C. equisetifolia	40	23	0.03	0.06	0.01	0.05
Eucalyptus gomphocephala	40	23	0.01	0.20	0.09	0.14
SHRUBS						
Atriplex lentiformis	32	15	10.20	28.89	21.53	17.63
A. rhagodioides	18	15	5.91	14.07	15.55	16.37
A. undulata	64	15	2.81	5.91	7.72	7.20

1—control, no fertilizer
2—commercial compound fertilizer at rate of 50g per plant
3—single superphosphate (20% P_2O_5) at rate of 500 g per plant
4—Combination of 2 and 3 plus 50g ammonium nitrate per plant after plant established
Source : Hill (1977)

In experiments with grasses, Hill (1977) showed that the use of mulch and/or compound fertilizers increased yields of 5 species grown over the dumps at the Trojan Mine. The data are shown in Table 5.7. In general the most suitable species were the tree *Acacia setigera*, the shrubs *Atriplex* spp., and the grasses *Cynodon aethiopicus* and *C. dactylon*. Plate 5.2b shows revegetation of nickel tailings at the Epoch Mine, Filabusi, Zimbabwe.

The search for suitable colonisers of serpentinic mine dumps will continue to occupy scientists for many years and it would seem from past experience that the best results will be achieved with native trees, shrubs and grasses already adapted to both serpentine and the local climatic conditions. Another avenue of approach which has not yet been explored, is the development of cultivars from such serpentine-endemic or serpentine-tolerant taxa, which could be more suitable for carrying out the task of revegetation. This is already commonplace with higher-yielding food crops for human and animal consumption, and there is no reason why it could not be done for this entirely different purpose.

TABLE 5.7 Yields (kg of dry matter per hectare) of Grasses Grown on the Serpentinic Wastes at the Trojan Nickel Mine, Zimbabwe

Species	Control— no fertilizer		1000 kg/ha compound fertilizer	
	No mulch	With mulch	No mulch	With mulch
Cyanodon aethiopicus	510	890	5180	9890
C. dactylon	80	130	3860	4640
Dactyloctenium geminatum	320	400	3710	2610
Paspalum vaginatum	30	720	2040	2430
Sporobolus virginicus	450	440	5670	3180

Source: Hill (1977)

REFERENCES

Becklake, M. R., 1976. Asbestos-related diseases of the lung and other organs: their epidemiology and implications for clinical practice. *Am. Rev. Respir. Dis.* 114: 187–227.

Chittenden, E. T., Stanton, D. J. and Watson, J., 1964. Solubility of magnesium in serpentine from six localities in New Zealand. *N.Z. J. Exp. Agr.,* 1: 49–50.

Desaulniers, G., P'an, A., Lecomte, R., Paradis, R., Landsberger, S. and Monaro, S., 1979. On the use of a proton-induced x-ray emission method to determine river water pollution in asbestos mining areas. *Int. J. Appl. Radiat. Isotopes,* 30: 261–262.

During, C., 1972. *Fertilizers and Soils in New Zealand Farming.* Govt. Printer, Wellington.

Frank, A. L., Rohl, A. N., Wade, M. J. and Lipkin, E., 1979. Biological activity in vitro of chrysotile compared to its quarried parent rock (platy serpentine). *J. Environ. Path. Toxicol.,* 2: 1041–1046.

Fujiwara, A. and Kikuchi, T., 1950. Studies on the minor elements (1) Zinc and nickel. *J. Sci. Soil Manure* Japan, 21: 37–40.

Germine, M. and Puffer, J. H., 1981. Distribution of asbestos in the bedrock of the northern New Jersey area. *Environ. Geol.,* 3: 337–351.

Hallenbeck, W. H. and Patel-Mandliak, K. J., 1979. Presence of fibers in the urine of a baboon gavaged with chrysotile asbestos. *Environ. Res.,* 20: 335–340.

Halstead, R. L., 1968. Effects of different amendments on yield and composition of oats grown on a soil derived from serpentine matter. *Can. J. Soil Sci.,* 48: 301–305.

Hill, J. R. L., 1977. Establishment of vegetation on copper- gold- and nickel-mining wastes in Rhodesia. *Trans. Inst. Min. Metall.,* Sec.A, 86: 135–146.

Hogg, D. E., 1962. Studies on soil magnesium. I A laboratory investigation into the displacement and replacement of magnesium in soils. *N.Z. J. Sci.,* 5: 64–73.

Hogg, D. E. and Dorofaeff, F. D., 1976. Residual effects of various magnesium fertilizers in grassland. *N.Z. J. Exp. Ag.,* 4: 127–133.

Hunter, J. G. and Vergnano, O., 1952. Nickel toxicity in plants. *Ann. Appl. Biol.,* 39: 279–284.

Iizuka, T., 1975. Interactions and nickel, iron, and zinc in mulberry trees grown on serpentine soils. *Soil Sci. Pl. Nutr.,* 21: 47–55.

McNaught, K. J., Karlovsky, J. and Hogg, D. E., 1968. Serpentine-superphosphate and dolomite as magnesium sources on Whakarewarewa sandy loam. *N.Z. J. Ag. Res.,* 11: 849–862.

McNaught, K. J., Dorofaeff, F. D., Ludecke, T. E. and Cottier, K., 1973. Effect of potassium fertilizer, soil magnesium status and soil type on uptake of magnesium by pasture plants from magnesium fertilizers. *N.Z. J. Exp. Ag.,* 1: 329–347.

Mizuno, N., 1979. Studies on the chemical composition of serpentine soils and mineral deficiencies and toxicities of crops. *Rep. Hokk. Pref. Ag. Exptl. Stns.,* 29: 1–77.

Moore, T. R. and Zimmermann, R. C., 1977. Establishment of vegetation on serpentine asbestos mine wastes, southeast Quebec, Canada. *J. Appl. Ecol.,* 14: 589–599.

Proctor, J. and Cottam, D. A., 1982. Growth of oats, beet and rape in four serpentine soils: *Trans. Bot. Soc. Edinb.,* 44: 19–25.

Puffer, J. H., Germine, M., Hurtubise, D. O., Mrotek, K. A. and Bello, D. M., 1980. Asbestos distribution in the central serpentine district of Maryland-Pennsylvania. *Environ. Res.,* 23: 233–246.

Rohl, A. N., Langer, A. M. and Selikoff, I. J., 1977. Environmental asbestos pollution related to use of quarried serpentine rock. *Science,* 196: 1319–1322.

Soane, B. D. and Saunder, D. H., 1959. Nickel and chromium toxicity of serpentine soils in Southern Rhodesia. *Soil Sci.,* 88: 322–330.

Shiotani, S., 1939. About the mottle leaf of citrus. *J. Sci. Soil Manure* Japan, 13: 53.

Takagishi, H., Higashino, S. and Iizuka, T., 1973. Studies on abnormal features of mulberry plants grown on the soil derived from serpentine. Part 1, Chemical analysis of serpentineous soils and mulberry plants injured by nickel toxicity. *J. Sericult. Sci.* Japan, 42: 135–143.

Tanaka, S., 1960. *Studies on citrus chlorosis in Japan*. II Studies on zinc deficiency of citrus. Tokai-Kinki Ag. Exp. Stn. Hort. Stn. Spec. Bull. No. 1: 29–47.

Wade, M. J., Lipkin, L. E., Frank, A. L., 1979. Studies of in vitro asbestos-cell interaction. *J. Environ. Path. Toxicol.*, 2: 1029–1039.

Wallace, A., Romney, E. M. and Kinnear, J. E., 1977. Metal interactions in bush bean plants grown in a glasshouse in amended serpentine soils from California. Commn. *Soil. Sci. Pl. Nutr.*, 8: 7727–732.

Wild, H., 1965. The flora of the Great Dyke of Southern Rhodesia with special reference to serpentine soils. *Kirkia*, 5: 49–86.

Wild, H. and Wiltshire, G. H., 1971a. The problem of vegetating Rhodesian mine dumps examined. *Chamber Mines J.* (Salisbury), 13: 26–29.

Wild, H. and Wiltshire, G. H., 1971b. The problem of vegetating Rhodesian mine dumps examined. II Suggestions for future research and practical trials. *Chamber Mines J.* (Salisbury), 13: 35–37.

Wild, H. and Hill, J. R. C., 1979. Stabilization of Rhodesian mining wastes with indigenous and exotic plant species. In, (G. Kunkel ed.) *Taxonomic Aspects of African Economic Botany*. Proc. IX Plenary Meeting AETFAT, Las Palmas: 88–90.

Chapter 6

PLANT EVOLUTION AND SERPENTINE

6.1 INTRODUCTION

The subject of adaptation of plant species to the total environment of serpentine soils has occupied scientists for many years. Studies began with Prat (1934) who first identified the presence on mine wastes, of species tolerant to heavy metals. The work was advanced by the extensive studies of Bradshaw and his coworkers at Liverpool University (Bradshaw, 1952; Gregory and Bradshaw, 1965). Their earlier work was concerned with the use of the grass *Agrostis tenuis* which readily develops strains capable of colonising mineralized or contaminated ground. Much of these earlier studies have been summarized by Antonovics et al. (1971).

Tolerant strains of a taxon such as *Agrostis tenuis* are normally surrounded by non-tolerant strains of the same species in the surrounding terrain and gene flow between the two populations is therefore possible. Tolerance across a geochemical boundary, changes abruptly over a few metres (Jain and Bradshaw, 1966; McNeilly, 1968; Antonovics and Bradshaw, 1970). The self fertility of metal-tolerant populations is usually much greater than that of non-tolerant taxa and is presumably a strategy to reduce reduction of tolerance by flow of non-tolerant genes from the surrounding populations.

The review by Antonovics et al. (1971) is an important contribution to the literature on this subject but is concerned primarily with the so-called "mine taxa" in essentially man-made environments and it not concerned to any degree with serpentine soils. Adaptation of plants to serpentine soils has clearly occupied a much longer time span than the few hundred years or less of typical mine taxa. This adaptation will be considered further below.

Before leaving this brief introduction, some mention should be made of the terms *facultative* and *obligate* as applied to serpentine plants. *Facultative* taxa are plants which will grow quite well on serpentine soils without having a specific requirement for any of the edaphic or physical properties of the substrate. *Obligate* species are presumed to grow on serpentine because of a specific nutritional or other requirement which only such soils can provide. Great care must be taken in definition of the term *obligate*. It is my experience that all serpentine-endemics will grow quite well on non-serpentine soils until they succumb to either fungal attack or competition from vigorous weed species. It would seem (see also Chapter 5) that these plants are *obligate* to serpentine only insofar as such soils provide a refuge from biotic factors present in non-serpentine substrates. There is at present no firm evidence that any serpentine plant has a specific nutritional requirement for any of the constituents of its supporting soils.

6.2 NEOENDEMISM, PALAEOENDEMISM AND THE TIME FACTOR

6.2.1 Neoendemism and Palaeoendemism

Plants growing on serpentine can be said to have evolved by either a *neoendemic* or *palaeoendemic* process. *Palaeoendemic* plants (Stebbins, 1942; Turrill, 1951) are taxa which have a widespread but highly disjunct distribution and which are confined mainly to 'islands' of metalliferous soils. Because of this widespread distribution, the plants must at one time have colonised a much greater range of substrates but have now been restricted by competitive pressures or climatic changes to their present sites. These plants are therefore remnants of once highly successful taxa. The second type of endemic plant (Stebbins, 1942) is the *neoendemic* which represents a taxon which has evolved on a metalliferous soil and which has derived from a neighbouring non-metallophyte in response to the unfavourable edaphic and environmental conditions of the colonised substrate.

Although we are perhaps more familiar today with the terms *neo-* and *palaeoendemic*, the original terminology of Stebbins (1942) used the words *insular* and *depleted*, respectively.

A fuller description of the processes of *neoendemism* and *palaeoendemism* as applied to serpentine plants has been given by Kruckeberg (1954) who proposed the following sequence of events for the development of *palaeoendemic* species on this type of substrate. He first suggested that a non-serpentine plant extends its range into a region where serpentine and non-serpentine soils coexist. A certain percentage of the population of this plant will have a greater tolerance to the edaphic, biotic and physical factors of serpentine, and its seeds will fall upon the serpentine or on to the transitional soils. Some of the most tolerant seeds will germinate and produce plants which in turn will eliminate more of the non-tolerance genes by the selective effect of the serpentine environment. The serpentine plant ultimately develops into a biotype adapted to life on this substrate.

6.2.2 The Time Factor

The time factor is of great importance in a discussion of the evolution of serpentine plants. In the northern part of Europe and North America, glaciation during the Ice Ages has meant that serpentine plants have only had about 10,000 years to develop. Fig. 6.1 shows the extent of the ice sheets during the last Ice Age. Though 10,000 years is short on the geological time scale, it is very long compared with the relatively few years needed for tolerant strains of grasses (see above) to develop over mine wastes. Antonovics et al. (1971) for example have reported that such strains can develop in as little as 30 years. Proctor and Woodell (1975) reported introduced Mediterranean grasses (*Avena* and *Bromus*) growing on and off serpentine in California, having been established perhaps only 100 years ago. It must be remembered, however, that tolerant and non-tolerant strains of grasses and other plants are often not morphologically distinct from each other. The time needed for a morphologically-distinct species to evolve will clearly be very much longer.

6.2.3 Differences Between Tropical and North Temperate Serpentine Floras

Wild (1978) and Wild and Bradshaw (1977) have compared evolutionary processes on African (non-glaciated) and northern European (glaciated) ultramafic terrain. The serpentine flora of the Zimbabwean Great Dyke was the African model chosen for this comparison and is clearly a very old flora dating back to the Mesozoic era. The angiosperms are believed to have evolved from their tropical source at this time (Takhtajan, 1969), and as the Great Dyke predates the Mesozoic, it is probable that its serpentine flora has had 200–300 million years to evolve.

Because of the very great difference in the allowable time span for evolution of serpentine plants in northern Europe and tropical Africa, the following characteristics (Wild and Bradshaw, 1977; Wild, 1978) might have been expected to distinguish the two floras:

(a) the African flora will be much richer in species

(b) the African flora will be much more distinctive in physical and chemical characters

(c) the African flora will have more species which have attained the status of separate taxa and yet have close relatives off serpentine

(d) the African flora will have more species which have now lost their closest relatives (biotype depletion)

(e) the African species will have developed distinct but related taxa in separate areas of the ultramafic formations

(f) the two floras will have a different distribution of families in their make-up.

The above expected differences will now be discussed in terms of the realities of the two situations.

Numbers of species occupying serpentine soils

The Zimbabwean serpentine flora of the Great Dyke and other regions has 320 tolerant species of which 22 are endemic (Wild, 1965). By comparison, Lounamaa (1956) has reported only about 20 species of serpentine-tolerant plants in northern Finland, none of which is endemic at the specific level (though there are several endemics at the subspecific level such as *Viscaria alpina* subsp. *serpentinicola*).

The greater distinctiveness of the populations

There is a much greater difference of morphological adaptation to serpentine in Zimbabwe than in northern Europe. Zimbabwean plants from the Great Dyke such as *Helichrysum leptolepis*, *Euclea linearis* and *Merremia pesdraconis* display great differences in morphology compared with their probable parents or with strains of the same species growing off-serpentine. Howard-Williams (1971) has observed morphological differences in specimens of the famous copper flower *Becium homblei* (Howard-Williams, 1970) growing on serpentine at Tipperary Claims, Zimbabwe, compared with plants from the normal copper-rich habitat. Corolla dimensions of these specimens were invariably lower in the plants from the nickeliferous substrate. This work also showed that a plant adapted already to one heavy metal (copper) appears to have an inherent ability to adapt to anomalous concentrations of another. Morphological differences in the leaf shape of these two populations were also observed by Wild and Heyting (1966).

Tolerant species attaining the status of distinct and endemic taxa.

As detailed by Wild and Bradshaw (1977), a further stage in evolutionary divergence occurs when a species occupying both anomalous and normal habitats splits into two distinct species, one of which is endemic to serpentine soils and is surrounded by the other non-tolerant taxon.

Among the serpentine plants of Zimbabwe, some rather unusual situations arise. The endemic taxa do not form islands in the middle of a sea of non-tolerant cousins, but such relatives do indeed exist though separated by a long distance from the endemic taxa, as illustrated in Table 6.1. An intermediate stage is represented by partially endemic plants whose other representatives (morphologically indistinct) of the same species, are also separated by some distance from the endemic taxa. This is shown in Table 6.2.

The inference from the above observations is that evolution occurred in the distant past, and that species whose closest relatives are a long way away, biotypic depletion has removed the nearby non-tolerant representatives. In the case of partially-endemic taxa (Table 6.2), the process of evolution is still continuing. Although biotype depletion has removed nearby representatives, some of these non-tolerant species remain a long way away though ultimately they will become extinct and the serpentine plant will become truly *palaeoendemic*.

The available evidence is that most of the Zimbabwean serpentine plants are palaeo-endemic as compared with the northern European plants which are neoendemic at the sub-specific levels and given enough time will be so at the specific level.

An interesting intermediate flora from the standpoint of plant evolution is the serpentine flora of Turkey and southeastern Europe. The genus *Alyssum* (see also Chapter 8) displays a highly unusual character confined to section Odontarrhena of this genus. This character is the hyperaccumulation of nickel. According to Brooks et al. (1977), such a

Plate 5.2   (a) Above: Revegetation of asbestos tailings in the Eastern Townships region of Quebec. The tailings were treated with sawdust and fertilizer and now support a thick grassy cover. Photo by T. R. Moore.
(b) Below: Revegetation of nickel tailings at Epoch Mine, Filabusi, Zimbabwe. Photo supplied by the Editor of the Chamber of Mines Journal (Zimbabwe).

Plate 8.1 Drawing of *Alyssum robertianum* from Corsica.
By courtesy of Mme. M. Conrad. Reprinted by permission of Association pour l'Etude écologique du Maquis (Corsica), publisher of Flora Corsicana Iconographia.

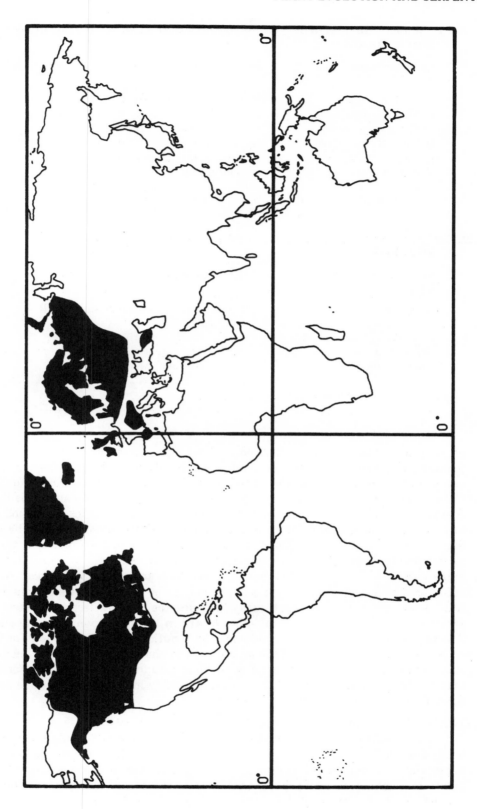

Fig. 6.1.   The extent of glaciation during the Ice Ages.

TABLE 6.1   Endemic Species of Serpentine Areas of Zimbabwe and the Location of their Nearest Relatives

Endemic taxon	Related species	Location of related species
Barleria molensis	B. longissima	Somalia
Euphorbia wildii	E. monteiri	Angola and Botswana
Lasiocorys aggerestis	L. capensis	South Africa
Lasiocorys hephaestis	L. argyrophylla	Somalia
Lotononis serpentinicola	L. prostrata	South Africa (Cape Province)
Pearsonia metallifera	P. marginata	South Africa
Vernonia accommodata	V. usafuensis	Tanzania

Source: Wild and Bradshaw (1977)

TABLE 6.2   Species Partially-Endemic to Serpentine in Zimbabwe but also Occurring Elsewhere.

Serpentine species	Additional distribution
Crotalaria variegata	Angola
Cyphostemma humile	South Africa (Transvaal and Natal)
Euclea linearis	South Africa
Indigofera williamsonii	South Africa (Natal)
Sutera brunnea	South Africa (Natal)
Tragia cannabina	India, Northeast Africa

Source: Wild and Bradshaw (1977)

plant is one which contains >1000 μg/g (0.1%) nickel in its dry matter. This is about 10 times the nickel content of other serpentine plants and about 500 times the nickel content of non-serpentine taxa. Brooks et al. (1979) have identified 45 hyperaccumulators among the 168 species of this genus (Dudley, 1964). Nearly all of these specialised plants are from Anatolia and southeastern Europe. If they were true palaeoendemics, we would not expect to find non-accumulating relatives around the area of distribution of each hyperaccumulating species, since biotype depletion should have removed such plants. If we now consider subsection Samarifera of section Odontarrhena of the genus, we find 8 hyperaccumulating species of fairly local distribution in Anatolia and a very widespread non-accumulating species A. peltarioides. This is illustrated in Fig. 6.2 and shows that the latter taxon and its subsp. peltarioides and subsp. virgatiforme occupy terrain contiguous to the serpentine islands colonised by the other 8 taxa in the subsection. The Alyssum flora of Anatolia is clearly at the neoendemic stage and insufficient time has elapsed for the process of biotype depletion to render it palaeoendemic in character. It should be mentioned that since Anatolia has never been glaciated, the time span for evolution is considerably greater than the 10,000 years of northern Europe, but possibly much shorter than the time span of the African serpentine floras.

Serpentine-endemic plants which have lost their closest relatives

The subject of serpentine-endemic plants which have lost their closest relatives has been discussed to some extent above. However, a few additional comments are appropriate. In southern Africa (see Table 6.1), close relatives of many serpentine-endemic plants of Zimbabwe, which have given rise to these serpentinophytes, are sometimes situated some hundreds of kilometres distant. These African endemics often belong phytogeographically not to the Sudano-Zambesian region, but to the non-tropical Cape

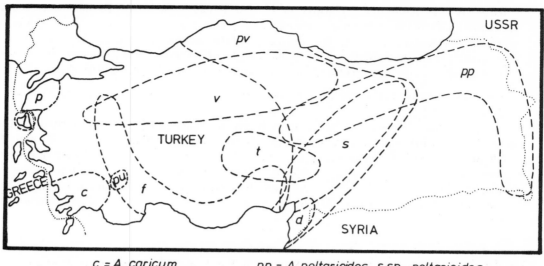

c = A. caricum
d = A. dubertretii
f = A. floribundum
l = A. lesbiacum
p = A. pinifolium
pu = A. peltarioides s.sp. undetermined

pp = A. peltarioides s.sp. peltarioides
pv = A. peltarioides s.sp. virgatiforme
s = A. samariferum
t = A. trapeziforme
v = A. virgatum

Fig. 6.2. The distribution of eastern Mediterranian species of subsection Samarifera of section Odontarrhena of *Alyssum*.
Source: Morrison (1980).

phytogeographic region of South Africa. A good example is the nickel hyperaccumulator *Pearsonia metallifera* which grows on the Great Dyke but whose nearest relative is *P. marginata* from the Cape region.

In the Mediterranean region, as mentioned above, potential precursors of serpentine-endemic plants often remain in the vicinity on non-serpentine substrates as is the case in subsection Samarifera of section Odontarrhena of *Alyssum*. In series Crenulata of subsection Compressa of this genus, however, it has not been possible to find a non-accumulating possible precursor for the 5 hyperaccumulators of nickel contained in this series. It is possible, however, that a parent taxon has now disappeared so that *palaeoendemism* rather than *neoendemism* is a more appropriate description in this instance. In spite of this example, it seems that the Mediterranean serpentine floras are not as old as those of the Great Dyke (though much older than those of northern Europe) and that there has been insufficient time for biotype depletion to proceed far enough to justify classifying the whole flora as palaeoendemic.

The occurrence of distinct but related serpentine endemics in different parts of the same region

The Great Dyke of Zimbabwe is divided into 2 halves by a large norite intrusion. Wild (1965) has observed that there are 7 endemics occurring on the northern half only and a further 2 confined to the south. A number of other species are endemic to both halves of this structure. Wild and Bradshaw (1977) and Wild (1978) have suggested that this is evidence that a large area of serpentine is necessary for distinct taxa to evolve in separate areas of the same structure. These authors claim that such a process does not occur in Europe because the areas of contiguous serpentine are too small. This is certainly true for northern Europe which has no serpentine areas rivalling the 3000 km^2 of the Great Dyke.

However, we have found (Brooks et al. 1979) that in southern Europe and Anatolia, morphologically-distinct endemic species of *Alyssum* can evolve over adjacent (though not contiguous) serpentine areas that are only a few hectares in extent. An example is *A. lesbiacum* found in a small area of the island of Lesbos only a few kilometres from the site of another nickel hyperaccumulator, *A. pinifolium,* on the Anatolian coast.

The independent pattern of evolution of tolerance among the families of different serpentine floras

The final difference to be expected between tropical and temperate serpentine floras lies in their different distribution among families. Wild and Bradshaw (1977) and Wild (1978) compared the percentages of serpentine-tolerant species in different families for serpentine floras of Zimbabwe and Japan. Their data are shown in Table 6.3. An analysis of these data, led Wild (1978) to conclude that differences in distribution among families were related mainly to the distribution of families among the pool of surrounding non-serpentine taxa.

TABLE 6.3   Comparison of Numbers of Species in Families on Serpentines in Zimbabwe and Japan Expressed as a Percentage of the Entire Flora of the Country

Family	Zimbabwe		Japan	
	Total No.	% on serpentine	Total No.	% on serpentine
Anacardiaceae	43	14.0	5	60.0
Vitaceae	30	16.7	10	30.0
Mimosaceae	67	6.0	3	0
Caesalpinaceae	60	6.7	5	0
Papilionaceae	35	10.0	100	2.0
Aceracae	0	0	27	33.0
Caprifoliaceae	0	0	62	17.7
Protaceae	14	35.7	0	0
Polygalaceae	23	30.4	4	0
Euphorbiaceae	52	25.0	28	7.1
Lamiaceae	110	9.1	100	7.0
Scrophulariaceae	108	7.4	77	7.9
Asclepiadaceae	129	7.0	27	7.4
Rubiaceae	287	3.1	55	12.7
Poaceae	413	11.5	200	10.0
Liliaceae	142	7.7	180	10.0
Asteraceae	367	6.5	280	9.3
Campanulaceae	62	6.5	31	16.1

Source: Wild and Bradshaw (1977)

6.3 STUDIES OF SPECIATION AMONG SERPENTINE PLANTS

There has been some discussion above, on field observations of endemism in serpentine plants, and it is now appropriate to consider specific quantitative experiments designed to study speciation in selected taxa. Two important benchmark papers on this subject are by Kruckeberg (1954, 1967). He carried out experiments on plants classified as *bodenvag* and *bodenstets* using the terminology of Unger (1836). *Bodenvag* plants occur both on- and off-serpentine whereas *bodenstets* species are restricted to serpentine. This nomenclature will be used consistently throughout this book. Clearly *bodenvag* taxa are likely to provide strains capable of colonising either type of soil. Kruckeberg (1954) studied different strains of *bodenvag* plants by means of seed gathered from serpentine and non-serpentine sites. The paired populations were then grown on serpentine soils amended by different levels of calcium. The serpentine-tolerant strains were invariably more tolerant to low calcium levels in the soils.

A surprisingly large number of serpentine-tolerant strains was observed by Kruckeberg 1954) among the *bodenvag* taxa. Of 21 species of several plant families investigated, 12 displayed differentiation into serpentine and non-serpentine races. This work was of great importance in that it pointed out probable reasons for the exclusion of serpentine endemics from non-serpentine soils. These studies involved the endemic species *Streptanthus glandulosus* and a number of weeds. The *Streptanthus* grew perfectly well on any type of soil but was immediately smothered when weed seedlings were grown in the same plots. The weeds were unable to grow on serpentine however. This reciprocal exclusion indicated that edaphic factors were important in the one case and biotic and dynamic factors in the other (i.e., on non-serpentine soil).

Experiments similar to those of Kruckeberg were carried out by Proctor in 1971 (unpub. work—see Proctor and Woodell, 1975), in which serpentine-endemic *Plantago erecta* was seeded in cleared and uncleared plots of a sandstone soil adjacent to serpentine. Only in the cleared plots did the plant survive and flourish.

Climatic stress when added to edaphic stress can also affect the degree to which plant species will colonise serpentine. For example Duvigneaud (1966) reported that the fern *Notholaena marantae,* is restricted to serpentine in the northern part of its range in France, but not in the south. Other workers such as Rune (1953) have reported a reverse effect in which exclusive colonisers of serpentine soils occur only in the more southerly parts of Sweden. It is probable that climatic effects are responsible for these disjunct occurrences on and off serpentine. The competitive ability of serpentinophytes may well be affected by these climatic changes.

The ecotypic response of plants to ultramafic soils was studied by Kruckeberg (1967) in another important paper on this subject. He tested the responses of 18 species of which all but three were divided into strains with tolerance or non-tolerance to serpentine. Growth performance was tested by pot trials, field trials, and by transplants in the wild. Herbaceous perennials such as *Achillea millefolium, Fragaria virginiana, Prunella vulgaris* and *Rumex acetosella* showed the best ecotypic differences among the two types of race. Comparison of growth in strains of 8 herbaceous plants grown in pot containing a dunite soil, are shown in Fig. 6.3. The bar diagrams show clearcut differences in *Achillea millefolium, Erigeron compositus, Prunella vulgaris* and *Spiraea douglasii,* compared with the poor differentiation among four other species.

A particularly important observation by Kruckeberg (1967) was that non-tolerant strains of *Achillea* from localities adjoining serpentine, grew better on serpentine than strains of the same species selected from sites a long way away from ultramafic rocks. These experiments suggest a certain amount of gene flow between contrasting edaphically-specialized populations.

To summarize, we may use the words of Kruckeberg (1967):

Ecotypic differentiation of species is now an assumed consequence of infraspecific diversification. Indeed it is an axiom of population biology. Genetically controlled response to physical and biotic influences of the environment is expected and is usually found wherever it is looked for. Where edaphic differences between habitats are pronounced, genotypic specialization for substrate can be readily detected by the simple tests of this study.

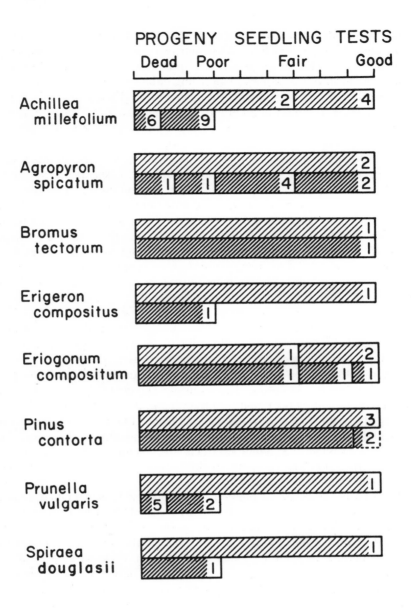

Fig. 6.3. Comparison of growth responses for ultramafic (upper bar) with non-ultramafic (lower bar) strains of plant species growing in a dunite soil. Number of strains tested is indicated by the numerals. Source: Kruckeberg (1967).

REFERENCES

Antonovics, J., Bradshaw, A. D. and Turner, R. G., 1971. Heavy metal tolerance in plants. Adv. Ecol. Res., 7: 1–85.

Bradshaw, A. D., 1952. Populations of Agrostis tenuis resistant to lead and zinc poisoning. Nature, 169: 1098.

Brooks, R. R., Reeves, R. D., Lee, J. and Jaffré, T., 1977. Detection of nickeliferous rocks by analysis of herbarium specimens of indicator plants. J. Geochem. Explor., 7: 49–57.

Brooks, R. R., Morrison, R. S., Reeves, R. D., Dudley, T. R. and Akman, Y., 1979. Hyperaccumulation of nickel by Alyssum Linnaeus. Proc. Roy. Soc. Lond. Sec. B, 203: 387–403.

Dudley, T. R., 1964. Synopsis of the genus Alyssum. J. Arn. Arbor., 45: 358–373.

Duvigneaud, P., 1966. Note sur la biogéochimie des serpentines du sud ouest de la France. Bull. Soc. Roy. Bot. Belg., 99: 271–329.

Gregory, R. P. G. and Bradshaw, A. D., 1965. Heavy metal tolerance in populations of Agrostis tenuis Sibth. and other grasses. New Phytol., 64: 131–143.

Howard-Williams, C., 1970. The ecology of Becium homblei in Central Africa with special reference to metalliferous soils. J. Ecol., 58: 741–763.

Howard-Williams, C., 1971. Morphological variation between isolated populations of Becium homblei growing on heavy metal soils. Vegetatio, 23: 141–151.

Jain, S. K. and Bradshaw, A. D., 1966. Evolutionary divergence among adjacent plant populations. I. The evidence and its theoretical analysis. Heredity, 21: 407–441.

Kruckeberg, A. R., 1954. The ecology of serpentine soils. III Plant species in relation to serpentine soils. Ecology, 35: 267–274.

Kruckeberg, A. R., 1967. Ecotype response to ultramafic soils by some plant species of southwestern United States. Brittonia, 19: 133–151.

Lounamaa, J., 1956. Trace elements in plants growing wild on different rocks in Finland. Ann. Bot. Soc. Zool.-Bot. Fenn. "Vanamo", 29: 1–196.

McNeilly, T., 1968. Evolution in closely adjacent plant populations. III Agrostis tenuis on a small copper mine. Heredity, 23: 99–108.

Morrison, R. S., 1980. Aspects of the Accumulation of Copper, Cobalt and Nickel by Plants. PhD Thesis, Massey University, Palmerston North, New Zealand.

Prat, S., 1934. Die Erblichkeit der Resistenz gegen Kupfer. Ber. Dt. Bot. Ges., 52: 65–67.

Proctor, J. and Woodell, S. R. J., 1975. The ecology of serpentine soils. Adv. Ecol. Res., 9: 255–366.

Rune, O., 1953. Plant life on serpentines and related rocks in the north of Sweden. Acta Phytogeogr. Suecica, 31: 1–139.

Stebbins, G. L., 1942. The genetic approach to rare and endemic species. Madroño, 6: 241–272.

Takhtajan, A., 1969. Flowering Plants: Origin and Dispersal. Oliver and Boyd, Edinburgh.

Turrill, W. B., 1951. Some problems of plant range and distribution. J. Ecol., 39: 205–227.

Unger, F., 1836. Uber den Einfluss des Bodens auf die Vertheilung der Gewächse nachgewiesen in der Vegetation des nordöstlichen Tirols. Rohtmann and Scheigerd, Vienna.

Wild, H., 1965. The flora of the Great Dyke in Southern Rhodesia with special reference to the serpentine soils. Kirkia, 5: 49–86.

Wild, H., 1978. The vegetation of heavy metal and other toxic soils. In, (M. J. A. Werger ed.) Biogeography and Ecology of Southern Africa. Junk, The Hague, 1301–1332.

Wild, H. and Bradshaw, A. D., 1977. The evolutionary effects of metalliferous and other anomalous soils in south-central Africa. Evolution, 31: 282–293.

Wild, H. and Heyting, A., 1966. An analysis of variation of leaf dimensions in Becium homblei and Becium obovatum. Bot. Notisier., 119: 308–316.

Chapter 7

ANIMALS AND SERPENTINE

7.1 INTRODUCTION

Any study of the ecology of serpentine soils cannot be complete without considering the role played by animals. In contrast to the very extensive literature on serpentine plants, very few studies have been carried out on "serpentine animals". They, particularly insects, are highly dependent on the food supply provided by the serpentine environment, and this brings the question of nutrition into consideration since all the factors which render serpentine infertile to plants (see Chapter 4), such as low levels of plant nutrients, high concentrations of toxic nickel and chromium, and the unfavourable Ca/Mg quotient, are equally unfavourable for animal nutrition. Animals adapted to serpentine must have adopted strategies to combat the adverse biotic and edaphic factors of the serpentine environment. It may also be the case that just as plants are believed to have retreated to serpentine to avoid competition from other plants, animals may have done so to avoid competition from other animals.

The very sparse literature on "serpentine animals" is mainly devoted to the lower animals such as insects, rather than to more advanced biota. It is probable that future investigations in this field are likely to be concentrated on these insects since they are much more diverse than other classes of animals and have a greater likelihood of endemism.

7.2 MAMMALS AND SERPENTINE

Although it is probably true to say that serpentine-endemic mammals do not exist, some mammals do prefer a serpentine environment for a number of reasons. Proctor and Whitten (1971) noted the abundance of the gopher *Thomomys bottae* on a serpentine soil near Stanford University as compared with its relative rarity on adjacent non-serpentine soils. This was surprising since serpentine soils have a tendency to be shallow and rocky, hence unfavourable for burrowing animals.

The gopher population was assessed by Proctor and Whitten (1971) by measuring the number of mounds on selected quadrats (1500 m^2). The mean percentage cover by gopher mounds was 35% on serpentine and 3% on the adjacent non-serpentine soil. It has been observed by these workers that gopher activity in serpentine soils is useful in disturbing the ground and bringing subsoil to the surface so that plants growing over the mounds are larger and remain green longer during dry periods. They speculated that this resulted in providing more food for various insects during such periods.

The gopher diet consists primarily of underground fleshy parts of forbs which are reached by subterranean tunnels close to the surface. In this way the animal is protected from predators while feeding. It was observed by Proctor and Whitten (1971) that the corm of *Brodiaea* spp. was the main component of the diet of these animals. These species were much less common over non-serpentine terrain.

It is reasonable to suppose that gopher predators should also be more abundant in the serpentine environment, particularly as the ground cover is much reduced, so rendering the gophers more visible. The above authors report finding fecal pellets of a predator bird which contained not only gopher remains but also a residue of *Brodiaea* corms consumed by these mammals.

Nutrition with a large excess of magnesium is probably just as unfavourable for animals as for plants. The Ca/Mg quotient for the serpentine soils near Stanford University was about 0.17, whereas for the *Brodiaea* corms the value was 0.28, a higher though still unfavourable level. It is not clear to what extent the gopher *T. bottae* has adapted to a diet with this unfavourable elemental composition; however, it has been shown by Vaughn (1967) that the diet of gophers is 5–10 times richer in magnesium than that of herbivores on normal soils. The same is true of seed-eating animals as has been shown by Russell (1950) and Baumeister (1958).

7.3 FISH, REPTILES AND SERPENTINE

As reported by Proctor and Woodell (1975), Stebbins (1949) has observed that certain cases of intergradation between subspecies of the salamander *Ensatina eschscholtzia* are related to serpentine. He was unable to find any evidence for deleterious effects of serpentine upon this animal.

In a highly original investigation by Warren et al. (1971), it was suggested that the copper, lead and zinc levels in livers of rainbow and cutthroat trout could be used as indicators of mineralization in the watershed of the rivers which supported these fish. There is no reason why the same principle should not apply to the detection of serpentine rocks by such means, using indicator elements such as chromium, magnesium and nickel.

The potential of shellfish for indicating the presence of serpentine minerals is much greater than that of pelagic fish. This is because shellfish can enrich trace elements in their ambient water by a factor of several millions. For example Brooks and Rumsby (1965) reported an enrichment of cadmium in the scallop *Pecten novaezelandiae* which reached a factor of 2,260,000 in the soft portions of the organism. Nickel was also enriched by a factor of 12,000 in the scallop, 4000 in the oyster (*Ostrea sinuata*) and 24,000 in the mussel (*Mytilus edulis*). Factors for chromium, another serpentine indicator, were 200,000, 60,000 and 320,000 respectively. Under normal conditions there is no reason why using shellfish to detect serpentine rocks would be either economic or desirable. However, in certain parts of the world where land access is difficult and where little geological mapping has been performed, the use of shellfish for the above purpose might be contemplated. An obvious site for such work is Greenland where Bollingberg (1975) has already shown that marine organisms may be used for prospecting for copper, lead and zinc, as well as for monitoring pollution from mining activities.

7.4 INSECTS AND SERPENTINE

The relationship between insects and serpentine has been investigated more thoroughly than for any other animals. A number of insects are endemic or nearly endemic to serpentine because of specific nutritional requirements for vegetation not found elsewhere. For example, Johnson et al. (1968) have studied the population biology of the butterfly *Euphydryas editha* (Western Checkerspot Butterfly) which occurs in the San Francisco Bay area in scattered colonies apparently always associated with serpentine. This insect is largely, though not entirely, restricted to habitats supporting *Plantago erecta* which is very abundant on serpentine soils, though it is not endemic to them (Thomas, 1961).

The area of distribution of *E. editha* exceeds that of *Plantago erecta* as it is also found on a few other hosts such as *P. lanceolata* and *P. major*. In the San Francisco Bay area, however, the butterfly is confined to serpentine soils because the latter two species of *Plantago* do not exist in this region.

A further link between butterflies and serpentine was established by Shapiro (1981). Larvae of the pierid butterflies *Pieris sisymbrii* and *P. sara*, preferentially feed on serpentine-endemic species of *Streptanthus*. Some plants develop non-green callosities at the tips of the marginal teeth which mimic *Pieris* eggs and deter oviposition by the butterflies.

The role of animals in mineral exploration has been reported by Brooks (1983) who described the use of termites in prospecting for gold. The fact that termite mounds can be used for gold exploration was known in antiquity when Herodotus (450 B.C.) reported that certain "tribes" in India used the mounds for this purpose: ". . . There is found in this desert a kind of ant of great size—bigger than a fox though not as big as a dog. These creatures as they burrow underground throw up the sand in heaps, just as our own ants throw up the earth, and they are very like ours in shape. The sand has a rich content of gold, and it is this that the Indians are after when they make their expeditions into the desert." Herodotus seems to have exaggerated the size of the termites, but there is no reason why they could not have been used for prospecting even then.

The use of termite mounds for prospecting for gold reached its climax in Zimbabwe a few years ago due to the work of West (1965) who reported that: ". . . Termite colonies abound in this country and they cannot exist without water. Owing to the intermittent rainfall they must depend on underground water supplies to keep them alive for six to nine months each year and the water must come from water-carrying fissures. In the Leopard Mine their water-carrying passages extend down to 60 m which is the present water level. The termites mine their way down the softer sections of the surface rocks to obtain the water, these softer sections obviously being the dried-up portions of the water-carrying fissures, and in the case of the Leopard Mine, the ore-bearing fissure. In mining their way down to water, they remove the necessary spoil and bring it to the surface to be deposited in the form of a heap known as an ant heap. . . . Some of the termite heaps on the Leopard and Leopardess Mines yield more than 3 oz of gold per tonne (84 μ/g). . . . The plotting and sampling of termite heaps, irrespective of the nature of the overburden (such as Kalahari sands) is a useful and accurate method of prospecting as the onerous part of the work has already been done by the termites at no cost to the prospector."

Fig. 7.1 shows a plan of termite mounds above the Leopard Mine in Zimbabwe. The ultimate justification of the above method of exploration is to be found in the presence of an operating gold mine in Zimbabwe, which is known as "Termite Mine" and was discovered by analysing the spoil from termite mounds.

It is admittedly true that the above studies were concerned primarily with the discovery of gold rather than serpentine rocks. There is, however, no reason why the same principles should not be applied to the discovery of serpentine rocks in countries such as those of southern and southwestern Africa where the terrain is often overlain by ubiquitous Kalahari sand which renders geological mapping very difficult because of the lack of outcrops.

Perhaps one of the most thorough investigations of the relationship between termites and serpentine was a study by Wild (1975) on termites of the Great Dyke, Zimbabwe. The termite *Odontotermes transvaalensis* is a common mound-building species in the 800 mm rainfall area of Mashonaland in Zimbabwe. A number of mounds were found on quite steep slopes on the Great Dyke between Mtoroshanga Pass and Merrie's Pass, always on serpentine soils and always on south-facing slopes. The species *Trinervitermes dispar* was also present though it builds a nest rather than a mound.

The termite mounds supported a denser growth of more palatable grasses than the surrounding serpentine. These grasses were *Setaria lindenbergiana*, *S. anceps* and *Panicum novemnerve*. The surroundings were dominated by such grasses as *Loudetia simplex*, *Themeda triandra* and *Andropogon gayanus*. The type of vegetation indicated that the mounds were more fertile than their surrounding soils. Table 7.1 shows concentrations of calcium, chromium, magnesium and nickel in the spoil of the mounds, in the surrounding serpentine, and in termites and tenebrionid beetles (*Catamerus* sp.) found on or near the mounds.

The general findings of Wild (1975) were:

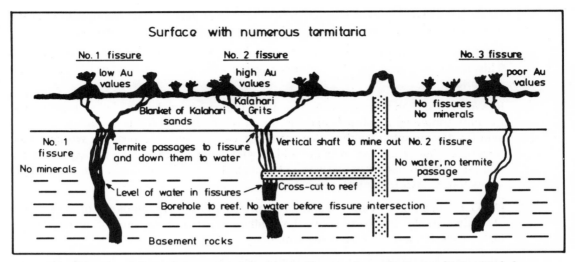

Fig. 7.1. Schematic representation of a termite mound over the Leopard Mine Zimbabwe. Source: West (1970).

TABLE 7.1 Elemental Levels in Soils, Termite Mounds, Termites and Tenebrionid Beetles (*Catamerus* sp.) from the Great Dyke, Zimbabwe (values for calcium and magnesium in soils are for the exchangeable percentage as determined by extraction with 1M ammonium acetate).

Species	Sample	pH	Ca(%)	Cr(μg/g)	Mg(%)	Ni(μg/g)	Ca/Mg*
Odontotermes	Workers		0.28	1500	1.43	4600	0.12
transvaalensis	Soldiers	—	0.06	300	0.14	300	0.24
	Queens	—	0.07	100	0.12	20	0.34
	Soil of mound	6.7	0.10	75000	0.19	9600	0.32
	Surrounding soil	6.0	0.05	65000	0.16	6800	0.19
Trinervitermes	Workers	—	0.12	500	0.46	500	0.16
dispar	Soldiers	—	0.40	90	0.65	90	0.36
	Soil of nest	6.0	0.05	79700	0.13	8400	0.23
	Surrounding soil	5.9	0.05	104000	0.11	7300	0.28
Catamerus sp	Adults	—	0.13	2500	1.48	2000	0.06
	Larvae	—	0.10	7700	1.80	3500	0.03

*mole quotient
After: Wild (1975)

(1) There seemed to be some increase in the nickel content of the mounds compared with the surrounding serpentine.

(2) There was no pattern for the chromium content of the mounds.

(3) In *Odontotermes* mounds on serpentine, the amounts of both calcium and magnesium were increased but the Ca/Mg quotient was increased to a more favourable level. This rendered the mounds more fertile for grasses such as *Setaria lindenbergiana* which has poor tolerance to serpentine and produces a dense green sward on the mounds, in sharp contrast to the poor *Loudetia-Themeda-Andropogon* grassland on the surrounding serpentine.

(4) Both species of termite selected in favour of finer particle sizes building their nests. This favoured clays and of course increased soil fertility for the overlying vegetation.

(5) There was a sharp increase in pH on the mounds compared with the surroundings. This again increased fertility by lowering the availability of phytotoxic nickel and chromium.

(6) Workers of both termite species contained quite high levels of nickel and chromium. Soldiers contained much less and the queen of *O. transvaalensis* contained quite in-significant amounts of either element. This was presumably because workers feed directly on vegetation, whereas the soldiers and queen are fed by the workers on saliva and regurgitated liquids which has had some of the nickel and chromium removed by the workers' own regulatory mechanisms.

(7) The tenebrionid beetle *Catamerus* sp. contained large amounts of nickel and chromium as did its larvae. Both the beetle and larvae feed directly on vegetation, hence explaining these high concentrations.

(8) The Ca/Mg quotient is lower in both species of termite than in the serpentine soil, but is elevated (as are nickel and chromium) in the soldiers of both species and even more so in the queen of *O. transvaalensis*. There is a consistent pattern of protection of these types of termite from the unfavourable nutritional factors, a protection afforded by the more numerous and therefore more expendable workers.

The role of animals in the ecology of serpentine is a fascinating subject and it is surprising that so little has been done in this field. It is hoped that this chapter will do something to stimulate such research in the future.

REFERENCES

Baumeister, W., 1958. Die Aschenstoffe. In (W. W. Rühland ed.) *Handbuch der Pflanzenphysiologie* v. 4. Springer, Berlin, 27.

Bollingberg, H. J., 1975. Geochemical prospecting using seaweed, shellfish and fish. *Geochim. Cosmochim. Acta*, 39: 1567–1570.

Brooks, R. R., 1983. Geozoology in mineral exploration. *Episodes*, 1983: 27–32.

Brooks, R. R. and Rumsby, M. G., 1965. The biogeochemistry of trace element uptake by some New Zealand bivalves. *Limn. Oceanogr.*, 10: 521–527.

Herodotus 450 BC. English translation by A. de Selincourt. Penguin Classics, London.

Johnson, M. P., Keith, A. D. and Ehrlich, P. A., 1968. The population biology of the butterfly *Euphydryas editha*. *Evolution*, 22: 422–423.

Proctor, J. and Whitten, K., 1971. A population of the Valley Pocket Gopher (*Thomomys bottae*) on a serpentine soil. *Am. Midl. Nat.*, 85: 517–521.

Russell, E. J., 1950. *Soil Conditions and Plant Growth*. Longmans Green, London, 483.

Shapiro, A. M., 1981. Egg mimics of *Streptanthus* (Brassicaceae) deter oviposition by *Pieris sisymbrii* (Lepidoptera: Pieridae). *Oecologia*, 48: 142–143.

Stebbins, G. L., 1949. *Speciation in salamanders of the Plethodontid genus Ensatina*. Univ. Calif. Pubs. Zool., 48: 377–526.

Vaughn, T. A., 1967. Food habits of the northern pocket gopher on shortgrass prairie. *Am. Midl. Nat.*, 78: 176–179.

Warren, H. V., Delavault, R. E., Fletcher, K. and Peterson, G. R., 1971. The copper, lead and zinc content of trout livers in the search for favourable areas to prospect. *Can. Inst. Min. Metall. Spec.* Vol. 11: 444–450.

West, W. F., 1965. Some unconventional ideas on prospecting. *Chamber Mines J.* (Rhodesia), 7: 40–42.

West, W. F., 1970. Termite prospecting. *Chamber Mines J.* (Rhodesia), 12: 32–35.

Wild, H., 1975. Termites and the serpentines of the Great Dyke of Rhodesia. *Trans. Rhod. Sci. Ass.*, 57: 1–11.

Chapter 8

THE DISTRIBUTION AND PHYTOCHEMISTRY OF PLANTS WHICH HYPERACCUMULATE NICKEL

8.1 INTRODUCTION

Nearly 40 years ago, Minguzzi and Vergnano (1948) reported the unusually high accumulation of nickel by the serpentine-endemic crucifer *Alyssum bertolonii*. Dried leaves of this plant contained over 1% nickel, a concentration perhaps 100 times greater than had ever been reported before for any flowering plant. A few years later, Doksopulo (1961) reported over 1% nickel in leaves of *A. murale*.

In the 1970s a third "hyperaccumulator" of nickel, *Hybanthus floribundus* was found in Western Australia by Severne and Brooks (1972) and Cole (1973). This taxon contained 9800 μg/g (0.98%) nickel in its dry leaves. Shortly afterwards, Jaffré and Schmid (1974) discovered a very high nickel concentration in *Geissois pruinosa*, *Homalium guillainii* and *Hybanthus austrocaledonicus* growing over ultramafic soils in New Caledonia.

The discovery of two species of *Hybanthus* with inordinately high nickel levels led Brooks et al. (1977a) to investigate the nickel content of as many species as possible from this genus as well as in *Homalium*, which also contained a taxon with this extraordinary accumulation of nickel. To carry out this work, these authors used herbarium material. Some description of the nature and use of herbaria might now be appropriate.

The world's herbaria store some 200 million dried plant samples. There are about 2000 of these institutions listed in the *Index Herbariorum* (Stafleu, 1974). Among the oldest of these is the Basel Herbarium (1588) and the Paris Herbarium which was founded in 1635 by King Louis XIII and which contains about 6 million specimens. Similar numbers are held by the famous Kew Gardens Herbarium and by the British Museum.

Herbarium specimens of flowering plants are customarily dried between sheets of heavy blotting paper under pressure so that the dried specimen is flat. Although the colours of the flowers fade very quickly, herbarium specimens will last indefinitely, some being over 200 years old.

A herbarium is the most essential tool for research in plant taxonomy and serves as a permanent record of the distribution of each species, its range of variability and the correlation of that variability with geography and habitat. A botanist writing up the flora of a region relies very heavily on herbarium material which he studies against a background of his own observations on living plants. He can hope to see only a small percentage of the species under natural conditions in their various habitats and at different years and seasons, so the herbarium is a *sine qua non* without which his work is impossible.

When Minguzzi and Vergnano first discovered the unusual accumulation of nickel by *Alyssum bertolonii*, they thought of analysing herbarium material to see if this character was possessed by other species of the genus. Their approach to the curator of the Florence Herbarium evoked such consternation that they were obliged to withdraw their request. The reason for this reaction is not hard to understand. The technique of emission spectrography used at that time would have destroyed the entire herbarium specimen.

The first person to perform routine analyses of herbarium material was probably Chenery (1948) who determined aluminium in representatives of all of the 259 recognized families of dicotyledons. He performed semi-quantitative colorimetric tests on leaf fragments about 6 cm^2 in area.

In recent years, new techniques in chemical analysis such as atomic absorption and plasma emission spectrometry have resulted in the minimum size of sample being reduced to only about 1 cm² (ca. 50 mg) or less.

With a sample this size, 20 or more elements can be determined by plasma emission methods with high sensitivity and good reproducibility. During the past few years, my own research group has analysed about 20,000 herbarium specimens for a number of different projects including the study of serpentine floras.

Returning now to the work of Brooks et al. (1977a) on the genera *Hybanthus* and *Homalium*, they determined nickel in about 2000 specimens of 128 out of 240 *Homalium* species, and 104 out of 150 *Hybanthus* species, collected from all parts of the tropical and warm-temperate world and which corresponded with a sampling density of one specimen per 2000 km². The survey resulted in the reidentification of all previously known hyperaccumulators of nickel and in the discovery of five additional taxa possessing this character. From the collection localities of these plants, it was possible to pinpoint many of the world's major serpentine occurrences. The principle was obviously applicable to other genera with significant numbers of serpentine-tolerant constituent species. In this study, Brooks et al. (1977a) coined the term "hyperaccumulators" or "nickel plants" to describe taxa containing more than 1000 μg/g nickel (0.1%) in dried aerial parts of the plant.

Table 8.1 lists the 144 hyperaccumulators of nickel which have been discovered so far. The list is not likely to become much larger in the course of time because most of the genera and species likely to contain hyperaccumulators have already been examined.

The choice of a cut-off point of 1000 μg/g nickel for hyperaccumulators is not arbitrary. Fig. 8.1 shows histograms of nickel concentrations in 167 species of *Alyssum* (Brooks et al. 1979). There is a marked gap between the highest nickel concentration in non-hyperaccumulators (500 μg/g) and the lowest value (1000 μg/g) for the nickel plants.

Fig. 8.2 places hyperaccumulators of nickel in their proper perspective against the nickel content of rocks and other plants. From this figure it can be seen that the nickel content of dried leaves of many hyperaccumulators is equal to, or exceeds, that of the ultramafic rocks which provide the supporting soils. The nickel content of the ash of these plants greatly exceeds that of the rocks because the conversion factor from dry weight to ash weight usually involves an increase of about 15 times for the elemental contents.

TABLE 8.1 List of Plants Which Hyperaccumulate Nickel (> 1000 μg/g in dry leaves)

No.	Genus	Species	Location	Max Ni (μg/g)	References
1	Agatea (Violac.)	deplanchei	New Caledonia	2500	36
2	Alyssum	akamasicum	Cyprus	9090	1
3	(Brassicac.)	alpestre	S. Europe	4480	2, 3
4		anatolicum	Anatolia	8170	1
5		argenteum	Italy	29400	1, 3, 4, 13
6		bertolonii	Italy	13400	2, 3, 5
7		subsp. scutarinum	Italy	10200	13
8		callichroum	Anatolia	10900	1
9		caricum	Anatolia	16500	1, 13
10		cassium	Anatolia	20000	1
11		chondrogynum	Cyprus	16300	1
12		cilicicum	Anatolia	13500	1
13		condensatum	Syria, Iraq	4990	1, 13
14		constellatum	Anatolia	18100	1
15		corsicum	Anatolia, Corsica	13500	1
16		crenulatum	Anatolia	10400	1
17		cypricum	Cyprus	23600	1

No.	Genus	Species	Location	Max Ni (μg/g)	References
18		davisianum	Anatolia	19600	1
19		discolor	Anatolia	11700	1
20		dubertretii	Anatolia	16500	1
21		eriophyllum	Anatolia	11500	1
22		euboeum	Euboea	4550	2, 13
23		fallacinum	Crete	3960	2
24		floribundum	Anatolia	7700	1
25		giosnanum	Anatolia	7390	1
26		heldreichii	Greece	12500	2
27		hubermorathii	Anatolia	13500	1
28		janchenii	Albania	9610	1
29		lesbiacum	Lesbos	22400	1
30		malacitanum	Spain	10000	6, 37
31		markgrafii	Albania	13700	1, 13
32		masmenaeum	Anatolia	24300	1
33		murale	Balkans	7080	1, 2, 7
34		obovatum	Russia	4590	1
35		oxycarpum	Anatolia	7290	1
36		peltarioides subsp. virgatiforme	Anatolia	7600	1, 13
37		penjwinensis	Iraq	7860	1
38		pinifolium	Anatolia	21100	1, 13
39		pintodasilvae	Portugal	9000	2, 8, 9
40		pterocarpum	Anatolia	22200	1, 13
41		robertianum	Corsica	12500	1
42		samariferum	Anatolia	18900	1, 13
43		singarense	Iraq	1280	1
44		smolikanum	Greece	6600	2
45		syriacum	Syria	10200	1
46		tenium	Tinos	3420	2
47		trapeziforme	Anatolia	11900	1
48		troodii	Cyprus	17100	1, 13
49		virgatum	Anatolia	6320	1
50	Argophyllum (Escalloniac.)	grunowii	New Caledonia	1375	36
51		laxum		1900	36
52	Blepharis (Acanthaceae)	acuminata	Zimbabwe	2000	10
53	Bornmuellera (Brassicac.)	baldaccii subsp. baldaccii	Greece	21300	13
54		subsp. markgrafii	Albania	27300	13
55		subsp. rechingeri	Greece	12000	13
56		glabrescens	Anatolia	19200	13
57		tymphaea	Greece	31200	13
58		$\times$ petri	Greece	11400	13
59	Buxus (Buxaceae)	flaviramea	Cuba	4500	11
60	Cardamine (Brassicac.)	resedifolia	Italy	1050	4, 34

No.	Genus	Species	Location	Max Ni (µg/g)	References
61	*Casearia* (Flacourticeae)	*silvana*	New Caledonia	1490	12
62	*Chrysanthemum* (Asteraceae)	*alpinum*	Italy	3200	34
63	*Cleidion* (Euphorbiac.)	*lasiophyllum*	New Caledonia	9900	36
64	*Geissois* (Cumoniaceae)	*hirsuta*	New Caledonia	4000	14
65		*intermedia*		22900	14
66		*magnifica*		3250	14
67		*montana*		5740	14
68		*pruinosa*		34000	14, 15
69		*racemosa*		1000	14
70		*trifoliolata*		6250	14
71	*Homalium*	*austrocaledonicus*	New Caledonia	1805	12, 16
72	(Flacourtiac.)	*deplanchei*		1850	12, 16
73		*francii*		14500	12, 16
74		*guillainii*		6926	12, 15, 16
75		*kanaliense*		9420	16–18
76		*mathieuanum*		1694	12, 16
77		*rubrocostatum*		1157	12, 16
78	*Hybanthus*	*austrocaledonicus*	New Caledonia	17600	15, 18, 19
79	(Violaceeae)	*caledonicus*		8800	16, 17
		floribundus			
80		subsp. *adpressus*		3000	20
81		subsp. *curvifolius*		9000	20
82		subsp. *floribundus*	W. Australia	9800	20–22
83	*Lasiochlamys* (Flacourtiaceae)	*peltata*	New Caledonia	1000	12
84	*Leucocroton* (Euphorbiaceae)	*flavicans*	Cuba	7700	11
85	*Linaria* (Scrophulariaceae)	*alpina*	Italy	1990	34
86	*Luzula* (Juncaceae)	*lutea*	Italy	2050	34
87	*Merremia* (Asclepiacaceae)	*xanthophylla*	Zimbabwe	1400	10
88	*Minuartia* (Caryophyllaceae)	*laricifolia*	Italy	1910	34
89	*Myristica* (Myristicaceae)	*laurifolia* var. *bifurcata*	Obi (Indon.)	1100	23

No.	Genus	Species	Location	Max Ni (µg/g)	References
90	*Noccaea*	aptera	Yugoslavia	13600	24
91	(Brassicac.)	boeotica	Greece	23400	24
92		firmiensis	France	16200	24
93		tymphaea	Greece	11800	24
94	*Oncotheca* (Oncothecac.)	balansae	New Caledonia	2500	36
95	*Pancheria* (Cunoniaceae)	engleriana	New Caledonia	6300	36
96	*Pearsonia* (Fabaceae)	metallifera	Zimbabwe	10000	35
97	*Peltaria*	emarginata	Greece	34400	25
98	(Brassicac.)	dumulosa (= #42)	Asia Minor	18900	25
99	*Phyllanthus*	aeneus	New Caledonia	2100	26
100	(Euphorbiac.)	balansaeanus		1820	26
101		cataractarum		1450	26
102		chrysanthus		1180	26
103		induratus		1480	26
104		kanalensis		1090	26
105		maytenifolius		1420	26
106		ngoyensis		9550	26
107		peltatus		2830	26
108		serpentinus		38100	26
109	*Planchonella* (Sapotaceae)	oxyedra	Indonesia	19600	23
110	*Psychotria* (Rubiaceae)	douarrei	New Caledonia	19900	15, 19, 33
111	*Rhus* (Anacardiaceae)	wildii	Zimbabwe	1600	10
112	*Rinorea*	bengalensis	S.E. Asia	17500	27
113	(Violaceae)	javanica	Borneo	2170	28
114	*Saxifraga*	aizoon	Italy	3840	34
115	(Saxifragac.)	exarata	Italy	2970	34
116	*Sebertia* (Sapotaceae)	acuminata	New Caledonia	11700	29
117	*Stachys* (Lamiaceae)	recta	Italy	2600	30
118	*Streptanthus* (Brassicac.)	polygaloides	W. USA	14800	31
119	*Thlaspi*	alpestre	Central Eu.	4000	24

No. Genus	Species	Location	Max Ni (µg/g)	References
120 (Brassicac.)	subsp. *virens*	France	4100	24
121	*alpinum subsp. sylvium*	Central Eu.	31000	24
122	*bulbosum*	Greece	2000	24
123	*epirotum*	Greece	3000	24
124	*goesingense*	Austria	12000	24
125	*graecum*	Greece	12000	24
126	*montanum*			
127	var. *californicum*	W. USA	7940	32
	var. *montanum*	W. USA	5530	32
128	var. *siskiyouense*	W. USA	11200	32
129	*ochroleucum*	Greece	4000	24
130	*rotundifolium*	Central Eu.	18300	24
131	var. *corymbosum*	Central Eu.	2000	24
132 *Trichospermum* (Tiliaceae)	*kjellbergii*	Celebes	1600	23
133 *Trifolium* (Leguminosae)	*pallescens*	Italy	2000	34
134 *Xylosma*	*boulindae*	New Caledonia	1930	12
135 (Flacourtiac.)	*confusum*		1630	12
136	*dothioense*		1780	12
137	*kaalense*		1900	12
138	*molestum*		1140	12
139	*pancheri*		1130	12
140	*peltatum*		1000	36
141	*pininsulare*		1280	12
142	*serpentinum*		1490	12
143	*tuberculatum*		1600	12
144	*vincentii*		3750	12

1—Brooks et al. (1979)
2—Brooks and Radford (1978)
3—Vergnano Gambi et al. (1979)
4—Vergnano Gambi and Gabbrielli (1979)
5—Minguzzi and Vergnano (1948)
6—Brooks et al. (1981)
7—Doksopulo (1961)
8—Menezes de Sequeira (1969)
9—Dudley (1986a)
10—Brooks and Yang (1984)
11—Berazain Iturralde (1981)
12—Jaffré et al. (1979b)
13—Reeves et al. (1983a)
14—Jaffré et al. (1979a)
15—Jaffré and Schmid (1974)
16—Brooks et al. (1977a)
17—Brooks et al. (1974)
18—Lee et al. (1977a)
19—Kelly et al. (1975)
20—Severne (1972)
21—Severne and Brooks (1972)
22—Cole (1973)
23—Wither and Brooks (1977)
24—Reeves and Brooks (1983b)
25—Reeves et al. (1980)
26—Kersten et al. (1979)
27—Brooks and Wither (1977)
28—Brooks et al. (1977b)
29—Jaffré et al. (1976)
30—Lisanti (1952)
31—Reeves et al. (1981)
32—Reeves et al. (1983b)
33—Baker et al. (1984)
34—Vergnano Gambi and Gabbrielli (1981)
35—Wild (1970)
36—Jaffré (1980)—see ref. at end of Chapter 19
37—Dudley (1986b)

NB. An undescribed subspecies of *Alyssum serpyllifolium* from La Coruña, Spain contained 11,482 µg/g nickel and is probably a new species.

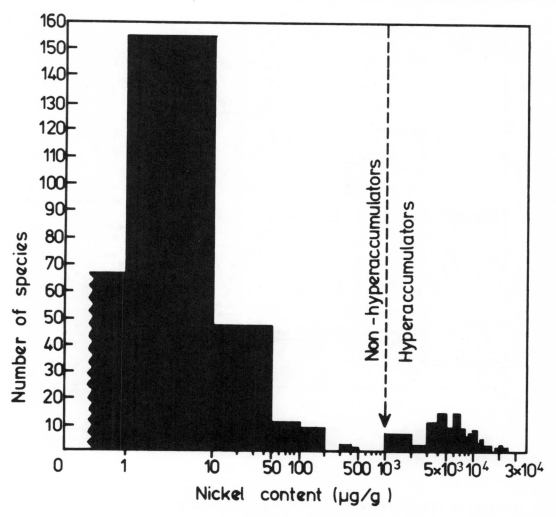

Fig. 8.1 Histograms of the abundance of nickel in *Alyssum* species. All the values >1000 μg/g dry weight are from section Odontarrhena.

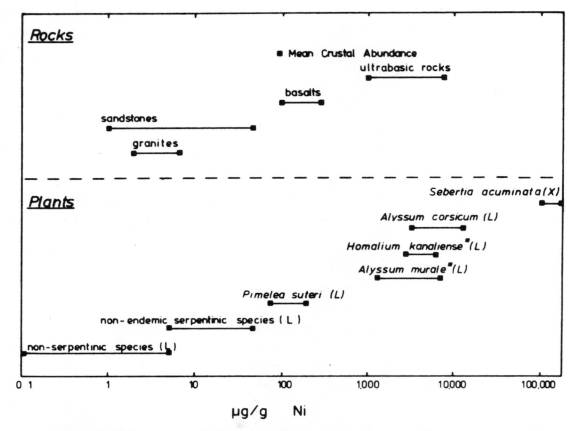

Fig. 8.2 Range of values for nickel concentrations in plants and various rock types (L = leaves, X = sap).

8.2 THE DISTRIBUTION OF HYPERACCUMULATORS OF NICKEL

8.2.1 Alyssum

The geographical distribution of hyperaccumulators of nickel is shown in Fig. 8.3. It is apparent that all of the nickel plants so far discovered have been found in one or more of seven distinct regions: 1—New Caledonia, 2—Western Australia, 3—southern Europe and Asia Minor, 4—The Malay Archipelago, 5—Cuba, 6—western United States, 7—Zimbabwe (Great Dyke). It will also be noted that hyperaccumulators are never found over previously-glaciated terrain (see also Chapter 6).

It might perhaps be argued that the distributions shown above are fortuitous rather than real and may have arisen from extensive studies of selected parts of the world. However, in the original herbarium survey of Brooks et al. (1977a) involving the genera *Hybanthus* and *Homalium*, hyperaccumulators were found in only two of the above seven regions despite a relatively uniform distribution of samples throughout the world.

The genus with the greatest number of hyperaccumulators of nickel (see Table 8.1) is *Alyssum* (Dudley, 1964) which contains 48 species of nickel plant (Brooks et al. 1979). A drawing of a typical plant of this type, *A. robertianum* from Corsica is portrayed in Plate 8.1.

The distribution of hyperaccumulating *Alyssum* species is unusual. They are confined to ultramafic substrates in southern Europe and Asia Minor stretching from Portugal in the west to the Iraq/Turkey/Iran border areas in the east. Anatolia is the site of their maximum

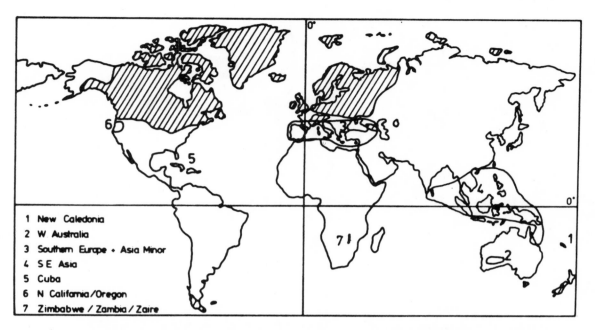

1 New Caledonia
2 W Australia
3 Southern Europe • Asia Minor
4 S E Asia
5 Cuba
6 N California/Oregon
7 Zimbabwe / Zambia / Zaire

Fig. 8.3 Worldwide distribution of hyperaccumulators of nickel. The shaded areas indicate the limits of the ice sheets during the last glaciation.
Source: Brooks (1983).

multiplicity and diversity. The distribution of 13 of these plants in southern Europe is shown in Fig. 8.4 (Brooks and Radford, 1978). Another nickel plant, *Alyssum malacitanum* (Dudley, 1986b; Brooks et al., 1981) has subsequently been identified from Malaga in southeastern Spain, followed by another on serpentine at La Coruña, in the northwest of the same country (F. F. Guitian Ojea—pers comm.). This latter is a subspecies of *A. serpyllifolium* with 1.15% nickel in dried leaves. The Iberian species of *Alyssum* give an excellent illustration of the evolutionary concept of neoendemism (see Chapter 6). The hyperaccumulators *A. pintodasilvae* (Portugal), *A. malacitanum* (Malaga), and *A.* sp. (La Coruña), are all close relatives of the ubiqutous *A. serpyllifolium* found throughout the Iberian Peninsula. This "precursor" species surrounds "serpentine islands" colonised by the three nickel plants.

Fig. 8.5 shows the distribution according to *vilayets* (provinces) of Anatolian: *Alyssum* from section Odontarrhena (which contains all the hyperaccumulating taxa of this genus). The figure classifies the plants into four categories depending on their nickel content: >10000 μg/g, 1000–10000 μg/g, 100–999 μg/g, and <100 μg/g. The locations of the plants correspond exactly with the areas of ultramafic rocks in Anatolia. There is hardly a single serpentine outcrop in the territory, however small, which does not contain at least one distinctive hyperaccumulator of nickel of the genus *Alyssum*.

Although species of *Alyssum* extend through central Asia and even across the Bering Strait to Alaska and the Yukon, hyperaccumulators are not found beyond a point just east of Turkey, despite the fact that there are plenty of serpentine soils in Asia and northwestern North America. Only *A. penjwinensis* (northwestern Iran) and *A. singarense* (northeastern Iraq) have the ability to hyperaccumulate nickel anywhere to the east of Turkey.

An interesting observation can be made about *A. corsicum*. This taxon was once thought to be endemic to a small ultramafic occurrence of a few hectares in extent, situated

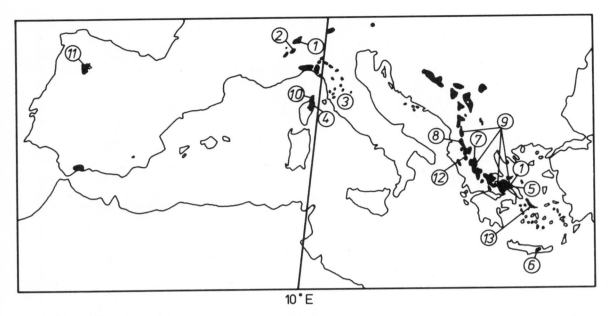

Fig. 8.4 Ultramafic rocks (solid black) and the distribution of *Alyssum* hyperaccumulators in southern Europe. 1—*A. alpestre*, 2—*A. argenteum*, 3—*A. bertolonii*, 4—*A. corsicum*, 5—*A. euboeum*, 6—*A. fallacinum*, 7—*A. heldreichii*, 8—*A. markgrafii*, 9—*A. murale*, 10—*A. robertianum*, 11—*A. pintodasilvae*, 12—*A. smolikanum*, 13—*A. tenium*.
Source: Brooks and Radford (1978).

on the outskirts of Bastia in Corsica. Later work, however, showed that this species originated in western Anatolia and was later spread to Corsica as weed seeds in grain carried to those islands by the Venetian traders in the 15th century. The seeds fell fortuitously literally on "stony ground" as they required an ultramafic substrate upon which to germinate and flourish. The site in Bastia is at present under threat from developers who can see no virtue in the preservation of a few "weeds".

It has been proposed by Brooks et al. (1979) that the magnitude of the areal distribution of a nickel plant is inversely related to its nickel content. For example, of the 18 species of *Alyssum* in section Odontarrhena containing over 10000 μg/g nickel in their dry leaves only one (*A. constellatum*) has a wide distribution, and even that is confined to eastern Turkey and northern Iraq. *Alyssum* species containing 1000–5000 μg/g nickel have a much wider dissemination. Examples of this are *A. alpestre* and *A. obovatum*. There is, therefore, a relationship in *Alyssum* species between diversity, proliferation and endemism on the one hand, and extraordinarily high concentrations of nickel on the other.

Multiplicity and diversity of species recognized by morphological discontinuities, together with a high level of endemism, have often been associated with ancient disturbed floras. A third characteristic may now be added: hyperaccumulation of nickel. This cannot be regarded as a universal characteristic of ancient floras, however, because of the comparative rarity of ultramafic rocks which are obviously a prerequisite for extreme nickel uptake.

It would seem that hyperaccumulation of nickel, like endemism, is an evolutionary adaptation typical of many ancient floras. In their extraordinary ability to accumulate massive concentrations of normally phytotoxic nickel, some genera such as *Alyssum* have

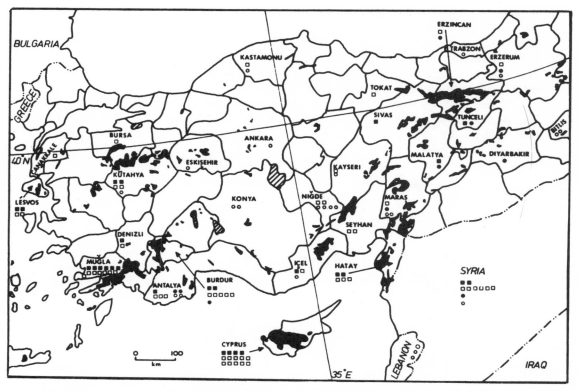

Fig. 8.5 Ultramafic rocks (solid black) and the distribution of *Alyssum* hyperaccumulators in Anatolia and the eastern Mediterranean. Solid squares = >10000 μg/g, open squares = 1000–10000 μg/g, solid circles = 100–999 μg/g, open circles = <100 μg/g.
Source: Brooks et al. 1979.

adjusted phylogenetically to very hostile edaphic conditions. The development of this physiological tolerance may perhaps be a survival or defence strategy against competition from other taxa. Certainly within section Odontarrhena of *Alyssum*, there is no question that the hyperaccumulators of nickel have been enormously successful. This triumph over the environment is illustrated by several taxa that occur on serpentine outcrops as extensive or nearly pure populations with an almost total absence of any other competing species. Examples of such "weedy" colonisers and superadaptors are *A. murale* which occurs microspeciated throughout the Balkans and particularly in the Pindus mountains of Greece (see colour plates in Chapter 14), and *A. corsicum* and *A. cypricum* throughout western Anatolia.

8.2.2 Thlaspi

Like *Alyssum,* the genus *Thlaspi* contains a number of hyperaccumulators of nickel and tends to occupy the same types of ecological niche in central and southern Europe. However, *Thlaspi* nickel plants are also represented in Anatolia. For about a century, one species of *Thlaspi* (*T. calaminare*) has had the reputation of hyperaccumulating zinc. Baumann (1885) reported 17.1% zinc in the ash of specimens growing over calamine deposits in western Germany. More recent work by Ernst (1968) continues to demonstrate the extraordinary ability of this taxon to hyperaccumulate zinc. He showed that normal zinc levels were around 1% in dried leaves of the plant. Reeves and Brooks (1983a) have reported hyperaccumulation of zinc and lead in *T. rotundifolium* subsp. *cepaeifolium* from the Cave del Predil region of northern Italy and have recently (Reeves and Brooks, 1983b) shown that several of the southern European taxa of this genus can hyperaccumulate nickel. They found at least 12 species with this character. The centre of maximum diversity and multiplicity appears to be in Greece (Fig. 8.6) where there are 7 taxa which may be classified as nickel plants. Other hyperaccumulators of nickel in the genus *Thlaspi* are to be found in the Switzerland/Italy/France alpine border area, in southcentral France, and in Austria and Yugoslavia. American varieties of *T. montanum* have also been found to hyperaccumulate nickel and are discussed in section 8.2.5 below.

It will be noted from Table 8.1 that several nickel plants are classified as *Noccaea* but had been assigned to *Thlaspi* until the genus was revised by Meyer (1973). Reeves and Brooks (1983b) showed that 38 out of 54 taxa studied were also able to hyperaccumulate zinc.

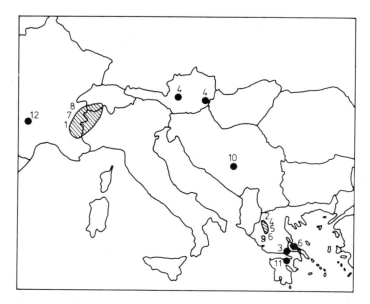

Fig. 8.6 Distribution of *Thlaspi* throughout southern and central Europe. 1—*T. alpestre*, 2—*T. graecum*, 3—*T. bulbosum*, 4—*T. goesingense*, 5—*T. epirotum*, 6—*T. ochroleucum*, 7—*T. alpestre* subsp. *sylvium*, 8—*T. rotundifolium*, 9—*Noccaea tymphaea*, 10—*N. aptera*, 11—*N. boetica*, 12 —*N. firmiensis*.
Source: Reeves and Brooks (1983b).

8.2.3 The Nickel Plants of New Caledonia

An example of the clear relation between nickel hyperaccumulation and endemism and multiplicity of taxa is shown by the flora of New Caledonia. Nearly 50 hyperaccumulators of nickel from 14 genera and 8 different plant families have been reported from this Pacific island. These New Caledonian nickel plants belong to the following genera and families: *Agatea* (Violaceae), *Argophyllum* (Escalloniaceae), *Casearia* (Flacourtiaceae), *Cleidion* (Euphorbiaceae), *Geissois* (Cunoniaceae), *Homalium* (Flacourtiaceae), *Hybanthus* (Violaceae), *Lasiochlamys* (Flacourtiaceae), *Oncotheca* (Oncothecaceae) *Pancheria* (Cunoniaceae), *Phyllanthus* (Euphorbiaceae), *Psychotria* (Rubiaceae), *Sebertia* (Sapotaceae), and *Xylosma* (Flacourtiaceae).

Among the above genera, the largest number of hyperaccumulators is found in *Homalium*. Out of the 16 New Caledonian species recognized by Sleumer (1974), 7 possess this unusual accumulatory character. Not only are these 7 taxa endemic to New Caledonia, but they are severely restricted to ultramafic substrates.

8.2.4 The Nickel Plants of Southeast Asia

Several hyperaccumulators of nickel have been reported from Southeast Asia. A fuller description of this work is given in Chapter 18 and it will therefore suffice at this stage to give a brief resume of the studies. Brooks and Wither (1977) found hyperaccumulation of nickel by *Rinorea bengalensis* which grows throughout the region and extends from Sri Lanka to Queensland. Although not all specimens of the herbarium material analysed contained >1000 μg/g nickel, it was clear that such levels were attained or exceeded whenever the plant was growing on ultramafic rocks. Brooks and Wither used the nickel content of the herbarium specimens to identify previously undiscovered ultramafites from Indonesian New Guinea.

In an analagous investigation of herbarium material, Wither (1977) and Wither and Brooks (1977) identified hyperaccumulation of nickel by *Planchonella oxyedra* and *Trichospermum kjellbergii* and used the information to detect previously-unrecorded ultramafic rocks from the Moluccas. Details of the nickel content of all of the above three taxa are given in Table 8.1.

8.2.5 Nickel Plants from other Regions

Only brief mention will be made of hyperaccumulators from other parts of the world. Perhaps the most important of the remaining areas is the Great Dyke in Zimbabwe. Wild (1970) reported the presence of the hyperaccumulator *Pearsonia metallifera* and later, Brooks and Yang (1984) found a further 3 nickel plants (*Blepharis acuminata, Merremia xanthophylla* and *Rhus wildii*) from this area.

Apart from 2 species in Cuba (*Buxus flaviramea* and *Leucocroton flavicans*) reported by Berazain Iturralde (1981) and 3 from Western Australia (*Hybanthus floribundus* subsp. *floribundus,* subsp. *adpressus* and subsp. *curvifolia*) reported by Severne (1972, 1973), Severne and Brooks (1972) and Cole (1973), the only other hyperaccumulators of nickel found elsewhere in the world are from the western United States. In this region, Reeves et al. (1981, 1983) discovered hyperaccumulation of nickel by *Streptanthus polygaloides* and by 3 varieties of *Thlaspi montanum* (var. *californicum,* var. *montanum* and var. *siskiyouense*). The development of serpentine-tolerant forms of *Thlaspi montanum* is another example of neoendemism (see also Chapter 6). The existence of forms intermediate between *T. montanum* and var. *siskiyouense* has been observed at Waldo, Oregon by Holmgren (1971). A taxon in this intermediate category contained 12,850 μg/g (1.28%) nickel.

8.3 THE PHYTOCHEMISTRY OF HYPERACCUMULATORS OF NICKEL

8.3.1 Inorganic Constituents

The first investigation of the chemical composition of hyperaccumulators of nickel was that of Minguzzi and Vergnano (1948) who determined SiO_2, Fe_2O_3, MgO, CaO and NiO in various organs of *Alyssum bertolonii*, a nickel plant from Tuscany. These data are shown in Table 8.2. A relatively constant Ca/Ni atom quotient was found in all plant parts except the seeds. Minguzzi and Vergnano (1948) suggested that the plant is able to compensate for increased nickel levels by increased uptake of calcium.

Morrison (1980) carried out a thorough investigation of the nickel content of various plant parts of *Alyssum heldreichii*. His findings are summarized in Table 8.3. It will be seen that the greatest accumulation of nickel occurred in the leaf material and the least in the roots. The lower stem and middle stem zones had lower nickel levels than the upper stems, and lower lateral stems. This is of some significance because the last two plant parts were green whereas the former were brown and woody. It would seem that nickel can be preferentially accumulated in photosynthetic tissues rather than in non-photosynthetic material. Similar observations were made by Minguzzi and Vergnano (1948) and Vergnano

TABLE 8.2   Percentage of Nickel and Other Oxides in *Alyssum bertolonii*

Organ	Ash %	SiO$_2$	Fe$_2$O$_3$	MgO	CaO	NiO	Ca/Ni*	Ca/Mg*
Roots	6.89	0.90	0.59	0.69	1.35	0.40	4.85	1.39
Leaves	15.50	0.33	0.18	1.14	5.15	1.55	4.42	3.21
Flowers	8.39	0.08	0.08	0.63	2.39	0.69	4.54	2.67
Fruits	10.00	0.21	0.09	0.84	2.65	0.74	4.71	2.26
Seeds	6.70	0.20	0.17	0.50	1.64	0.78	2.77	2.32

*—mole quotients
Source: Minguzzi and Vergnano (1948)

TABLE 8.3   The Distribution of Nickel Among Various Organs of *Alyssum heldreichii*

Organ	% of total wt	Ni (μg/g) in dry organ	% of total Ni
Lower Roots	11.9	4330	4.5
Upper roots	9.4	9150	7.6
Lower stems	10.0	7190	6.4
Middle stems	5.4	9660	4.6
Upper stems	3.4	16740	5.0
Lower lateral stems	10.0	17060	15.1
Lower lateral leaves	27.2	12150	29.2
Midstem leaves	12.9	11890	13.5
Upper stem leaves	7.6	14070	9.5
Apical buds	2.2	23400	4.6
Seeds		1880	

Source: Morrison (1980)

Gambi et al. (1977) using *A. bertolonii*. The same workers concluded that the degree of accumulation of nickel was related to the length of the growing period rather than to the nickel content (total or exchangeable) of the soil.

Several studies have been carried out to determine the relationship between hyperaccumulation of nickel and the uptake of other trace elements. In a study on nickel and 15 other elements in endemic plants of the Great Dyke in Zimbabwe, Brooks and Yang (1984) found that the nickel content of leaf material was correlated positively only with other siderophiles such as cobalt, chromium and manganese but was not related to any of the plant nutrients. A similar study by Yang et al. (1985) on serpentine-endemic Flacourtiaceae from New Caledonia showed an almost identical pattern: i.e., nickel in leaves correlated positively only with other siderophiles, though in this case there was also correlation with sodium and zinc.

From the above studies, it does not seem that nickel is able to affect the nutrient balance of serpentinophytes to any marked degree in spite of its hyperaccumulation by some taxa.

8.3.2 Organic Constituents

A few years ago, Jaffré et al. (1976) determined that the sap of *Sebertia acuminata* (sève bleue), a serpentine-endemic tree from New Caledonia, contained an inordinately high nickel content in its blue-green sap (hence the French common name for the tree). The tree is portrayed in Plate 19.1 and was reported by these workers to have a nickel content of 25.7% in the dried sap (11.2% in the fresh material). The leaves, trunk bark, twig bark, fruits and wood contained respectively: 1.17, 2.45, 1.12, 0.30, and 0.17% nickel. The 11.2% nickel contained in the fresh latex represents by far the highest nickel content recorded for any living material. Lee et al. (1977b) isolated and characterised the nickel compound in this material and in leaves of other hyperaccumulators such as *Homalium francii*, *H. guillainii*, *H. kanaliense*, *Hybanthus austrocaledonicus* and *H. caledonicus*. Experiments with high-voltage paper electrophoresis (Fig. 8.7) showed that at pH 6.5, an aqueous extract of *Sebertia acuminata* gave peaks corresponding to $Ni(H_2O)_6^{2+}$ and a negatively-charged 2:1 citrato-nickel complex. An extract of *Homalium guillainii* showed only the presence of the citrato complex. The identity of these peaks was further confirmed by a combination of gas-liquid chromatography and mass spectrometry. The counter-cation to the nickel citrato complexes was a mixture of $Ni(H_2O)_6^{2+}$ and hydrated Ca^{2+} and Mg^{2+} ions in the case of the *Homalium* and *Hybanthus* plants but was only the aquo complex of nickel in the latex of *S. acuminata*.

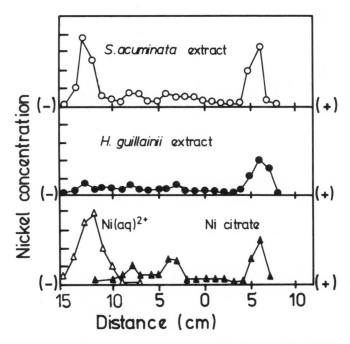

Fig. 8.7 Results of high-voltage electrophoresis on extracts of *Sebertia acuminata* and *Homalium guillainii* at pH 6.5. The *Sebertia* extract shows positively- and negatively-charged species corresponding to a nickel aquo complex and a citrato complex respectively. The *Homalium* extract shows only the citrato complex.
Source: Lee et al. (1977b). Copyright 1977 by Pergamon Press, reprinted by permission.

The relationship between nickel and citric acid was further investigated by Lee et al. (1978) who found both constituents in mature leaves of 15 New Caledonian hyperaccumulators and in two *Alyssum* species as well as in the Zimbabwean nickel plant *Pearsonia metallifera*. This association is shown in Fig. 8.8 and it is clear that the two variables are closely related. The same workers also found traces of malic and malonic acids in the extracts, though these were minimal in the latex of *S. acuminata*.

Further work on the composition of nickel complexes was performed by Kersten et al. (1980) using both gel and ion-exchange chromatography, as well as high performance liquid chromatography (HPLC), and a combination of gas-liquid chromatography and mass spectrometry. In their work on *Psychotria douarrei*, these workers showed that the nickel was present mainly as a negatively-charged malate complex balanced by a cationic nickel aquo complex. In contrast, the hyperaccumulator *Phyllanthus serpentinus* had its nickel bound as 42% citrate and 40% malate.

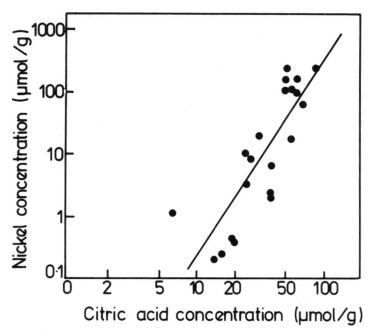

Fig. 8.8 The relationship between nickel and citric acid in hyperaccumulators of the *Genera Homalium, Hybanthus, Sebertia, Geissois, Psychotria, Alyssum* and *Pearsonia*.
Source: Lee et al. (1978). Copyright 1978 by Pergamon Press, reprinted by permission.

Nickel plants are ideal subjects for phytochemical studies of their organic constituents because the nickel contents are usually so high that it is readily possible to isolate milligram quantities of these complexes rather than the microgram amounts possible with "normal" plants. Despite this obvious advantage, it is surprising to find that only one other group outside that at Massey University, New Zealand, has carried out extensive studies on these interesting plants. I refer to the work of O. Vergnano Gambi and her associates at the University of Florence who identified nickel complexes in *Alyssum bertolonii* (Pelosi et al. 1974). These workers used gel chromatography to separate soluble nickel complexes and deduced that the nickel was bound mainly to an organic acid. Later, Pelosi et al. (1976) purified a nickel complex from the same species, again using gel chromatography. The purified product was examined by a mixture of gas-liquid chromatography and mass spectrometry and was found to contain a mixture of malic and malonic acids. The association of nickel with these acids in *A. bertolonii* and in *A. pintodasilvae* was further investigated by Pancaro et al. 1978a (see also Pancaro et al. 1978b for an English summary of this work). These workers used as a control, specimens of *A. bertolonii* grown in ordinary non-serpentine garden soil. The results of their survey are shown in Table 8.4. They found that nickel in leaves of plants grown on serpentine soil was mainly associated with malic and malonic acids present in an approximately 1:1 mole ratio (ca. 200 μmol/g dry mass). Control samples of *A. bertolonii* obtained from plants grown on ordinary garden soil and therefore deficient in nickel (< 40 μg/g), contained malic and malonic acid concentrations an order of magnitude lower. High levels of malic acid (120 μmol/g) related to high nickel concentrations (166 μmol/g) were found in the leaves of *A. pintodasilvae*, though in this case the level of malonic acid was very low. Experiments on purified extracts from *A. bertolonii* confirmed the involvement of the organic acids in the nickel metabolism of the leaf tissues which contained 1400 μgmol/g of malonic acid and 800 μgmol/g of malic acid. In the seeds of this plant, nickel was bound mainly to malic acid (300 μmol/g).

TABLE 8.4 **The Concentrations (μmol/g) of Malic and Malonic Acids and of Inorganic Constituents in Dried Leaves of (A)** *Alyssum bertolonii* **(Italy) and (B)** *A. pintodasilvae* **(Portugal).**

Species	Collection date	Locality	Organic acids			Cations				
			Malic	Malonic	Total	Ni	K	Ca	Mg	Total
A	17/2/75	Pomaia	304	176	480	238	390	1060	175	1863
	7/9/75	(on serp.)	257	208	465	213	399	723	269	1604
	11/11/75		153	162	315	272	374	686	238	1570
	11/1/76		161	140	301	341	325	661	245	1572
	10/7/76	On Non-	10	38	48	0.56	351	1260	101	1712
	10/1/77	serp. soil	29	44	73	0.65	508	1320	87	1915
B	15/5/77	On serp.	120	36	156	166	465	1448	124	2203

Source: Pancaro et al. (1978)

From the above work, it is possible to draw the conclusion that nickel is bound primarily to malic and malonic acids in *Alyssum* and to citric acid in many other hyperaccumulators such as *Sebertia acuminata, Homalium*, and *Hybanthus*. There little direct evidence for an association between citric acid and nickel in *Alyssum*.

It would be somewhat facile to assume that nickel in hyperaccumulators is bound only to citric, malic and malonic acids. Morrison (1980) studied the organic constituents of several *Alyssum* species and found many organic constituents other than these three organic acids. Many of these were derivatives of one or more of these acids such as the trimethyl esters of citric and homocitric acid. The latter parent acid has also been identified in the Zimbabwean *Pearsonia metallifera* by Stockley (1980).

The phytochemistry of Zimbabwean serpentine-tolerant plants has also been investigated by Ernst (1972). He studied *Indigofera setiflora* and *Dicoma niccolifera* from the Great Dyke area. The latter species contains up to 700 μg/g nickel in dried leaves and does not quite qualify for hyperaccumulator status. It has, however, been included for the sake of completeness. The same is true of *I. setiflora* (415 μg/g nickel). Ernst found 73 μg/ml of nickel in the cell sap of *D. niccolifera* and also carried out sequential extraction of root material from this species and in leaves of *I. setiflora*. These data are shown in Table 8.5. The proportion of nickel extractable with water from leaves of both species closely followed the nickel content of the cell sap. It appeared, therefore, that much of the water-soluble fraction was located within the leaf vacuole system.

As reported by Ernst (1972), about 75% of the nickel in leaves of *I. setiflora* was relatively tightly bound to the plant material and could only be removed by solvents with a high exchange capacity such as sodium chloride and citric acid. Ernst concluded that an appreciable proportion of the nickel in the residue was bound to the cell walls. He suggested that fixation at these sites was a mechanism whereby the nickel could be detoxified by storage and removed from the plant at leaf fall. When nickel levels in the substrate were high, these storage sites became saturated and the nickel burden in the cells was characterised by an increased water-soluble fraction.

Perennial organs such as roots present an entirely different problem compared with leaves. In the latter case, leaf fall can lead to removal of toxic metals, whereas in roots the same mechanism cannot be operative. In roots the capacity to tolerate heavy metals depends on the capacity to render the metals either soluble or insoluble and to retain the insoluble fraction while permitting the soluble fraction to translocate to the leaves for subsequent

TABLE 8.5 Percentage of Total Nickel in Various Extracts of Organs of *Dicoma niccolifera* **and** *Indigofera setiflora*.

Species	Organ	a	b	c	d	e	f	g
I. setiflora	Leaves	0.2	23.4	3.5	34.3	34.3	4.3	415
D. niccolifera	Root cortex	—	21.2	6.2	21.1	19.4	32.1	510
	Root xylem	29.3	21.2	13.3	20.1	13.4	2.7	238

After: Ernst (1972)
a—butanol
b—water
c—sodium chloride solution
d—citric acid solution
e—hydrochloric acid
f—insoluble residue
g—total nickel (μg/g dry weight)

TABLE 8.6 Percentage of Total Nickel in Extracts of Leaves of *Pearsonia metallifera*.

Extractant	Percentage nickel
Ethanol (95%)	2.79
Water (first extract)	55.76
Water (second extract)	15.33
Water (third extract)	4.74
Hydrochloric acid (0.2M)	20.35
Acetone-insoluble fraction from above	Trace
Perchloric acid (0.5M)	0.84
Acetone-insoluble fraction from above	0.03
Sodium hydroxide (2M)	0.12
Residue	0.05

Source: Stockley (1980)

removal at leaf fall. The data in Table 8.6 for roots of *Dicoma niccolifera* show that residual nickel is much more abundant in the root cortex than in the woody material. In general the older roots are predominant sites for the inactivation of heavy metals accumulated by these plants. The nickel in the wood was characterised by a high percentage of water-soluble and easily-exchangeable forms.

The phytochemistry of the Zimbabwean hyperaccumulator *Pearsonia metallifera* was investigated by Stockley (1980) using a sequential extraction system (Bowen et al. 1962 as modified by Lee, 1977). The percentage of total nickel in each fraction is shown in Table 8.6. It will be noted that over 75% of the nickel was extractable with water. The aqueous fractions were subjected to gel chromatography to separate a green crystalline material which contained most of the nickel. The extract was methylated and passed through a gas-liquid chromatographic column coupled to a mass spectrometer. Two peaks were obtained of which one was the trimethyl ester of citric acid. The other appeared to be the trimethyl ester of 3-hydroxy–3-carboxylhexanedioic acid.

Stockley (1980) also found malonic acid in the crude extract of the plant material and proposed that this causes the tricarboxylic acid cycle (Krebs Cycle) to be inhibited at the step involving conversion of succinate to fumarate. Because of this, the conversion of oxaloacetate to citrate is controlled by the amount of malate produced from back-to-back condensation of acetate units, and by the small residual conversion of succinate to fumarate.

The phytochemistry of *Pearsonia metallifera* is obviously much more complicated than that of other hyperaccumulators such as *Sebertia acuminata*.

A process of sequential extraction was also used by Brooks et al. (1981) to study nickel in *Alyssum serpyllifolium* and its close relatives *A. pintodasilvae* and *A. malacitanum*. They found that more than half of the nickel was soluble in water and dilute acid showing that it was present as polar complexes. They also found an association between nickel and citric, malic and malonic acids (cf. Pelosi et al. 1974, 1976).

8.4 GENERAL DISCUSSION

Although the 144 hyperaccumulators of nickel in Table 8.1 are distributed among 6 superorders, 17 orders, 22 families, and 38 genera (Table 8.7), it is remarkable that 117 of the species are in superorder Dilleniidae (using the system of Cronquist, 1968). Moreover 95 of these are found in the two families Brassicaceae and Flacourtiaceae. The concentration of nickel plants in such a small number of families presupposes some sort of evolutionary factor perhaps linked with families with a ready ability to produce organic acids capable of complexing with nickel. In contrast with the above findings, hyperaccumulators of cobalt and copper (Brooks et al. 1980) are found predominantly in the Asteridae, a superorder poorly represented in nickel plants. Hyperaccumulation of a particular element by plants is clearly a very selective event.

It will be appropriate at this stage to discuss mechanisms of hyperaccumulation of nickel by plants. It would seem that most, if not all, of these nickel plants are *facultative* rather than *obligate* (see Chapter 6 for a definition of these terms) since they will usually grow quite well in non-serpentine soils though they are liable to fungal attack and will not usually tolerate much competition from other plants. Even the unusual *Sebertia acuminata* from New Caledonia with its latex of almost pure nickel citrate is probably not obligate on serpentine. The latex serves most likely as an efficient agent in transporting phytotoxic nickel from the root systems to the leaves for storage until leaf fall.

All the above studies have shown that uptake of nickel by plants is a selective process not accompanied to any marked extent by accumulation of other elements to an inordinate degree. Still and Williams (1980) have discussed this point and proposed that the accumulation of nickel is due to a selective transport ligand in the root membrane. This "selector" is restricted to the membrane, so that other organic compounds such as citric and malic acids would be needed to act as "transport" ligands. A mechanism of hyperaccumulation based on the work of Still and Williams (1980) has been proposed by Morrison (1980). When the former examined the transport of nickel in plants they were unable to decide whether the transporting ligand was able to cross the root membrane as part of a selector-transport-nickel complex or became complexed after the nickel had been released after crossing the membrane. Morrison (1980) proposed that the transport ligand forms a ternary (mixed ligand) complex with the selector-nickel complex on the internal surface of the root membrane. Thus the method proposed (Fig. 8.9) has the selector ligand (S) complex with the aquonickel(II) ions of the soil solution on the external surface of the root membrane. The selector-nickel complex (SNi) then moves through the membrane to the inner surface where a ternary complex (SNiT) is formed with the transport ligand (T) which is most probably an oxygen donor.

Sigel (1973) has shown that not only are mixed ligand systems generally more stable than binary systems, but mixed nitrogen-oxygen systems are more stable than nitrogen- or oxygen-dominated systems. Still and Williams (1980) have proposed that since the ligand has a nitrogen donor, the transport ligand is most favourably an oxygen donor. It is the breakdown of the ternary complex which releases the transport-nickel complex into the xylem. The selector ligand is then free to move back across the root membrane to repeat the process. This

TABLE 8.7 Taxonomic Classification of Hyperaccumulators of Nickel (using system of Cronquist, 1968).

Superorder	Order	Family	Genus	No.
Asteridae	Asterales	Asteraceae	*Chrysanthemum*	1
	Gentianales	Asclepiadaceae	*Merremia*	1
	Lamiales	Lamiaceae	*Stachys*	1
	Rubiales	Rubiaceae	*Psychotria*	1
	Scrophulariales	Acanthaceae	*Blepharis*	1
		Scrophulariaceae	*Linaria*	1
Caryophyllidae	Caryophyllales	Caryophyllaceae	*Minuartia*	1
Commelinidae	Juncales	Juncaceae	*Luzula*	1
Dilleniidae	Capparales	Brassicaceae	*Alyssum*	48
			Bornmuellera	6
			Cardamine	1
			Noccaea	4
			Peltaria	1
			Streptanthus	1
			Thlaspi	13
	Ebenales	Oncothecaceae	*Oncotheca*	1
		Sapotaceae	*Planchonella*	1
			Sebertia	1
	Malvales	Tiliaceae	*Trichospermum*	1
	Violales	Flacourtiaceae	*Casearia*	1
			Homalium	7
			Lasiochlamys	1
			Xylosma	11
		Violaceae	*Agatea*	1
			Hybanthus	5
			Rinorea	2
Magnoliidae	Magnoliales	Myristicaceae	*Myristica*	1
Rosidae	Cunoniae	Escalloniaceae	*Argophyllum*	2
		Cunoniaceae	*Geissois*	7
			Pancheria	1
	Euphorbiales	Buxaceae	*Buxus*	1
		Euphorbiaceae	*Cleidion*	1
			Leucocroton	1
			Phyllanthus	10
	Fabales	Fabaceae	*Pearsonia*	1
			Trifolium	1
	Rosales	Saxifragaceae	*Saxifraga*	2
	Sapindales	Anacardiaceae	*Rhus*	1

proposal of nickel complexation via a selector-transport-nickel complex has one particularly important advantage: free aquonickel(II) ions, the cause of nickel toxicity to plants, are not formed internally. Within the plant cells the nickel is always in a complexed form. The transport-nickel complex moves through the xylem to the leaf cells. Here it crosses the plasmalemma, cytoplasm and tonoplast to enter the vacuole. In the vacuole, the transport-nickel complex reacts with a terminal "acceptor" ligand (A) to form the acceptor-nickel complex (NiA), and releases the transport ligand. The acceptor-nickel complex accumulates within the vacuole where it cannot interfere with the cell's physiological processes. The

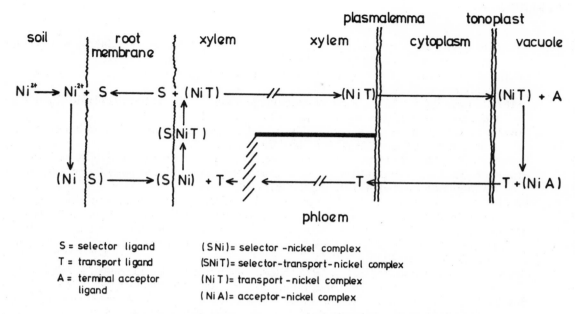

Fig. 8.9 Proposed mechanism for the uptake of nickel by *Alyssum*. Source: Morrison (1980).

tonoplast must, therefore, be impermeable to this complex. The transport ligand moves out of the vacuole, the tonoplast being permeable to this ligand, through the cytoplasm and plasmalemma into the phloem and hence to the roots where it diffuses back into the xylem. It is not impossible that in some cases (e.g., citric acid), the transport and acceptor ligands could be the same species. The combination of roles would mean that a non-cyclic system is developed with the transport-nickel complex moving through to the vacuole where it accumulates while a fresh supply of ligand is always made available to the roots.

Before leaving this chapter, a brief mention will be made of phytochemical work on other serpentine plants. Lyon et al. (1969a, 1969b) found chromate ion in the sap of the serpentine-tolerant *Leptospermum scoparium* from New Zealand. The plant seedlings had been fed chromium artificially as the chromate ion. In leaf tissue, the chromium was complexed as the trisoxalatochromate(III) ion. The transport of chromium in the xylem sap was analogous to that of sulphur and phosphorus which are transported principally as anions in xylem sap (Tolbert and Wiebe, 1955). Lyon et al. (1969b) showed that most of the chromium was retained in the root system in the form of three oxalato-complexes. This is clearly a mechanism for reducing uptake of this phytotoxic element by serpentine plants.

A great deal of research still remains to be done on hyperaccumulators of nickel. So far such work has been carried out mainly at two institutions, Massey University, New Zealand and the Istituto Botanico, Florence, Italy. It is suggested that fruitful avenues of research on these interesting plants should be centred on mechanisms of nickel uptake. Such work may well lead to progress in colonising serpentine areas with suitable crop plants and help to raise the standard of living of many Third World countries where so much potentially-arable land is unexploited due to serpentine and lateritic soils.

REFERENCES

Baker, A. J. M., Brooks, R. R., Kersten, W. J. and Lee, J., 1985. Accumulation of nickel by *Psychotria* species of the Pacific Basin. *Taxon,* 34: 89–95.

Baumann, A., 1885. Das Verhalten von Zinksalzen gegen Pflanzen und in Böden. *Landwirtsch. Vers.-Stn.,* 31: 1–53.

Berazain Iturralde, R., 1981. Sobre el endemismo de la florula serpentinicola de "Lomas de Galindo", Canasi, Habana. *Rev. Jard. Bot. Nac. (CUBA),* 2: 29–59.

Bowen, H. J. M., Cawse, P. A. and Thick, J., 1962. The distribution of some inorganic elements in plant tissue extracts. *J. Exp. Bot.,* 13: 257–267.

Brooks, R. R., 1983. *Biological Methods of Prospecting for Minerals.* Wiley, New York.

Brooks, R. R., Lee, J. and Jaffré, T., 1974. Some New Zealand and New Caledonian plant accumulators of nickel. *J. Ecol.,* 62: 523–529.

Brooks, R. R., Lee, J., Reeves, R. D. and Jaffré, T., 1977a. Detection of nickeliferous rocks by analysis of herbarium specimens of indicator plants. *J. Geochem. Explor.,* 7: 49–77.

Brooks, R. R., Morrison, R. S., Reeves, R. D., Dudley, T. R. and Akman, Y., 1979. Hyperaccumulation of nickel by *Alyssum* Linnaeus (Cruciferae). *Proc. Roy. Soc. Lond. Sec. B,* 203: 387–403.

Brooks, R. R. and Radford, C. C., 1978. Nickel accumulation by European species of the genus *Alyssum. Proc. Roy. Soc. Lond. Sec. B.,* 200: 217–224.

Brooks, R. R., Reeves, R. D., Morrison, R. S. and Malaisse, F., 1980. Hyperaccumulation of copper and cobalt—a review. *Bull. Soc. Roy. Bot. Belg.,* 113: 166–172.

Brooks, R. R., Shaw, S. and Asensi Marfil, A., 1981. The chemical form and physiological function of nickel in some Iberian *Alyssum* species. *Physiol. Plantarum,* 51: 167–170.

Brooks, R. R. and Wither, E. D., 1977. Nickel accumulation by *Rinorea bengalensis* (Wall.) O.K. *J. Geochem. Explor.,* 7: 295–300.

Brooks, R. R., Wither, E. D. and Zepernick, B., 1977b. Cobalt and nickel in *Rinorea* species. *Pl. Soil,* 47: 707–712.

Brooks, R. R. and Yang, X. H., 1984. Elemental levels and relationships in the endemic serpentine flora of the Great Dyke, Zimbabwe, and their significance as controlling factors for this flora. *Taxon,* 33: 392–399.

Chenery, E. M., 1948. Aluminium in the plant world. Part I General survey in dicotyledons. *Kew Bull.,* 1948: 173–183.

Cole, M. M., 1973. Geobotanical and biogeochemical investigations in the sclerophyllous woodland and scrub associations of the eastern Goldfields area of Western Australia with partial reference to the role of *Hybanthus floribundus* (Lindl.) F. Muell. a nickel indicator and accumulator plant. *J. Appl. Ecol.,* 10: 269–320.

Cronquist, A., 1968. *The Evolution and Classification of Flowering Plants.* Nelson, London.

Doksopulo, E. P., 1961. Nickel in rocks, soils, waters and plants adjacent to the Chorchanskaya Group (in Russ.). *Izd. Tbiliskovo Univ., Tbilisi.*

Dudley, T. R., 1964. Synopsis of the genus *Alyssum. J. Arn. Arbor.,* 45: 358–373.

Dudley, T.R., 1986a. A new nickelophilous species of *Alyssum* (Cruciferae) from Portugal, *Alyssum pintodasilvae* T. R. Dudley, sp. nov. *Fedd. Rep.* 97: 135–138.

Dudley, T. R., 1986b. A nickel hyperaccumulating species of *Alyssum* (Cruciferae) from Spain: *Alyssum malacitanum* (Rivas Goday) T. R. Dudley, comb et stat. nov. *Fedd. Rep.* 97: 139–142.

Ernst. W., 1968. Zur Kenntnis der Soziologie und Okologie der Schwermetallvegetation Grossbritaniens. *Ber. Dt. Bot. Ges.,* 81: 116–124.

Ernst, W., 1972. Ecophysiological studies on heavy metal plants in south Central Africa. *Kirkia,* 8: 125–145.

Holmgren, P. K., 1971. A biosystematic study of North American *Thlaspi montanum* and its allies. *Mem. N.Y. Bot. Gard.,* 21: 1–106.

Jaffré, T., Brooks, R. R., Lee, J. and Reeves, R. D., 1976. *Sebertia acuminata* a nickel-accumulating plant from New Caledonia. *Science* 193: 579–580.

Jaffré, T., Brooks, R. R. and Trow, J. M., 1979a. Hyperaccumulation of nickel by *Geissois* species. *Pl. Soil,* 51: 157–162.

Jaffré, T., Kersten, W. J., Brooks, R. R. and Reeves, R. D., 1979b. Nickel uptake by the Flacourtiaceae of New Caledonia. *Proc. Roy. Soc. Lond. Sec. B*, 205: 385–394.

Jaffré, T. and Schmid, M., 1974. Accumulation du nickel par une Rubiacée de Nouvelle Calédonie, *Psychotria douarrei* (G. Beauvisage) Däniker. *C. Rend. Acad. Sci. Paris Sér. D*, 278: 1727–1730.

Kelly, P. C., Brooks, R. R., Dilli, S. and Jaffré, T., 1975. Preliminary observations on the ecology and plant chemistry of some nickel-accumulating plants from New Caledonia. *Proc. Roy. Soc. Lond. Sec. B.*, 189: 69–80.

Kersten, W. J., 1979. *Ecological and Phytochemical Studies on Nickel-accumulating Plants from the Pacific Basin Region.* MSc Thesis, Massey University, New Zealand.

Kersten, W. J., Brooks, R. R., Reeves, R. D. and Jaffré, T., 1979. Nickel uptake by New Caledonian species of *Phyllanthus. Taxon*, 28: 529–534.

Kersten, W. J., Brooks, R. R., Reeves, R. D. and Jaffré, T., 1980. Nature of nickel complexes in *Psychotria douarrei* and other nickel-accumulating plants. *Phytochemistry*, 19: 1963–1965.

Lee, J., 1977. *Phytochemical and Biogeochemical Studies in Nickel Accumulation by some New Caledonian Plants.* PhD Thesis, Massey University, New Zealand.

Lee, J., Brooks, R. R., Reeves, R. D., Boswell, C. R. and Jaffré, T., 1977a. Plant-soil relationships in a New Caledonian serpentine flora. *Pl. Soil*, 46: 675–680.

Lee, J., Reeves, R. D., Brooks, R. R. and Jaffré, T., 1977b. Isolation and identification of a citrato complex of nickel from nickel-accumulating plants. *Phytochemistry*, 16: 1503–1505.

Lee, J., Reeves, R. D., Brooks, R. R. and Jaffré, T., 1978. The relationship between nickel and citric acid in some nickel-accumulating plants. *Phytochemistry*, 17: 1033–1035.

Lisanti, E. L., 1952. Contributo allo studio delle morfosi che si riscontrano sui serpentini. *Nuov. G. Bot. Ital.*, 14: 349–360.

Lyon, G. L., Peterson, P. J. and Brooks, R. R., 1969a. Chromium-51 transport in the xylem sap of *Leptospermum scoparium* (manuka). *N.Z. J. Sci.*, 12: 541–545.

Lyon, G. L., Peterson, P. J. and Brooks, R. R., 1969b. Chromium-51 distribution in tissues and extracts of *Leptospermum scoparium. Planta*, 88: 282–287.

Morrison, R. S., 1980. *Aspects of the Accumulation of Cobalt, Copper and Nickel by Plants.* PhD Thesis, Massey University, New Zealand.

Menezes de Sequeira, E., 1969. Toxicity and movement of heavy metals in serpentinic rocks (northeastern Portugal). *Agron. Lusit.*, 30: 115–154.

Meyer, F. K., 1973. Conspectus der *Thlaspi* Arten Europas, Afrikas und Vorderasiens. *Fedd. Rep.*, 84: 449–470.

Minguzzi, C. and Vergnano, O., 1948. Il contenuto di nichel nelle ceneri di *Alyssum bertolonii* Desv. *Mem. Soc. Tosc. Sci. Nat. Ser. A*, 55: 49–74.

Pancaro, L., Pelosi, P., Vergnano Gambi, O. and Galoppini, C., 1978a. Ulteriori indagini sul rapporto tra nichel e acidi malico e malonico in *Alyssum. G. Bot. Ital.*, 112: 141–146.

Pancaro, L., Pelosi, P., Vergnano Gambi, O. and Galoppini, C., 1978b. Further contribution on the relationship between nickel and malic and malonic acids in *Alyssum. G. Bot. Ital.*, 112: 282–283.

Pelosi, P., Galoppini, C. and Vergnano Gambi, O., 1974. Sulla natura dei composti del nichel presenti in *Alyssum bertolonii* Desv. Nota I. *Agric. Ital.*, 29: 1–5.

Pelosi, P., Fiorentini, R. and Galoppini, C., 1976. On the nature of nickel compounds in *Alyssum bertolonii* Desv. II. *Agric. Biol. Chem.*, 40: 1641–1642.

Reeves, R. D. and Brooks, R. R., 1983a. Hyperaccumulation of lead and zinc by two metallophytes from a mining area in Central Europe. *Environ. Pollut.*, 31: 277–287.

Reeves, R. D. and Brooks, R. R., 1983b. European species of *Thlaspi* L. (Cruciferae) as indicators of nickel and zinc. *J. Geochem. Explor.*, 18: 275–283.

Reeves, R. D., Brooks, R. R. and Dudley, T. R., 1983a. Uptake of nickel by species of *Alyssum. Bornmuellera* and other genera of Tribus Alyssae. *Taxon*: 184–192.

Reeves, R. D., Brooks, R. R. and McFarlane, R. M., 1981. Nickel uptake by Californian *Streptanthus* and *Caulanthus* with particular reference to the hyperaccumulator *S. polygaloides* Gray (Brassicaceae). *Am. J. Bot.*, 68: 708–712.

Reeves, R. D., Brooks, R. R. and Press, J. R., 1980. Nickel accumulation by species of *Peltaria* Jacq. (Cruciferae). *Taxon*, 29: 629–633.

Reeves, R. D., Macfarlane, R. M. and Brooks, R. R., 1983b. Accumulation of nickel and zinc by western North American genera containing serpentine-tolerant species. *Am. J. Bot.*, 70: 1297–1303.

Severne, B. C., 1972. *Botanical Methods for Mineral Exploration in Western Australia*. PhD Thesis, Massey University, New Zealand.

Severne, B. C., 1973. Nickel accumulation by *Hybanthus floribundus*. *Nature*, 248: 807–808.

Severne, B. C. and Brooks, R. R., 1972. A nickel-accumulating plant from Western Australia. *Planta*, 103: 91–94.

Sigel, H., 1973. Structural aspects of mixed-ligand complex formation in solution. In, *Metal Ions in Biological Systems*. Dekker, New York.

Stafleu, F. A., 1974. *Index Herbariorum*. Part I The Herbaria of the World. Oosthoek, Scheltema and Holkema, Utrecht.

Sleumer, H., 1974. A concise revision of the Flacourtiaceae of New Caledonia and the Loyalty Islands. *Blumea*, 22: 123–147.

Still, E. R. and Williams, R. J. P., 1980. Potential methods for selective accumulation of nickel II ion in plants. *J. Inorg. Biochem.*, 13: 35–40.

Stockley, E., 1980. *Biogeochemical Studies on the Nickel Complex Contained in the Nickel-accumulating Legume Pearsonia metallifera from the Great Dyke Area, Zimbabwe*. BSc Hons Thesis, Massey University, New Zealand.

Tolbert, N. E. and Wiebe, H., 1955. Phosphorus and sulphur compounds in plant xylem sap. *Pl. Physiol.*, 30: 499–504.

Vergnano Gambi, O., Pancaro, L. and Formica, C., 1977. Investigations on a nickel-accumulating plant *Alyssum bertolonii* Desv. I Nickel, calcium and magnesium content and distribution during growth. *Webbia*, 32: 175–188.

Vergnano Gambi, O., Brooks, R. R. and Radford, C. C., 1979. L'accumulo di nichel nelle specie italiane del genere *Alyssum*. *Webbia*, 33: 269–277.

Vergnano Gambi, O. and Gabbrielli, R., 1979. Ecophysiological and geochemical aspects of nickel, chromium and cobalt accumulation in the vegetation of some Italian ophiolitic outcrops. *Ofioliti*, 4: 199–208.

Vergnano Gambi, O. and Gabbrielli, R., 1981. La composizione minerale della vegetazione degli affiorimenti ofiolitici dell'Alta Vale de Ayas. *Rev. Valdôtaine d'Hist. Nat.*, 35: 51–61.

Wild, H., 1970. Geobotanical anomalies in Rhodesia 3.—The vegetation of nickel-bearing soils. *Kirkia* 7 Suppl. 1–62.

Wither, E. D. and Brooks, R. R., 1977. Hyperaccumulation of nickel by some plants of Southeast Asia. *J. Geochem. Explor.*, 8: 579–583.

Yang, X. H., Brooks, R. R. and Jaffré, T., 1985. Elemental levels and relationships in the Flacourtiaceae of New Caledonia and their significance for the evaluation of the "serpentine problem." *Pl. Soil*, 87: 281–292.

Chapter 9

KIMBERLITES, CARBONATITES AND THEIR VEGETATION

9.1 INTRODUCTION

Because of the scattered and worldwide occurrence of kimberlites and carbonatites, they are discussed in Part I of this book rather than in the regionally-orientated Part II. Kimberlites occur as small *diatremes* (volcanic pipes), dykes, veins and sills and appear to be associated with linear structural trends. They can be considered as belonging to three main groups (Wyllie, 1961): (i) clusters of diatremes forming elongated chains; (ii) dykes and sheets on a regional scale; (iii) central complex kimberlites associated with alkalic carbonatites.

There is increasing evidence of a genetic linkage between kimberlites, carbonatites and alkalic ultrabasic complexes. According to Dawson (1967), a hypothesis relating kimberlites to rocks of the nepheline syenite—carbonatite suite (including olivine melilite) most accurately reflects the chemical composition of kimberlites and its association with these rock types.

The main emphasis in this chapter will be on groups (i) and (iii) above. The former because of its importance as a source of diamond, and the latter because of its association with carbonatite complexes which support an unusual vegetation, easily recognizable by aerial photography and satellite imagery.

9.2 THE COMPOSITION AND DISTRIBUTION OF KIMBERLITES

Although often classified as ultramafic rocks, kimberlites differ from other ultramafites by their much higher levels of titanium, potassium, calcium and phosphorus due to their high content of perovskite (Ti), and apatite (P), and also because they are associated with carbonate-rich carbonatites. This is shown in Table 9.1 which gives the chemical composition of kimberlites in comparison with that of other igneous rocks including other ultramafites.

Because of their high phosphorus content, higher nutrient status and more favourable Ca/Mg quotient compared with most other ultramafites, soils derived from kimberlites are considerably more fertile than serpentine soils or even those of the non-ultramafic rocks surrounding diatremes and carbonatite complexes. This greater fertility can be used in the search for diamonds because of the more luxuriant, and therefore more recognizable, vegetation which covers diatremes. The distribution of kimberlites throughout the world is shown in Fig. 9.1. They occur in 17 distinct regions as follows:

(i) **North America.** The kimberlites of North America are found mainly in a broad band along the western rim of the Appalachians from New York State to Kentucky, and across to Kansas through Arkansas, Missouri and southern Illinois. They have been described by Watson (1967). Kimberlites also occur in Ontario and Quebec (Satterley, 1948; Watson, 1955) and also in the Colorado Plateau (Watson, 1967).

(ii) **Brazil.** Brazil was the world's foremost producer of diamonds immediately prior to the South African discoveries, and even in the early 19th Century Spix and Martius (1824) claimed to have discovered plant indicators of diamonds, the gems having been discovered a century earlier by Bernado de Fonseca Lobo. Most of the diamond finds in Brazil have been alluvial and there have been relatively few discoveries of kimberlites except for some in the state of Minas Gerais (Draper, 1923), and in the Bagagem region (Rimann, 1931). Both of these kimberlite zones are associated with, or are near, the carbonatite centres of Catalao,

Patrocinio, Salitre and Araxa. The most recently discovered diamondiferous region is in the Matto Grosso at Poxoreo.

(iii) **Australia.** Kimberlites occur in several states of Australia, notably in New South Wales and northern Western Australia. The deposits in the east do provide alluvial diamonds, but the most exciting discoveries were made fairly recently in Western Australia. These kimberlites are said to have a potential output exceeding that of Southern Africa.

(iv) **Solomon Islands.** The island of Malaita in the Solomons, contains outcrops of alnoite (lamprophyre) with ultramafic inclusions and the kimberlite indicator minerals pyrope, chrome-diopside and picro-ilmenite (Allen and Deans, 1965).

(v) **Kalimantan—Indonesia.** Alluvial diamond fields exist in southeast Kalimantan (Borneo) in Indonesia. The fields are situated near the Pamali river. At present further diamond exploration is being carried out to the west of the island.

(vi) **India.** Until recently, only one diamondiferous kimberlite occurrence was recorded in India. This was at Majhgawan (Mathur, 1962) and was the source of all India's diamond production. Recently a new diatreme has been discovered nearby at Hinota together with others in South India (Alexander, 1983). The vegetation of the Hinota pipe is discussed below.

(vii) **Siberia.** The Yakutia area of northern Siberia is the second-most extensive region of diamondiferous kimberlites in the world (i.e., after Southern Africa). The main area is in the Anabarsk shield. The kimberlites are associated with a wide variety of carbonatitic, alkalic and ultramafic rock types (Sheinmann, 1957; Butakova and Egorov, 1962). The vegetation of the diatremes is very distinctive and is also discussed below.

(viii) **Czechoslovakia.** Two kimberlites and three breccia pipes are known from the northern flanks of the Bohemian Massif in Czechoslovakia (Kopecky, 1960).

(ix) **Fennoscandia.** Kimberlites associated with carbonatites occur at Alnö in Sweden, Fen in Norway, and almost certainly at Sokli in Finland. The Sokli Carbonatite Massif (see below) has one of the world's most spectacular vegetation anomalies associated with this rock type.

(x) **West Africa.** Kimberlites have been found at Kenieba, Mali and also in Sierre Leone (Grantham and Allen, 1960). Alluvial diamonds are also found in Liberia, Ghana, Ivory Coast, Gabon, Angola and Zaïre. The Zairean production is quite considerable.

(xi) **Tanzania.** Kimberlites are widely distributed in the Central Plateau of Tanzania. Over 100 occurrences are known, of which the most famous is the Mwadui diamondiferous pipe (Edwards and Howkins, 1966).

(xii) **Zimbabwe.** Four kimberlites occur in the Lochard area near Bulawayo (McGregor et al. 1937).

(xiii) **South Africa.** Kimberlite pipes are more abundant in South Africa than anywhere else on earth. They are spread over a wide area from north of the Cape Mountains to South West Africa. Carbonatite dykes cut the kimberlite of the famous Premier Mine (Daly, 1925).

(xiv) **South West Africa.** Over 40 kimberlite occurrences have been found in the Gibeon-Keetmanshoop region in southern South West Africa (Janse, 1964). The kimberlites here are associated with carbonatites. Further north there is a large area of ring complexes including carbonatites (Martin et al. 1960).

(xv) **Lesotho.** Several kimberlite pipes and numerous dykes are known in Lesotho (Dawson, 1962, 1980). Mining for diamonds commenced in 1977 at Letsengla-Terai in the Maluti Mountains.

(xvi) **Botswana.** A number of kimberlites are known from Botswana (Cole, 1980) and are associated with vegetation anomalies recognizable from aerial photographs. These anomalies are also described below.

(xvii) **Swaziland.** Industrial diamonds have been discovered in the Ngomane area of Swaziland and at Ehlane in the north of the country near the Dokolwayo kimberlite pipe.

TABLE 9.1 The Major Element Composition (%) of Kimberlites and Other Igneous Rocks

Constituent	Ultramafites	Basic rocks	Felsic rocks	Kimberlites
SiO_2	40.60	50.30	69.20	35.20
TiO_2	0.05	1.50	0.40	2.32
Al_2O_3	0.85	16.50	14.50	4.40
FeO	12.60	10.90	3.50	9.80
MnO	0.19	0.26	0.70	0.11
MgO	42.90	7.40	0.93	27.90
CaO	1.00	9.40	2.30	7.60
K_2O	0.04	0.99	4.00	0.98
Na_2O	0.77	2.60	3.70	0.32
$H_2O + CO_2$	0.04	0.04	0.10	10.70
P_2O_5	0.04	0.32	1.60	0.70
NiO	0.02	0.02	0.005	0.13
Cr_2O_3	0.27	0.01	0.005	0.22
Total	99.73	100.24	100.94	100.38

Sources: various including Dawson (1980) for last column.

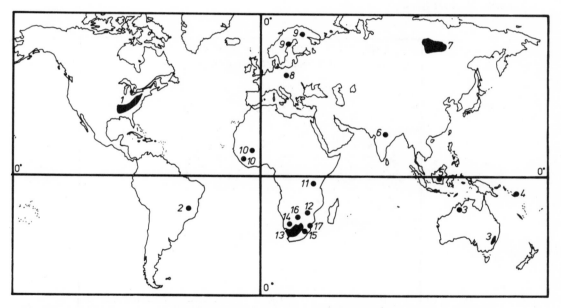

Fig. 9.1 Worldwide distribution of kimberlites: (1) North America, (2) Brazil, (3) Australia, (4) Solomon Islands, (5) Kalimantan (Borneo), (6) India, (7) Siberia, (8) Central Europe, (9) Fennoscandia, (10) West Africa, (11) Tanzania, (12) Zimbabwe, (13) South Africa, (14) South West Africa, (15) Lesotho, (16) Botswana, (17) Swaziland.

9.3 THE VEGETATION OF KIMBERLITES AND CARBONATITES

9.3.1 India

One of the most thorough studies of the vegetation of a single diatreme was carried out in India by Alexander (1983) and Alexander and Shrivastava (1983) at the Hinota pipe in the Penna district of Madhya Pradesh State. A simplified map of this location is shown in Fig. 9.2. The kimberlite intrudes the Kaimur sandstone and measures about 215 × 180 m. Petrologically, the kimberlite is predominantly micaceous, but basaltic-type and kimberlitic breccia can also be found. The geology, mineralogy and geochemistry of this pipe have been reported by Mathur (1961), Paul et al. (1975) and Ktesten and Paul (1976). The surrounding country rock is a hard indurated quartz arenite with a ferruginous siliceous cement. The soil has a pH of 6.2 in sharp contrast with the pH of 7.7 over the kimberlite. The trace element concentrations in the two contrasting rocks types are shown in Table 9.2.

The entire tree layer over the diatreme is characterised by a healthier growth of several species, compared with those over the quartzite (Fig. 9.3), and is visually obvious from a considerable distance. Fig. 9.4 shows the relative heights of six tree species from the pipe and the country rock. The Hinota diatreme not only supports a more luxuriant vegetation, but also has a greater number of species growing over it compared with the quartzite.

The undergrowth on the quartzite is very scanty and the grass has a height of only 10–20 cm compared with 50–100 cm over the diatreme. The Hinota pipe is readily identifiable from aerial photographs.

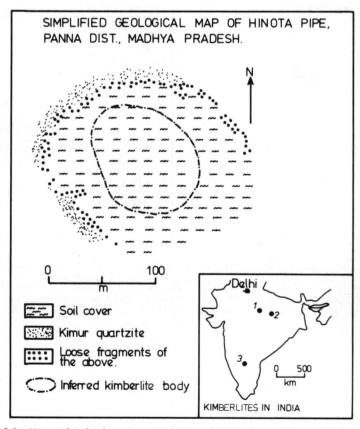

Fig. 9.2   Map of the Hinota kimberlite pipe, northern India. Kimberlites in the inset are: (1) Hinota and Majhagawan, (2) Jungal, (3) South India.
Source: Alexander (1983).

TABLE 9.2   Composition (%) of the Quartzite Country Rock and Kimberlite of the Hinota Diatreme, India.

Constituent	Quartzite	Kimberlite
SiO_2	96.71	36.50
TiO_2	0.13	6.92
Al_2O_3	0.95	3.51
Fe_2O_3	0.92	8.20
MnO	0.01	0.12
MgO	0.34	23.95
CaO	0.07	5.20
Na_2O	0.15	0.13
K_2O	0.19	1.65
P_2O_5	0.01	2.79
Loss on ignition	0.45	10.20
Cr_2O_3	0.008	0.18
NiO	0.002	0.12

Source: Alexander and Shrivastava (1983)

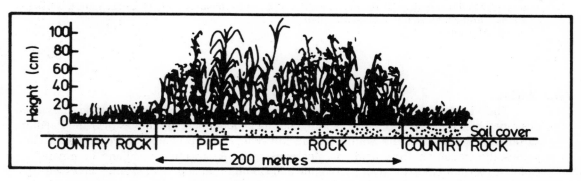

Fig. 9.3   A representation of the difference of density and height of the undergrowth off and on the Hinota kimberlite pipe, northern India.
Source: Alexander (1983).

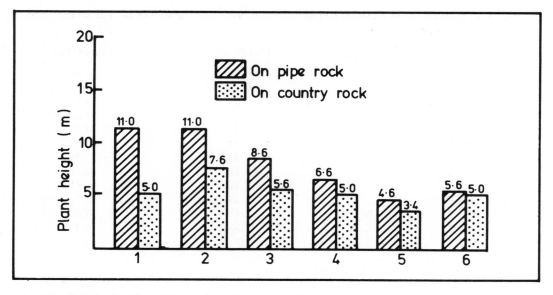

Fig. 9.4   Relative heights of six tree species growing off and on the Hinota kimberlite pipe, northern India. (1) *Madhuca indica*, (2) *Tectona grandis*, (3) *Diospyros melanoxylon*, (4) *Butea monosperma*, (5) *Lannea coromandelica*, (6) *Emblica officinalis*.
Source: Alexander (1983).

9.3.2 Africa

The vegetation overlying kimberlites and carbonatites in Southern Africa has been described by Cole (1980). She has reported strong geobotanical anomalies over the Palabora carbonatite complex of the South African lowveld. A sharp change of vegetation accompanies the transition from acid to calcareous soils. A savanna woodland dominated by *Colophospermum mopane* over pyroxenite and *Combretum* spp. over syenite, gives way to a thick cover of *Acacia nigrescens, Dichrostachys cinerea. Ormocarpum trichocarpum* and *Zizyphus zeyheriana* over carbonatite. The relatively luxuriant vegetation over the carbonatite was due to enhanced levels of phosphorus and potassium in the soils.

In eastern Botswana, Cole (1980) reported that although kimberlites were masked by a thick cover of residual brown loam, calcrete and Kalahari sand in the Orapa area, the more important pipes supported a denser and more diversified vegetation than the surrounding savanna underlain by basalt. The Orapa pipe (1.5 km diameter) was also well delineated from aerial photography. Near Ghanzi in western Botswana, other circular vegetational anomalies were not related to kimberlites.

As reported by Cole (1980), kimberlites in the high Maluti mountains of Lesotho are very different to those of the savanna areas. Here circular depressions are formed by the diatremes, and they are colonised by a species-rich mat of forbs and grasses in sharp contrast with the sparse grasses of the surrounding basaltic country rock.

9.3.3 Siberia

Some of the earliest work on vegetational anomalies over kimberlites was carried out in Siberia in the Yakutia region (Kobets, 1960; Lukicheva, 1960; Zagrebina, 1961, 1965). A study by Buks (1965) was centred around 8 kimberlite pipes in Yakutia. The kimberlites were covered with a thin larch forest dominated by *Larix dahurica*. The forest was always denser over the kimberlites and the characteristics of this vegetation compared with that of the surrounding country rock are summarized in Table 9.3.

Buks (1965) ascribed the healthier vegetation of the kimberlites to the higher apatite content of the substrate compared with that of the country rock. He also recorded a much more luxuriant undergrowth in the large forest overlying kimberlites. This undergrowth was characterised by a relative abundance of alder and associated mosses. He emphasized the importance of aerial observation and photography in detecting the kimberlites.

TABLE 9.3   Physical differences in *Larix dahurica* Forest Growing over Kimberlites and Country Rock in the Yakutia Region of Siberia.

	Kimberlites	Country rock
Undergrowth	abundant	sparse
Mean tree height (m)	9–11	4–8
Mean tree diameter (m)	0.25	0.15
Number per hectare	94	178
Mean age (years)	400	550

Source: Buks (1965)

9.3.4 Fennoscandia

The Sokli Carbonatite Massif (Plate 9.1) of northeastern Finland is associated with the Archaean gneiss granite basement of that part of the country and which is composed primarily of gneissic granites, amphibolites and ultramafic rocks. The carbonatite massif (5 km diam.) consists mainly of calcite-rich rocks (sövites and silicosövites) surrounded by a 1–2 km wide fenite aureole (Paarma and Talvitie, 1976; Paarma et al. 1977). According to Cole (1980), circular structures, possibly kimberlites, have been identified from aerial photography, and are situated at the periphery of the carbonatite. Even if kimberlites have not yet been positively identified at this site, the close association with carbonatites throughout the world, renders the Sokli Carbonatite Massif an obvious target for such exploration.

There have been extensive investigations of the Sokli carbonatite since its discovery about 20 years ago. These studies have involved LANDSAT imagery, reflectance radiometry, aerial photography, geobotany and geophysics (Paarma and Talvitie, 1976; Paarma et al. 1968, 1977; Talvitie, 1979).

The vegetation cover of the nutrient-poor Archaean basement rocks of northeastern Finland consists mainly of low woodland (<4 m in height) of *Picea alba* and *Pinus sylvestris* alternating with large bogs. In sharp contrast, the Sokli carbonatite supports a luxuriant forest of *Betula pubescens* exceeding 15 m in height. The shrub layer is' dominated by *Juniperus communis* and the ground layer contains numerous grasses, herbs and dwarf shrubs such as *Vaccinium*. Within the carbonatite itself, the vegetation is influenced by soil depth, drainage and phosphate concentrations in the soil. When the latter is exceptionally high (> 21% P_2O_5), *Ribes sylvestre* and *Equisetum* spp. are abundant.

In the course of geobotanical investigations over the Sokli Carbonatite Massif, Talvitie (1979) carried out several flights over the area using a 10-channel Daedalus scanner operating over the entire wavelength range of 0.4 to 1.1 μm. From the reflectance spectra obtained in this way, he identified 10 spectral classes of vegetation related to the nature of the bedrock. He used channels 7 (0.65–0.70 μm), 8 (0.70–0.80 μm) and 10 (0.92–1.10 μm) in various combinations and with the data printed out in a number of false-colours and tones. The ten spectral classes are shown in colour in the upper part of Plate 9.1. The geology is shown below in the same plate. The relations between the spectral classes of vegetation and their substrate can be summarized as follows:

Classes 1–4 (brown, blue, red and pink) cover silicate rocks with the blue indicating mainly ultramafites.

Classes 6, 8 and 9 (orange, black and green) are over carbonatite rocks with classes 8 and 9 representing specifically rocks high in phosphate.

Classes 5 and 7 (greens) overly rocks intermediate between silicates and carbonatites.

Class 6 (orange) represents vegetation growing exclusively on carbonatite.

Class 10 (yellow) is related to luxuriant bogs over carbonatite.

Field observations showed that in the tree layer, *Pinus sylvestris* was dominant in classes 1–4 (silicate rocks) and *Betula pubescens* in classes 5–8 (carbonatites). Classes 9 and 10 are treeless. In the shrub layer, the silicate rocks (classes 1–4) are covered with immature specimens of *Pinus sylvestris*. Typical shrubs of the carbonatite (classes 6, 8 and 9) are *Juniperus communis* and *Betula nana*. For the ground layer, the silicate rocks are covered with an abundance of dwarf shrubs with sparse grasses and herbs, whereas over the carbonatite, the situation is reversed.

The carbonatite is distinguishable not so much from its species composition but rather from the degree of luxurance of this vegetation. This is illustrated in Table 9.4 which shows the density percentages of the vegetation in 6 classes.

The work carried out at Sokli is perhaps one of the best examples of an integrated survey of carbonatites and/or kimberlites. It shows what can be done by cooperation between scientists of different disciplines and should serve as a valuable model for further exploration for kimberlites in other parts of the world.

TABLE 9.4 Density Percentage of Species Showing Exceptional Luxuriance over the Sokli Carbonatite Massif, Finland.

Species	Class Index					
	5	6	7	8	9	10
Selaginella selaginoides	1		+		3	
Equisetum scirpoides	+	+				
Carex capitata			5			
Mohringia lateriflora	1					
Thalictrum simplex	+		+	17		
Saxifraga hirculus						3
Cirsium helenioides	1			45	+	
Sphagnum subsecundum					8	
S. teres			1			
S. warnstorfii			15		20	55
Campylium stellata			13			
Paludella squarrosa				25		5
Tomenthypnum nitens			1		15	

+ = luxuriant but not determined quantitatively
Source: Talvitie (1979)

REFERENCES

Alexander, P. O., 1983. Looking for diamonds ? Try geobotany. *Indiaqua*, 36: 33–38.

Alexander, P. O. and Shrivastava, V. K., 1983. Geobotanical expression of a blind kimberlite pipe, Central India. *Proc. 3rd Int. Kimberlite Conf.*, Clermont Ferrand, France.

Allen, J. B. and Deans, T., 1965. Ultrabasic eruptives with alnoitic-kimberlitic affinities from Malaita, Solomon Islands. *Mineral. Mag.*, 34: 16–34.

Buks, I. I., 1965. The use of the geobotanical method in the search for kimberlite tubes in the Yakutian Polar region. In (A. G. Chikishev ed.) *Plant Indicators of Soils, Rocks and Subsurface Waters*. Consultants Bureau, New York, 173–175.

Butakova, E. L. and Egorov, L. S., 1962. The Meimecha-Kotui complex of alkalic and ultrabasic rocks (in Russ.). In, *Petrography of Eastern Siberia*. Akad. Nauk, Moscow-Leningrad, 417–489.

Cole, M. M., 1980. Geobotanical expression of orebodies. *Trans. Inst. Min. Metall. Sec. B*, 89: 73–91.

Daly, R. A., 1925. Carbonate rocks of the Premier Mine, Transvaal. *J. Geol.*, 33: 659–684.

Dawson, J. B., 1962. Basutoland kimberlites. *Bull. Geol. Soc. Am.*, 73: 545–560.

Dawson, J. B., 1967. The kimberlite/carbonatite relationship. *Proc. 4th Gen. Meet. Int. Mineral. Ass. New Delhi*.

Dawson, J. B., 1980. *Kimberlites and their Xenoliths*. Springer, Berlin.

Draper, D., 1923. Additional evidence regarding the origin of the high-level diamond-bearing breccias of Diamintina, Brazil. *Trans. Geol. Soc. S. Afr.*, 26: 7–13.

Edwards, C. B. and Howkins, J. B., 1966. Kimberlites in Tanganyika. *Econ. Geol.*, 61: 537–554.

Grantham, D. R. and Allen, J. B., 1960. Kimberlites in Sierre Leone. *Overseas Geol. Mineral. Res.*, 8: 6–25.

Janse, A. J. A., 1964. *Kimberlites and Related Rocks of the Nama Plateau, South West Africa*. PhD Thesis, Univ. Leeds.

Kobets, N. V., 1960. *The application of aerial methods in prospecting for kimberlite bodies in the Daldynsk diamond-bearing region of the Yakutia region*. (in Russ.). Izd. Akad. Nauk SSSR, Moscow.

Kopecky, L., 1960. Diamond prospecting in the Czech massif (in Russ.). *Izv. Akad. Nauk SSSR Ser Geol.*, No. 12: 46–55.

Ktesten, P. and Pauk, D. K., 1976. Mineralogy of Indian kimberlites: a thermal and x-ray study. *Can. Mineral.*, 14: 487–490.

Lukicheva, A. N., 1960. The vegetation cover as an indicator of kimberlite cores (in Russ.). *Geol. Geofiz.* No. 1.

Martin, H., Mathias, M. and Simpson, E. S. W., 1960. The Damaraland subvolcanic ring complexes in South West Africa. *Rep. 21st Int. Geol. Congr. Copenhagen*, 13: 156–174.

Mathur, S. M., 1961. *Report on the geological mapping on aerial photographs of the diamond-bearing areas and investigation of newly-located ultramafic pipes in Panna, Madhya Pradesh*. Geol. Surv. India Rep.

Mathur, S. M., 1962. Geology of the Panna diamond deposits. *Rec. Geol. Surv. India*, 87: 787–818.

MacGregor, A. M., Ferguson, J. C. and Amm, F. L., 1937. The geology of the country round the Queens Mine, Bulawayo District. *S. Rhod. Geol. Surv. Bull.*, No. 30.

Paarma, H. and Talvitie, J., 1976. Deep fractures—Sokli carbonatite. *Contrib. Dep. Geophys. Univ. Oulu*, No. 65: 1–5.

Paarma, H., Raevaara, H. and Talvitie, J., 1968. On the interpretation of Ektachrome infrared aerofilm type 8443 photographs used in mineral reconnaissance and geological surveys. *Photogramm. J. Finl.*, 2: 3–22.

Paarma, H., Vartiainen, H. and Penninkilampi, J., 1977. Aspects of photogeological interpretation of Sokli carbonatite massif. In, *Prospecting in Areas of Glaciated Terrain*. Inst. Min. Metall., London, 25–29.

Paul, D. K., Rex, D. C. and Harris, P. G., 1975. Chemical characteristics and K-Ar age of Indian kimberlites. *Bull. Geol. Soc. Am.*, 86: 364–366.

Rimann, E., 1931. Uber das Muttergestein der Diamanten von Minas Gerais, Brasil. *Fortsch. Mineral. Krist. Petrogr.*, 16: 93–96.

Satterley, J., 1948. *Geology of Michaud township.* Ont. Dep. Mines Ann. Rep., 57, Pt. 4.

Sheinmann, Yu.M., 1957. Location and age of alkalic ultrabasic rocks of the Siberian Platform (in Russ.). *Razved. Okhr. Nedr,* 23: 12–16.

Spix, J. B. von and Martius, C. F., 1824. *Travels in Brazil in the years 1817–1820 undertaken by command of His Majesty the King of Bavaria.* Longmans, London.

Talvitie, J., 1979. Remote sensing and geobotanical prospecting in Finland. *Bull. Geol. Surv. Finl.,* 51: 63–73.

Watson, K. D., 1955. Kimberlites at Bachelor Lake, Quebec. *Am. Mineral.,* 40: 565–579.

Watson, K. D., 1967. Kimberlites of eastern North America. In (P. J. Wylie ed.) *Ultramafic and Related Rocks.* Wiley, New York, 312–323.

Wyllie, P. J., 1967. *Ultramafic and Related Rocks,* Wiley, New York, 240.

Zagrebina, N. L., 1961. The landscape method of discovering kimberlite bodies (in Russ.). In, *The Use of Aerial Methods in the Investigation of Natural Resources.* Izd. Akad. Nauk SSSR, Moscow-Leningrad.

Zagrebina, N. L., 1965. The relationship between vegetation and rock lithology in the Daldynsk region of the Yakutian ASSR from aerial photographs. In (A. G. Chikishev ed.) *Plant Indicators of Soils, Rocks and Subsurface Waters.* Consultants Bureau, New York, 120–123.

PART TWO

SERPENTINE VEGETATION OF THE WORLD

Chapter 10

INTRODUCTION TO SERPENTINE VEGETATION OF THE WORLD

If part I of this book could be described as "The ecology of serpentine", this second part might be described as "The floristics of serpentine vegetation of the world." The term floristics is used here in a very broad sense and includes such topics as biogeochemistry and biogeochemical prospecting which have only a very tenuous link with floristics but are better placed in this second part of the work because of their strong regional importance.

In deciding the subjects to be covered in this second edition, I have been greatly assisted by the famous benchmark paper by O. Rune who, in 1953, studied the serpentine floras of North America and Northwest Europe. He set out 6 important characteristics of serpentine vegetation as follows:

1—the paucity in species and individuals of serpentine floras compared with their non-ultramafic neighbours;

2—ecotypic differentiation resulting in taxa which are distinct both ecologically and morphologically;

3—spectacular disjunctions involving sometimes several hundred kilometres (as for example at Mt Albert in Quebec);

4—the coexistence of both acidicolous and basicolous plants on serpentine;

5—the xerophytic nature of serpentine plants;

6—the dominance of certain families or genera in a particular region, as for example the Caryophyllaceae in serpentines of northwest Europe (see Chapter 13), or the Flacourtiaceae in New Caledonia (Chapter 19).

These characteristics will be considered, and in addition there will be a listing of serpentine-endemic plants whenever this is feasible. Although it is very easy to list the serpentine-endemic species of Great Britain since there are only a few, in the case of countries such as The Philippines, Sulawesi or New Caledonia, the number of serpentine-endemic taxa is so large that space limitations preclude a listing of the hundreds of taxa involved.

It will be immediately apparent in the region-by-region description of serpentine floras (which follows) how uneven the coverage has been. Although virtually every serpentinic nook and cranny in Europe has been studied by one or more workers, the effort has been prompted more by availability than by degree of interest. Virtually only Europe and the more "civilised" parts of Asia were open to the earlier botanists of the period 1850–1950. They quickly covered the terrain using the excellent railway networks then available, and before World War I were virtually unhindered by the political restraints of passports and visas. Indeed at the turn of the century, it was possible to travel by train from London to Vladivostok without needing the latter form of documentation. On the other hand, any journey involving extensive sea travel was not really feasible, so the world remained ignorant (as it does indeed to some extent today) of the vast ultramafic floras of the Malay Archipelago.

During the 1960s and 1970s, the remote areas of the world became accessible due to the development of cheap air travel. For a brief period it looked as if the secrets of tropical ultramafic floras were about to be revealed. Recently, however, a new element of doubt has crept into the situation. In many countries such as the Philippines, extensive areas are controlled by anti-government insurgents often choosing to operate in the remote serpentine massifs. Of all the islands of this country which contain extensive areas of serpentine, only Palawan so far is free of the "New People's Army."

Political problems have made the task of the botanist more difficult in many other countries, such as for example Albania, which has been closed to foreigners for 40 years, though it is now beginning to open up a little. Similarly it is difficult to imagine that a botanist could operate successfully today in the serpentine areas of Afghanistan or Iran.

Even if political and logistic problems can be settled in the near future, it is unlikely that the serpentine vegetation of the Malay Archipelago will be studied as extensively as that of Europe because the task is just too great. It is a relatively simple matter to classify the British serpentine flora down to the subspecific and varietal rank, but the task of similarly classifying a serpentine flora of over 1000 taxa, will not be achieved in the foreseeable future. With some notable exceptions, such as Japan, it is probably not too outrageous to state that our knowledge of serpentine floras is inversely proportional to their floristic amplitude and richness, due to accidents of geography or politics.

To determine the extent of research on serpentine plants, Table 10.1 records the number of papers which describe such vegetation. It relates this work to the area of each territory, by a term involving total papers divided by the total area and multiplied by 10^6. Using this expression, values range downwards from 1368 for New Caledonia to 0.06 for South America. The countries which have been most extensively studied are, as might be expected, New Caledonia, Japan and a number of European countries.

The criteria used for determining the extent of research are of course open to criticism. For example, it might have been more appropriate to determine number of papers divided by area of serpentines only. This would not greatly change the picture, however, beyond perhaps promoting the Soviet Union and United States to a higher level in the list. There is moreover the great difficulty of gauging with any accuracy the true area of serpentine in many of the countries. The value for New Zealand (98) is probably inflated, since I, an author living in New Zealand, might be expected to know of every single paper on the subject compared with say the Soviet Union, where the language problem is another barrier to appreciation of the true extent of the literature (see also Chapter 1).

It is appropriate at this stage to mention the major floristic regions of the world. With the exception of a few disjunctions, serpentine floras are in the main derived from their surrounding non-ultramafic floras. These floristic regions are portrayed in Fig. 10.1 which is based on data by Good (1974) who has listed 37 regions, each of which is roughly equivalent in floristic value and importance, though not in size. Using the number of serpentinicolous plants as the criterion, the richness of the floristic regions are in descending order of importance: New Caledonia (#21), Malesia (#19), Cuba (#24), The Mediterranean (#5), and Japan (#3). The serpentine floras of North America and Northwest Europe are extremely impoverished due to the effects of the Pleistocene Ice Ages resulting in an allowable evolutionary time of only 10,000 years compared with about 80 m.y. for the flora of the Malay Archipelago.

A vast subject is to be covered here, so no attempt has been made to give an *in depth* appreciation of a particular topic or region. The emphasis is on *simplicity* and *wide coverage*. Bibliographies are as complete as possible, and I do not believe that any major reference has been excluded. The purpose of this extensive bibliography is to enable the reader to investigate selected fields to a greater depth if desired.

The following pages are a guided tour of the serpentine areas of the world on all continents, in order to provide the reader with a broad appreciation of the nature and extent of serpentine plant communities.

TABLE 10.1   Degree of Research into Serpentine Floras as Measured by Total Number of Papers ($\times 10^6$) Divided by the Area (km²) of the Territory.

Territory	Area (km²)	Total papers	Papers/Area $\times 10^6$
New Caledonia	19,000	26	1368
Austria	81,000	16	197
Japan	363,000	58	159
Greece	130,000	15	115
Czechoslovakia	125,000	14	112
Albania	28,000	3	107
New Zealand	263,000	26	98
Italy	296,000	25	84
Great Britain	240,000	20	83
Cuba	107,000	7	65
Yugoslavia	253,000	14	55
Portugal	89,000	4	45
Norway	317,000	11	35
Zimbabwe	384,000	13	34
Germany (West)	243,000	7	29
Finland	332,000	8	24
Hungary	89,000	2	22
Spain	499,000	10	20
Turkey	757,000	9	12
Poland	304,000	2	6.6
France	542,000	3	5.5
United States	9,254,000	45	4.9
Philippines	294,000	1	3.4
Sweden	442,000	1	2.2
Indonesia	1,881,000	4	2.1
Australia	7,595,000	11	1.4
South Africa	1,208,000	1	0.82
Canada	9,858,000	7	0.70
India	3,072,000	2	0.65
Soviet Union	21,939,000	7	0.32
Puerto Rico	8,700	1	0.11
South America	17,648,000	1	0.06

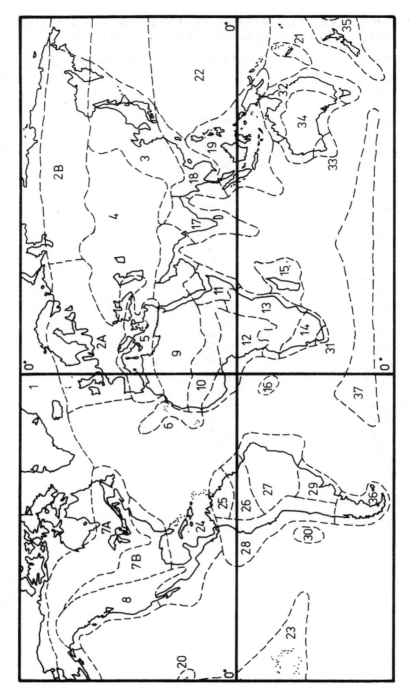

Fig. 10.1 Floristic regions of the world. 1—Arctic, 2—Euro-Siberian, 3—Sino-Japanese, 4—West and Central Asiatic (Indo-Turanian), 5—Mediterranean, 6—Macronesian, 7—Atlantic North American, 8—Pacific North American, 9—African-Indian desert, 10—Sudanese park steppe, 11—Northeast African highland, 12—West African rain forest, 13—East African steppe, 14—South African, 15—Madagascar, 16—Ascension and St. Helena, 17—Indian, 18—Continental Southeast Asiatic, 19—Malaysian, 20—Hawaiian, 21—New Caledonia, 22—Melanesia and Micronesia, 23—Polynesia, 24—Caribbean, 25—Venezuela and Guiana, 26—Amazon, 27—South Brazilian, 28—Andean, 29—Pampas, 30—Juan Fernandez, 31—Cape, 32—North and East Australian, 33—Southwest Australian, 34—Central Australian, 35—New Zealand, 36—Patagonian, 37—South-temperate oceanic islands. After: Good (1974)—reference at end of Chapter 21.

Chapter 11
NORTH AMERICA

11.1 GEOLOGY AND TECTONICS

The geology and tectonics of North America have been recently reviewed by Derry (1980). The North American continent is built around a foundation of early Precambrian cratons surrounded in the east by folded rocks of the Appalachians resulting from alternate collision with and parting from the Eurasian and African Plates. To the west, the continent is bounded by the Cordilleran Range resulting from collision of the American and Pacific Plates.

The Appalachian folding took place some 500–320 million years (m.y.) ago affecting an area from Alabama to Newfoundland. During periods of reversal (rebound of the plates) sediment deposition occurred between pulses of folding, intrusion and alteration. In some places along the sutures, parts of the ocean floor were thrust up on the eastern edge of the continent to form ophiolites, particularly in Newfoundland.

About 180 m.y. ago, the Eurasian and African continents separated from North America along the Mid-Atlantic Ridge, followed by Greenland and Britain separating from Canada about 80 m.y. ago. Greenland then parted from Eurasia some 20 m.y. later.

The North American Plate drifted westward and was underthrust by the thinner oceanic crust of the Pacific Plate to produce the folding which resulted in the formation of the Cordilleras, beginning some 225 m.y. ago. The Cordilleran orogeny has continued to the present day with faulting, folding, granitic intrusion and periodic vulcanism.

Several very large faults such as the Denali (Alaska) and San Andreas (California) are still active today. The latter shows evidence of a lateral displacement of some 260 km, which still continues.

The region is marked by continuing vulcanism as is evidenced by continuing geothermal activity and the recent eruption of Mt St Helens.

To summarize, ultramafic rocks in North America are found in two main regions. The first of these is the narrow belt of ophiolites forming the western Mountain chain of North America stretching from Santa Barbara in the south (Central California) to Alaska and the Yukon in the north. The second region is a mirror image of the first and stretches from Alabama in the south, through the Appalachians, Gaspé Peninsula, Newfoundland, and northern Quebec to Ungava. Details of local geology will be given below as appropriate.

11.2 WESTERN NORTH AMERICA

11.2.1 California

The Distribution of Serpentine Rocks

Ultramafic rocks in California are distributed in 2 broad bands on each side of the Great Central Valley (Fig. 11.1). These bands range from Santa Barbara county in the south to Del Norte county in the north where they merge into the extensive outcrops in southwest Oregon in the Siskiyou and Klamath Mts. As described by Kruckeberg (1984a), the early geologists were aware of Californian serpentine as early as 1826 when it was mapped by naturalists working from *HMS Blossom*, a British survey vessel. Extensive serpentine areas were mapped by Whitney in 1865, though he failed to notice the connection between the bedrock and the serpentine barrens which he encountered at many places in the state. The serpentine

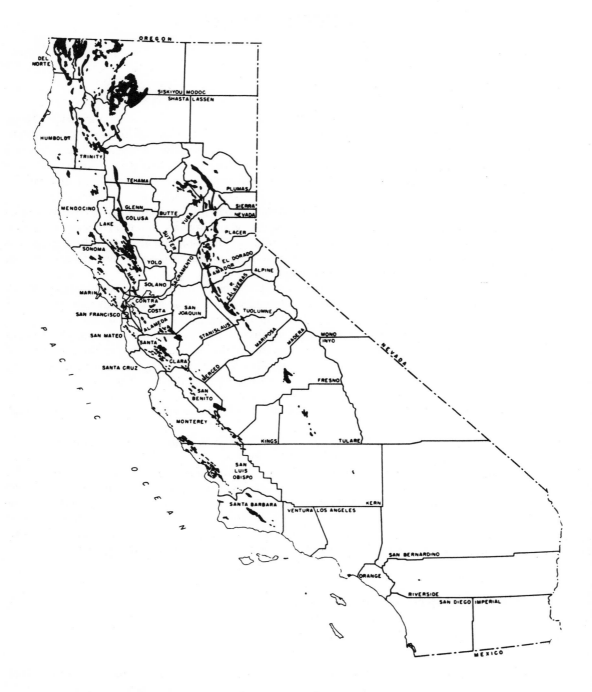

Fig. 11.1 Map of California showing serpentine areas (black).
Source: California Division of Mines and Geology.

rocks of California occupy about 3000 km². The most massive and extensive are near the Oregon border in Del Norte county. The ultramafites cover a great diversity of terrain from arid to mesic and from low elevation to the summits of the highest mountains such as Mt Eddy, Preston Peak and Scott Mt (Kruckeberg, 1984a). There are well-known serpentine occurrences north of San Francisco in northern Napa county, and in Sonoma and Marin counties. To the south and southwest of San Francisco are the serpentine outcrops in the Santa Lucia Mts and Diablo Range.

The serpentines of California were probably first exposed in the middle Mesozoic (150 m.y. ago), though some occurrences are much younger due to the continuing movement of the San Andreas fault.

The Communities of Serpentine Vegetation in California

Table 11.1 is a listing of references pertaining to the serpentine flora of North America. Some of the most useful recent papers on the serpentine flora of California are those by Kruckeberg (1984a, b, c) who has identified four major vegetation types occurring on serpentine: coniferous woodland, oak woodland, grassland, and chaparral. The effect of serpentine upon each of these communities is dramatic. Numbers and quality of species are reduced and the species distribution is different from that of the surrounding rock types. In the north coast ranges a high-yield mixed coniferous forest gives way to stands of Jeffrey pine (*Pinus jeffreyi*—see Plate 11.1a) and incense cedar (*Calocedrus decurrens*). Sometimes the coniferous forest is replaced by a chaparral (scrub association) with serpentine-tolerant or-endemic shrubs such as *Quercus durata, Ceonothus jepsonii* and *Garrya congdonii*. Else-

TABLE 11.1 References Describing Natural Serpentine Vegetation in North America.

Western North America	Eastern North America
Barker (1984)	Braun (1950)
Callizo and Clifton (1984)	Dearden (1975, 1979)
Callizo and Ruygt (1984)	Fernald (1907, 1911, 1925)
Crittenden and Grundmann (1984)	Harshberger (1903, 1904)
Goforth (1984)	Lawrence and Goss (1984)
Griffin (1984)	Legault and Blais (1968)
Kruckeberg (1950, 1951,	Low (1884)
1964, 1967, 1969a, b,	Mansberg and Wentworth
1983, 1984a, b, c)	(1984)
Latimer (1984)	Miller (1977)
Maas and Stuntz (1969)	Pennell (1910, 1912, 1930)
Main (1984)	Radford (1948)
Mason (1946)	Raymond (1950)
McCormick (1984)	Rune (1954)
McLeod (1984)	Scoggan (1950)
Medeiros (1984)	Shreve (1910)
Sawyer (1984)	Wherry (1963)
Schlising (1984)	Worthley (1984)
Sommers (1984)	
Stebbins (1984)	
Vogl (1973)	
Walker (1948)	
Whipple (1984)	
Whittaker (1954, 1960)	

where typical mesic forest is replaced by *Pinus sabiniana* (digger pine), cypress or chaparral woodland dominated by serpentine-endemic *Cupressus sargentii* and *C. macnabiana*.

These contrasting vegetation types are well represented over ultramafites in parts of Napa and Lake counties where grassland becomes sparse and contains indicator or endemic species such as *Streptanthus niger*, *Calochortus tiburonensis* and *Castilleja neglecta*. A number of serpentine-tolerant and endemic species are shown in Fig. 11.2 in relation to their nickel content, which in the case of the hyperaccumulators (Chapter 8) *Streptanthus polygaloides* and varieties of *Thlaspi montanum*, is considerably higher than that of the soils.

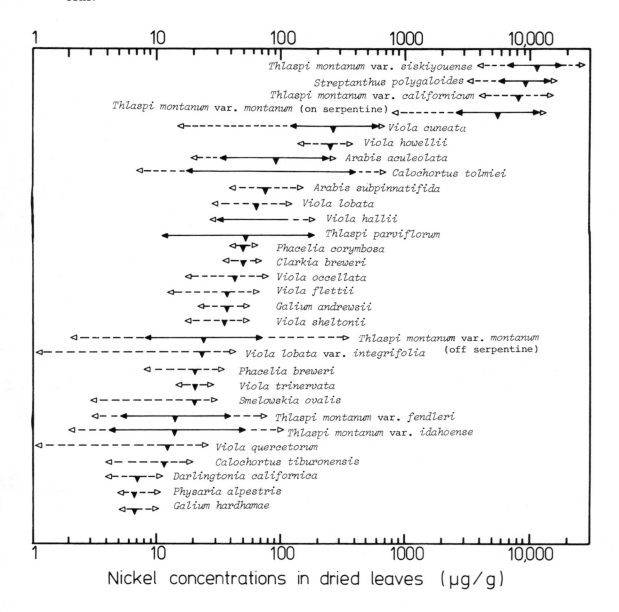

Fig. 11.2 The nickel content of Californian serpentine-endemic and serpentine-tolerant taxa. The geometric means (inverted triangles) are encompassed by the standard deviations (continuous lines) and ranges (broken lines).
Source: Reeves et al. 1983.

The vegetation of serpentine in California has also been studied by Barbour and Major (1977). They describe a typical serpentine chaparral as being an open low type associated with serpentine soils from San Luis Obispo northward through the coastal ranges and foothills of the Sierra Nevada. The shrubs display typically xeromorphic characteristics and severe nanism. The dominant shrubs are *Adenostoma fasciculatum*, and *Heteromeles arbutifolia* together with local endemics such as *Arctostaphylos viscida*, *Ceonothus jepsonii*, *Cupressus sargentii*, *Garrya congdonii* and *Quercus durata*. Serpentine chaparral often forms the understorey beneath trees of the foothills of the Sierra Nevada such as *Pinus sabiniana*, *P. jeffreyi*, *P. ponderosa*, *P. attenuata* and *Pseudotsuga menziesii*.

An excellent study by Whittaker (1954, 1960) on the vegetation of the Siskiyou Mts of Oregon and California provides first-rate data on the vegetation of contrasting rock types from diorite through gabbro to serpentine. He found that the gradient from wet to dry on any particular rock type, produces an ecocline in the vegetation. On serpentine, mesic forms of *Chamaecyparis lawsoniana* and *Pinus monticola* found near water, are transformed to xeric chaparral on dry ridges. These transitions are shown schematically in Fig. 11.3. Whittaker (1954) observed that much of the contrast between the vegetation of the two rock types was due to exclusion from one rock type of growth forms important on the other. For example, broad leaved trees are absent on serpentine, whereas shrubs and pines are of minor importance on diorite. The important work by Whittaker (1954, 1960) will be discussed further below.

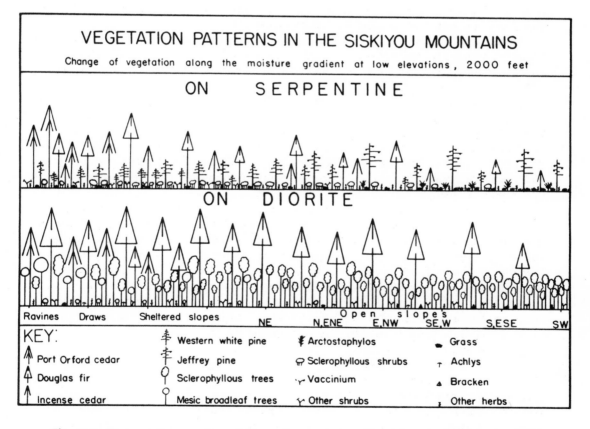

Fig. 11.3 Transect diagram of vegetation patterns on serpentine and quartz diorite in the Siskiyou Mts, southwest Oregon. The sequence is for most mesic to most xeric sites going from left to right. From "The Ecology of Serpentine Soils" by R. H. Whittaker. Copyright 1966 by *Ecology*. Reprinted by permission.

The relationship between water retention and vegetation on serpentine was also studied by Vogl (1973) who investigated stands of knobcone pine (*Pinus attenuata*) growing in the Santa Ana Mts of California, the most southerly of the ultramafites of California. *P. attenuata* is confined here to hydrothermally-modified serpentinite which supports only limited plant growth compared with the surrounding dense chaparral. The pine grows on the serpentine by tolerating the edaphic conditions and because competition is reduced in this hostile site. The water retention capacity of the ultramafic substrate is about double that of the soils supporting the chaparral. The pines are able to intercept moist marine air and produce considerable fog drip which is readily held by the soil.

The Serpentine-Endemic Vegetation of California

Perhaps one of the most useful reviews and listings of the serpentine-endemic vegetation of California is that of Kruckeberg (1984c).

Many of the pioneer Californian botanists, W. L. Jepson, E. L. Greene, K. Brandegee and A. Eastwood, failed to record whether a given species grew exclusively or otherwise on serpentine. More modern floras such as that of Munz and Keck (1959) are much more specific in this respect.

As already pointed out in earlier chapters of this book, a prominent characteristic of many serpentine floras is their high degree of endemism. The Californian serpentine vegetation is no exception to this rule, and is perhaps the richest of all temperate serpentine floras. We may define a serpentine-endemic taxon as a plant confined to serpentine throughout its range. Some endemic plants such as *Streptanthus breweri* and *Quercus durata* have a very wide range, whereas species such as *Layia discoidea* (at New Idria) and *S. batrachopus* (at Mt Tamalpais) are restricted to only one locality.

Although *Q. durata* is considered to be serpentine endemic, it has occasionally been found off serpentine, as for example at Mt Vaca in northern California. However, work by Forde and Faris (1962) suggests that these specimens may have been hybrids between *Q. dumosa* and *Q. durata*.

It is probable that the serpentine-endemic flora of California is only rivalled in species numbers by those of Cuba, Turkish Anatolia and New Caledonia. Kruckeberg (1984) lists about 215 vascular plants (including varieties and subspecies) which are wholly or partly confined to serpentine in California. This is only a rough estimate because the true status of many plants of the flora has yet to be established. This number of plants represents some 10% of the total endemic flora of California, though ultramafites cover only about 1% of the total area of the state.

Occurrence of endemism in serpentine plants of California is biased in favour of families such as the Asteraceae, Apiaceae, and Brassicaceae. There are also 3 genera of monocotyledons (*Allium, Calochortus* and *Fritillaria*) which have a number of serpentine-endemic representatives. Other genera with several endemic species are: *Eriogonum, Lomatium, Phacelia, Navarretia, Arctostaphylos, Ceonothus, Linum* and *Streptanthus*. Because of the great climatic diversity of the serpentine outcrops of California which range in latitude from 35°–43°N and in altitude from sea level to several thousand metres, as well as encompassing a wide range of rainfall, several phytogeographical provinces can be recognized. These have been defined by Kruckeberg (1984b) as:

1—the south coast ranges,
2—the San Francisco Bay area,
3—the north coastal ranges,
4—the Sierra Nevada.

The same author has listed 86 of 215 known serpentine-endemic taxa of the Californian flora. These are shown in Table 11.2. The reader is referred to Kruckeberg (1984c) for the full listing.

1—**The South Coast Ranges.** Kruckeberg lists 36 endemics in this phytogeographical province. The southernmost coastal ranges of California (San Raphael near Santa Barbara)

TABLE 11.2 Some Serpentine-endemic Plants of California

SOUTH COAST RANGES

Acanthomintha lanceolata
Arctostaphylos obispoensis
Camissonia benitensis
Cirsium campylon
Dudleya bettinae
Fritillaria falcata
Layia discoidea
Navarretia mitracarpa subsp. jaredii
Streptanthus amplexicaulis var.
   barbarae
Sidalcea hickmanii var. anomala

Allium howellii var. sanbenitensis
Calochortus clavatus
Ceonothus ferrisae
Delphinium parryi var. eastwoodii
Eriogonum argillosum
Galium hardhamiae
Monardella benitensis
Phacelia breweri
Streptanthus insignis

SAN FRANCISCO BAY AREA

Acanthomintha obovata subsp. duttonii
Calochortus tiburonensis
Clarkia franciscana
Eriophyllum latilobum
Lessingia ramulosa var. micradensis
Streptanthus batrachopus

Arctostaphylos hookeri subsp.
   franciscana
Cirsium vaseyi
Eriogonum caninum
Hesperolinon congestum
Montia spathulata var. rosulata
Streptanthus niger

NORTH BAY AREA

Allium fimbriatum var. purdyi
Calycadenia pauciflora
Cordylanthus pringlei
Delphinium uliginosum
Hesperolinon drymarioides
Monardella viridis
Senecio clevelandii
Streptanthus morrisonii and subsp.

Arctostaphylos bakeri
Ceonothus jepsonii
Cryptantha hispidula
Erythronium helenae
Madia hallii
Navarretia jepsonii
Streptanthus hesperidis

NORTH COAST AND KLAMATH—SISKIYOU RANGES

Allium hoffmanii
Arabis aculeolata
Arnica cernua
Astragalus breweri
Ceonothus pumilus
Eriogonum alpinum
Fritillaria glauca
Lomatium howellii
Phacelia corymbosa
Polystichum lemmonii
Rudbeckia californica var. glauca
Sanicula tracyi
Senecio greenei
Streptanthus howellii
Veronica copelandii

Antennaria suffrutescens
Arenaria howellii
Asclepias solanoana
Calochortus vestae
Epilobium rigidum
Erythronium californicum
Hieracium bolanderi
Perideridia leptocarpa
Poa piperi
Raillardella pringelei
Salix delnortensis
Sedum laxum subsp. eastwoodiae
Silene hookeri subsp. bolanderi
Thlaspi montanum var. californicum*
Viola cuneata

SIERRA NEVADA

Allium sanbornii
Chlorogalum grandiflorum
Githopsis pulchella var. serpentinicola
Lupinus spectabilis
Senecio lewisrosei

Arabis constancei
Cryptantha mariposae
Lomatium congdonii
Sedum albomarginatum
Streptanthus polygaloides*

*Hyperaccumulators of nickel
Source: Kruckeberg (1984b)

are hosts to Sargent cypress (*Cupressus sargentii*) and to *Streptanthus amplexicaulis* var. *barbarae*. Further north near San Luis Obispo, serpentine-endemic plants include *Calochortus obispoensis* and *Carex obispoensis*. At the southern end of the San Benito valley, especially at New Idria, *Layia discoidea*, *Streptanthus insignis* and *Monardella benitensis* are typical serpentine endemics. Kruckeberg and Morrison (1983) have reported a new endemic subspecies of *Streptanthus* from this area, *S. insignis* subsp. *lyonii* (western Merced county). *Fritillaria falcata* (Plate 11.2c) is a particularly striking plant of the South Coast Ranges. Another serpentinicolous *Fritillaria* is *F. plurifolia* shown in Plate 11.2d.

2—**The San Francisco Bay Area.** There are about 19 serpentine-endemic plants in the San Francisco Bay area. At the Presidio are to be found *Clarkia franciscana* and *Arctostaphylos franciscana*. The serpentines of the Tiburon Peninsula are colonized by *Streptanthus niger*, *Castilleja neglecta* and *Calochortus tiburonensis*. On Mt Tamalpais, a classical serpentine site whose soils have been described by Robinson et al. (1935), serpentine endemics include: *Cirsium vaseyi*, *Sidalcea hickmanii* subsp. *viridis*, *Streptanthus batrachopus* and *S. glandulosus* subsp. *pulchellus*. At Crystal Springs Reservoir in San Mateo county, *Acanthomintha obovata* subsp. *duttonii*, *Cirsium fontinale* var. *fontinale* and *Eriophyllum latilobum* are to be found.

3—**The North Coast Ranges.** According to Kruckeberg (1984c), there are about 90–100 serpentine-endemic taxa in the north coast ranges. The richness of this specialized flora is probably due to the more favourable climate in this phytogeographical province. The southernmost counties of this area (Napa, Sonoma and Lake) support a number of notable serpentine endemics including: *Arctostaphylos stanfordiana* subsp. *bakeri*, *Erythronium helenae*, *Senecio clevelandii* and several species of *Streptanthus*. Kruckeberg (1983) has recently described a new species of *Streptanthus*, *S. drepanoides* from Tehama and Trinity counties near the Oregon border. Near this border, the number of serpentine endemics increases rapidly. Many of the taxa listed in Table 11.2 are from this border area. The region also supports a large number of serpentine indicators such as *Silene californica* (Plate 11.3a). The mild climate near the border area seems to be the main cause of this increase.

4—**The Sierra Nevada.** The list of serpentine endemics from the foothills of the Sierra Nevada (16 taxa) is not great, perhaps because of the less favourable climate of this region. Typical endemics are however: *Allium sanbornii*, *Chlorogalum grandiflorum*, *Lupinus spectabilis*, *Streptanthus polygaloides* and *S. tortuosus* var. *optatus*. *S. polygaloides* is well known as a hyperaccumulator of nickel (see Chapter 8 and Reeves et al. 1981, 1983), one of a very few taxa possessing this character in North America.

Several Californian serpentine-endemic taxa are found in two or more of these four regions. Examples include *Streptanthus breweri* and *Quercus durata*. Other papers on the serpentine endemics of California are by: Barker (1984), Calizo and Clifton (1984), Calizo and Ruygt (1984), Crittenden and Grundmann (1984), Goforth (1984), Griffin (1984), Latimer (1984), Main (1984), Medeiros (1984), McCormick (1984), McLeod (1984), Sawyer (1984), Schlising (1984), Sommers (1984), Stebbins (1984), and Whipple (1984).

Californian Serpentine-Tolerant Plants

A clear distinction must be made between endemic species restricted to serpentine and "indifferent" taxa (*bodenvag*) found on and off this substrate. Examples of *bodenvag* woody plants (Kruckeberg, 1984b) are: *Ceanothus cuneatus*, *Calocedrus decurrens*, *Pinus jeffreyi*, and *P. attenuata* (knobcone pine).

Several annuals and herbaceous perennials are also partially endemic to serpentine. Examples of these are *Cirsium breweri*, *Darlingtonia californica* (Plate 11.3c), *Eriogonum umbellatum* subsp. *bahiaeforme*, *Festuca tracyi*, *Streptanthus glandulosus* subsp. *glandulosus*, and *Zygadenus fontanus*.

11.2.2 The Pacific Northwest (Oregon, Washington, and British Columbia)

The Location and Nature of Serpentine Occurrences

The Pacific Northwest of North America may be considered a single floristic unit, thanks to the uniform of moist cool climate throughout the region. It encompasses within its boundaries, Oregon, Washington and southern British Columbia. Serpentine occurrences within the region are shown in Fig. 11.4 and are at:

1—Bralorne (BC),
2—Upper Tulameen River (BC),
3—Sumas Mt (WA),
4—Twin Sisters Mt (WA),
5—Double Eagle Lakes (WA),
6—Wenatchee Mts (WA),
7—Fields Creek (OR),
8—Baldy Mt (OR),
9—Siskiyou/Klamath Mts (OR).

The geology of these areas has been described by Kruckeberg (1969a) and by Whittaker (1954, 1960). The latter three references provide a good understanding of the floristics and ecology of the Pacific Northwest.

In the Siskiyou Mts of southwestern Oregon, the serpentine supports a highly diverse flora which has been thoroughly studied by Whittaker (1954, 1960). Further north in the state of Washington, the largest and most important serpentine occurrence is in the Wenatchee Mts, a spur of the Cascade range. Outcrops here range up to several square km in area. The region is very complex lithologically as the ultramafites are interspersed with altered volcanics, sediments, gneisses, schists and igneous granodiorites. The terrain is very rugged with steep slopes culminating in peaks of up to 3000 m in height. All of the Wenatchee Mts serpentine areas are covered with coniferous forest.

Another important occurrence of ultramafites is in the northwest corner of Washington State in the counties of Snohomish, Skagit and Whatcom (#3–5 in Fig. 11.4). The outcrop at Twin Sisters Mt is probably the most prominent of these. Here there is a very sharp contrast between the vegetation of the serpentine and non-serpentine rocks. The luxuriant Western Red Cedar and Western Hemlock forest gives way to stunted *Pseudotsuga menziesii* (Douglas Fir), *Pinus contorta* (Lodgepole Pine), *P. monticola* (Western Red Pine) and shrubby *Juniperus communis* over the ultramafic substrates.

The Serpentine Flora of Southwest Oregon

The serpentine vegetation of the Siskiyou-Klamath Mts in southwest Oregon adjoins that of northern California, with which it has many features in common (see Table 11.2). The vegetation is extremely rich and contains a number of endemic species. The area covers about 500 km² of more-or-less continuous serpentine rocks. Vegetation patterns on-and-off serpentine have already been discussed (Fig. 11.3) and are much influenced by the moisture status of the soil. Two papers by Whittaker (1954, 1960) give a very thorough account of the floristics and ecology of the area.

Over serpentine, *Chamaecyparis lawsoniana* (Port Orford cedar) and *Pseudotsuga menziesii* (Douglas fir) are dominant in the mesic extremes of the vegetation pattern and form open stands with *Pinus monticola* and other species. *Rhododendron occidentale* is the most important shrub. The herb layer shows a number of rare serpentine-tolerant and -endemic species including *Trillium rivale*, *Lilium howellii*, and *Cypripedium californicum*.

At the intermediate (less mesic) sites on serpentine, are mixed stands of *Pseudotsuga menziesii*, *Pinus monticola*, *P. lambertiana*, *P. jeffreyi*, and *Calocedrus decurrens* (incense cedar) with a dense stratum of shrubs including *Quercus chrysolepis* var. *vaccinifolia*, *Arctostaphylos nevadensis* and *Garrya buxifolia*. The shrub layer is dominated by

Fig. 11.4 Ultramafic rock outcrops (solid areas) in the Pacific Northwest. 1—Bralorne (BC), 2—Upper Tulameen River (BC), 3—Sumas Mt (WA), 4—Twin Sisters Mt (WA), 5—Double Eagle Lakes (WA), 6—Wenatchee Mts. (WA), 7—Fields Creek (OR), 8—Baldy Mt (OR), 9—Siskiyou/Klamath Mts (OR).

scelerophyllous species. The tree layer is almost entirely coniferous. The broadleaf trees, so common on the adjacent diorite are virtually absent on serpentine.

Shrubs form a continuous phase in the non-mesic parts of the serpentine terrain and give way to open grassland in the more xeric areas. In the latter, dwarfed Jeffrey pine is the dominant tree whereas Douglas fir, white pine and sugar pine dominate the more mesic parts. Shrubs are virtually absent in the most xeric areas. Grasses include *Stipa lemmoni* and *Sitanion jubatum*.

Typical serpentine-endemic herbs of the Siskiyou ultramafites are *Vancouveria chrysantha, Lomatium howellii, Galium ambiguum, Iris bracteata, Hieracium cynoglossoides* var. *nudicaule, Sanicula peckiana, Horkelia sericata* and *Ceonothus pumilus*.

The data listed in Fig. 11.3 give some indication of the floristics of serpentine compared with the adjacent diorite of the Siskiyou Mts. However, over 100 species occur on both types of substrate. Table 11.3 provides a breakdown of the 2 floras according to growth forms. It is clear that serpentine supports far fewer trees than does diorite, but that the degree of endemism is much greater. Only 11.5% of the taxa are found on both substrates even though they occur in the same climatic and elevational environments. Seventeen of the serpentine endemics are restricted to the narrow area of the Siskiyou Mts and a further 13 to the Klamath Mts.

Whittaker (1960) has studied the life form spectra of the flora of lower elevations in the Siskiyou Mts. His findings are summarized in Table 11.4 together with data from Kruckeberg (1969a) for comparison.

In the Siskiyou Mts, from diorite through gabbro to serpentine, the phanerophytes and geophytes decrease in abundance while chamaephytes and hemicryptophytes increase.

Whittaker (1960) has also studied the species diversity of vegetation on the various rock types in the Siskiyou Mts. His data are summarized in Table 11.5. A number of trends can be seen from this table:

1—The total number of species decreases from diorite, through gabbro to serpentine.

2—The total number of shrubs increases from diorite, through gabbro to serpentine and decreases in the sequence mesic-xeric for all rock types.

3—The total number of forbs increases from diorite, through gabbro to serpentine.

4—The number of grasses remains constant except for a large increase over xeric serpentine sites.

Although Whittaker (1960) observed the above trends in one region of the Siskiyou Mts, he noted a large decrease in numbers of serpentine-tolerant species in the west-east progression from maritime to continental climate. The total number of species in a given serpentine area decreased by 40% from Emigrant Creek in the west to Mill Creek in the east.

To summarize the floristics of southwest Oregon, Whittaker (1954) concluded that the serpentine flora of the Siskiyou Mts was a climax vegetation and not a seral stage in the vegetation of other soils. He based these conclusions on the following 5 criteria:

1—The dominant trees on serpentine (except *Pinus attenuata* knobcone pine) continue to reproduce.

2—The serpentine soils are just as mature as those derived from diorite.

3—Islands of each rock type in the dominant area of the other type show persistence in differences of vegetation.

4—The stand-to-stand regularity or predictability of patterns (Whittaker, 1953) indicate that the serpentine vegetation has stabilized.

5—Successions in the serpentine and diorite regions are different.

TABLE 11.3 Floristics of Serpentine and Diorite Floras of the Siskiyou and Klamath Mts of Southwest Oregon.

Growth form	Number of species		Number of endemics	
	Diorite	Serpentine	Diorite	Serpentine
Grasses and sedges	8	17	0	0
Other herbs	58	71	2	25
Shrubs	19	17	0	5
Trees	16	8	0	0
Total	101	113	2	30

After: Whittaker (1954)

TABLE 11.4 Life Form Spectra (% of each class) of Vegetation Growing on Serpentine and other Substrates in the Pacific Northwest.

Location	Habitat		P	C	H	G	T	Total	Ref
Siskiyou	Diorite	—mesic	35	14	28	21	2	72	1
		—intermediate	33	10	33	22	2	79	1
		—xeric	31	8	42	13	6	47	1
	Gabbro	—mesic	34	11	33	21	1	73	1
		—intermediate	30	22	35	12	1	72	1
		—xeric	29	23	38	8	2	66	1
	Serpentine	—mesic	27	19	35	18	1	88	1
		—intermediate	25	24	39	12	1	102	1
		—xeric	15	17	43	14	11	76	1
Wenatchee	Serpentine	—barrens	0	14	80	6	0	51	2
		—glades	2	15	77	6	0	70	2
		—wooded slopes	9	23	61	4	3	74	2
	Non-serp.	—wooded slopes	6	21	67	4	2	112	2
Normal			46	9	26	6	13		3

1—Whittaker (1960), 2—Kruckeberg (1969a), 3—Raunkiaer (1934).
P—phanerophytes, H—hemicryptophytes, G—geophytes, T—therophytes.

TABLE 11.5 Relationship Between Growth Form and Species Diversity in the Central Siskiyou Mts. Numbers Refer to Individual Species Encountered in Experimental Transects.

Rock type		Trees	Shrubs	Forbs	Grasses	Total
Diorite	—mesic	15	11	42	4	72
	—intermed.	15	11	48	5	79
	—xeric	9	6	27	5	47
Gabbro	—mesic	16	10	40	7	73
	—intermed.	10	13	44	5	72
	—xeric	10	11	40	5	66
Serpentine	—mesic	9	18	56	5	88
	—intermed.	9	19	68	6	102
	—xeric	6	7	49	14	76

Source: "The Ecology of Serpentine Soils", by R. H. Whittaker. Copyright 1966 by *Ecology*. Reprinted by permission.

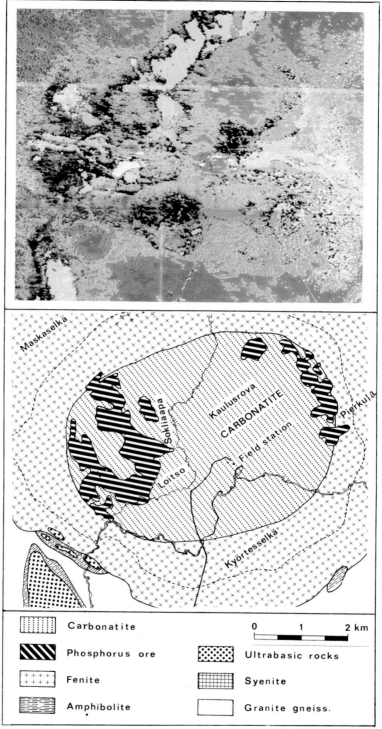

Plate 9.1 Above: Reflectance data for an aerial survey of the Sokli Carbonatite Massif using various combinations of three channels of a 10-channel Daedalus scanner. Colours are all in false colour and are divided into 10 classes: (1) brown, (2) blue, (3) red, (4) pink, (5) light green, (6) orange, (7) dark green, (8) black, (9) grey, (10) yellow. See text for significance of the classes.
Below: geology of the bedrock of the Sokli Carbonatite Massif.
Source: Talvitie (1979).

Plate 11.1 (a) Above: *Pinus jeffreyi* (Jeffrey Pine) over barren serpentine in northern California.
Photo by A. R. Kruckeberg.
(b) Below: The serpentinicolous fern *Adiantum pedatum* var. *aleuticum* over serpentine in
Newfoundland.
Photo by P. Dearden.

Lack of space precludes a further discussion of the serpentine flora of southwest Oregon and the reader is referred to Whittaker (1954, 1960) for further information on this subject.

The Serpentine Vegetation of Washington and British Columbia

Wenatchee Mts. The most comprehensive work on the serpentine flora of the Pacific Northwest is by Kruckeberg (1969a). The author gives a fairly detailed description of the floristics of about 100 localities from British Columbia to Oregon. Some of the elements of this work are presented below.

One of the areas showing the most impressive contrast between serpentine and non-ultramafic substrates is in the Wenatchee Mts (#6 in Fig. 11.4) of central Washington. Table 11.6 is a condensation of some of Kruckeberg's floristic observations in this area. Twenty-

TABLE 11.6 Typical Species of Serpentine Areas of the Wenatchee Mts Washington.

Species	Abundances		Type
	On-serpentine (36 releves)	Off-serpentine (30 releves)	
TREES			
Pinus contorta var. latifolia	4	2	+
P. monticola	7	2	+
SHRUBS			
Juniperus communis	7	6	+
Ledum glandulosum	2	0	++
Salix brachycarpa	1	0	++
FERNS			
Cheilanthes siliquosa	21	4	+++
Polystichum mohrioides var. lemmonii	17	1	+++
Adiantum pedatum var. aleuticum	6	0	++
GRASSES			
Poa curtifolia	13	0	+++
Festuca viridula	9	4	+
FORBS			
Eriogonum compositus	11	7	+
E. pyrolaefolium	15	3	++
Polygonum newberryi	5	3	+
Arenaria obtusiloba	7	0	++
Silene parryi	11	5	+
Claytonia nivalis	7	0	++
Lewisia colombiana	5	2	+
Anemone drummondii	11	2	++
Thlaspi alpestre	20	4	++
Ivesia tweedyi	4	0	++
Lomatium cuspidatum	9	1	+++
L. geyeri	3	0	+
Douglasia nivalis var. dentata	10	1	++
Cryptantha thompsonii	4	2	+
Castilleja elmeri	8	2	+
Agoseris glauca var. dasycephala	4	0	+
Chaenactis thompsonii	2	0	+
Eriophyllum lanatum	4	1	+

+++ = serpentine endemic   + = weak serpentinophyte
++ = strong serpentinophyte   After: Kruckeberg (1969a)

nine species are typical of serpentine occurrences in the Wenatchee Mts. They include only three serpentine-endemic species, in sharp contrast with the number in southwest Oregon and California. This is probably because of the more continental climate of inland Washington. Two of the endemics are the ferns *Polystichum mohrioides* var. *lemmonii* and *Cheilanthes siliquosa* (Kruckeberg, 1964) and the other is the well-known *Poa curtifolia*.

In summarizing the serpentine vegetation of the Wenatchee Mts, Kruckeberg (1969a) has drawn five main conclusions about the life form spectra of the area (Table 11.4):

1—Extremely barren serpentine occurrences are impoverished in species numbers and especially in tree and shrub life forms.

2—The serpentine occurrences are characterized by endemic and indicator species (Table 11.6).

3—Conifers do not show any marked edaphic preference.

4—There are at least 35 taxa which are serpentinophobes. They include *Pinus ponderosa*, 7 shrubs, 3 ferns, 3 grasses, 20 forbs and 1 lichen. This is particularly noticeable at geological boundaries.

5—A substantial number of *bodenvag* (serpentine-indifferent) species occur. Among these are Douglas fir, *Abies lasiocarpa*, *Pinus albicaulis*, *Tsuga mertensiana*: 3 shrubs; 1 grass *Agropyron spicatum*; and 18 forbs.

Although only 3 serpentine endemics are listed in Table 11.6, several additional species are virtually endemic to ultramafites in the Wenatchee Mts. They are: *Arenaria obtusiloba*, *Claytonia megarhiza* var. *nivalis*, *Anemone drummondii*, *Ivesia tweedyi*, *Lomatium cuspidatum*, *Douglasia nivalis* and *Chaenactis thompsonii*.

Del Moral (1972) studied diversity patterns in the vegetation of the Wenatchee Mts. He concluded that maximum diversity occurs where a closed upper storey canopy is not achieved and where edaphic conditions are not so severe as to prevent specialization. This supports the work of Whittaker (1960) in the Siskiyou Mts where the highest degree of diversity occurred in serpentine sites intermediate between the extremes of mesic and xeric conditions.

In a further study on the serpentine flora of the Wenatchee Mts, Del Moral (1982) studied herb patterns on serpentines and on adjacent sandstones using binary discriminant analysis of data. Species patterns suggested that control by soil moisture is far more pronounced on serpentine than on sandstone where light and its correlates are far more important. He suggested that the adverse edaphic conditions of serpentine soils select against intolerant species and that survivors respond primarily to moisture conditions.

Northwestern Washington. The vegetation of the ultramafic occurrences to the northwest of Washington State (Nos. 3 and 4 in Fig. 11.4) consists mainly of lowland coniferous forest west of the Cascade ranges. One of the most notable of these areas is at Twin Sisters Mt (#4 in Fig. 11.4) which consists mainly of dunite. In the steep talus of the mountain, *Pinus contorta* var. *latifolia* has adopted a gnarled "Krummholz" habit. Floristic contrast between serpentine and non-ultramafic substrates at Twin Sisters is not as pronounced as in the Wenatchee Mts. In the shrub layer, the two serpentine-endemic ferns *Polystichum mohrioides* var. *lemmonii* and *Cheilanthes siliquosa* again make their appearance.

The most northerly of the serpentine occurrences in Washington State is at Sumac Mt (#3 in Fig. 11.4). Dunite is the dominant rock type at this site. The general aspect is one of a dry open forest. Woody species are dominated by stunted *Pseudotsuga menziesii* and *Pinus contorta*. The indicator fern, *Cheilanthes siliquosa* is again prevalent in the understorey.

British Columbia. One of the most spectacular expressions of serpentine in British Columbia is at Tulameen River (#2 in Fig. 11.4) on Olivine Mountain which is composed largely of ultramafic rocks. According to Kruckeberg (1969a) the plant cover is somewhat xeric and the faithful indicator fern, *Cheilanthes siliquosa* again makes its appearance.

The Bralorne area (#1 in Fig. 11.4) is the most northerly of the serpentine areas studied by Kruckeberg in the Pacific Northwest. The sparse and stunted vegetation at the site is similar to that of the Tulameen area. A sparse grass-forb ground layer is interspersed with stunted *Pinus contorta*. As usual *Cheilanthes siliquosa* is abundant in rock crevices and open talus, habitats which it shares with *Polystichum* aff. *scopulinum*.

11.2.3 A summary of the Serpentine Vegetation of the Pacific Northwest

Kruckeberg (1969a) has summarized a number of characteristics of the serpentine vegetation of the Pacific Northwest as follows:

1—The physiognomy of the vegetation is altered in a striking manner at contacts between serpentine and non-serpentine. Coniferous forest becomes sparse and stunted and is often replaced by a grass-forb cover.

2—Serpentine vegetation assumes a typically alpine character. Numbers of species are reduced and the life forms are reduced to 3 classes of herbaceous perennials: hemicryptophytes (80%), chamaephytes (14%) and geophytes (6%).

3—The mixture of azonal serpentine soils with zonal "ordinary" soils affects the distribution of the conifers. Subalpine species such as *Pinus albicaulis, Abies lasiocarpa,* and *Juniperus communis* are found on serpentine at lower altitudes than otherwise. In contrast, lower montane species such as *P. ponderosa., P. contorta* var. *latifolia* and *Pseudotsuga menziesii* are displaced upwards.

4—Species composition changes abruptly at geological boundaries with ultramafites. Several whole genera fail to appear over serpentine.

5—Three species of fern are excellent indicators of serpentine: *Cheilanthes siliquosa, Polystichum mohrioides* var. *lemmonii* and *Adiantum pedatum* var. *aleuticum.* The first of the these is the most faithful of the indicators and is also found over ultramafites along the eastern seaboard of North America.

6—Serpentine endemics are few over the Pacific Northwest ultramafites. Apart from the 3 ferns listed above, only the Wenatchee Mountains contain angiosperm endemics: *Poa curtifolia, Lomatium cuspidatum,* and *Chaenactis thompsonii.*

7—*Bodenvag* (indifferent) angiosperms appear in abundance only in the Wenatchee Mountains of central Washington.

8—The *bodenvag* species include several conifers and a number of herbaceous perennial grasses and forbs.

11.3 THE EASTERN UNITED STATES

11.3.1 Ultramafic Rocks

The geological province known as the Piedmont Upland (Fig. 11.5) is a northeast-trending belt of metamorphic rocks extending from Alabama to Trenton, New Jersey. It forms part of a very long belt of ultramafites extending further through New York state, the Gaspé Peninsula (Quebec), Newfoundland, to the northern tip of Quebec in the Ungava Peninsula in Arctic Canada (Figs. 11.6 and 11.7).

Perhaps the most important part of the Piedmont Upland (at least floristically) is the section passing through Maryland, Pennsylvania and Delaware where the ophiolitic belt is

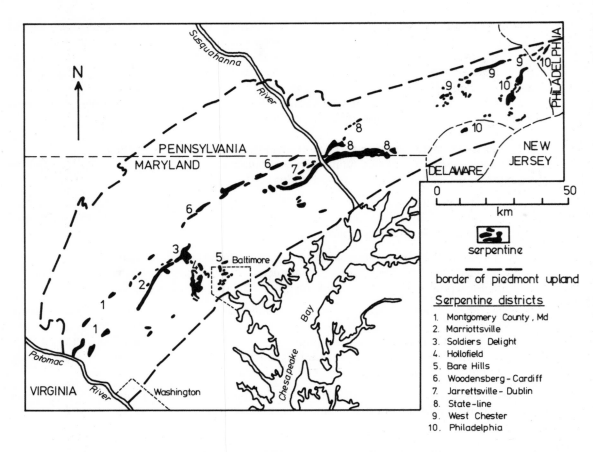

Fig. 11.5 Serpentine sites of the Piedmont Upland of the eastern United States. Source: Pearre and Heyl (1960).

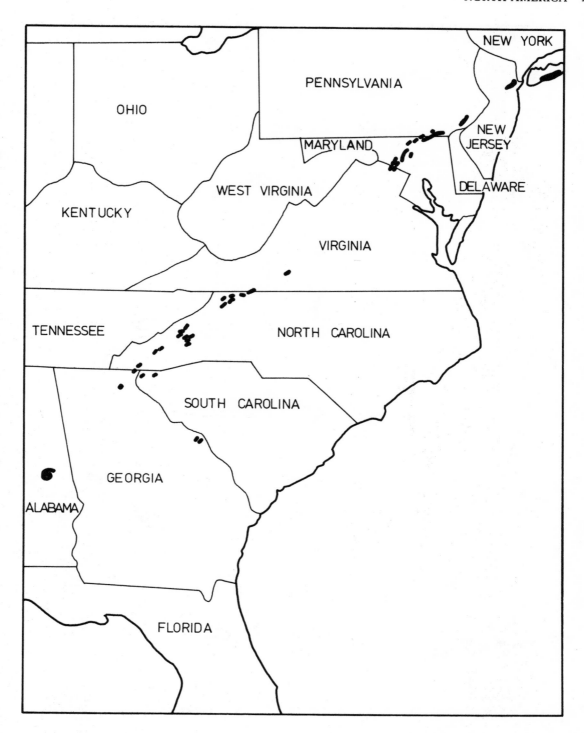

Fig. 11.6 Ultramafic rock outcrops (solid areas) of the eastern United States.

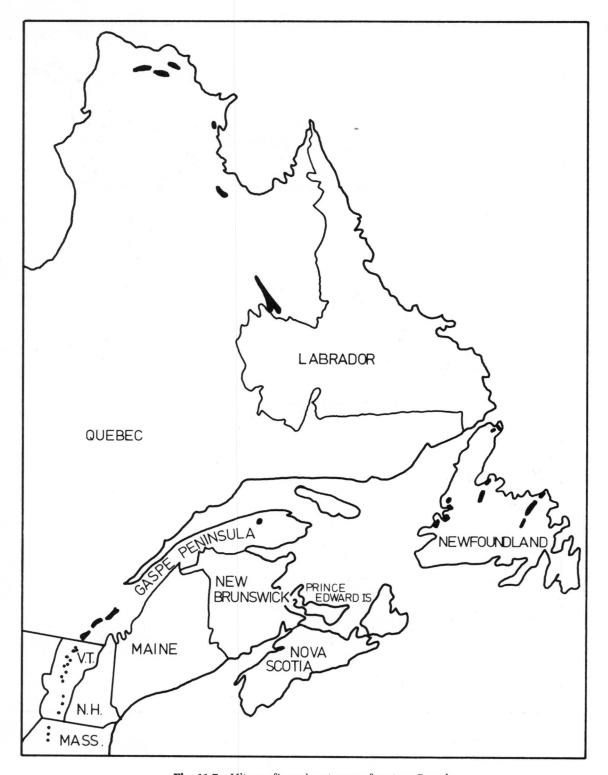

Fig. 11.7 Ultramafic rock outcrops of eastern Canada.

about 250 km long and 80 km at its greatest width. The geology of the structure has been described by Pearre and Heyl (1960), from which the following extract is taken.

> Rocks that underlie the province are the Baltimore gneiss of Precambrian age and quartzite, gneiss, schist, marble, phyllite and greenstone, which make up the Glenarm series of early Palaeozoic age. They are intruded by granitic, gabbroic and ultramafic igneous rocks. Most of the ultramafic rocks, originally peridotite, pyroxenite, and dunite, have been partly or completely altered to serpentine and talc; they are all designated by the general term serpentine. The bodies of serpentine are commonly elongate and conformable with the enclosing rocks. Many have been extensively quarried for building, decorative, and crushed stone. In addition, chromite, titaniferous magnetite, rutile, talc and soapstone, amphibole asbestos, magnesite, sodium-rich felspar and corundum have been mined, or prospected for, in the serpentine.
>
> Both high-grade massive chromite and lower-grade disseminated chromite occur in very irregular and unpredictable form in the serpentine. Placer deposits of chromite are in, or near streams that drain areas underlain by serpentine.
>
> Chromite was first discovered in the United States at Bare Hill, Md, around 1810. Between 1820 and 1850, additional deposits were found and mined in Maryland and Pennsylvania, including the largest deposit of massive chromite ever found in the United States—the Wood deposit in the State Line district. About 150,000 tonnes of chromite ore was mined before 1900.

11.3.2 The Flora of the Serpentine Barrens of the Piedmont Upland

The unique flora of the serpentine barrens of the Piedmont Upland was originally described by Harshberger (1902), Pennell (1910, 1912, 1930), Shreve (1910), Wherry (1963) and Radford (1948). Other reports such as those of Worthley (1984) and Mansberg and Wentworth (1984) have been concerned with the vegetation of individual serpentine barrens (Soldiers' Delight and Buck Creek respectively).

Soldiers' Delight

The Soldiers' Delight serpentine barren (see Fig. 11.5) is situated in Maryland some 15 km west of Baltimore and comprises about 800 hectares of serpentine barren and forest dotted with a number of old chrome mines. The name is believed to have been derived from a number of sources. One story is that the soldiers of King George III gave it that name because being open terrain, attacks from marauding Indians were less successful. Another (perhaps more likely) story is that the local "ladies" entertained the soldiery at this site which was an army camp at that time.

The flora of Soldiers' Delight was originally described by Shreve (1910) and has since been studied by Worthley (1984) and Lawrence and Goss (1984). The typical stunted trees of this area include *Quercus marilandica* (blackjack oak), *Q. stellata* (post oak) and Virginia pine (*Pinus virginiana*).

It does not seem that the trees at Soldiers' Delight represent the climax vegetation since studies by Knox (1984) on the age spectrum of these trees, showed distinct age clusters in 3 of the 4 stands studied. This suggests past episodes of recruitment caused by fire or drought.

Approximately 1200 plant species have been found on the serpentine barrens of the Piedmont Upland in Maryland, Delaware and Pennsylvania. These include 140 lichens, 200 bryophytes, 35 ferns and about 1000 phanerogams. Worthley (1984) has recognized 3 main plant associations within the Soldiers' Delight reserve. The first of these is the group of 7 species found on entirely barren ground. Among these is the serpentine-endemic *Cerastium arvense f. villosissimum* (villose field chickweed). This low herb is perhaps one of the most typical of the endemic plants of the serpentine barrens of the Piedmont Upland. Another endemic plant is *Polygonum tenue,* a plant found on most serpentine barrens in the region. It is noteworthy that Soldiers' Delight does not contain the serpentine endemic *Aster depauperatus* which is common on many other barrens (Hart, 1980).

Worthley (1984) has also described the *Andropogon* and the *Andropogon*-oak associations on Soldiers' Delight, the floristics of these and of the "bare ground" association are recorded in Table 11.7.

Very few studies have been carried out on the lower plants of serpentine barrens, though Maas and Stuntz (1969) examined fungi on serpentine in the Cascade Mts of Washington state. However, at Soldiers' Delight, Terlizzi and Karlander (1979) studied soil algae which consisted of members of the Cyanophyta, Chlorophyta and Chrysophyta. Composition of the soil flora at the division level, was similar to that of more favourable soil

TABLE 11.7 Plant Associations of the Soldiers' Delight Serpentine Barren, Maryland

BARREN AREA ASSOCIATION

Arabis lyrata var. *parvisiliqua*	*Cerastium arvense* f. *villosissimum**
Gerardia decemloba	*Houstonia coerulea*
Linum medium	*Polygonum tenue*
Talinum teretifolium	

ANDROPOGON ASSOCIATION

Acerates viridiflora	*Agrostis perennans*
Andropogon scoparius	*Aristida purpurescens*
Aristida dichomata	*Aster ericoides*
Aster lateriflorus	*Cassia fasciculata*
Carex glaucodea	*Eleocharis tenuis*
Festuca rubra	*Fimbristylis autumnalis*
Juncus platyphyllus	*Juncus secundus*
Juncus tenuis var. *dudleyi*	*Lobelia inflata*
Oenthera tetragona var. *brevistipata*	*Panicum clandestinum*
Panicum dichotomiflorum	*Panicum linearifolium*
Poa pratensis	*Polygala verticillata*
Sabatia angularis	*Scleria pauciflora*
Senecio smallii	*Sisyrinchium mucronatum*
Solidago juncea	*Solidago canadensis*
Sorghastrum nutans	*Spenopholis obtusata*
Viola fimbriatula	

ANDROPOGON—OAK ASSOCIATION

Anaphalis obtusifolium	*Apocynum cannabinum*
Asclepias verticillata	*Aureolaria pedicularia*
Cunila origanoides	*Desmodium marilandicum*
Dianthus armeria	*Erigeron ramosus*
Eupatorium perfoliatum	*Hieracium venosum*
Hypericum gentianoides	*Hypericum perforatum*
Hypericum punctatum	*Lespedeza virginica*
Liatris graminifolia	*Linaria vulgaris*
Lobelia spicata var. *scaposa*	*Oxalis stricta*
Phlox subulata var. *eusubulata*	*Pinus virginiana*
Potentilla canadensis	*Prunella vulgaris*
Pycnanthemum flexosum	*Quercus marilandica*
Quercus stellata	*Rosa virginiana*
Sericocarpus asteroides	*Verbascum blaterium*
Vernonia noveborensis	*Viola pedata* var. *lineariloba*

* = serpentine endemic
Source: Worthley (1984)

types. This indicated possible adaptations to high nickel and chromium concentrations and a low Ca/Mg quotient. Among the Cyanophyceae were three genera known to contain species which fix nitrogen. It was suggested that they are a source of nitrogen input to this generally nitrogen-deficient soil.

Nottingham

The Nottingham serpentine barren (near West Chester—see Fig. 11.5) has been described by Lawrence and Goss (1984) and is situated in southeast Pennsylvania. It occupies about 400 hectares and is the sole remaining relatively undisturbed barren in the state. It is believed that the presence of certain species at this site reflects changes during the advance and retreat of the most recent ice sheet (the Wisconsin). For example the Aleutian maiden-hair fern (*Adiantum pedatum* var. *aleuticum*) is found in Canada, Alaska and the Nottingham barren. When the Wisconsin ice sheet reached its southern limit just north of this site, it produced an Arctic climate where only tundra-type vegetation could survive. The fern adapted itself to these cold conditions and established itself here. When the climate changed again, the fern retreated to the serpentine barrens where there was less competition from more vigorous southern invaders.

In contrast to the behaviour of the ferns, Small's ragwort (*Senecio smallii*) present on this barren, is not found north of Virginia except on serpentine. During the warm interglacial period, when the climate was warmer than today, the plant extended its range northward, but as the climate cooled, competition from other species crowded this southerner from all but edaphically-unfavourable soils such as serpentine.

The Nottingham barren also supports grasses of the western prairies such as *Bouteloua curtipendula* (grama grass), *Andropogon scoparius* (little bluestem beardgrass) and *Sorghastrum nutans* (Indian grass). Other typical plants of this area are: *Talinum teretifolium* (flame flower)—again a plant at the northern limit of its range, *Phlox subulata* (moss pink), *Asclepias verticillata* (whorled milkweed), and *Arabis lyrata* (lyre-leaved rockcress). The ubiquitous serpentine endemics, *Aster depauperatus* and *Cerastium arvense* f. *villosissimum* are also found at Nottingham. An extensive forest of pitch pine (*Pinus rigida*) is a characteristic feature of this serpentine barren. Although *T. teretifolium* is not a serpentine endemic, studies by Pinion (1973) indicated that specimens growing on serpentine in Pennsylvania had an induced tolerance compared with those growing on granite in Georgia.

Pink Hill

The Tyler Arboretum (see Lawrence and Goss, 1984) includes the only relatively undisturbed serpentine barren (Pink Hill) in Pennsylvania (near site 10 in Fig. 11.5). Typical plants of this area are *Quercus marilandica*, *Pycanthemum tenuifolium* (slender mountain mint) and *Asclepias verticillata*. The faithful serpentine-endemic *Aster depauperatus* and *Cerastium arvense* f. *villosissimum* also occur at this site.

The outstanding display on Park Hill in the Tyler Arboretum is the flowering of *Phlox subulata* in late April and early May. This species is not a serpentine endemic, but grows in dry sandy soils throughout the mid-Atlantic region and retreats to these sites to avoid competition from other species.

Buck Creek

The Buck Creek serpentine barren is the most southerly of the sites described in this section of the chapter. It is situated in Clay County, North Carolina. An excellent survey of the vegetation and soils of this area has been given by Mansberg and Wentworth (1984). The ultramafites consist primarily of unaltered olivine and serpentinized dunite. The site has remained virtually undisturbed since 1932.

Mansberg and Wentworth (1984) compared the plant communities on serpentine with those of the adjacent mica gneiss. An open canopy of stunted *Pinus rigida* (see also Nottingham in Pennsylvania) dominates the serpentine. The understorey is composed primarily of caespitose grasses alternating with clumps of tall shrubs. The community was described as pine-savanna.

Species representation in the canopy of serpentine and mica-gneiss sites is shown in Table 11.8 and demonstrates the small number of canopy species on serpentine and the great dominance of *P. rigida*.

TABLE 11.8   Species Representation in the Canopy of Serpentine and Mica-Gneiss Sites at Buck Creek, N. Carolina (numbers refer to mean importance values with percentage constancy in parentheses).

Species	Serpentine (n = 11)	Mica-gneiss (n = 5)
Pinus rigida	83.3 (100)	
Tsuga canadensis	6.1 (64)	1.4 (40)
Quercus alba	4.9 (45)	13.9 (100)
Acer rubrum	3.1 (55)	19.4 (100)
Sassafras albidum	1.3 (18)	
Oxydendrum arboreum	0.9 (18)	6.4 (60)
Betula lutea	0.3 (9)	
Amelanchier arborea		3.3 (60)
Quercus rubra		31.8 (100)
Q. coccinea		6.8 (60)
Robinia pseudoacacia		4.4 (40)
Quercus prinus		3.5 (40)
Carya glabra		3.1 (60)
Nyssa sylvatica		2.2 (40)
Ilex ambigua		2.0 (20)

n refers to the number of experimental quadrats
Source: Mansberg and Wentworth (1984)

Several forbs and grasses are good indicators of serpentine and do not occur on the adjacent mica-gneiss. These species are also rare in the southeastern United States and include: *Agropyron trachycaulum*, *Castilleja coccinea*, *Sporobolus heterolepis*, *Parnassia grandiflora*, *Sanguisorba canadensis*, *Tsuga canadensis* (hemlock), and the tall shrub *Polygala paucifolia*.

The life form spectra for serpentine and mica-gneiss communities at Buck Creek are given in Table 11.9 which shows that hemicryptophytes exceed phanerophytes numerically. This same pattern was observed on the west coast barrens of the United States (see Table 11.4).

TABLE 11.9   Life Form Spectra of Plants Growing in Serpentine and Mica-gneiss at Buck Creek, N. Carolina.

| Life form | Percentage | |
	Serpentine (n = 11)	Mica-gneiss (n = 5)
Phanerophytes	31.6	33.7
Chamaephytes	6.3	2.1
Hemicryptophytes	41.8	32.6
Geophytes	7.6	12.6
Therophytes	1.3	5.3
Lianas	3.8	3.2
Other	7.6	10.5

n refers to the number of experimental quadrats
Source: Mansberg and Wentworth (1984)

The Buck Creek serpentine vegetation displays an affinity with that of the mid-western United States and has a number of species disjunct for their normal range. Examples are *Senecio plattensis* (central North America), and *Sporobolus heterolepis*. Other species such as *Agropyron trachycaulum*, *Deschampsia caespitosa* subsp. *glauca* and *Muehlenbergia glomerata* occur here at the periphery of their ranges.

Ecotypic differentiation, so typical of serpentine, is also evident on the Buck Creek serpentine. Examples are a stoloniferous form of *Hexastylis*, a hybrid *Aster*, an unusually small form of *Thalictrum macrostylum* and a low stoloniferous form of *Rhododendron viscosum*. A surprising feature of the Buck Creek serpentine barren is the complete absence of serpentine endemics, at least as far as is known.

The pine-savanna community of the above site appears to be a stable edaphic climax closely resembling in its physiognomy and structure, the vegetation of serpentine barrens of the northern part of the Piedmont Upland such as at Lancaster County, Pennsylvania (Miller, 1977).

Another well-known serpentine barren in N. Carolina is located near Webster and is shown in Plate 11.3d. The boundary is indicated by the line of trees in the background.

11.4 EASTERN CANADA

11.4.1 The Gaspé Peninsula—Eastern Townships

Introduction

The long train of serpentine outcrops beginning in Alabama and ending at the tip of the Ungava Peninsula in Quebec, has an extremely important section in the Eastern Townships area of Quebec in the southern part of the Gaspé Peninsula (Fig. 11.7). Near Thetford, an important mining centre for asbestos (see Chapter 5), there is a strip of more or less continuous serpentine occurring in an area 100 km long and 25 km wide which stretches from Richmond in the southeast to East Broughton in the northwest (Fig. 11.8). Asbestos production from this region accounts for nearly 40% of the world output.

The Serpentine Vegetation of the Eastern Townships Region

The Eastern Townships is a well-forested area dominated on non-serpentine soils by *Acer saccharum*, *Betula lutea*, *Picea glauca*, *Abies balsamea*, *Pinus strobus* and *Tsuga canadensis*.

A typical succession of serpentine vegetation has been described by Legault and Blais (1968) at Mt Silver, a few km from Thetford. Table 11.10 lists the principal serpentine-tolerant species on this hill. A similar site is to be found at Cheilanthes Hill (500 m) some 20 km southeast of Thetford. The serpentine vegetation of this site is shown schematically in Fig. 11.9. The conifers at the bottom of the slope are mainly *Pinus strobus* and *Picea mariana*. The serpentine talus of the slope is dominated by a scrub association of *Juniperus communis* dotted with dwarfed *Betula papyrifera*.

The most interesting feature of the two sites is the occurrence of the serpentine-endemic fern *Cheilanthes siliquosa* which is rare on the east coast but is common on serpentines of the Pacific Northwest. According the Legault and Blais (1968), this taxon has been found at only four sites in the Eastern Townships and at Mt Albert further north. For establishment it apparently requires a combination of dry talus, steep slope, southern exposure, plentiful sunshine and low humidity. The Aleutian maidenhair fern (*Adiantum pedatum* var. *aleuticum*— Plate 11.1b) is also found on the serpentines of the Gaspé Peninsula as well as in Newfoundland and at some localities of the Piedmont Upland, in all cases on talus slopes.

Some mention should now be made of the use of satellite imagery for studying serpentine and other vegetation of the Eastern Townships region. Such studies were carried out by Bélanger (1980), Bélanger et al. (1979) and Bélanger and Rencz (1983). LANDSAT

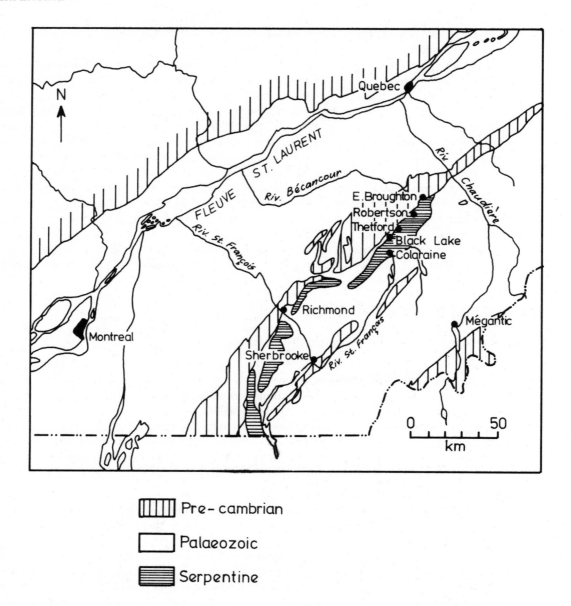

Fig. 11.8 Ultramafic rock outcrops in the Eastern Townships area of Quebec.
Source: Legault (1976).

TABLE 11.10 Plants of Serpentine on Mt Silver, Eastern Townships, Quebec

TOP OF MOUNTAIN

Canopy	Undergrowth
Acer rubrum	Aralia nudicaulis
Alnus crispa	Aster johannensis
Betula papyrifera	A. longifolius
Picea glauca	A. radula
P. mariana	Carex scirpoidea
Pinus resinosa	Clintonia borealis
P. strobus	Ledum groenlandicum
Prunus pensylvanica	Maianthemum canadense
Viburnum cassinoides	Oryzopsis asperifolia
	Prenanthes trifoliolata
	Pteridium aquilinum var. laniginosum
	Saxifraga virginiensis
	Solidago randii
	Trientalis borealis

TALUS SLOPES

Adiantum pedatum var. aleuticum
Arenaria rubella
Campanula rotundifolia
Carex scirpoidea
Cerastium arvense var. ophiticola
Cheilanthes siliquosa
Festuca scabrella
Gnaphalium sylvaticum
Melampyrum lineare
Oryzopsis asperifolia
Puccinellia distans
Senecio pauperculus
Solidago hispida
S. randii
Spergularia rubra
Stellaria longipes

FOOT OF MOUNTAIN

Abies balsamea	Juniperus communis
Acer rubrum	Viburnum cassinoides
Alnus rugosa
Betula papyrifera
Larix laricina
Nemopanthus mucronatus
Picea mariana
Pinus resinosa
P. strobus

Source: Legault (1976)

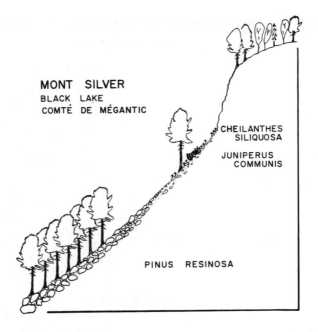

Fig. 11.9 Schematic representation of serpentine vegetation at Mt Silver, Thetford Mines area of the Eastern Townships, Quebec.
Source: Legault and Blais (1968).

satellites contain a multiband scanner (MSS) with bands at 500–600, 600–700, 700–800, and 800–1100 nm. These are known as MSS4, MSS5, MSS6, and MSS7 respectively. The terrain is scanned and the reflectance of each 79×79 m area (pixel) of the terrain is assigned a number from 0 to 256 depending on the degree of reflectivity. These numbers are stored on computer-compatible tape and are computer processed to give images in selected false colours. Each satellite "scene" contains 7,637,760 pixels (31,000 km^2). By use of various band ratios such as MSS5/MSS7 (biomass index), Bélanger and Rencz studied the dispersal train of enriched trace elments resulting from transport of rocks by glacial activity in the last ice age. This dispersal was evident in an area of 1000 km^2 "downice" from Thetford. The dominant tree species (*Abies balsamea* and *Picea glauca*) reflected the presence of mafic minerals in the soil. Chemical analysis showed up to 1800 μg/g (0.18%) nickel in ashed leaves in specimens pinpointed by poor spectral reflectance due to chlorosis of their leaves. Correlation analysis of the data showed a significant inverse relationship ($P < 0.01$) between the nickel content and spectral reflectance.

LANDSAT imagery can also give a clear indication of ultramafic substrates by the unusual reflectance patterns of vegetation. Bélanger (1980) has shown that false colour images of the biomass index gave distinctive patterns for serpentine vegetation in the Thetford area. Similarly, Brooks and McDonnell (1983) showed that most ultramafic occurrences in New Zealand could be easily identified by satellite imagery using various band ratios and computer processing in false colour (see Chapter 21).

11.4.2 The Gaspé Peninsula—Mt Albert

Mt Albert is the high point of the Shickshocks which are the northern extension of the Appalachians. Mt Albert is botanically most interesting because of its highly disjunct flora showing affinities with communities several hundred km further north in the Canadian Arctic.

American botanist Fernald (1925) also noted other disjunct vegetation distributions in the area of Mt Albert, such as the presence of elements of the western American montane flora. He ascribed this to incomplete glaciation of the Gaspé Peninsula during the Ice Ages when it was suggested that the mountain tops were exposed above the ice and retained the Arctic flora developed upon them. This hypothesis is not however accepted by modern botanists.

Nearly the whole of Mt Albert consists of serpentinized peridotite surrounded by dark amphibolite. The geological boundaries are very sharply defined by the vegetation. On amphibolite there is a close canopy of *Picea mariana*, *P. glauca*, and *Abies balsamea*. The serpentine is completely devoid of trees and appears as a desert nearly destitute of vegetation. The original discoverer (Low, 1884) described it as "a picture of the moon."

Rune (1954) noted a physiognomic and floristic resemblance between the flora of the Mt Albert "tableland" and that of the Arctic tundra. He suggested that serpentine is impermeable to water, hence duplicating the conditions of permafrost in the Arctic, so that moist conditions are maintained in winter and summer and the vegetation is subject to "frost heave" during the winter. Table 11.11 lists (in order of decreasing abundance) characteristic plants of the serpentines of Mt Albert. One of these taxa, *Minuartia marcescens*, is endemic to serpentine at Mt Albert and in Newfoundland.

The disjunct nature of the serpentine flora at Mt Albert is emphasized by consideration of the main geographical groups of the plants (Rune, 1954). These are as follows:

1—Arctic species with a southern outpost at Mt Albert. *Deschampsia alpina*, *Carex lachenalii*, *Arenaria humifusa*, *Minuartia biflora*, *Lychnis alpina*, *Armeria scabra* subsp. *labradorica*, *Campanula rotundifolia* var. *langsdorfiana*, *Artemisia borealis*, *Solidago multiradiata*.

2—Arctic species with a range extending to the high mounts of New England. *Carex scirpoidea*, *Minuartia rubella*, *Silene acaulis* subsp. *exscarpa*, *Rhododendron lapponicum*, *Vaccinium uliginosum* var. *alpinum*, *Ledum palustre* subsp. *groenlandicum*.

3—Northwestern species with disjunct appearance at Mt Albert. *Polystichum mohrioides* var. *scopulinum*, *Adiantum pedatum* var. *aleuticum*, *Cheilanthes siliquosa*, *Festuca scabrella*, *Danthonia intermedia*, *Salix brachycarpa*, *Minuartia marcescens*, *Solidago chrysolepis*, *Aster foliaceus*.

Cheilanthes siliquosa is perhaps one of the most interesting of the taxa recorded at Mt Albert (see also Legault and Blais, 1968) because of its role as an indicator of serpentine on both the eastern and western seaboards of North America. *Minuartia marcescens* is closely related to *M. obtusiloba* of the Rocky Mts and is probably a serpentinicolous variety of the latter.

TABLE 11.11 **Characteristic Vascular Plants of the Serpentine Barrens on Mt Albert, Gaspé Peninsula (listed in order of abundance)**

Minuartia marcescens	*Rhododendron lapponicum*
Carex scirpoidea	*Cerastium arvense*
Lychnis alpina	*Campanula rotundifolia* var. *langsdorfiana*
Armeria scabra subsp. *labradorica*	*Artemisia borealis*
Arenaria humifusa	*Minuartia rubella*
Silene acaulis subsp. *exscarpa*	*Salix brachycarpa*
Minuartia biflora	

Source: Rune (1954)

11.4.3 Newfoundland

Ultramafic Rocks of Newfoundland

Ultramafic rocks are found in 3 parallel belts in Newfoundland (excluding Labrador) as is shown in Fig. 11.8. They form part of the long line of ophiolitic rocks from Alabama to the Ungava Peninsula in Quebec. The most westerly of the 3 bands in Newfoundland is the most important and forms part of the Bay of Islands Ophiolitic Complex covering about 650 km^2 of which 50% comprises ultramafic rocks (Smith, 1958; Thayer, 1967). The Bay of Islands complex has also been described by Coleman (1977) and has been very well surveyed geologically (there are 15 geological references in Coleman, 1977 alone). The complex is shown in Fig. 11.10. The peridotites have a distinct layered or banded structure with steep (up to 70°) northeast dips in Table Mt and North Arm Mt. The peridotite consists mainly of dunite and harzburgite with banding resulting from variation in the amounts of olivine and orthopyroxene.

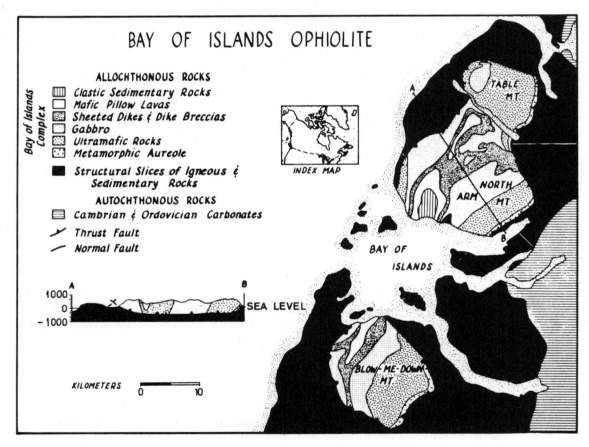

Fig. 11.10   The geology of the Bay of Islands ophiolitic complex, western Newfoundland. Source: Coleman (1977).

Plate 11.2 (a) Top left: *Campanula rotundifolia* over serpentine, Newfoundland. Photo by P. Dearden. (b) Top right: *Lychnis alpina* over serpentine in Newfoundland. Photo by P. Dearden. (c) Below left: *Fritillaria falcata* on Californian serpentine. Photo by Mary Gamble. (d) Below right: *Fritillaria pluriflora* on Californian serpentine. Photo by T. Nelson.

Plate 11.3 (a) Above: *Silene californica* on Californian serpentine. Photo by A. R. Kruckeberg. (b) Below: Serpentine barren at Winterhouse Canyon, Bay of Islands, Newfoundland. Photo by P. Dearden.

Plate 11.3 (c) Above: *Darlingtonia californica* on Californian serpentine. Photo by A. R. Kruckeberg. (d) Below: Serpentine barren on the north bank of the Tuckanegee River, near Webster, North Carolina. The line of trees in the background shows the boundary. Photo by W. R. Lauder.

Plate 12.1 *Pinus caribaea* on laterized serpentine at Loma de Cajalbana, Cuba. Photo by E. E. Smith.

The Serpentine Vegetation of Newfoundland

The typical vegetation of the diorites and gabbros adjacent to the serpentines of the Bay of Islands complex consist of a forest dominated by *Abies balsamea*, *Picea glauca*, *P. mariana*, and occasionally *Betula papyrifera*. This terminates abruptly at the ultramafite geological boundary with ultramafites where an entirely different vegetation appears. Plate 11.3b shows the serpentine barren at Winterhouse Canyon, Bay of Islands, Newfoundland.

There is a brief description by Roberts (1980a) of the more important constituents of the flora of the Newfoundland serpentine barrens and a further listing has been given by Dearden (1977, 1979) in his study of the plant communities of this area. Table 11.12 list the plant species found in these communities. Among these is the well-known serpentinicolous *Campanula rotundifolia* (Plate 11.2a) as well as *Lychnis alpina* (Plate 11.2b), both of which are common on serpentine in northwestern Europe (see Chapter 13).

In his study of the factors influencing the composition and location of plant communities on serpentine bedrock in Newfoundland, Dearden (1979) used indirect ordination analysis to identify these communities (Table 11.12). Compositional variation was found to be significantly correlated with levels of available calcium in the soil. A schematic representation of 4 of the communities observed by Dearden is shown in Fig. 11.11.

A second important factor affecting the composition of plant communities in the Newfoundland serpentine was the effect of topography which also influenced the type of

TABLE 11.12 Typical Plant Communities of Serpentine Barrens in Newfoundland (Table Mountain).

Community	pH	Exch. conc. (μg/ml) in soil			Constituent species
		Ca	Mg	Ni	
A—Arctic— alpine in most exposed locations	6.66	12	269	0.41	*Adiantum pedatum* var. *aleuticum* (F) *Androsace septentrionalis* (H) *Armeria labradorica* (H) *Arenaria humifusa* (H) *A. marcescens* (H) *Betula pumila* (S) *Cerastium beeringianum* (H) *C. terraenovae* (H) *Diapensia lapponica* (H) *Juniperus communis* (S) *Potentilla fruticosa* (S) *Racomitrium lanuginosum* (M) *Rhododendron lapponicum* (S) *Sagina nodosa* (H) *Salix arctica* (S) *Saxifraga oppositifolia* (H) *Silene acaulis* (H) *Vaccinium uliginosum* (S)
B—Arctic— in less exposed locations	6.76	10	259	0.47	*Andromeda glaucophylla* (S) *Carex echinata* (SE) *Juncus trifidus* (SE) *Juniperus horizontalis* (S) *Lychnis alpina* var. *americana* (H) *Myrica gale* (S) *Racomitrium lanuginosum* (M) *Scirpus cespitosus* (SE) *Saxifraga aizoides* (H)

Community	pH	Exch. conc. (µg/ml) in soil			Constituent species
		Ca	Mg	Ni	
C—Ecotone dominated by shrubs and sedge	6.27	13	237	0.72	Betula pumila (S) Carex scirpoidea (SE) Juncus balticus (SE) Juniperus communis (S) Ledum groenlandicum (S) Myrica gale (S) Rubus pubescens (S) Scirpus cespitosus (SE) S. hudsonianus (SE) Thalictrum alpinum (S) Vaccinium oxycoccos (S) V. uliginosum (S)
D—Peat— lands and sedge meadows	5.78	42	540	3.10	Betula michauxii (S) Carex buxbaumii (SE) C. echinata (SE) C. exilis (SE) C. lineolata (SE) C. paupercula (SE) C. scirpoidea (SE) Empetrum nigrum (S) Eriophorum angustifolium (H) E. chamissionis (H) Festuca rubra (G) Juncus balticus (SE) J. filiformis (SE) J. trifidus (SE) Vaccinium oxycoccos (S)
E—Fell— field	7.63	7	289	1.51	Alnus crispa (S) Betula pumila (S) Juniperus communis (S) Larix laricina (S)
F—Scarp foot in sheltered locality	7.63	132	78	0.07	Acer rubrum (T) Betula papyrifera (T) Circaea alpina (H) Cornus canadensis (H) Epigaea repens (S) Gaylussacia dumosa (S) Gaultheria hispidula (S) Kalmia polifolia (S) Lonicera villosa (S) Maianthemum canadense (H) Nemopanthus mucronatus (T) Pinus strobus (T) Rhododendron canadense (S) Trientalis borealis (H) Vaccinium angustifolium (S) V. macrocarpum (S) V. vitisidaea (S)

T = tree, S = shrub, SE = sedge, M = moss, H = herb.
After: Dearden (1979)

clay in the substrate (kaolinite or montmorillonite) and hence the nature of the plant community. The Arctic-alpine community in the most exposed localities has some resemblance to the tundra-type community described by Rune (1954) on the tableland of Mt Albert, alleged to have been derived from periglacial phenomena on poorly-drained soils. It is interesting to note that this Newfoundland community also includes the serpentine-tolerant fern *Adiantum pedatum* var. *aleuticum* (Plate 11.1b).

Biogeochemical Studies of the Newfoundland Serpentine Vegetation

Roberts (1980b) has presented data for the chemical composition of some of the plants growing over serpentine in Newfoundland. He determined iron, zinc, copper, nickel, chromium, cobalt and aluminium in 29 plant species from the region. Nickel uptake was far greater than that for chromium and cobalt and had its maximum level in *Arenaria humifusa* and *A. marcescens*, where values of 2330 and 2365 μg/g (dry weight) were reported. Corresponding levels for chromium were 530 and 416 μg/g, and for cobalt were 113 and 123 μg/g. Unless these values are partly due to contamination from wind-blown dust, they indicate that the 2 taxa have hyperaccumulator status as far as nickel is concerned and would be the only recorded case of hyperaccumulators ever found in previously-glaciated regions of the earth.

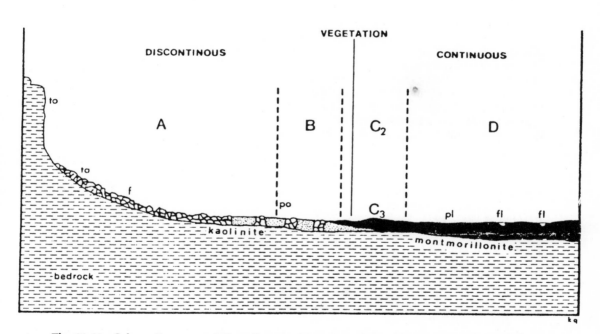

Fig. 11.11 Schematic representation of vegetation community types over serpentine in the Bay of Islands Ophiolitic complex, western Newfoundland. (to, tor, ta) = talus, f = felsenmeer, pu = polygons, pl = peatland, fl = flarks. A = Arctic alpine community in most exposed localities, B = as A but less exposed, C = ecotone dominated by shrubs and sedges, D = peatland and sedge meadow. Source: Dearden (1979).

REFERENCES

Barbour, M. G. and Major, J., 1977. *Terrestrial Vegetation of California*. Wiley, New York.

Barker, L., 1984. Serpentine flora in California—Scott Mountain—China Mountain crest zone. *Fremontia*, 11: 13–14.

Bélanger, J. R., 1980. LANDSAT et les gisements miniers. *Geos (Summer)*: 10–12.

Bélanger, J. R. and Rencz, A. N., 1983. Prospecting in glaciated terrain—Integrating airborne and LANDSAT MSS. *Adv. Space Res.*, 3: 187–191.

Bélanger, J. R., Shilts, W. W. and Rencz, A. N., 1979. Pattern of glacial dispersion of heavy metals as reflected by staellite imagery. In (F. Bonn ed.) *Télédétection et Géstion des Ressources*. Association Québecoise de Télédétection, Ste Foy.

Braun, E. L., 1950. *Deciduous Forest of Eastern North America*. Blakiston, Philadelphia.

Brooks, R. R. and MacDonnell, M. J., 1983. Detection of New Zealand ultramafic rocks by computer processing of digital data from satellite imagery. *N.Z. J. Sci.*, 26: 65–71.

Callizo, J. and Clifton, G., 1984. Serpentine flora in California—Yolo County. *Fremontia*, 11: 16–17.

Callizo, J. and Ruygt, J., 1984. Serpentine flora in California—Cedar Roughs. *Fremontia*, 11: 17–18.

Coleman, R. G., 1977. *Ophiolites*. Springer, Berlin.

Crittenden, M. and Grundmann, A., 1984. Serpentine flora in California—Jasper Ridge. *Fremontia*, 11: 20–21.

Dearden, P., 1975. *The Biogeography of Table Mountain, Bonne Bay, Newfoundland. An Investigation of Plant Community Composition and Distribution on a Serpentinic Bedrock*. MSc Thesis, Memorial University, St. Johns.

Dearden, P., 1979. Some factors influencing the composition and location of plant communities on a serpentine bedrock in western Newfoundland. *J. Biogeogr.*, 6: 93–104.

Del Moral, R., 1972. Diverse patterns in forest vegetation of the Wenatchee Mountains, Washington. *Bull. Torrey Bot. Club*, 99: 57–64.

Del Moral, R., 1982. Control of vegetation on contrasting substrates: herb patterns on serpentine and sandstone. *Am. J. Bot.*, 69: 227–238.

Derry, D. R., 1980. *World Atlas of Geology and Mineral Deposits*. Mining Journal Books, London.

Fernald, L. M., 1907. The soil preferences of certain alpine and subalpine plants. *Rhodora*, 9: 149–193.

Fernald, L. M., 1911. A botanical expedition to Newfoundland and South Labrador. *Rhodora*, 13: 109–162.

Fernald, L. M., 1925. Persistence of plants in unglaciated areas of boreal America. *Mem. Am. Acad. Arts Sci.*, 15.

Forde, M. B. and Faris, D. G., 1962. Effects of introgression on the serpentine endemism of *Quercus durata*. *Evolution*, 16: 338–347.

Goforth, D., 1984. Serpentine flora in California—Gasquet Mountain. *Fremontia*, 11: 11–12.

Griffin, J., 1984. Serpentine flora in California—San Benito Mountain. *Fremontia*, 11: 22–23.

Harshberger, J. W., 1903. The flora of serpentine barrens of southeastern Pennsylvania. *Science*, 18: 339–343.

Harshberger, J. W., 1904. A phytogeographical sketch of southeast Pennsylvania. *Bull. Torrey Bot. Club*, 31: 125–159.

Hart, R., 1980. The coexistence of weeds and restricted native plants on serpentine barrens in southeast Pennsylvania. *Ecology*, 61: 688–701.

Knox, R. G., 1984. Age structures of forests on Soldiers' Delight, a Maryland serpentine area. *Bull. Torrey Bot. Club*, 111: 498–501.

Kruckeberg, A. R., 1950. *An Experimental Inquiry into the Nature of Endemism on Serpentine Soils*. PhD Thesis, University of California, Berkeley.

Kruckeberg, A. R., 1951. Intraspecific variability in the response of certain native plant species in serpentine soils. *Am. J. Bot.*, 38: 408–418.

Kruckeberg, A. R., 1964. Ferns associated with ultramafic rocks in the Pacific Northwest. *Am. J. Bot.*, 54: 113–126.

Kruckeberg, A. R., 1967. Ecotypic response to ultramafic soils by some plant species of the northwestern United States. *Brittonia,* 19: 133–151.

Kruckeberg, A. R., 1969a. Plant life on serpentinite and other ferromagnesian rocks in northwestern North America. *Syesis,* 2: 15–114.

Kruckeberg, A. R., 1969b. Soil diversity and the distribution of plants with examples from western North America. *Madroño,* 20: 129–154.

Kruckeberg, A. R., 1984a. California's serpentine. *Fremontia,* 11(4): 11–17.

Kruckeberg, A. R., 1984b. The flora of California's serpentine. *Fremontia,* 11(5): 3–10.

Kruckeberg, A. R., 1984c. *Californian Serpentines: Flora, Vegetation, Geology, Soils, and Management Problems.* Univ. Calif. Press, Berkeley.

Kruckeberg, A. R. and Morrison, J. L. 1983. New *Streptanthus* taxa (Brassicaceae) from California. *Madroño,* 30: 230–244.

Latimer, H., 1984. Serpentine flora in California—Eastern Fresno County. *Fremontia,* 11: 29–30.

Lawrence, S. and Goss, B., 1984. *The Audubon Society Field Guide to the Natural Places of the Mid Atlantic States.* Pantheon, New York.

Legault, A., 1976. *Field trip to the serpentine area of Black Lake—Thetford Mines, Province of Quebec, Canada.* Can. Bot. Ass. Unpub. Rep.

Legault, A. and Blais, V., 1968. Le *Cheilanthes siliquosa* Maxon dans le nord-est Americain. *Naturaliste Can.,* 95: 307–316.

Low, A. P., 1884. *Report on explorations and surveys in the interior of the Gaspé Peninsula.* Geol. Surv. Can. Rep. 1882–1884.

Maas, J. L. and Stuntz, D. D., 1969. Mycoecology on serpentine soil. *Mycologia* 61: 1106–1116.

Main, L. P., 1984. Serpentine flora in California—Red Mountains in the Mt Hamilton range. *Fremontia,* 11: 21–22.

Mansberg, L. and Wentworth, T. R., 1984. Vegetation and soils of a serpentine barren in western North Carolina. *Bull. Torrey Bot. Club,* 111: 273–286.

Mason, H. L., 1946. The edaphic factor in narrow endemism. *Madroño,* 8: 209–226, 241–257.

McCormick, S., 1984. Serpentine flora in California—Ring Mountain. *Fremontia,* 11: 18–19.

McLeod, M., 1984. Serpentine flora in California—Cuesta Ridge. *Fremontia,* 11: 24.

Medeiros, J., 1984. Serpentine flora in California—The Red Hills. *Fremontia,* 11: 28–29.

Miller, G. L., 1977. An ecological study of the serpentine barrens in Lancaster County, Pennsylvania. *Proc. Penn. Acad. Sci.,* 51: 169–176.

Munz, P. A. and Keck, D. D., 1959. *A Californian Flora.* University of California Press, Berkeley and Los Angeles.

Pearre, N. C. and Heyl, A. V. Jr., 1960. Chromite and other mineral deposits in serpentine rocks of the Piedmont Upland, Maryland, Pennsylvania and Delaware. *U.S. Geol. Surv. Bull.,* 1082K: 707–827.

Pennell, F. W., 1910. Flora of the Conowingo barrens of southeastern Pennsylvania. *Proc. Acad. Sci. Philadelphia,* 62: 541–584.

Pennell, F. W., 1912. Further notes on the floras of the Conowingo barrens of southeastern Pennsylvania. *Proc. Acad. Sci. Philadelphia,* 62: 541–584.

Pennell, F. W., 1930. On some critical aspects of the serpentine barrens. *Bartonia,* 12: 1–28.

Pinion, G. E., 1973. Edaphic variations in *Talinum teretifolium,* Portulaceae. *Va. J. Sci.,* 24: 137.

Radford, A. E., 1948. The vascular flora of the olivine deposits of North Carolina and Georgia. *J. Elisha Mitchell Sci. Soc.,* 64: 45–106.

Raunkiaer, C., 1934. *The Life Forms of Plants and Statistical Plant Geography.* Clarendon Press, Oxford.

Raymond, M., 1950. Esquisse phytogéographique du Québec. *Mem. Jard. Bot. Montréal,* 5: 1–147.

Reeves, R. D., Brooks, R. R. and Macfarlane, R. M., 1981. Nickel uptake by Californian *Streptanthus* and *Caulanthus* with particular reference to the hyperaccumulator *Streptanthus polygaloides* Gray (Brassiccaceae). *Am. J. Bot.,* 68: 708–712.

Reeves, R. D., MacFarlane, R. M. and Brooks, R. R., 1983. Accumulation of nickel and zinc by western North American genera containing serpentine-tolerant species. *Am. J. Bot.*, 70: 1297–1303.

Roberts, B. A., 1980a. Some chemical and physical properties of serpentine soils from western Newfoundland. *Can. J. Soil Sci.*, 60: 231–240.

Roberts, B. A., 1980b. *Concentrations of micronutrients (trace elements) in native plants growing on serpentine soils from western Newfoundland.* Abs. Paper Univ. Brit. Columbia, Vancouver 12–16 July: 95.

Robinson, W.. O., Edgington, G. and Byers, H. G., 1935. *Chemical studies of infertile soils high in magnesium and generally high in chromium and nickel.* U.S. Dep. Ag. Tech. Bull. 471: 1–28.

Rune, O., 1954. Notes on the flora of the Gaspé Peninsula. *Svensk. Bot. Tidskr.*, 48: 117–138.

Sawyer, J., 1984. Serpentine flora in California—The Lassics. *Fremontia*, 11: 15–16.

Schlising, R. A., 1984. Serpentine flora in California—Magalia in Butte County. *Fremontia*, 11: 25–26.

Scoggan, H. J., 1950. The flora of Bic and the Gaspé Peninsula. *Bull. Natn. Mus. Canada*, 115: 1–399.

Shreve, F., 1910. *The Plant Life of Maryland.* John Hopkins Univ. Press, Baltimore.

Smith, C. H., 1958. *The Bay of Islands igneous complex western Newfoundland.* Geol. Surv. Can. Mem. 290.

Sommers, S., 1984. Serpentine flora in California—Edgewood Park. *Fremontia*, 11: 19–20.

Stebbins, G. L., 1984. Serpentine flora in California—The northern Sierra Nevada. *Fremontia*, 11: 26–28.

Terlizzi, D. E. and Karlander, E. P., 1979. Soil algae from a serpentine Maryland formation. *Soil Sci. Biochem.*, 11: 205–207.

Thayer, T. P., 1967. Chemical and structural relationships of ultramafic and felspathic rocks in alpine intrusive complexes. In (P. J. Wyllie ed.) *Ultramafic and Related Rocks.* Wiley, New York.

Vogl, R. J., 1973. Ecology of the knob cone pine in the Santa Ana Mts, California USA. *Ecol. Monogr.*, 43: 125–143.

Walker, R. B., 1948. *A Study of the Serpentine Soil Infertility with Special Reference to Edaphic Endemism.* PhD Thesis, University of California, Berkeley.

Wherry, E. T., 1963. Some Pennsylvania barrens and their flora. *Bartonia*, 33: 7–11.

Whipple, J., 1984. Serpentine flora in California—Mt Eddy. *Fremontia*, 11: 14–15.

Whittaker, R. H., 1953. A consideration of climax theory: the climax as a population and pattern. *Ecol. Monogr.*, 35: 275–288.

Whittaker, R. H., 1954. The ecology of serpentine soils. IV The vegetation response to serpentine soils. *Ecology*, 35: 275–288.

Whittaker, R. H., 1960. Vegetation of the Siskiyou Mountains, Oregon and California. *Ecol. Monogr.*, 30: 279–338.

Worthley, E. G. Sr., 1984. *A nature walk for Soldiers' Delight, Baltimore County, Maryland.* Soldiers' Delight Conservation Inc., Unpub. Rep.

Chapter 12
TROPICAL AMERICA

12.1 INTRODUCTION

Ultramafic rocks in tropical America occur mainly in Cuba, Puerto Rico and Brazil. Elsewhere there are a few sporadic occurrences along the line of the Andes and in Guyana, but in general it can be said that ultramafites occupy a smaller proportion of the area of South America than of any other continent. In tropical America, the most important and best studied serpentine areas are in the Greater Antilles, particularly Cuba. A number of workers have studied the flora of Cuba (Table 12.1) and a study of the serpentine flora of Tropical America essentially involves the Cuban plants. Although Cuba lies only just inside the Tropics, its serpentine flora is so different from that of the United States that it is indeed appropriate that it be considered in a separate chapter. The paucity of information on the serpentine plants of the fairly extensive ultramafites of Brazil is surprising and it would seem that here is a virtually untapped floristic field which should amply reward research in the future.

TABLE 12.1 Papers Describing Natural Serpentine Vegetation in Tropical America

Cuba	Puerto Rico	Brazil
Beard (1953)	Holdridge (1945)	Carmo Lima e Cunha (1985)
Berazain Iturralde (1976, 1981a, 1981b)		
Carabia (1945)		
Seifriz (1940, 1943)		

12.2 CUBA

12.2.1 Geology, Geomorphology, and Soils of Cuban Ultramafic Rocks

Cuba is the largest of the Greater Antilles and has a length of about 1200 km coupled with an average width of about 80 km. The area is 110,000 km^2. Topographically the island consists of a long central plain flanked in the west by the Organos Mts and in the east by the Sierra Maestra. The plain is interrupted in the middle of the island by a group of mountains in Villa Clara, Cienfugos, and Sancti Spiritus provinces (Fig. 12.1).

Ultramafic rocks occupy an important position in the geology of Cuba and cover a total area of about 5000 km^2 at elevations from sea level to 1100 m. The distribution of ultramafic rocks in Cuba is shown in Fig. 12.2, and their relative areas are shown in Table 12.2.

As with those of most other ultramafic occurrences, the Cuban serpentine soils are characterised by an abundance of iron and magnesium, a deficiency of calcium and silica, and pH levels in the range 6.0–6.5. The soils are of two main types:

1—shallow skeletal poorly-developed soils.

2—deep developed soils resulting from laterization.

12.2.2 Vegetation Types on Cuban Serpentines

The vegetation of Cuba has been described by various workers including Carabia (1945) and Seifriz (1943). The latter is perhaps the more complete of the two, since the former paper

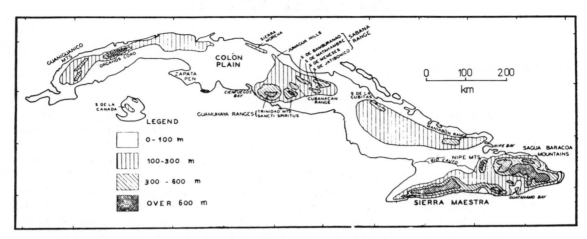

Fig. 12.1   Relief map of Cuba.

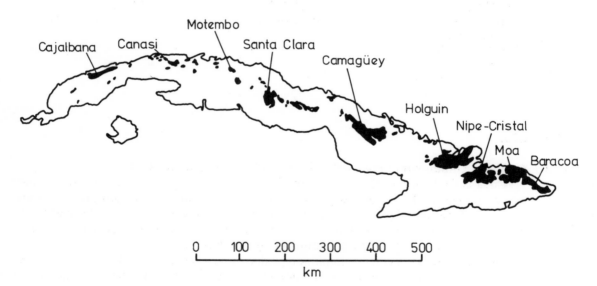

Fig. 12.2   Ultramafic rock outcrops in Cuba.
Source: Berazain Iturralde (1976).

TABLE 12.2 Characteristics of the Cuban Serpentine Flora

Region	Area (km²)	No. of Endemics*	End./km²	Endemic species of the genus								
				A	B	C	D	E	F	G	H	I
Cajalbana	140	36	0.25	1	—	1	—	1	—	—	—	1
Canasi	180	19	0.105	1	—	—	1	1	2	—	1	—
Motembo	137	5	0.036	—	—	—	—	—	—	—	—	—
Santa Clara	735	10	0.013	—	—	—	1	1	1	—	1	—
Camaguey	1030	6	0.005	—	—	—	6	1	—	1	—	4
Holguin	897	14	0.014	—	—	—	1	—	—	1	1	1
Nipe-Cristal	894	184	0.205	1	2	1	5	6	1	1	—	2
Moa	1130	189	0.166	3	2	1	3	4	1	—	—	1
Baracoa	246	48	0.190	1	1	1	1	1	—	—	1	—
Total	5389	511	0.109	7	4	4	18	15	5	3	4	9

*endemic to one region only
A—Moacroton, B—Tetralix, C—Heptanthus, D—Buxus, E—Leucocroton,
F—Harpalyce, G—Spirotecoma, H—Melocactus, I—Gochnatia.
After: Berazain Iturralde (1976).

was concerned with the flora (principally serpentinicolous) of one region of Cuba (Sierra de Nipa). A paper by Beard (1953) is a general description of the Cuban flora which is described as mainly belonging to the savanna flora, remarkable in both its richness and high degree of endemism.

Berazain Iturralde (1976) has reported the presence of four types of vegetal formation on the Cuban serpentines. These are, using the vernacular names, as follows:

1—*Cuabal* (named after "Cuaba" a Euphorbiaceous plant of the community): a community of xeromorphic shrubby evergreen vegetation growing on poorly-developed soils. In more humid places, the community has a more mesomorphic appearance.

2—*Charrascal* (cf. chapparal = bushland): a community found on fairly shallow soils and comprising xero- and mesomorphic evergreen vegetation. This is found primarily in high-rainfall montane regions.

3—*Pinar* (pine-savanna): this community is found over deep soils (latosols) and comprises mainly an arboraceous, xeromorphic type in montane regions with poor rainfall. Plate 12.1 shows a stand of *Pinus caribaea* in this community.

4—*Pluviosilva de montaña* (rainforest): a mesolaurifoliar vegetation on deep soils in montane regions with good rainfall.

The distribution of serpentine plant communities in Cuba is shown in Fig. 12.3.

12.2.3 Characteristics of the Cuban Serpentine Flora

Endemism

The serpentine flora of Cuba is probably one of the richest of this type in the world. Of the 6700 phanerogams of the Cuban flora, 3437 (51.3%) are endemic and of these, 902 (13.5%) are endemic to serpentine (Berazain Iturralde, 1976). The number of serpentine endemics is tabulated region-by-region in Table 12.2.

One or two characteristics of the serpentine vegetation should be noted. In northern Oriente province there are 198 endemics common to the Nipe-Cristal, Moa, and Baracoa occurrences. There are 81 endemics found at two or more serpentine outcrops and there are 14 pancuban species found at all of the sites.

Endemism with respect to genus is also of interest in Cuba. Of the 67 endemic genera of

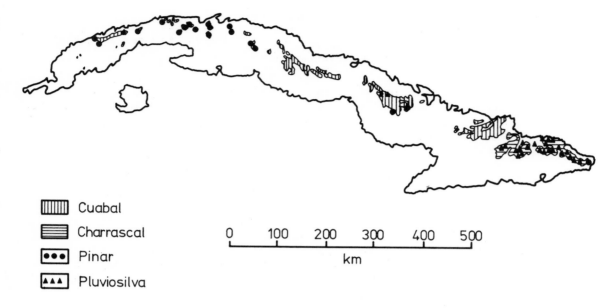

Cuabal

Charrascal

Pinar

Pluviosilva

0   100   200   300   400   500

km

Fig. 12.3   Vegetation communities over serpentine in Cuba.
Source: Berazain Iturralde (1976).

the Cuban flora, 23 (34.3%) are endemic to serpentine. The density of endemic species is also shown in Table 12.2 and shows the high degree of endemism in the Cajalbana province compared with Camaguey.

Disjunctiveness and Vicariousness

The disjunctiveness and vicariousness of serpentine-endemic taxa of Cuba has been discussed by Berazain Iturralde (1976). The former property is summarized in Table 12.2. Vicariousness is common among several of the serpentine-endemic genera of Cuba. For example one species of *Tetralix* is found on latosols in North Oriente province whereas another is found on skeletal soils at Moa.

Berazain Iturralde (1981a) investigated the serpentine flora of the Canasi outcrop west of Havana in order to determine the probable source of its constituent species. She collected 54 endemics of which 14 were solely of western origin, 13 were found in both western and central region, two were from the western and eastern zones, and 25 were pancuban. A further 18 species were *bodenvag* (indifferent) taxa occurring on and off serpentine.

The 4 main findings of the above study by Berazain Iturralde (1981a) were as follows:

1—The serpentine vegetation of Canasi is markedly occidental in its composition.

2—There are links with the central and eastern serpentine floras.

3—There is a high degree of endemism among the serpentinophytes of Canasi.

4—There is a high proportion of pancuban elements in the flora.

Each of the 4 characteristics listed above will now be discussed further:

1. The serpentine flora of Canasi is closely related to that of nearby Cajalbana. The soils at Canasi are extremely old (ca. 30 m.y.) and account for the apparent antiquity of the flora. There are notable examples of disjunctiveness and vicariousness between the *charrascales* of western Cuba and those of the eastern part of the island in Oriente province. Both regions have similar soils and a high degree of endemism. Berazain Iturralde (1981a) proposed that the western flora had been derived from the eastern flora some time before the Tertiary, during which migration patterns might have been interrupted by subduction of Central Cuba,

resulting in isolation of the western and eastern floras. At a later date, central Cuba arose again from the sea.

The reservoir of occidental species in western Cuba was also suggested as a source for recolonization of the central areas. It was also proposed that some elements in the western flora resulting from the primary (east-west) migration are palaeoendemic in nature. Examples of this are *Acalypha nana*, *Jacquinia brunnescens*, and *Ottoschmidtia dorsiventralis*.

2. The relationship between the eastern and central serpentine floras can be explained either by a continuation of migration during the Tertiary when the higher parts of central Cuba were not submerged, or by a more recent secondary migration from west to east after the ocean has retreated (see above). Again many elements of the central serpentine flora can be considered to be palaeoendemic in nature. Examples of this are: *Moacroton revolutus* (central Cuba) which resembles *M. lanceolatus* of northeast Oriente province, more than it does *M. trigonocarpus* of the eastern region. Similarly, *Buxus flaviramea* is closer to *B. heterophylla* (Holguin), and *Acacia daemon* is closer to *A. bucherii* (Moa, Holguin).

3. The high degree of endemism in Canasi is probably a result of the extremely hostile edaphic conditions in the serpentine soils coupled with the xeric conditions in this region. This prevents colonization by other competing species. The Canasi area is characterized by plants with a very restricted distribution such as: *Borreria matanzasia*, *Bucida ophiticola*, *Guilleminea brittonii* subsp. *brittonii*, *Moacroton revolutus*, *Myrtus matanzasia*, *Reynosia intermedia*, and *R. microphylla*. Plants such as *R. intermedia* (closely related to *R. microphylla* and *R. mucronata*) and *B. matanzasia* (related to *B. eritrichoides*), are probably neoendemics. The high degree of endemism contributes to the floristic richness of the region which which appears to be a centre of speciation for adjacent ultramafic outcrops with a poorer flora.

4. The abundance of pancuban species is a factor in favour of the theory of continuation of the east-west migration pattern even during the Tertiary, since the longitudinal distribution of species favours such a pattern.

To give a checklist of all of the 511 serpentine-endemic species of Cuba is well beyond the scope of this book. Table 12.3 therefore presents a listing of most of the serpentine endemics of a single area (Canasi), a region however typified by a large number of such endemics. The same table shows their occurrence in other parts of Cuba. For another listing of serpentine plants from a single area (Nipe), the reader is referred to Carabia (1945).

TABLE 12.3 Serpentine-endemic Plants of the Canasi Area of Cuba and their Distribution in other Serpentine Sites in the Island

Species	Family	W	W & C	W & E	Pancuban
Anthacanthus nannophyllus	Acanthaceae		X		
Guilleminea brittonii subsp. *brittonii*	Amaranthaceae		X		
Agave legrelliana	Agavaceae	X			
Mesechites rosea	Apocynaceae				X
Neobracea valenzuelana					X
Plumeria clusioides					X
Rauwolfia cubana			X		
Coccothrinax miraguama subsp. *roseocarpa*	Arecaceae	X			
Copernicia macroglossa			X		
Buxus flaviramea	Buxaceae		X		
Rheedia brevipes	Clusiaceae		X		
R. fruticosa				X	
Bucida ophiticola	Combretaceae	X			

Species	Family	W	W & C	W & E	Pancuban
Acalypha nana	Euphorbiaceae	X			
Chamaesyce brittonii					X
Leucocroton flavicans		X			
Moacroton revolutus		X			
Phyllanthus discolor			X		
P. orbicularis					X
Savia clussifolia				X	
Galactia savannarum	Fabaceae				X
Harpalyce suberosa		X			
Piscidia cubensis					X
Acacia daemon	Mimosaceae		X		
Calliandra pauciflora					X
Calyptranthes decandra	Myrtaceae				X
Eugenia camarioca					X
E. cyphophloea			X		
E. tuberculata				X	
Myrtus matanzasia		X			
Ouratia ilicifolia var. *savannarum*	Ochnacaceae		X		
Tetramicra eulophiae	Orchidaceae				X
Passiflora foetida var. *polyadena*	Passifloraceae				X
Andropogon reedii	Poaceae		X		
Coccoloba armata	Polygonaceae				X
C. microphylla					X
C. praecox					X
Portulaca cubensis	Portulacaceae				X
Reynosia intermedia	Rhamnaceae	X			
R. microphylla		X			
R. mucronata					X
Borreria eritrichoides	Rubiaceae				X
B. matanzasia		X			
Guettarda echinodendron					X
Mitracarpum squarrosum					X
Rondeletia camarioca					X
Zanthoxylum dumosum	Rutaceae				X
Manilkara jaimiqui subsp. *wrightiana*	Sapotaceae				X
Brunfelsia nitida	Solanaceae		X		
Jacquinia brunnescens	Theophrastac.	X			
Anemia cuneata	Schizaceae				X
A. cajalbanica		X			
Selaginella stolonifera	Selaginellaceae				X

W = west, E = east, C = central.
After: Berazain Iturralde (1981a).

General Conclusions

A number of general conclusions can be made about the serpentine vegetation of Cuba:

1. The serpentine flora has a very high degree of endemism. This is partly because of the extreme toxicity of the soils, requiring a high degree of specialization for successful colonization.

2. The degree of competition on serpentine soils resulting from the extreme ecological conditions, permits a major variability in species.

3. Because of its numerous endemic species, the *charrascal* community provides a major floristic resource for other younger communities such as the *cuabal*. This process is in the course of full development as indicated by the small number of species extending over the whole island. It is proposed that the process originated in northeast Oriente province (Moa and Baracoa) which contains 77% of the endemic serpentinicolous species of Cuba and 84% of the endemic genera.

4. Certain similarities are evident in the species composition of the *charrascales* of northern Oriente in the east and of Canasi and Cajalbana in the west. These similarities are believed to result from east-west migration before the Tertiary when central Cuba was subducted. Similarities between the flora of the western and central parts of Cuba are postulated as being due to a secondary, more recent, west-east migration (or possibly a continuation of the east-west migration during the Tertiary via islands of unsubmerged mountain peaks).

12.2.4 Biogeochemical Investigations on the Cuban Serpentine Flora

Chemical analysis of Cuban serpentine plants was first carried out by Brooks et al. (1977) in their investigation of the genera *Hybanthus* and *Homalium* (see Chapter 8). Although no hyperaccumulators of nickel (> 1000 μg/g in dried material) were discovered, an unusually high nickel content was reported in the Cuban *Hybanthus linearifolius* and *H. wrightii* (107 and 350 μg/g respectively). Later, Berazain Iturralde (1981b) determined nickel and other elements in 6 serpentine endemic species from Cuba. Unfortunately the data were presented on an ash weight basis and no conversion factor to dry weight was given. However, using a conversion factor of 0.05, it is quite clear that 2 species at least are hyperaccumulators of nickel. Nickel concentrations shown in parentheses (μg/g dry weight) were as follows: *Leucocroton flavicans* (5725), *Buxus flaviramea* (3170), *Myrtus matanzasia* (445), *Neobracea valenzuelana* (60), *Ternostroemia peduncularis* (10), *Coccothrinax miraguama* subsp. *rosecarpa* (25). The first two species are among the very few hyperaccumulators for nickel so far discovered in the Americas. It might be assumed that further work on the Cuban flora will turn up other hyperaccumulators. It must, however, be remembered that plants of this type tend to be concentrated in a very small number of families such as the Flacourtiaceae, Violaceae and Brassicaceae, none of which is well represented in the Cuban serpentine flora.

12.3 PUERTO RICO

Ultramafic rocks cover a significant area of Puerto Rico in the Greater Antilles (Fig. 12.4) and run southeast from Mayaguez on the west coast of the island to the southeast of the territory. The serpentine breaks down to a slippery red clay in the wet season and bakes to a hard dry pan in periods of drought. The soils are very infertile as are most serpentine soils in tropical climates, and are hardly exploited for agriculture, primarily because of the very low phosphorus content.

The vegetation of the Puerto Rican serpentines is typically xeromorphic (Holdridge, 1945) and this rock type supports a mixture of endemic and drought-tolerant taxa derived from other parts of the island. Typical plants of the serpentine are: *Amomis grisea, Byrsonima cuneata, Mayepea domingensis, Tabebuia haemantha, Clusia rosea, Taonabo pachyphylla* and *Ilex guianensis*.

Brooks et al. (1977) in their study of hyperaccumulators of nickel in the genera *Hybanthus* and *Homalium*, found up to 343 μg/g nickel (about ten times the normal nickel content of serpentine plants) in dried leaves of *Hybanthus pleiandrum* growing on ultramafic rocks near Mayaguez. It is noteworthy that the genus contains several hyperaccumulators of nickel in Western Australia and New Caledonia (see Chapter 8).

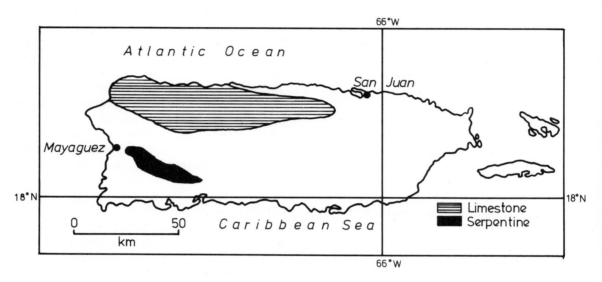

Fig. 12.4 Ultramafic rocks in Puerto Rico.
After: Holdridge (1945)

12.4 BRAZIL

12.4.1 Geology

As mentioned in the introduction to this chapter, South America is relatively deficient in ultramafic rocks except in Brazil where extensive outcrops occur in Goiás state near Brasilia in the central uplands of the country. These deposits are the 7th largest in the world and are heavily laterised (Trescases et al. 1981). The locations of these and other ultramafic areas are given in Fig. 12.5 and include scattered outcrops in the states of Bahia (site #2), Minas Gerais (site #3), and Rio Grande do Sul (site #4) as well as in Goiás (site #1).

The large outcrops in Goiás are primarily stratiform whereas those in the rest of the country are mainly of the alpine (ophiolitic) type and are partly or wholly serpentinized. The deposits are all extremely old and range from 3000 m.y. for those of Goiás to 600 m.y. in Pará (a continuation of the Goian outcrops). The ultramafites of Rio Grande do Sul (see below) are about 2000 m.y. old.

12.4.2 A Serpentine Plant Community in Brazil

Carmo Lima e Cunha (1985) has made brief notes of a serpentine plant community at São Sepe in Rio Grande do Sul (site #4 in Fig. 12.5). The area has a central core of peridotites surrounded by gabbro and in turn by granites. The vegetation over the granite is very dense and comprises trees of medium height (*Scutia buxifolia*) and numerous shrubs. The transi-

Fig. 12.5 Ultramafic rocks in Brazil. 1—Goias, 2—Bahia, 3—Minas Gerais, 4—Rio Grande do Sul.

tion to gabbro is marked by a predominance of grasses and caespitose cushion plants forming a so-called "campos sujos" (dirty fields).

Over ultramafic rocks the *Scutia* is reduced to a shrub not exceeding 2 m in height and occurs in association with plants of the Anacardiaceae, Lauraceae, and Podocarpaceae (cf. New Zealand—Chapter 21). The physiognomy of the serpentine plants reflects the usual xeromorphic adaptation of nanism and small leaf size. The leaves generally have a deep green colour.

12.4.3 Biogeochemical Studies

Carmo Lima e Cunha (1985) has carried out biogeochemical investigations at the São Sepe ultramafic outcrop whose vegetation has been described above. She determined nickel and 11 other elements in the ash of *Scutia buxifolia*. Some of the data are shown in Fig. 12.6 and indicate that the nickel content of this plant gives a good indication of the presence of ultramafic rocks in the substrate, so that this species has an obvious potential for biogeochemical prospecting particularly as it is an extremely common plant throughout the region.

Intra-plant correlation analysis of the elemental data showed an inverse significant relationship ($P < 0.05$) between nickel and potassium and between magnesium and potassium in the plant material. This indicated antagonism to potassium uptake by excess accumulation of either of the other 2 elements. The Ca/Mg mole quotient in *Scutia buxifolia* (0.40) was extremely low and demonstrates the high tolerance of this species to ultramafic rocks. This taxon is clearly able to tolerate not only this adverse quotient, but also antagonism to uptake of the plant nutrient potassium.

There can be little doubt that Brazil will provide a rich field of research into serpentine plants in the future since so little work has been done so far, and it is to be hoped that ecologists, botanists and other scientists will take up the challenge and begin to exploit this vast potential field.

REFERENCES

Beard, J. S., 1953. The savanna vegetation of northern tropical America. *Ecol. Monogr.*, 23: 167–171.

Berazain Iturralde, R., 1976. Estudio preliminar de la flora serpentinicola de Cuba. *Ciencias Ser. 10; Botanica*, 12: 11–26.

Berazain Iturralde, R., 1981a. Sobre el endemismo de la florula serpentinicola le "Lomas de Galindo", Canasi, Cuba. *Revist. Jard. Bot. Nac. Cuba*, 2: 29–47.

Berazain Iturralde, R., 1981b. Reporte preliminar de plantas serpentinicolas acumuladoras e hiperacumuladoras de algunos elementos. *Revist. Jard. Bot. Nac. Cuba*, 2: 48–59.

Brooks R. R., Lee, J., Reeves, R. D. and Jaffré, T., 1977. Detection of nickeliferous rocks by analysis of herbarium specimens of indicator plants. *J. Geochem. Explor.*, 7: 49–57.

Carabia J. P., 1945. The vegetation of Sierra de Nipe. Cuba. *Ecol. Monogr.*, 15: 321–341.

Carmo Lima e Cunha, M. Do, 1985. Estudos biogeoquimicos no complexo basico-ultrabasico de Pedras Pretas, São Sepe, R.S. *Revist. Brasil. Geocienc.*, 15: 147–153.

Holdridge, L. R., 1945. A brief sketch of the Puerto Rican flora. In (F. Verdoorn ed.) *Plants and Plant Science in Latin America*. Chronica Botanica, Waltham Mass.

Seifriz, W., 1940. Die Pflanzengeographie von Kuba. *Bot. Jrb.*, 70: 441–462.

Seifriz, W., 1943. The plant life of Cuba. *Ecol. Monogr.*, 13: 375–426.

Trescases, J. J., Melfi, A. J. and Barros de Oliveira, S. M., 1981. Nickeliferous laterites of Brazil. In (V. S. Krishnaswamy ed.) *Laterisation Processes*. Oxford and IBH Publishing Co., New Delhi.

Plate 13.1   (a) Above left: *Arenaria norvegica* growing on serpentine scree at Keen of Hamar, Shetland.
Photo by D. R. Slingsby.
(b) Above right: The serpentine-endemic *Cerastium nigrescens* on serpentine scree at Keen of Hamar, Shetland.
Photo by D. R. Slingsby.
(c) Below left: *Armeria maritima* at Meikle Kilrannoch, Scotland.
Photo by A. J. M. Baker.
(d) Below right: *Cochlearia Pyrenaica* in a mat of *Cherleria sedoides* at Meikle Kilrannoch, Scotland.
Photo by A. J. M. Baker.

Plate 13.2   (a) Above: View of Hallival, Island of Rhum.
Photo by W. R. Lauder.
(b) Below: Serpentine scree at Keen of Hamar, Shetland.
Photo by D. R. Slingsby.

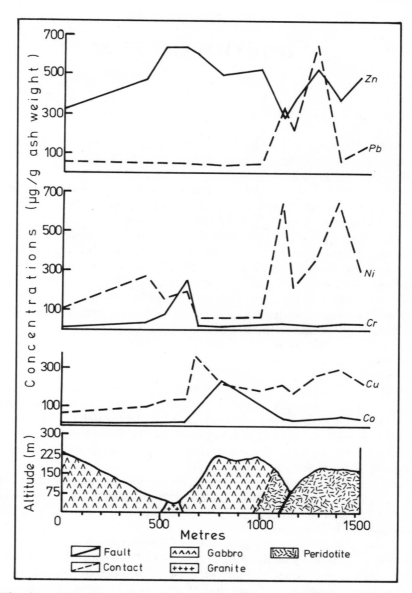

Fig. 12.6   The elemental content of the ash of *Scutia buxifolia* growing over various rock types near São Sepe, Rio Grande do Sul, Brazil.
Source: Carmo Lima e Cunha (1985).

Chapter 13

NORTHWEST EUROPE

13.1 GEOLOGY AND TECTONICS

Ultramafic rocks in Europe are found in 2 main zones. The first of these is in a long train of outcrops stretching from the Hebrides in the southwest and along the line of the Caledonian mountains (Caledonides or Scandes) in Scandinavia into northern Norway. Subsidiary outcrops branch out into northern and central Finland. The second major zone is the much younger belt of ophiolites extending from southeastern Spain through the Alps, Yugoslavia and Greece and into the Aegean sea.

In a global framework, the ultramafites of northwestern Europe form the northwestern part of the Eurasian tectonic plate stretching from the Mid-Atlantic Ridge to the Pacific Ocean and from the Arctic regions to the Mediterranean. This region of Europe is known as Palaeo-europa (Ager, 1980) and will be discussed further in Chapter 14.

About 1800 m.y. ago, northwestern Europe formed part of the North American continent and became separated about 1000 m.y. ago by a trough or series of troughs which formed the Proto-Atlantic Ocean. Sediments and volcanics accumulated in the troughs and were compressed by repeated convergence of the sides to form the continuous structure of which the Appalachians are now part. The northern part of this structure was the present Caledonides.

The separation of the Eurasian plate from the North American plate began about 100 m.y. ago. At first the separation involved movement of Greenland away from Canada (80 m.y. ago) and continued for a further 20 m.y. until what is now northwestern Europe separated from Greenland and is still doing so at the present time. A glance at Fig. 2.2 will show that the ophiolites of the Caledonides and Appalachians would fit perfectly together if separation of the plates had not occurred.

An important ultramafic outcrop in northwestern Europe, the Lizard Peninsula in Cornwall, England, is not part of the ophiolites of the region and is believed to have been derived from the Variscan (Hercynian) orogeny (280 m.y. ago) resulting from the collision of the Eurasian and African plates.

Because of the identical origin of the Caledonides and the Appalachians, it is not surprising to find many similarities in their petrology, mineralogy, and geochemistry. The floras likewise are rather similar, at least as regards the Canadian extension of the Appalachians, though such floras do not date back to the original separation of the continents since glaciation removed the entire vegetation cover of both regions. Table 13.1 lists papers which describe the serpentine floras of northwestern Europe.

13.2 GREAT BRITAIN

13.2.1 Rocks and Soils

Outcrops of ultramafic rocks in Britain occur mainly at Lizard Peninsula in England and at numerous localities in Scotland from Rhum to Shetland. The Scottish outcrops form part of the Caledonian Ophiolitic Belt and have their greatest areal extent in Aberdeenshire and at Unst and Fetlar in Shetland. The location of 19 of these occurrences is shown in Fig. 13.1.

Soils developed on serpentine have been described by Proctor and Woodell (1971), Wilson and Berrow (1978) and by Birse (1982). Heslop and Bown (1969) have classified these

TABLE 13.1 Papers which Describe Serpentine Vegetation of Northwestern Europe

Britain	Norway	Sweden	Finland
Birse (1982)	Bjørlykke (1938)	Rune (1953)	Kotilainen (1944)
Carter et al. (1986)	Dahl (1912)		Kotilainen and
Coombe and Frost	Jørgensen (1974)		Seivala (1954)
(1956a, b)	Knaben (1952)		Lounamaa (1956)
Ferreira (1959)	Kotilainen and		Mikkola (1938)
Halliday (1960)	Seivala (1954)		Rintanen (1968)
Hunter and	Nordhagen (1936,		Rune (1953)
Vergnano (1952)	1966)		Takala and Seaward (1978)
Johnston and	Rune (1953, 1954)		Vuokko (1978)
Proctor (1979, 1980)	Svenonius (1883)		
Marrs and Proctor	Vogt (1942)		
(1978, 1979)			
Marshall (1959)			
Proctor and			
Johnston (1977)			
Proctor and			
Woodell (1971)			
Shewry and			
Peterson (1975, 1976)			
Spence (1957, 1958,			
1969, 1970)			
West (1912)			

as separate from other soil groups; they are now known as brown magnesian soils (a subgroup of brown soils) and magnesian gleys (within the group of gleys). A brief description of both types of soil follows (see also Table 4.1):

1—Magnesian skeletal soils (BMR). These are debris soils such as are found on Keen of Hamar, Shetland. The surface layer is composed of coarse debris overlying finer material. The Ca/Mg quotient is extremely low (ca. 0.03) and toxic levels of nickel and chromium are present.

2—Brown magnesian soils (BMS and GMS). These soils include well-drained and poorly-drained (gleyed = GMS) soils. There is a tendency for a marked humus layer to develop·and the domination of magnesium over calcium is not attained until the C horizon is reached. Typical soils of this type are found at Strathdon, Aberdeenshire.

3—Magnesian gleys (BMG). These are soils of very poorly drained sites. The Ca/Mg quotient of the upper horizons can be much greater than 0.1 due to the presence of glacial drift over the serpentine. Typical soils of this type are also found at Strathdon.

4—Alpine magnesian soils. These are subdivided into alpine brown magnesian (MBM) and alpine magnesian gley (MMG). Both soil types are found at Meikle Kilrannoch.

5—Loessic soils over serpentine. It has been observed by Coombe and Frost (1956a) that the true serpentine soil of the Lizard Peninsula in Cornwall is a red-brown friable loam, rich in humus, found in shallow pockets over serpentine. The whole area is, however, covered with a thick layer of loess (Coombe and Frost, 1956b) which is chemically not ultramafic in nature. These soils therefore have a comparatively high calcium content (see Table 4.1) and do not therefore feature in the British classification of serpentine soils.

In a well-known benchmark paper on British serpentine vegetation, Proctor and

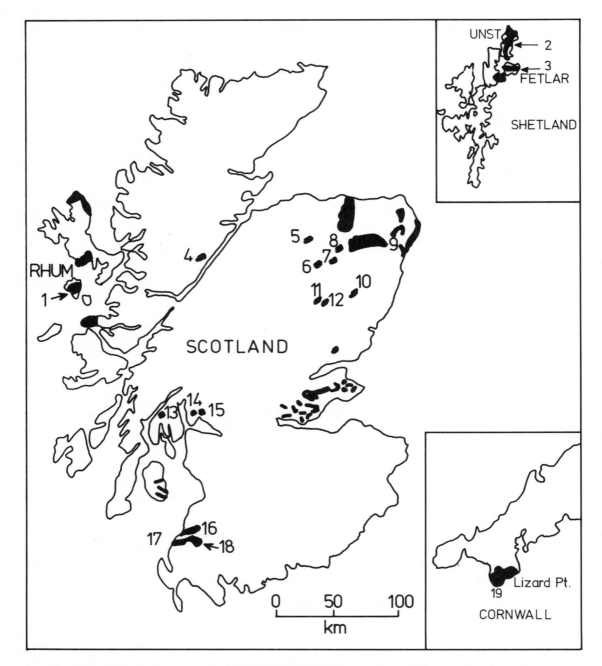

Fig. 13.1 Ultramafic rocks in the British Isles (solid black areas). 1—Rhum, 2—Unst, 3—Fetlar, 4—Glen Urquhart, 5—Blackwater, 6—Green Hill (Strathdon), 7 = Glenkindie, 8—Hill of Towanreef, 9—Beauty Hill, 10—Coyles of Muick, 11 and 12—Meikle Kilrannoch, 13—Glendaruel, 14 and 15—Loch Lomond, 16—Girvan, 17—Balmahie Hill, 18—Grey Hill, 19—Lizard Point.

Woodell (1971) classified serpentine sites into 2 groups as follows:

1—those with vegetation with characteristic serpentine features (e.g., Unst), and;

2—those supporting vegetation lacking characteristic features (e.g., the Lizard Peninsula).

Although there has been some argument as to whether edaphic or climatic factors have had a controlling influence on the British serpentine vegetation, Slingsby and Brown (1977) assert that edaphic factors are at least a contributory factor. These workers analysed a large number of serpentine soils from Lizard, Unst, Haaf Gruney (near Unst), Coyles of Muick, Greenhill of Strathdon, Whitecairns (Aberdeenshire), and Holyhead (Wales). The soils were analysed for total and extractable Al, Ca, Co, Cr, Fe, K, Mg, Na, Ni, P, Si, and Ti, and for % organic material. Principal components analysis (PCA) was used to interpret the data. The first component (46% of the total variance) sorted the soils according to their "serpentineness", i.e., low concentrations of K, Al, Si, Ca, Na and P, and high levels of Ni, Cr, Co, Mg and Fe. The second component (a further 13% of the variance) was dominated by total magnesium, the Ca/Mg quotient, and the acetic acid—soluble iron. Plant-available nickel as determined by bioassay of oat plants was also a factor and implied that soils rich in total magnesium tended to have low exchangeable magnesium and vice versa.

Ordination of serpentine sites after PCA analysis by Slingsby and Brown (1977), is shown in Fig. 13.2 and clearly shows the Lizard soils as a distinct group (B). Group C comprises two inland quarries in Lizard Peninsula. Group A shows the Haaf Gruney (HG) and Holyhead (H) soils which like those of Lizard (L), do not carry a characteristic serpentine vegetation. Group D is composed of sedge-grass sites from Coyles of Muick (CM) and Sobul (U9) on Unst, which are distinguishable from other serpentine sites by their higher potassium and phosphorus levels. Group E is a heterogeneous group of Hamar (U), Greenhill (GH) and Coyles of Muick sites. Group F comprises Keen of Hamar debris sites and group G is for the Nikkavord site at Unst characterised by high available nickel levels and a low total Ca/Mg quotient. A map of Unst (Fig. 13.3) is shown below to facilitate understanding of Fig. 13.2. In general, serpentine sites with the most characteristic vegetation occur to the left of Fig. 13.2, whereas those without a characteristic flora are found on the right-hand side. The "characteristic" sites are those where soils most closely resemble unweathered serpentine rock and have the highest nickel content.

Slingsby and Brown (1977) have also suggested that the maritime influence is instrumental to some degree in ameliorating the infertility of serpentine soils. They suggested that sea spray adds nutrients such as sodium and potassium, and has the effect of raising the Ca/Mg quotient by leaching of soluble magnesium salts. This hypothesis is borne out to some extent by the observation that the most maritime Shetland sites (U1, HG1 and HG2) lie well to the right in Fig. 13.3

There will be a further discussion of British serpentine soils under the heading of the individual sites described below.

13.2.2 British Sites with a Characteristic Serpentine Vegetation

General

Spence (1970) has attempted to treat the serpentine vegetation of all Scottish sites as a single unit and has described a number of plant communities, Associations and Subassociations using the system of the northern European phytosociologists. This method is different from the more modern system of Braun-Blanquet as used by Birse (1982) for the same vegetation. In this book, however, the presentation of vast, complicated and confusing phytosociological tables will be avoided as far as possible, though there will be occasions when this cannot be done. In its place, I will use a more empirical method to give some indication of the nature of plant communities on serpentine throughout the world. As regards

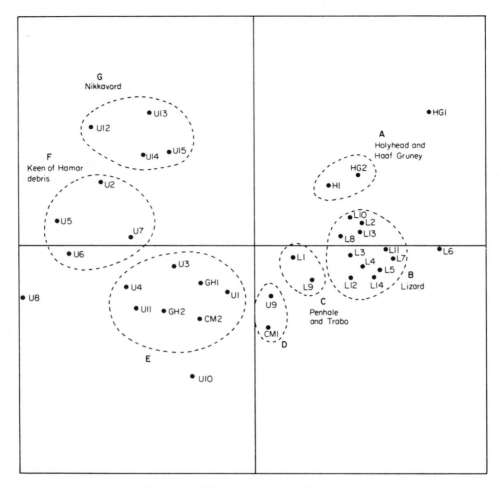

Fig. 13.2 Ordination of British serpentine soils.
Source: Slingsby and Brown (1977).

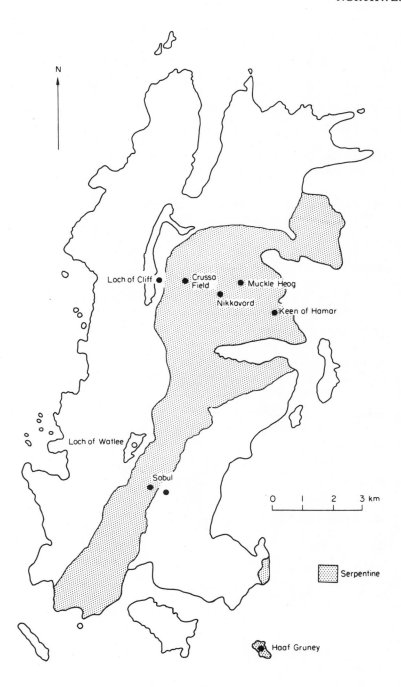

Fig. 13.3 Map of Unst, Shetland, showing serpentine sites.
Source: Slingsby and Brown (1977).

the phytosociology of Scottish serpentine vegetation it will suffice to say that according to Birse (1982), it belongs to the *Violetea calaminariae* class which is represented in Table 13.2. This class is divided into:

A—a Subassociation of the Sileno-Armerietum maritimae metallicolae (1–3),

B—the *Cerastium nigrescens—Armeria maritima* Association (4–6), and

C—the *Lychnis alpina—Armeria maritima* (7–8) Association.

A typical type A Association is found in the Strathdon area of Aberdeenshire. It is an open community on shallow soils covering serpentine outcrops. Frost heave is active

TABLE 13.2   The Phytosociology of British Serpentine Plant Communities

	A			B			C	
Releve #	1	2	3	4	5	6	7	8
Character species of subassociation A								
Cerastium holosteoides	4	3	2				1	2
Cochlearia pyrenaica	1	4	4		4		3	2
Racomitrium lanuginosum	1	2		3		1	5	5
Character species of Association B								
Cerastium nigrescens				2	2	1		
Differentials of Association B								
Arenaria norvegica var. norvegica				1	2	2		
Cardaminopsis petraea				1	1	1		
Character species of Association C								
Lychnis alpina								2
Differential of Association C								
Cherleria sedoides							5	3
Differential of Order Violetalia								
Festuca ovina	6	4	5					
Character species of Class Violetea calaminariae and of Association C								
Minuartia verna	5	5	5					
Companion species								
Festuca rubra	4	5	1	4	4	1	4	4
Agrostis canina subsp. montana	1	4		4	4	4		2
Armeria maritima	2	1		3	1	1		
Plantago maritima				3	3	3		
Silene acaulis				3	1	3		
Anthyllis vulneraria				3	1	1		
Thymus praecox subsp. arcticus				3	3	3		
Deschampsia caespitosa			1				1	
Silene maritima				1	1			
Antennaria dioica				2		1		
Scilla verna					2	2		
Rhinanthus minor				1	1			

A = Sileno-Armerietum maritimae metallicolae Subassociation with *Cochlearia officinalis* (1–3), B = *Cerastium nigrescens—Armeria maritima* Association, C = *Lychnis alpina—Armeria maritima* Association.
NB: numerals refer to relative abundances.
After: Birse (1982).

due to the open nature of the vegetation and the sliding propensity of the material weathered from serpentine.

Although the serpentine vegetation of Unst was originally classified into the A Association by Ernst (1976), Birse (1982) formulated the B Association of *Cerastium nigrescens—Armeria maritima* to describe this vegetation. The serpentine-endemic *C. nigrescens* (considered by Clapham et al. (1981) to be a subspecies of *C. arcticum*, subsp *edmondstonii*) is the character taxon of this Association. It is confined to Keen of Hamar and one other hill on Unst and is the only serpentine-endemic plant confined to Britain.

The small outcrops of serpentine at Meikle Kilrannoch carry vegetation assigned to the *Lychnis alpina—Armeria maritima* Association (C) with *Lychnis alpina* as the character species and *Cherleria sedoides* as the differential.

Lychnis alpina is found at only 2 other sites in the British Isles: on serpentine on the island of Rhum in the Inner Hebrides and at Hobcarton Crag in the English Lake District (Proctor and Johnston, 1977). Although the English site is not on serpentine it appears to be over pyrite mineralization which is not surprising in view of the reputation of this plant as a *kisplante* (pyrite plant) in Scandinavia (Vogt, 1942).

As mentioned above, the only true serpentine plant community is the Violetea calaminariae class with its three Associations. All other plant communities over serpentine in Britain can be fitted into a number of other classes.

Serpentine sites with characteristic serpentine vegetation as defined by Proctor and Woodell (1971) will now be discussed in general terms using the data of Spence (1970). The latter has recognized five community types growing on five Scottish serpentine sites carrying characteristic vegetation. These localities are on the island of Rhum (Ruinsival and Hallival), Unst and Hoo Fell (Shetland), Coyles of Muick, and Meikle Kilrannoch. His five communities are shown in Table 13.3 and comprise the following:

1—Herb-rich submontane sedge-grass-heath of soils of high base status. A sedge grassland develops after grazing.

2—A base-rich *Carex flacca—C. demissa* mire.

3—A base-poor *Schoenus nigricans—Molinia caerulea* mire.

4—Vegetation of base-rich crevices including *Asplenium viride* and *A. adiantum-nigrum*.

5—An *Arenaria norvegica—Cardaminopsis petraea* community on serpentine-derived scree.

It must be emphasized that the above communities do not fit into the Braun-Blanquet system and should not be confused with those reported by Birse (1982) above. The first of the Spence communities is found frequently on Unst and Ruinsival where *Erica cinerea* is a common subdominant. *Juniperus communis*, often found on Rhum, is absent on Unst and rare on Coyles of Muick.

The base-rich *Carex flacca—C. demissa* sedge grassland forms a cropped turf with bare soil visible between the plants. There are some floristic similarities between both of the above communities. The 3 dominants of the sedge grassland (*Carex pulicaris, Festuca vivipara,* and *Agrostis stolonifera*), are constants in the heath community. *Calluna vulgaris,* the main dominant of the heath, is also found in the sedge grassland community.

The mire communities (#2 above) are often dominated by the *Carex flacca—C. demissa* sociation (on Unst and Coyles of Muick) which is found on serpentine in flat-bottomed drainage hollows or along streams. Soils under the community are level and stratified with a thick organic layer overlaying clay.

Under the *Schoenus nigricans—Molinia caerulea* mire there is standing water at the stony soil surface. This community is found typically at Hoo Fell (Shetland).

The plants of the base-rich crevices (#3 above) are noteworthy in that they contain the ferns *Asplenium viride* and *A. adiantum-nigrum* which are common on serpentine. Other species of this community are recorded in Table 13.3.

The plant communities on serpentine scree (#4 above) are the most characteristic of Scottish serpentine sites. Spence (1970) has described the *Arenaria norvegica* (Plate 13.1a)—*Cardaminopsis petraea* sociation which occurs typically on Unst. The dominant taxa (see Table 13.3) are confined to serpentine sites. In order to avoid confusion with the Birse (1982) data, full details of Spence's classification system will not be given. On the island of Rhum, the *Arenaria—Cardaminopsis* community occurs near the summit of Ruinsival and on the Coyles of Muick is found on steep talus slides lying at the base of a series of steep crags. Debris on Meikle Kilrannoch is found on an open area of the summits in which the rich community includes *Armeria maritima, Cerastium holosteoides, Cherleria sedoides, Cochlearia pyrenaica, Festuca ovina, Cardaminopsis petraea, Silene maritima* and *Lychnis alpina* in its only Scottish station apart from Rhum.

TABLE 13.3   Dominant Taxa of Plant Communities on Scottish Serpentine Sites Carrying a Characteristic Serpentine Flora

Sedge-grass-heath	Base-rich mire	Base-poor mire	Base-rich crevices	Scree
Calluna vulgaris	*Carex flacca*	*Carex demissa*	*Asplenium viride*	*Arenaria norvegica*
Erica cinerea	*Agrostis stolonifera*	*Schoenus nigricans*	*Asplenium adiantum-nigrum*	*Cardaminopsis petraea*
Carex pulicaris				
Juniperus communis	*Ranunculus flammula*	*Armeria maritima*	*Draba incana*	*Silene maritima*
			Cystopteris fragilis	
Deschampsia flexuosa	*Carex pulicaris*		*Silene maritima*	
			Avenula pratensis	
Polygala serpyllifolia	*Festuca rubra*		*Cardaminopsis petraea*	

After: Spence (1970)

A useful summary of the dominant and characteristic taxa of these 5 serpentine stations in Scotland has been given by Spence (1970). The taxa are subdivided into basiphile, calciphile, plants on substrates rich in magnesium and sodium, plants on mineral-rich soils, and plants with serpentine-differentiated races. The data are shown in Table 13.4. For a fuller description of serpentine plants growing at various Scottish serpentine sites, the reader is referred to Proctor and Woodell (1971).

The characteristics of serpentine vegetation at various British sites are described below, from various sources including Proctor and Woodell (1971), Spence (1970) and Birse (1982). The numbering of the sites follows Fig. 13.1.

1. **Rhum.** The island of Rhum is dominated by the twin peaks of Ruinsival and Hallival which are composed of mainly ultramafic rocks. A picture of Hallival is shown in Plate 13.2a. Some description of the sedge-grass-heath community dominated by *Calluna vulgaris* and *Racomitrium lanuginosum* moss has already been given above. The scree slopes of Hallival near the summit have about 10% cover and are dominated by *Thymus praecox* subsp. *creticus, Plantago maritima,* and *Festuca* spp.

2. **Unst.** The vegetation of the extensive area of serpentine vegetation on Unst (see Fig. 13.3) has been described by Birse (1982), Proctor and Woodell (1971) and Spence (1957, 1958,

TABLE 13.4   Plants of Scottish Serpentine Outcrops at Shetland, Rhum, Coyles of Muick and Meikle Kilrannoch.

Species	Habitat		
	Scree	Sedge-grass	Mire
BASIPHILES			
Anthyllis vulneraria	2		
Arenaria norvegica	2		
Asplenium viride	4		
A. adiantum-nigrum	4		
Cerastium alpinum	1		
C. nigrescens	1		
Galium verum	1		
Juncus triglumis	2		
Koeleria macrantha	1	1	
Helictotrichon pratense	1		
Lychnis alpina	1		
Polygonum viviparum	1	1	
Rubus saxatilis	2		
Botrychium lunaria		4	
Coeloglossum viride		4	
Schoenus nigricans			2
Carex flacca	2	3	3
Sagina nodosa	1		
Saxifraga hypnoides	1		
CALCIPHILES			
Cystopteris fragilis	4		
Draba incana	3		
Gentianella amarella		2	
Plagiochila asplenoides		1	
MG- OR CA-RICH SUBSTRATES			
Cochlearia scotica	1		
C. pyrenaica	1		
Silene maritima	4		
Armeria maritima	4		
Plantago maritima	2	3	3
MINERAL-RICH SOILS WITH LITTLE PLANT COVER			
Cardaminopsis petraea	4		
Cherleria sedoides	2	1	
Silene acaulis	3	1	
SPECIES WITH SERPENTINE-DIFFERENTIATED RACES			
Cerastium fontanum	2		
Rumex acetosa	1		
Agrostis stolonifera	4	3	3
Silene dioica	1		

N.B. Numbers refer to relative abundance
After: Spence (1970)

1969, 1970). The vegetation is mainly of a closed type though there are several areas of debris associated with bedrock weathering *in situ*. The largest of these barrens is situated on Keen of Hamar (Plate 13.2b) which is also the site of several rare species such as *Cerastium nigrescens* (Plate 13.1b), the only serpentine-endemic plant confined to the British Isles and in this case only to Unst. The closed heath of Keen of Hamar is species-rich and similar to that over ultramafites elsewhere on Shetland.

The extensive serpentine flora of debris on Keen of Hamar has been ascribed by Spence (1957) to edaphic factors (high nickel), physical instability and exposure to wind. Spence and Millar (1963) demonstrated a phosphorus deficiency at this site, Amin (1954) noted that the well-vegetated part of Keen of Hamar was underlain mainly by pyroxene (higher calcium content than most other ultramafites), compared with the dunite bedrock of the barren debris.

3. **Fetlar.** The central part of the island of Fetlar culminating in Vord Hill (159 m) is of serpentine. The vegetation is mainly continuous but there are a few open patches of scree vegetation dominated by *Agrostis stolonifera, Plantago maritima,* and *Thymus praecox* subsp. *creticus.*

4. **Blackwater.** The serpentine outcrop at Blackwater (Banffshire) occupies about 0.5 km² with serpentine protuding out of the peat. There is little debris but the crevices support the serpentine indicator ferns *Asplenium viride* and *A. adiantum-nigrum.* The flatter parts are covered by a heath community.

6. **Greenhill of Strathdon.** The serpentine site at Greenhill (Aberdeenshire) is a hill about 570 m above sea level with an area of about 6 km². The vegetation is the usual sedge-grass-heath community described by Spence (1970). The hill includes an area of scree and debris dominated by *Festuca* spp. and with the appearance of the characteristic serpentine plant, *Minuartia verna.*

7. **Glenkindie.** The serpentine outcrop at Glenkindi (Aberdeenshire) is located on the northeast slope of Milhuie Hill and is covered with a *Molinia-Nardus* grassland or pine forest with an understorey of *Calluna* heath.

8. **Hill of Towanreef.** The serpentine body at Hill of Towanreef (Aberdeenshire) is a hill of 431 m with an area of about 5 km². The dominant vegetation community is heath. The slopes carry debris and the vegetation here is dominated by *Festuca* spp., and *Agrostis canina* with local patches of *Cerastium fontanum.*

10. **Coyles of Muick.** The vegetation of Coyles of Muick (Aberdeenshire) has been studied extensively by Spence (1970). The area is dominated by a series of crags (450–500 m) occupying only about 0.3 km². The serpentine is covered with grassland but there are areas of scree dominated by *Saxifraga hypnoides, Carex flacca, Cardaminopsis petraea, Armeria maritima* and *Festuca* spp.

11. and 12. **Meikle Kilrannoch.** The two adjacent hills at Meikle Kilrannoch (Plate 13.2c) in Angus, are among the most notable serpentine occurrences in the British Isles for a number of reasons. They are the most montane of all the occurrences and are one of only three sites for the occurrence of *Lychnis alpina.* They are also comparatively rich floristically. Typical plants of this site include *Cochlearia pyrenaica* (Plate 13.1d), *Agrostis canina, Armeria maritima* (Plate 13.1c), *Cherleria sedoides* (Plate 13.1d) and *Racomitrium lanuginosum.*

13. **Glendaruel.** The serpentine body at Glendaruel (Argyllshire) comprises a small steep outcrop of coarse rocks. Much of the outcrop is covered with grazed grassland, but there is a rich crevice flora dominated by *Asplenium adiantum-nigrum* closely resembling *A. cuneifolium.* Several calciphilous plants such as *Dryas octopetala. Neckera crispa* and *Porella platyphylla* have been recorded at the southern end of the outcrop which is traversed by a band of dolomite.

13.2.3 British Sites with Non-characteristic Serpentine Vegetation

Several British serpentine sites do not carry the type of vegetation usually associated with ultramafites. There are several reasons for this, and the first of these is the presence of surficial deposits not of serpentine origin (e.g., Lizard Peninsula). A second factor is the lack of debris, and the third is a less unfavourable Ca/Mg quotient in the soils. Some of these atypical sites will now be described. Numbering is as in Fig. 13.1.

2. **Haaf Gruney.** The islet of Haaf Gruney in Shetland (Fig. 13.2) has a surface area of only 0.25 km² and is completely overlain with serpentine. The vegetation is mainly pasture though there is an extensive community of *Plantago maritima* and *P. coronopus* (Slingsby and Brown, 1977) near the high-water mark. It is the most maritime of all the serpentine outcrops in Britain, a reason given by these authors (see above) for its non-characteristic vegetation.

4. **Glen Urquhart.** The serpentine outcrop at Glen Urquhart (Inverness-shire) is covered with a heath community indistinguishable from its surroundings. There is hardly any debris and the only recognizable serpentine feature of the vegetation is the presence of *Asplenium viride* in rock crevices.

9. **Beauty Hill.** Beauty Hill (Aberdeenshire) is covered almost entirely by glacial drift which effectively isolated the flora from the serpentinitic bedrock. Where erosion has produced small patches of debris, *Plantago maritima* can be found.

14. and 15. **Loch Lomond.** A band of serpentine crosses Loch Lomond (Dunbartonshire) and outcrops on both banks and on the Isle of Inchcailloch. On the east bank there is no serpentine vegetation, but on the west bank there is some covering of heath with slight features of a serpentine community.

16–18. **Girvan.** The Girvan area has several outcrops of serpentine but since there is an extensive covering of glacial drift, the vegetation is not typically serpentinic. Even where the drift is minimal in depth or even absent, there are still few signs of a characteristic serpentine flora. This may be due to the generally favourable Ca/Mg quotient which is appreciably higher than that of most other serpentine occurrences in Britain. The predominant vegetation of the area is dry grassland.

19. **The Lizard Peninsula.** The Lizard Peninsula (Cornwall) is the largest area of contiguous ultramafic rocks in the United Kingdom. These rocks occupy about 50 km². The geology of the area is shown in Fig. 13.4. The first detailed account of the flora of this area was given by Coombe and Frost (1956a). They recognized four major heath Associations as follows:

1—*Festuca ovina*—*Calluna vulgaris* ("rock heath") in shallow soil pockets among serpentine rocks.

2—*Erica vagans*—*Ulex europaeus* ("mixed heath") on well-drained brown earth soils.

3—*Erica vagans*—*Schoenus* spp. heath ("tall heath") in shallow valleys and depressions on seasonally-waterlogged soils.

4—*Agrostis setacea* ("short heath") on level but raised parts of the plateau.

Although the above vegetation is not typically serpentinitic, it does contain the unusual coexistence of basicolous and calcifuge taxa.

Further studies on the Cornish serpentine flora have been carried out by Marrs and Proctor (1978, 1979). In the earlier paper, the authors carried out normal and inverse association analysis (Williams and Lambert, 1959, 1961) using presence/absence data for all species found. They classified the plants into 19 groups (A–S) as shown in Table 13.5. The percentage representation of each species group at each of 13 sites is shown in Table 13.6. This table clearly shows groups corresponding with those proposed by Coombe and Frost (1956a).

In a later ecological study of the vegetation of the Lizard Peninsula, Marrs and

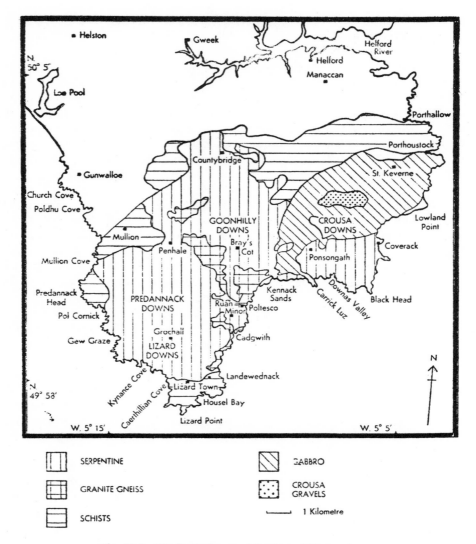

Fig. 13.4   Geological map of the Lizard Peninsula.
Source: Coombe and Frost (1956a).

Proctor (1979) showed that the heath types originally described by Coombe and Frost (1956a) could also be recognized by consideration of their dominant species which were as follows:

Rock heath—*Calluna vulgaris* and *Festuca ovina*.

Mixed heath—*Erica vagans* and *Ulex europaeus*.

Tall heath—*Erica vagans*, *Molinia caerulea* and *Schoenus nigricans*.

Short heath—*Agrostis setacea*, *Calluna vulgaris*, *Erica cinerea*, *E. tetralix*, *Molinia caerulea* and *Ulex europaeus*.

There are no truly endemic species growing over serpentine in the Lizard Peninsula, however the rare *Erica vagans* is nearly restricted to serpentine, and there is a morphological form of *Minuartia verna*, which, according to Clapham et al. (1962) is smaller, more glaucous and ciliate than normal forms of this taxon. Some taxonomists have given it subspecific status by calling it *M. verna* subsp. *gerardi* (Plate 13.4a).

TABLE 13.5 Species-groups of Cornish Serpentine Vegetation as Determined by Inverse Association Analysis

A — *Lecidea crustulata, Cladonia* spp.

B — *Pedicularis sylvatica, Cladonia impexa*

C — *Erica cinerea*

D — *Ulex gallii, Agrostis setacea, Erica tetralix, Molinia caerulea, Carex panicea*

E — *Dactylorhiza maculata, Potentilla erecta*

F — *Salix repens, Polygala serpyllifolia, Hypnum cupressiforme, Campylopus flexuosus*

G — *Schoenus nigricans, Succisia pratensis, Campylium stellatum, Anagallis tenella, Carex pulicaris*

H — *Sanguisorba officinalis*

I — *Viola riviniana, Genista anglica*

J — *Riccardia sinuata, Fissidens adianthoides, Carex hostiana, Hypericum humifusum, Juncus acutiflorus, Drepanocladus revolvens, Scorpidium scorpioides*

K — *Erica vagans, Festuca ovina, Carex flacca, Serratula tinctoria*

L — *Ulex europaeus, Betonica officinalis, Plantago maritime*

M — *Koeleria macrantha, Thymus praecox subsp. arcticus, Scilla verna, Genista tinctoria*

N — *Carex caryophyllea, Filipendula vulgaris*

O — *Agrostis stolonifera, Weisia microstoma, Chrysanthemum leucanthemum, Sieglingia decumbens*

P — *Genista pilosa, Hypochoeris maculata, Anthoxanthum odoratum, Frullania tamarisci, Leontodon taraxacoides*

Q — *Galium verum, Aira caryophyllea, Anthyllis vulneraria, Armeria maritima, Anagallis arvensis, Cerastium atrovirens*

R — *Lotus corniculatus, Hypochoeris radicata*

S — *Festuca rubra, Plantago lanceolata, Dactylis glomerata*

Source: Marrs and Proctor (1978)

TABLE 13.6   Percentage Representation of the Plant Groups in Table 13.5 in Four Types of Heath over the Cornish Serpentines. The Groups are Derived from Inverse Association Analysis.

| Site No. | 2 | 6 | 8 | 9 | 13 | 3 | 1 | 7 | 10 | 4 | 12 | 5 | 11 |
Heath type	SH	SH	SH	SH	SH	T/S	TH	TH	TH	MH	MH	RH	RH
Species group					Percentage representation								
A	37	50	45	60		27						15	5
B	12	50	50	25		10			15	12			
C	100	100	100	100	90	45			10	75	20	65	10
D	99	100	100	96	70	100	49	48	48	11	52		
E	22	60	35	75	10	35	32	45	40	37	45		
F	24	30	47	60	2	50	6	7	25	20	12	12	5
G		2		10		2	60	68	94	41	20		
H							20	80	10	15	10		
I	5	5	5				35	10	5	12	5	5	10
J							1	1	53	1	3		
K	1		5	20		50	75	65	90	60	42	35	12
L		3				3			7	63	53	12	10
M				2			1	5		79	15	79	25
N										2	35	62	
O							1			11	5	52	30
P										9	6	27	10
Q											3	38	37
R					10						10	45	40
S											7	73	83

SH = short heath, T/S mixed tall and short heath, TH = tall heath, MH = mixed heath, RH = rock heath.
Source: Marrs and Proctor (1978)

13.2.4 Some Characteristics of the British Serpentine Flora

Endemism and Disjunction

Serpentine floras typically contain endemic species and taxa with disjunct distributions. This has already been shown in Chapter 11 for the Californian flora with about 50 endemics and for the flora of the eastern seaboard of North America where some notable disjunctions occur. Endemism and disjunction in the British serpentine flora have been discussed by Proctor and Woodell (1971). The only distinct taxon endemic to British serpentines is *Cerastium nigrescens* from Keen of Hamar on Unst. It is, however, very closely related to *C. arcticum* (Clapham et al. 1962) and some authorities believe that the former is distinct only at the subspecific level.

A distinct form of *Plantago maritima* also exists on Unst. Drùce (1922) named it as a separate species *P. edmondstonii*. However, intermediates exist between *P. maritima* and the type of *P. edmondstonii* which tends to relegate to at most varietal status.

The small form of *Minuartia verna* (subsp. *gerardi*) already mentioned, is another example of possible endemism.

A number of disjunctions (80 km from the nearest non-serpentine locality) have been recorded by Proctor and Woodell (1971). These are given in Table 13.7.

Other features of British serpentine plants

The adjacent occurrence of basicolous and calcifuge plants on British serpentines is not unusual for many types of substrate. Taxa known to be calcifuge (*Blechnum spicant* and *Melampyrum pratense*) are always absent over serpentine, but strongly calcifuge plants such as *Calluna vulgaris* and *Empetrum* spp. are common over ultramafites, particularly in the serpentine heaths of the Lizard Peninsula.

It has been proposed by Rune (1953) that Fennoscandian serpentine floras are dominated by the Caryophyllaceae. This thesis was examined by Proctor and Woodell (1971) who noted that some members of the Caryophyllaceae such as *Minuartia verna*, *Lychnis alpina* and *Cerastium nigrescens* are common colonisers of serpentine debris. They are however conspicuous rather than dominant as their percentage of the total cover is usually around 1%.

TABLE 13.7 Disjunctions in British Serpentine Plants

Species	Serpentine site	Nearest non-serpentine site
Arenaria norvegica	Unst	Sutherland
Asplenium viride	Unst	Sutherland
Cardaminopsis petraea	Unst and Fetlar	Sutherland
Cerastium nigrescens	Unst	endemic
Lychnis alpina	Meikle Kilrannoch	Cumberland
Minuartia rubella	Unst (extinct)	Perthshire
M. verna	Lizard Peninsula	Somerset

Source: Proctor and Woodell (1971)

13.2.5 Biogeochemical Studies on British Serpentine Floras

Biogeochemical studies on plants are often undertaken with a view to carrying out biogeochemical prospecting for minerals (Brooks, 1983). However in Britain, where serpentine occurrences have been thoroughly recorded and their zones of mineralization well documented, biogeochemical prospecting over ultramafites is scarcely a viable option.

Studies on the chemical composition of British serpentine plants have been directed mainly towards an understanding of the physiological processes involved in element uptake by selected taxa (see Chapter 4), or towards experiments designed to find crops which can be grown on serpentine (see Chapter 5).

Johnston and Proctor (1979) determined the concentrations of Ca, Co, Cr, Fe, Mg, Ni, P and K in 9 plant species from the Lime Hill serpentine outcrop in Scotland. The mean nickel contents were relatively constant and ranged from 24 μg/g in dried leaves of *Teucrium scordonia* to 97 μg/g in *Asplenium trichomanes*. Chromium levels varied from 49 to 100 μg/g respectively. None of the plants showed any tendency to hyperaccumulate nickel (see Chapter 8). This lack of hyperaccumulation is typical of plant species from previously-glaciated parts of the globe and is clearly a character which takes a considerable time to develop. A similar pattern of element uptake was obtained by Johnston and Proctor (1977) for plants growing on serpentine at Hill of Towanreef. Maximum nickel values in phanerogams were 253 μg/g in dried leaves of *Cochlearia officinalis* and 319 μg/g in *Viola lutea*. The corresponding chromium levels were 67 and 173 μg/g.

Perhaps one of the most detailed biogeochemical surveys carried out in Britain is the work by Shewry and Peterson (1975, 1976) who determined the chemical composition of plants and soils from ultramafic occurrences in Shetland and Greenhill. The plant data are shown in Table 13.8. Nickel concentrations were about the same as reported by Johnston and Proctor (1971). The serpentinicolous *Cerastium nigrescens* contained almost the highest nickel content of all the plants studied. This behaviour is typical of serpentine-endemic plants. For example the nickel content of serpentine-endemic *Pimelea suteri* from New Zealand is the highest for any other taxon recorded from the Dun Mountain serpentine outcrop (Lee et al. 1975). Similarly, hyperaccumulators of nickel (> 1000 μg/g in dried

TABLE 13.8 Nickel and Chromium (μg/g dry weight) in Plants from Serpentine Sites in Scotland and Shetland.

Species	1 Ni	1 Cr	1 Ca/Mg	2 Ni	2 Cr	2 Ca/Mg	3 Ni	3 Cr	3 Ca/Mg	4 Ni	4 Cr	4 Ca/Mg	5 Ni	5 Cr
Agrostis stolonifera	22	4	0.30	—	—	0.47	—	—	—	—	—	—	—	—
Armeria maritima	52	8	0.30	68	7	0.68	160	12	0.25	—	—	—	2	1
Calluna vulgaris	80	21	0.57	—	—	—	41	15	0.89	96	12	0.45	—	—
Cerastium fontanum	—	—	—	—	—	—	—	—	—	83	9	0.06	—	—
*C. nigrescens**	84	70	—	—	—	0.11	—	—	—	—	—	—	—	—
Festuca ovina	—	—	—	—	—	—	—	—	—	39	6	0.38	—	—
F. rubra	—	—	—	15	3	0.50	24	5	0.60	—	—	—	—	—
F. vivipara	15	2	0.41	—	—	—	—	—	—	—	—	—	—	—
Juncus articulatus	30	5	0.80	—	—	—	36	4	0.12	—	—	—	—	—
Plantago maritima	49	5	0.23	—	—	—	—	—	—	—	—	—	1	0.30
Rubus saxatilis	95	2	0.29	—	—	—	—	—	—	—	—	—	—	—
Silene acaulis	—	—	—	—	—	—	—	—	—	—	—	—	—	—
Silene maritima	—	—	—	20	4	0.60	—	—	—	—	—	—	1	0.50
Succisa pratensis	—	—	—	—	—	—	25	3	0.42	—	—	—	—	—
Thymus praecox subsp. *arcticus*	42	5	1.08	68	8	0.38	—	—	—	—	—	—	3	2

*serpentine endemic

Ca/Mg quotients are in moles

Original data were on ash weight basis and have been converted to dry weight using factor of 0.1

1 = Hamar summit, Unst
2 = Hamar slope, Unst
3 = Dalepark, Keen of Hamar
4 = Greenhill, Aberdeenshire
5 = non-serpentine station at Silvadale, Unst.

After: Shewry and Peterson (1975, 1976)

leaves—see Chapter 8) are invariably colonisers of serpentine and are in most cases endemic to this type of substrate.

There was no evidence of inordinate uptake of chromium by any of the species studied by Shewry and Peterson (1976). This was to be expected in view of the low concentration of exchangeable chromium in the soil. It is also known that Ca/Mg quotients in serpentine-endemic plants tend to be lower than those of non-serpentine taxa (see Chapter 4). This is because serpentine plants tolerate a low calcium and high magnesium content in the soil. From the data of Shewry and Peterson (1975) shown in Table 13.8, the plants with the lower Ca/Mg quotients include the serpentine-endemic *Cerastium nigrescens* from Keen of Hamar. *Bodenvag* species such as *Calluna vulgaris* invariably had higher Ca/Mg quotients.

13.3 NORWAY

13.3.1 Introduction

Ultramafic outcrops in Norway occur at various sites along the Caledonides mountain chain (Fig. 13.5), which was once conterminous with the Appalachians. The most extensive outcrops occur in the Sunnmøre district (station 19 in Fig. 13.5) and in northern Norway just north of 70° latitude (stations 22–24). Further outcrops occur on the islands of Leka (station 20) and Rødøn (station 21).

The serpentine flora of Norway does not differ very greatly from that of Sweden (see Section 13.4 below) and is mainly derived from the mountain flora of the Caledonides (Scandes). The climate of Norway is, however, much milder than comparable latitudes in Sweden and there is therefore a number of floral elements characteristic of the milder climate of Central Europe. An example of this is the serpentine indicator fern *Asplenium adulterinum* which is found along with other serpentinicolous ferns such as *A. adiantum-nigrum*, *A. trichomanes* and *A. viride*. *A. adulterinum* grows as far north as the island of Rødøn just south of the Arctic Circle.

Several Norwegian species are also common to Scotland, Sweden and Finland. An example of this is *Arabis petraea* found at the Sunnmøre serpentine outcrop. It grows elsewhere in Fennoscandia wherever competition is low and is probably a serpentine relic (palaeoendemic). Other plants common to serpentine in Fennoscandia are *Asplenium viride*, *Lychnis alpina* subsp. *serpentinicola* and *Molinia caerulea*.

There has already been some mention of *Lychnis alpina* in Fennoscandia and Scotland. Though rare in Britain, this taxon is widespread on serpentine and other soils in Fennoscandia. Its occurrence has been linked with the presence of sulphide minerals in the substrate. Vogt (1942) listed its Norwegian distribution and noted its occurrence at the Røros copper deposits and at various serpentine sites such as those at Leka, Flakstad and Alvdal. He suggested that its distribution was related to sites with lack of competition from more vigorous species.

Before detailing the flora of specific serpentine areas in Norway, some mention should be made of the rare *Arenaria humifusa* which is a close relation of *A. norvegica*, itself a coloniser of serpentine. *A. humifusa* is a panarctic plant with a disjunct occurrence in the Gaspé Peninsula of southeast Quebec (see Chapter 11). In Fennoscandia, its occurrence is mainly in coastal districts at low altitude (Rune, 1954) and it cannot be classified as an alpine plant. The distribution of *A. humifusa* in Norway is shown in Fig. 13.6. It extends as far south as 66° N where it is found only on serpentine. Further north it is also found on calcareous rocks. This is again an example of a palaeoendemic species which colonised Fennoscandia after the retreat of the ice, but retreated to serpentine in the south due to competitive pressure from more vigorous later colonisers.

The flora of individual serpentine sites in Norway will now be described.

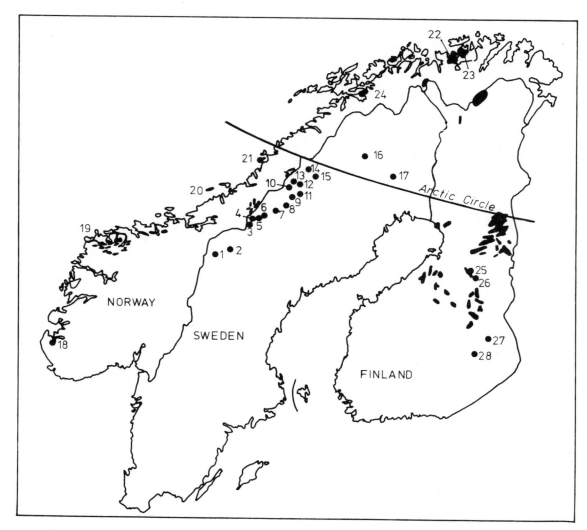

Fig. 13.5   Map of Fennoscandia showing serpentine occurrences. 1—Handöl, 2—Kall, 3—Muruhatten, 4—Junstern, 5—Lake Blasjön, 6—Lake Värgaren, 7—N. Burgfjällen, 8—Graipesvare, 9—Kittelfjäll, 10—Gränssjö, 11—Rönnbäck, 12—Tärna, 13—S. Storfjällen, 14—Lake Altsvattnet, 15—Ammarfjällen, 16—Kvikkjokk, 17—Gällivare, 18—Høle, 19—Sunnmøre, 20—Leka, 21—Rødøn, 22—Stjernøy, 23 Seiland, 24—Rana, 25—Paltamo, 26—Sotkamo, 27 Juuka, 28—Kaavi.

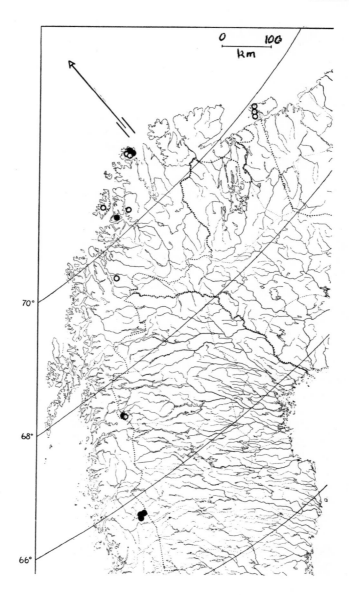

Fig. 13.6   Distribution of *Arenaria humifusa* in Norway on serpentine (solid dots) and on calcareous rocks (open circles).
Source: Rune (1954).

13.3.2 Norwegian Serpentine Plants

Sunnmøre

Sunnmøre (station 19 in Fig. 13.5) has the most extensive grouping of serpentine outcrops in Norway, though these are mainly quite small and in total area are probably less than those in the far north near Stjernøy. The serpentine flora is extremely rich due to the mild climate and was first recognised by Dahl (1912). In a very detailed study, Bjørlykke (1938) recorded the presence of 289 species growing on serpentine at one or more of the 30 stations in the region. A map of the area is shown in Fig. 13.7. This is in contrast to the discovery of only 48 phanerogams by Rune (1953) in his study of the flora of Swedish serpentines. Lack of space precludes a complete listing of Bjørlykke's data, but the more important serpentine plants growing at Sunnmøre are tabulated in Table 13.9. This list includes all of the serpentinicolous plants including *Arabis Petraea* (see above) which is confined to serpentine at Sunnmøre though it is found on calcareous rocks further north. It often accompanies *Lychnis alpina*. Various species of *Asplenium* are found at Sunnmøre including *A. adulterinum* which grew at 10 of the stations. A hybrid form with *A. viride* was also found at 7 stations, all of which carried *A. adulterinum* also. *A. viride* is even more abundant at Sunnmøre and is perhaps the most characteristic of all plants found on serpentine, although it is not endemic to this rock type.

Asplenium adiantum-nigrum is a common serpentine fern found in North America and throughout Northwest Europe. It is very variable in form and has sometimes been subdivided into subspecies such as subsp. *cuneifolium*.

Cerastium alpinum is another characteristic serpentine plant found at Sunnmøre. Kotilainen and Seivala (1954) have described a serpentinicolous form of *C. alpinum* which they named as *C. alpinum* var. *nordhagenii*.

The only tree of any size growing on serpentine at Sunnmøre is *Pinus sylvestris* found at 7 of the 30 stations. *Silene maritima* is another serpentinicolous species found also over ultramafites in Scotland. It was found at 4 of the Sunnmøre sites.

Bjørlykke (1938) recorded the presence of *Rumex acetosa* at Sunnmøre. This is normally a *bodenvag* species but he failed to notice that some of the specimens collected by him were in fact a serpentine-endemic subspecies named subsp. *serpentinicola* by Nordhagen (1966). This is one of the few serpentine-endemic plants in Norway and has been recorded at 6 stations in southern Norway. It grows only on dry serpentine scree with full insolation.

Bjørlykke (1938) has recognised 3 plant communities over serpentine at Sunnmøre. These are as follows:

1—Ultramafic rocky outcrops in unweathered rocks and crevices. Constant species are the following: *Anthoxanthum odoratum, Asplenium viride, A. adulterinum, Campanula rotundifolia, Deschampsia flexuosa, Euphrasia officinalis, Festuca rubra, Melica nutans,* and *Molinia caerulea.*
Common species not found at all stations are: *Agrostis capillaris, Carex panicea, C. pulicaris, Cerastium alpinum, C. caespitosum, Festuca vivipara, Juncus trifidus, Nardus stricta, Rubus saxatilis, Sagina procumbens, Selaginella selaginoides, Danthonia decumbens, Silene acaulis, S. rupestris,* and *Solidago virgaurea.*

2—Serpentine scree and talus. These are poorly vegetated especially on steep terrain and the plants show typical signs of nutrient deficiencies. Common plants are: *Agrostis capillaris, Anthoxanthum odoratum, Arabis petraea, Asplenium viride, Cerastium alpinum, Deschampsia caespitosa, D. flexuosa, Festuca rubra, F. vivipara, Juncus trifidus, Lychnis alpina,* and *Silene vulgaris.*

3—Pine forests—Typical localities are at Alkmklovdalen, Bjørkedalen, Rødbergvik and Onilsafeltet. The ground storey depends on the degree of openness of the canopy. The

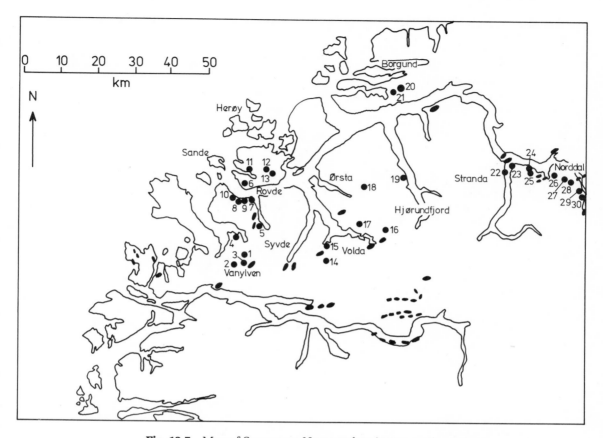

Fig. 13.7 Map of Sunnmøre, Norway showing serpentine outcrops.

following ferns, shrubs and herbs are found in these more open areas: *Agrostis capillaris, Anthoxanthum odoratum, Calluna vulgaris, Campanula rotundifolia, Carex panicea, C. pilulifera, C. stellulata, Deschampsia caespitosa, D. flexuosa, Dryopteris linnaeana, Empetrum nigrum, Eupteris aquilina, Festuca rubra, Helleborine atropurpurea, Juniperus communis, Linnaea borealis, Lotus corniculatus, Luzula campestris, L. pilosa, Lycopodium annotinum, Melampyrum pratense, M. sylvaticum, Melica nutans, Molinia caerulea, Oxalis acetosella, Potentilla erecta, Pyrola minor, P. secunda, P. uniflora, Silene vulgaris, Solidago virgaurea, Succisa pratensis, Trientalis europaea, Vaccinium myrtillus, V. uliginosum, V. vitis-idaea, Veronica officinalis, Viola canina, V. riviniana.*

Rødøn Island

Rødøn Island is a rocky islet in Nordland county (66° N—station 21 in Fig. 13.5). Rune (1953) has prepared brief notes on the vegetation of this serpentine site in which he recorded the dominance of *Molinea caerulea*, and *Racomitrium lanuginosum*, which with *Lotus corniculatus* and *Polygala vulgaris* form a richly-coloured pattern in the uniform vegetation mat. A few species such as *Asplenium viride, M. caerulea, Lychnis alpina* subsp. *serpentinicola, Cerastium alpinum* and *R. lanuginosum* are also found on Swedish serpentine sites.

Rana

Rana (station 24 in Fig. 13.5) is in northern Norway and is a source of nickel mineralization which has been mined in the past, and consists of pyrrhotite and pendlandite

TABLE 13.9   List of Characteristic Plants found at 30 stations on Serpentine at Sunnmøre, Norway.

Species	Reference numbers of stations at which found
Agrostis capillaris	1-3, 5, 7, 8, 11, 14, 16, 19-21, 24-27, 30
*Anthoxanthum odoratum	1-8, 11-28, 30
*Arabis petraea	1-3, 12, 14, 16, 20, 27, 29
*Asplenium adiantum-nigrum	1, 3, 11, 13-15, 22, 23, 26
*A. adulterinum	14, 15, 21-27, 29
*A. viride	1-20, 23, 24, 26-30
Calluna vulgaris	1-8, 10-30
*Campanula rotundifolia	1-30
Carex panicea	1-8, 11-14, 16, 20, 22, 23, 29
C. pilulifera	1-5, 7, 8, 10-27, 29
C. pulicaris	1-8, 10-14, 16-18, 20, 23, 24, 29
C. stellulata	1-4, 7, 8, 13, 14, 16, 20, 23, 28
*Cerastium alpinum	1-4, 9, 14, 16, 20, 22, 23, 26-30
C. caespitosum	1, 2, 4, 5, 7, 8, 11-14, 17-21, 24, 26, 28, 29
Danthonia decumbens	1-14, 20, 23, 26, 27
Deschampsia caespitosa	1-5, 7, 8, 12-14, 17, 19, 22, 23, 26, 27, 29
*D. flexuosa	1-30
Dryopteris linnaeana	1-5, 7, 8, 11-14, 16, 20, 23, 26, 27, 29
Empetrum nigrum	1-30
Eupteris aquilina	1, 14, 25, 29
*Festuca rubra	1-30
F. vivipara	1-5, 7-9, 11-14, 16, 19, 21, 23, 26, 27, 29
Helleborine atropurpurea	1, 14, 23, 29
Juncus trifidus	1-4, 6-14, 16, 19, 20, 26, 27
Juniperus communis	1-5, 7, 8, 10-14, 16, 20, 26, 27
Linnaea borealis	1, 2, 8, 12, 14, 20, 27, 29
Lotus corniculatus	1-6, 8, 11-27, 29
Luzula campestris	1-4, 6-8, 11-14, 17-20, 23-27, 29
L. pilosa	1, 3-5, 8, 13, 14, 23, 24, 26, 27, 30
*Lychnis alpina	1-3, 14, 16, 17, 19, 23, 24, 27-30
Lycopodium annotinum	1-3, 9, 13, 14, 16, 23, 27, 29
Melampyrum pratense	1-3, 5, 7, 8, 11-14, 17, 18, 20, 22-24, 26, 27, 29
M. sylvaticum	1, 3, 11, 12, 14, 18, 23, 24, 26, 27, 29
*Melica nutans	1-5, 7, 8, 10-9
*Molinia caerulea	1-5, 7, 8, 10-15, 17-27, 29
Nardus stricta	1-5, 7-9, 12-14, 16-20, 22-30
Oxalis acetosella	1-14, 16-20, 22-24, 26, 27, 29
Potentilla erecta	1-8, 10-14, 16-27, 29
Pyrola minor	1, 3, 8, 14, 29
P. uniflora	1, 14, 23, 29
Rubus saxatilis	1-5, 7, 8, 11-14, 17, 19, 20, 22-26, 29
Rumex acetosa	1-6, 11, 14, 17, 20, 21, 26, 27
Sagina procumbens	1-4, 6, 9, 11-14, 16, 18-24, 26, 27, 29
Selaginella selaginoides	1-14, 16-30
Silene acaulis	1-4, 7-10, 12, 16, 19, 27, 28, 30
*S. maritima	3, 5, 23, 28
S. rupestris	1-4, 12, 14, 16, 23, 26, 27, 29, 30
S. vulgaris	1-6, 11, 13, 14, 17-19, 22-27, 29, 30
Solidago virgaurea	1-6, 8, 10, 11, 13, 14, 17-19, 21-30
Succisia pratensis	1-6, 8, 11-14, 20, 26, 27, 29
Trientalis europaea	1-3, 8, 11, 12, 14, 20-24, 26, 27, 29
Vaccinium myrtillus	1-5, 7, 8, 11-14, 18-30

Species	Reference numbers of stations at which found
V. uliginosum	1-5, 8, 10-15, 18-20, 22-30
V. vitis-idaea	1-7, 9, 11-20, 22-30
Veronica officinalis	1, 2, 4, 5, 8, 10, 13, 14, 26, 27
Viola canina	1-3, 6, 11-14, 17, 22-24, 26, 27, 29

*confined to serpentine in the Sunnmøre area.

1—Almklovdalfeltet	2—Sundalsfeltet	3—Raudnausane
4—Vikfeltet	5—Tagsetnakken	6—Raudgrøte, Rovde
7—Flana	8—Sendeberget	9—Bjørlykkehornet
10—Vagan	11—Brandalsfeltet	12—Raudgrøte, Herøy
13—Raudskar	14—Bjørkedalen	15—Straumshamm
16—Norddalsseter	17—Ullelandsfeltet	18—Follestad
19—Gjøthaugen	20—Emblemsfjellet	21—Raudberget
22—Oksaugli	23—Rødbergvik	24—Ytterdal 1
25—Ytterdal 2	26—Fagervollfeltet	27—Raudnuten
28—Kalskaret	29—Onilsafeltet	30—Raudhaugane

After: Bjørlykke (1938)

disseminated in peridotite. The soils contain about 8500 μg/g nickel and 200 μg/g copper. The ore is covered with several metres of glacial till. The vegetation has been described by Lag and Bølviken (1977) and consists mainly of *Betula pubescens* and *Vaccinium* spp. In hollows where the nickel content is highest, local herbs predominate at the expense of shrubs.

Høle

The ultramafic deposit at Høle near Stavanger (station 18 in Fig. 13.5) has already been mentioned in Chapter 4. It is an unusual occurrence because it is a region of magnesium silicate mineralization without the accompanying high levels of chromium and nickel normally found with ultramafic rocks. It does however carry a flora which physiognomically is typically serpentine. A general view of the vegetation is given in Plate 13.3.

The vegetation of Høle was studied by Jørgensen (1974). As the area contains two quarry dumps of known age, it was an ideal natural laboratory for studying vegetation successions. The most common pioneer species were *Festuca ovina* and *Saxifraga aizoides*.

Despite the physiognomic similarity between this vegetation and serpentine floras, few taxa colonising the dumps were typical of serpentine communities elsewhere in Norway except in the case of *Euphrasia micrantha* and *Juniperus communis*.

13.4 SWEDEN

13.4.1 Swedish Serpentine Outcrops

The broad tectonic framework of the ultramafic occurrences in Fennoscandia has already been described earlier in this chapter. A brief description of serpentine outcrops in the Caledonides is contained in the monumental work by Rune (1953) on the serpentine flora of Sweden. The outcrops are of Ordovician age and are probably the oldest of the instrusions in the Caledonides. In Sweden they occur in N. Jämtland (Frostviken), in South Lapland from 64–66° N, and in two other localities (Kvikkjokk and Gällivare) in Central Lapland north of the Arctic Circle. In the west outcrops are largely phyllitic in form, and in the east are highly metamorphic. They occur as oval or lenticular outcrops ranging in length from a few metres to several kilometres and are usually very narrow. Because they are not readily weathered, the outcrops are often seen as knobs or reefs above the surrounding country rocks. They occur at varying altitudes from 400–1400 m. Their appearance is invariably barren even when they are below the tree line. They are easily recognisable from the reddish-yellow tints of their weathered surfaces.

During his investigation of the serpentine occurrences of Sweden, Rune (1953) visited almost all of the significant outcrops in Sweden. These are shown in Fig. 13.5 and are as follows: 1—Handöl, 2—Kall, 3—Muruhatten, 4—Junstern, 5—Bläsjön, 6—L. Värgaren, 7—Burgfjällen, 8—Graipesvare, 9—Kittelfjäll, 10—Gränssjö, 11—Rönnbäck, 12—Tärna, 13—S. Storfjällen, 14—L. Altsvattnet, 15—Ammarfjällen, 16—Kvikksjokk, 17—Gällivare.

It may be appropriate to translate some of the Swedish and Lapp names: fjäll = high mountain (cf. Eng. "fell"), berget = mountain, vare = high mountain, sjön = lake, tjärn = tarn, jaure = lake.

13.4.2 A General Overview of Swedish Serpentine Vegetation

It will be quite out of the question to attempt to cover in a few pages the extensive work by Rune (1953) on the serpentine vegetation of Sweden. He has however summarized the ecology and floristics of this flora at 31 sites of 9 of the districts shown in Fig. 13.5. The ecological data are shown in Table 13.10 and the distribution of the flora is shown in Table 13.11. Although the floras of all of the serpentine sites are superficially similar, they are not sufficiently homogeneous to classify them within a single phytogeographical unit. Only a few serpentinicolous plants occur at all or most of the sites, but examples of such a distribution are *Lychnis alpina* and *Asplenium viride*.

Plates 13.2d and 13.4b show typical serpentine barrens at Junsternklumpen (site #4 in Fig. 13.5) in Sweden.

TABLE 13.10   Ecological Data for Swedish Serpentine Sites. Regional Numbers are as in Fig. 13.5.

| | | Ecological characteristic | | | | | | | | | | | |
Reg.	Station	A	B	C	D	E	F	G	H	I	J	K	L	M
3	1	600	S	30	0	s	25	0	0	d	—	65	0.02	45
5	2	800	L	0	+	s	15	0	0	d	12	71	0.00	55
5	3	800	L	0	+	s	20	0	0	d	11	72	0.00	45
7	4	900	E	10	+	sg	20	0	0	n	10	67	0.00	30
7	5	900	L	0	+	s	20	0	0	vd	0.8	66	0.00	30
7	6	900	N	10	0	s	30	5	25	n	—	65	0.06	90
7	7	900	N	30	+	s	20	3	25	n	—	65	0.05	55
7	8	900	L	0	+	s	10	0	0	d	—	—	—	—
7	9	900	S	30	+	s	20	0	0	d	—	—	—	—
7	10	900	S	20	+	s	30	0	0	d	—	68	0.03	50
7	11	700	L	0	+	s	15	0	0	d	—	68	0.03	35
8	12	900	L	0	+	s	20	2	25	d	0.6	67	—	—
8	13	1000	N	10	+	s	10	0	0	d	1	68	0.03	45
8	14	1000	E	10	+	sg	30	0	0	d	14	75	0.01	45
8	15	900	W	10	+	sg	40	3	25	n	3.7	75	0.01	45
8	16	1100	L	0	+	s	10	0	0	d	—	63	0.02	60
9	17	900	L	0	+	s	20	0	0	d	—	63	0.07	65
9	18	900	L	0	+	s	20	0	0	d	—	—	—	—
9	19	900	L	0	+	s	20	0	0	d	—	—	—	—
9	20	900	S	20	+	s	40	0	0	d	—	62	0.03	63
10	21	800	S	10	+	sg	40	0	0	d	—	71	0.01	75
11	22	400	L	0	+	s	10	3	25	d	—	72	0.05	65
11	23	400	L	0	+	s	20	0	0	d	—	—	—	—
11	24	400	L	0	+	s	20	0	0	d	—	—	—	—

		Ecological characteristic												
Reg.	Station	A	B	C	D	E	F	G	H	I	J	K	L	M
11	25	400	L	0	+	s	20	0	0	d	—	—	—	—
11	26	400	L	0	+	s	20	0	0	d	—	—	—	—
11	27	400	L	0	+	s	20	0	0	d	—	—	—	—
11	28	400	L	0	+	s	15	0	0	d	—	—	—	—
11	29	400	S	10	+	s	15	5	50	n	—	69	25	350
13	30	1000	S	10	+	s	20	0	0	d	1.2	68	0.00	45
14	31	1000	L	0	+	s	25	0	0	d	—	68	0.02	25

Key: A = altitude (m), B = exposure (L = level), C = slope (degrees), D = wind exposure (+ = windy, 0 = sheltered), E = mechanical composition of soil (s = silt, g = gravel), F = thickness of mineral soil (cm), G = thickness of humus (cm), H = humus content of root horizon (%), I = moisture content of root horizon (n = normal, d = dry, vd = very dry), J = CaO content of soil (%), K = pH of root horizon ×10, L = soil phosphate (mg/100 g dry soil), M = soil potassium (mg/100g dry soil). After: Rune (1953).

TABLE 13.11 Floristics of Swedish Serpentine Outcrops (station numbers are as in Table 13.10).

Species	Stations
SERPENTINICOLOUS PLANTS	
Asplenium viride	9(1)
Agrostis stolonifera	2(1), 3(1), 21(1), 22(1), 24(1), 25(5), 27(5), 29(1)
Luzula spicata	4(1), 16(1), 18(1)
Rumex acetosa	2-5(1), 9(1), 11(1), 16(1), 19-23(1), 27(1), 31(1)
Cerastium alpinum var. serpentinicola	31(1)
C. glabratum	2-5(1), 8(1), 11(1), 17-20(1), 21(2), 30(1)
C. vulgatum var. kajanensis	22-24(1), 28(1)
Minuartia biflora	3-5(1), 8(1), 9(1), 11(1), 16(1), 20(1), 31(1)
Arenaria norvegica	3(2), 14(1), 19(1), 20(1), 22(2), 30(1)
Lychnis alpina	2(1), 5(1), 7(1), 9(1), 16-19(1), 22(1), 23(1), 24(2), 26(1), 27(2), 28(1), 31(1)
Silene acaulis	2(2), 3(1), 4(5), 5(5), 13-15(1), 17(2), 18(3), 30(1)
Silene dioica	1(1), 9(3), 23(1), 24(1), 29(5), 31(1)
SERPENTINE-INDIFFERENT PLANTS	
Agrostis borealis	4(1)
Deschampsia flexuosa	22-24(1), 26(1), 27(1)
Trisetum spicatum	16(1)
Festuca ovina	5(1), 7(4), 8(1), 9(1), 12(1), 14-18(1), 19(2), 20(1), 28(3), 29(2)
Carex lachenalii	7(1)
C. canescens	30(1)
Juncus trifidus	2(2), 6(2), 7(1), 8(1), 10(1), 16(2), 17(1), 18(2)
Salix herbacea	2(1), 7(1), 9(1), 18(1), 30(1)
Betula nana	6(5), 7(2), 9(1), 10(2), 17(1), 18(1)
Oxyria digyna	17(1)
Sedum rosea	30(1)
Saxifraga nivalis	16(1)

Species	Stations
Viola biflora	30(1)
Phyllodoce caerulea	6(2)
Arctostaphylos alpinus	10(2), 15(2)
Vaccinium vitis-idaea	10(1), 15(1), 22(1)
V. uliginosum	6(2), 10(1), 15(1), 17(1), 22(1)
Calluna vulgaris	17(3), 22(3)
Empetrum hermaphroditum	6(3), 10(5), 17(1), 22(5)
Campanula rotundifolia	30(1)
Solidago virgaurea	25(1), 26(5), 27(1)
CALCICOLOUS PLANTS	
Carex rupestris	13(1)
C. glacialis	12(2)
Tofieldia pusilla	15(1)
Leucorchis albida	15(1)
Salix reticulata	14(1), 15(1)
Minuartia rubella	14(1)
Thalictrum alpinum	15(1)
Draba norvegica	14(1)
Parnassia palustris	15(1)
Dryas octopetala	12(2), 13(5), 14(3), 15(5)
Saxifraga oppositifolia	14(1), 15(1)
Euphrasia lapponica	15(1)
Bartsia alpina	15(1)
Pinguicula vulgaris	15(1)
MOSS	
Racomitrium lanuginosum	12(1), 17(1), 18(5)

Numbers in parentheses are relative abundances
After: Rune (1953)

13.4.3 Plant Communities over Serpentine in Sweden

A description of plant communities over serpentine in Sweden has been given by Rune (1953). He recognised 3 communities comprising : (a) plants of rock crevices, (b) plants of serpentine scree and talus, and (c) the climax communities. Each will be described briefly.

The Asplenion viridis subarcticum Alliance of serpentine rock crevices

Nordhagen (1936) has described an Alliance of Fennoscandian calcareous rock crevices but also mentioned that this Alliance has a particular form on Norwegian serpentine characterised by the occurrence of *Asplenium viride, A. adulterinum, A. adiantum-nigrum, Lychnis alpina, Silene vulgaris, S. maritima* and *Arabis petraea.*

The above Alliance is also found in Sweden at most of the serpentine sites where *A. viride* is particularly abundant. Rune (1953) observed that this fern is accompanied by serpentinicolous moss such as *Tritomaria quinquedentata, Campylium stellatum, Drepanocladus uncinatus* and *Racomitrium lanuginosum.* Alpine elements such as *Cerastium alpinum, Silene acaulis, Juncus trifidus* and *Luzula spicata* are also present. The Alliance is shown in Table 13.12.

The Arenarion norvegicae Alliance on serpentine scree

The *Arenarion norvegicae* Alliance on unstable calcareous ground was first described by Nordhagen (1936). *Arenaria norvegica* is by far the most important indicator species in this Alliance which has also been described from Shetland (see above). Most of the plants of the

TABLE 13.12 The *Asplenion* **Serpentine Community in Northern Sweden (station numbers are as in Table 13.10).**

Species	Station								
	1	7	7	9	12	28	28	28	28
Asplenium viride	1	3	3	2	2	4	1	1	1
Arenaria norvegica				1					
Cerastium vulgatum var. kajanensis		1	1	1	1		1	1	1
Silene dioica	1	1	1			1		1	
Rumex acetosa	1	1	1	1	1		1	1	
R. acetosella				1					
Silene rupestris		1							
Lychnis alpina		1	1			1	1	1	1
Agrostis canina		1							
A. stolonifera					1		1	1	5
Deschampsia flexuosa		1		1		1	1		
Molinia caerulea		1							
Poa glauca			1						
Scirpus cespitosus	1								
Racomitrium lanuginosum					5				

After: Rune (1953)
Numbers in body of the table are relative abundances.

Alliance found on calcareous scree in Norway (Nordhagen, 1936) can also occur on serpentine. These components on serpentine stands are: *Arenaria norvegica*, *A. humifusa*, *Silene acaulis*, *Campanula rotundifolia*, *Cerastium alpinum* and *Festuca ovina*. Other constituents of this community are *Rumex acetosa* and *Cerastium glabratum*. This Alliance is shown in Table 13.13.

Climax communities on serpentine

A closed vegetation will never be found over serpentine unless the rock is covered with a thick layer of humus. This can be formed by *Racomitrium lanuginosum* which slowly invades bare soil patches. Most of the climax community of alpine serpentine soils can be regarded as a special form of the *Empetrion* Alliance characterised by *Empetrum hermaphroditum* and abundant stands of *Calluna vulgaris*, and serpentinicolous plants such as: *Asplenium viride*, *Lychnis alpina*, and *Silene acaulis*. This Alliance is essentially xerophytic and is well suited to the dry serpentine outcrops. In less exposed places where the vegetation is protected by snow in winter, the *Empetrum* heath is replaced by a *Vaccinium myrtillus* heath known as the *Myrtillion* Alliance.

The *Myrtillion* Alliance may well represent the true climax stage of serpentine vegetation in Sweden but the community is not very serpentinicolous in character because the thick humus layer shields the plants from the full effects of serpentine. The *Calluna* heaths of Cornwall (see above) are to some extent reminiscent of this Alliance.

13.4.4 The Distribution and Character of Swedish Serpentinicolous Plants

A list of serpentinicolous and serpentine-indifferent (*bodenvag*) plants found on serpentine in Sweden has been given Rune (1953) and has been shown in Table 13.11. The list does not include mosses (with one exception), lichens or plants only found occasionally on serpentine. It will be noted that there is no taxon at the specific rank which is truly serpentine-endemic in Sweden though there is a number of subspecies or varieties which have such status. The list is relatively short compared with the serpentine flora of Cuba (Chapter 12) or even of Norway (see above).

A number of Swedish serpentine taxa show disjunctions typical of this type of plant and are often restricted to serpentine in some areas and not so in others. Examples given by Rune (1953) are: *Arenaria humifusa, A. norvegica, Cerastium glabratum* and *Agrostis stolonifera*. These are considered to be serpentine relics (palaeoendemics—see Chapter 6).

Arenaria humifusa is restricted to about 10 serpentine localities in Fennoscandia (Fig. 13.6) and is also found in northeastern America. The main occurrence of this species is in northern Norway (Finnmark) north of 70° N. There are, however, several occurrences in Sweden. One is a serpentine station at Hattfjelldal and several occurrences have been reported (Rune, 1954) at Lake Salojaure. These disjunct distributions are similar to an occurrence at Mt Albert in the Gaspé Peninsula (Quebec) on serpentine, several hundred km to the south of its normal distribution in Arctic Canada.

Another *Arenaria* species, *A. norvegica,* has a bicentric distribution in Fennoscandia (Fig. 13.8). South of 66° N, it is virtually confined to serpentine (first centre of distribution) whereas in its second and northern distribution it can be found on non-serpentinitic substrates as well. It is suggested that this plant was originally a pioneer species as the first soil formed after the Ice Ages, but later succumbed to competition and retreated to serpentine except in the north where the climate did not favour competing species. A similar type of distribution has been noted by Rune (1953) for *Cerastium glabratum* which is common over calcareous rocks in northern Fennoscandia. In Jämtland, however, and in southern Lapland, this taxon is virtually confincd to serpentine. *Agrostis stolonifera* also appears to be a serpentine relic in southern Lapland.

TABLE 13.13 The *Arenarion* Serpentine Community in Northern Sweden (station numbers are as in Table 13.10)

Species	Station								
	2	3	5	11	14	19	20	21	30
Arenaria norvegica		2			1	1	1	2	1
Asplenium viride						1			
Campanula rotundifolia									1
Cerastium glabratum	1	1	1	1		1	1	2	1
Draba norvegica					1				
Minuartia biflora		1	1	1			1		
M. rubella					1				
Rumex acetosa	1	1	1	1		1	1	1	
Saxifraga oppositifolia					1				
Silene acaulis	2	1	5		1				1
Viola biflora ·									1
Lychnis alpina	1		1			1			
Agrostis stolonifera	1	1						1	
Festuca ovina			1			1	2	1	
Juncus trifidus	2								1
Dryas octopetala			3						2
Salix reticulata							1		
Bare soil	5	5	2	5	3	4	5	5	5

Numerals are relative abundances
After: Rune (1953)

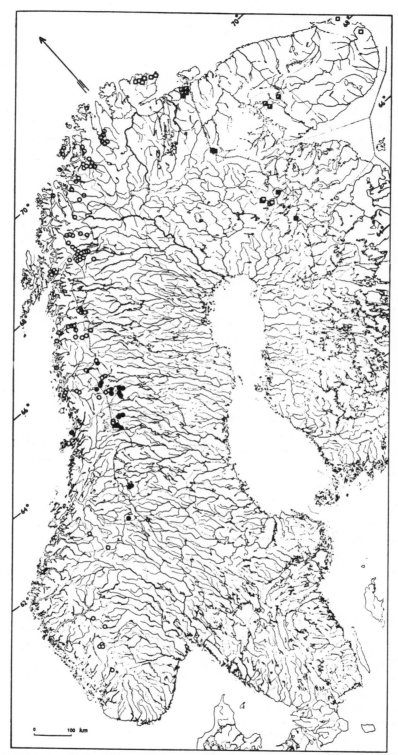

Fig. 13.8 Bicentric distribution of *Arenaria norvegica* in Fennoscandia (dots and circles), and of *A. ciliata* subsp. *pseudofrigida* (squares). Dots and black squares indicate occurrence on serpentine. Open circles and squares denote other rock types.
Source: Rune (1953).

13.4.5 A Comparison of the Serpentine Flora of Northeastern America and Northwestern Europe

Scottish serpentines are often colonised by characteristic plants of the Caryophyllaceae, which though not the main colonisers are among the most obvious. The serpentine flora of Sweden is even richer in Caryophyllaceae and in this respect is similar to the serpentine flora of northeastern America where common colonisers from this family are: *Arenaria humifusa, Minuartia rubella, M. marcescens, M. biflora, Lychnis alpina, Silene acaulis, Stellaria longipes* and *Cerastium arvense*. Some of these taxa are found in Fennoscandia and reflect the similarity of the two floras despite their wide geographical separation. Further south in Europe, the Caryophyllaceae are much less prominent over serpentine and are superseded by serpentinicolous plants of the families Fabaceae, Asteraceae and Brassicaceae.

Rune (1953) has made a comparison of the serpentine floras of northeastern America and northwestern Europe:

1—The physiognomy of the flora of both regions is similar due to the abundant occurrence of *Racomitrium lanuginosum* and due to extensive frost action on the soils.

2—There is a number of more-or-less serpentinicolous plants common to both regions. Some of these have been listed above and to this list we may add: *Armeria scabra* subsp. *labradorica* (in America) which is similar or identical to *Armeria scabra* subsp. *sibirica* in Europe. Other *bodenvag* species common to both regions are: *Scirpus cespitosus, Deschampsia cespitosa, D. flexuosa*, and *Vaccinium uliginosum*.

3—There is a number of plants which are serpentinicolous in northeastern America but which do not grow on serpentine in northwestern Europe. These are: *Rhododendron lapponicum, Carex scirpoidea, Stellaria longipes* and *Cerastium arvense*.

4—There are taxa which are serpentinicolous in northwestern Europe but do not grow on serpentine in northeastern America. Examples are: *Asplenium viride, Cerastium alpinum* and *Minuartia biflora* (= *Arenaria sajanensis* in America).

5—Both floras are conspicuously poor in endemics. This is because both regions have been strongly glaciated in the past so that a period of only 10,000 years has been available for endemic taxa to evolve.

In summary, the serpentine floras of northeastern America and northwestern Europe have many affinities because of similarities in their rock types, climate and past glaciation history.

13.5 FINLAND

13.5.1 Introduction

Serpentine outcrops are found in Finnish Lapland and in a broad belt of rocks known as the Karelides (Ager, 1980) which extends from Oulu in the northwest to Karelia in the southeast. They contain a great thickness of quartzites and dolomitic marbles and there is considerable development of basic and ultramafic volcanics whose origin is somewhat in doubt. The individual ultramafic outcrops are nowhere very extensive in area except perhaps in Finnish Lapland, but they are extremely numerous. They also give rise to several areas of nickel mineralization which are currently being mined.

Finnish serpentine vegetation was first studied by Mikkola (1938) and later by Kotilainen; however, the latter published very little on the floristics of these areas. Perhaps the most useful general work on the subject is a well-known paper by Lounamaa (1956) which was, however, mainly concerned with chemical analysis of the plant species recorded.

Plate 13.2 (c) Above: Serpentine at Meikle Kilrannoch, Scotland. Photo by A. J. M. Baker.
(d) Below: Eroded ultramafic rocks at Junstern Klumpen, Sweden. Photo by W. R. Lauder.

Plate 13.3   General view of the Høle magnesium silicate barren.
Photo by P. M. Jørgensen.

Much of the work on Finnish serpentine vegetation has been concerned with the mosses and lichens which are so prevalent in that country and these will be discussed together with phanerogams below.

13.5.2 Serpentinicolous Plants in Finland

Rune (1953) has described the alpine and subalpine serpentine flora of northern and central Finland in the districts of Laponnia kemensis, Laponnia inarensis, Ostrobottnia kajanensis, and N. Karelia. All of these outcrops are at an altitude of 100–400 m.

The serpentine flora of Lapland (Mikkola, 1938) has much in common with the flora of Swedish Lapland where species such as *Asplenium viride*, *Lychnis alpina*, *Cerastium alpinum*, *Minuartia biflora*, *Campanula rotundifolia* and *Molinia caerulea* are common. The Swedish serpentine flora has more affinity with that of Finland than that of Norway which is richer because of the oceanic influence. Though the climate of Central Finland is somewhat more severe that that of similar latitudes in Sweden, the lower altitudes compensate to some extent and produce marked floristic similarities.

Disjunctions, so common in the Scandinavian serpentine floras, are also found in Finland. For example, *Arenaria ciliata* subsp. *pseudofrigida* according to Rune (1953) is restricted to non-ultramafites in the extreme north of Fennoscandia but is appears disjunctively on serpentine further south (see Fig. 13.8). Another interesting disjunction is the appearance of the Central European fern *Asplenium adulterinum* in the Karelian serpentine areas (Kotilainen, 1921).

Rintanen (1968) has described the mountain flora of eastern Lapland and made field observations on the distribution of important serpentinicolous plants such as *Asplenium viride* (the commonest species on serpentine), *Cerastium alpinum* (not confined to serpentine), *Minuartia biflora*, *Arenaria ciliata* subsp. *pseudofrigida*, and *Lychnis alpina*.

Lounamaa (1956) analysed several hundred wild plants from various rock types in Finland, and although his work is primarily biogeochemical (see below), he did furnish a useful checklist of taxa found over serpentine in Central Finland. This list is given in Table 13.14. A comparison of the serpentine floras of Finland and Sweden can be made from the data in Tables 13.11 and 13.14. *Asplenium viride* is much more common in Finland than in Sweden, perhaps because of climatic stress caused by the greater altitude of the Swedish sites. The serpentinicolous *Lychnis alpina* is again common in both regions, and it is interesting to note that it displays a pattern similar to that of *Arenaria humifusa* and *A. norvegica* in that it is confined to serpentine only to the south of its normal range as for example in Scotland.

Lounamaa (1956) has listed a number of bryophytes and lichens over serpentine in Finland. However, the most intensive work in this field has been carried out by Takala and Seaward (1978). The work was centred around the Niinivaara serpentine outcrop near Kaavi (station 28 in Fig. 13.5). A total of 123 species of lichens growing on rocks, soils and mosses, was recorded. A further 27 species were found growing on trees. There was no serpentine-endemic lichen in this area.

13.5.3 Plant Communities over Serpentine in Finland

Plant communities on serpentine in Finland have not been studied to any great degree; however, some details have been given by Lounamaa (1956) and in later papers by Vuokko (1978) and Lounamaa and Vuokko (1978). They have recognised five types of serpentine vegetation as follows:

1—Rock vegetation principally composed of lichens and the moss *Racomitrium lanuginosum*.

2—Sparse, desert-like vegetation including serpentine specialists such as: *Asplenium viride, Cerastium alpinum, C. glabratum, Lychnis alpina, Minuartia biflora, Agrostis stolonifera,* and *Festuca ovina.*

3—Serpentine heath forests composed of open pine or sometimes birch forest with *Juniperus communis* and the usual dwarf shrubs of acid forest soil mixed with serpentine specialists.

4.—*Molinia caerulea* and *Scirpus cespitosus* meadow.

5—Paludified heath forest and peatlands.

TABLE 13.14   Check List of Plants Found at Seven Serpentine Sites in Finland (station numbers as shown in Fig. 13.5).

Species	Serpentine Stations						
	1	2	3	4	5	6	7
Actaea spicata							+
Agrostis stolonifers			+				
Alnus incana							+
Antennaria dioica				+			
Asplenium viride (F)	+	+		+	+	+	
A. septentrionale (F)					+		
Anthoxanthum odoratum					+		
Athyrium filix-femina (F)					+		
Betula verrucosa		+		+	+		+
Calluna vulgaris		+			+		
Campylium polyganum (M)		+					
Cerastium alpinum					+	+	
C. fontanum	+						+
C. holosteoides var. *kajanense*	+	+					
C. holosteoides var. *serpentini*		+	+				
Chamanerion augustifolium					+		
Cladonia alpestris (L)		+		+			
C. sylvatica (L)		+					
Coeloglossum viride							+
Covallaria majalis				+			
Cystopteris fragilis (F)					+		+
Daphne mezereum					+		
Deschampsia caespitosa	+	+			+		
D. flexuosa					+		
Dianthus superbus						+	
Dicranum fuscescens (M)		+					
D. muehlenbeckia var. *brevifolium* (M)		+					
Empetrum nigrum	+			+			+
Epilobium montanum							+
Festuca ovina	+				+		+
Hylocomium splendens (M)					+		
Juniperus communis	+	+			+		
Lastrea dryopteris (F)		+					
Lathyrus vernus					+		
Lychnis alpina		+	+		+		
L. vulgaris					+	+	
Melampyrum pratense		+					
Melica nutans							+
Molinia caerulea					+	+	
Parmelia centrifuga (L)	+	+					

Species	Serpentine Stations						
	1	2	3	4	5	6	7
Picea abies		+			+		
Pinus sylvestris	+	+		+			
Polypodium vulgare (F)					+		
Populus tremula					+		
Pyrola rotundifolia					+		
Racomitrium lanuginosum (M)					+		
Rosa acicularis							+
Rubus arcticus					+		
R. idaeus					+		
R. saxatilis		+		+	+		+
Sagina nodosa					+	+	
Sedum telephium					+		
Sorbus aucuparia					+		
Stellaria graminea							+
Stereocaulon paschale (L)	+				+		
Tortella tortuosa (M)		+		+	+		
Vaccinium uliginosum		+					
V. vitis-idaea		+			+		
Vicia sylvestris		+					
Woodsia ilvensis (F)				+	+		

M = moss, L = lichen, F = fern
Locations are to be found in Fig. 13.5 where: 1-3 = 25, 4 = 26, 5-6 = 28, and 7 = 27.
After: Lounamaa (1956)

13.6 BIOGEOCHEMICAL INVESTIGATIONS IN FENNOSCANDIA

Although the biogeochemical method of prospecting for minerals had its origins in Scandinavia with the pioneering work of Brundin (1939), it is noteworthy that none of his work involved serpentinitic substrates. Another Scandinavian pioneer of the biogeochemical method was Thorolf Vogt who analysed a number of serpentine-tolerant taxa including *Lychnis alpina* (Vogt, 1942). The most important biogeochemical paper on Fennoscandian serpentine plants is probably the work by Lounamaa (1956) who analysed a large number of Finnish serpentinophytes and their supporting rocks and soils. He analysed lichens, mosses, ferns, conifers, deciduous trees, dwarf shrubs, grasses and herbs. His findings are summarized in Table 13.15. The data had originally been expressed on an ash weight basis, but for the sake of consistency with the rest of this book, I have converted the data to a dry weight basis by use of a factor of 0.1.

There is a very clear trend in the data of Table 13.15 in which greatly enhanced levels of cobalt, chromium and nickel are found in plants growing over serpentine compared with granitic rocks. Concentrations of the nutrients boron, copper, molybdenum and zinc do not differ very greatly between plants on the two rock types except perhaps for the tendency for zinc levels in serpentine plants to be about half those of other vegetation. This deficiency, as well as the excess levels of cobalt, chromium and nickel are symptomatic of the "serpentine problem" (see Chapter 4).

Although Lounamaa's work was not specifically orientated towards biogeochemical prospecting, his data are useful in setting background values against which anomalous concentrations in vegetation may be determined during exploration surveys.

Before leaving this chapter, some mention will be made of a biogeochemical project involving determination of copper, lead and nickel concentrations in 700 herbarium specimens of *Lychnis alpina* and *Silene dioica* (*Melandrium dioicum*) sampled throughout Fennoscandia (Brooks et al. 1979). Levels exceeding 20 μg/g nickel in dried leaves of either species indicated the occurrence of an ultramafic substrate below the plant. The work is illustrated in Fig. 13.9 and resulted in the identification of most of the known occurrences of ultramafic rocks in Fennoscandia. These authors suggested that anomalous sites not known to bear ultramafic rocks should be examined at a later date by geologists for confirmation or negation of the findings.

It is noteworthy that none of the nickel concentrations found in Fennoscandian plants even approached the high levels (> 1000 μg/g) found in hyperaccumulator plants (see Chapter 8). This is of course because the whole of the region was glaciated 10,000 years ago and because hyperaccumulation appears to be a character found only in ancient floras. A second reason is probably that so many serpentinicolous plants in Fennoscandia belong to the Caryophyllaceae, a family which contains few if any hyperaccumulators of nickel even in more favourable regions of the earth.

Fig. 13.9   Distribution of *Lychnis alpina* in Fennoscandia showing localities corresponding to elevated nickel levels in dried leaves of herbarium specimens.
Source: Brooks et al. (1979).

TABLE 13.15 Trace Element Content (μg/g dry weight) of Rocks, Soils, and Aerial Parts (leaves, needles) of Plant Types from Serpentine Areas of Finland.

Sample	n	B		Co		Cr		Cu		Mn		Mo		Ni		Zn	
		x	ş	x	ş	x	ş	x	ş	x	ş	x	ş	x	ş	x	ş
Granitic rocks	170	11	1	6	1	87	14	50	4	610	59	3.1	0.1	38	3	180	17
Serpentine rocks	50	51	8	42	5	2200	260	27	4	1400	110	3.0	0.1	1500	150	100	29
Granitic soils	83	58	7	16	1	140	18	110	10	1500	150	3.4	0.2	91	11	320	50
Serpentine soils	23	41	6	140	15	4000	310	22	5	1200	150	3.0	0.1	1200	190	270	49
Lichens on granite	50	13	1	1	0.1	4	0.6	28	4	41	1	2.0	0.2	4	0.4	380	48
Lichens on serpentine	6	26	13	7	1.4	65	16	28	7	180	56	4.0	2.0	140	53	250	46
Mosses on granite	6	61	29	1	0.2	5	2	30	1	330	92	1.6	0.5	7	1.4	250	50
Mosses on serpentine	6	57	11	3	0.7	20	5	15	4	120	42	3.9	2.7	220	75	130	49
Ferns on granite	30	74	12	1	0.2	1	0.1	12	2	240	47	1.0	0.2	3	0.5	91	22
Ferns on serpentine	14	140	28	4	1.3	23	9	13	3	560	110	1.2	0.2	220	74	46	8
Conifers on granite	34	130	16	0.6	0.2	0.7	0.2	24	3	1400	130	0.2	0.1	3	0.6	150	25
Conifers on serp.	10	300	58	1.8	0.6	1.8	0.5	6	1	1600	380	1.5	0.8	120	28	90	25
Decid. trees on gr.	39	100	13	0.8	0.1	0.5	0.1	15	2	1200	120	0.5	0.1	4	0.7	210	33
Decid. trees on serp.	14	76	9	5.7	2.7	2.6	0.9	9	1	1500	320	2.8	0.9	120	29	120	33
Shrubs on granite	30	160	15	0.3	0.1	0.7	0.1	21	3	2200	190	1.0	0.3	3	1.1	81	12
Shrubs on serpentine	9	280	68	5.9	3.2	7.3	3.2	8	1	2100	350	1.4	0.4	130	61	80	29
Herbs on granite	63	64	9	0.6	0.1	0.8	0.2	13	2	720	84	1.3	0.2	3	0.3	93	13
Herbs on serpentine	31	98	17	1.2	0.4	10	4	9	1	370	56	2.2	0.5	72	18	33	4
Grasses on granite	12	27	10	0.4	0.2	0.9	0.3	12	3	810	230	3.3	0.9	2	0.4	140	32
Grasses on serpentine	12	32	8	2.0	0.8	4.6	1.2	10	2	500	160	2.9	0.7	70	27	62	8

Original data were on an ash weight basis and have been converted to dry weight using a factor of 0.1. x = mean. ş = standard deviation.

After: Lounamaa (1956)

REFERENCES

Ager, D. V., 1980. *The Geology of Europe*. McGraw-Hill, London.

Amin, M. S., 1954. Notes on the ultrabasic body of Unst. *Geol. Mag.*, 91; 399–406.

Birse, E. L., 1982. Plant communities on serpentine in Scotland. *Vegetatio*, 49: 141–162.

Bjørlykke, B., 1938. Vegetasjonen pa olivinsten pa Sunnmøre. *Nytt. Mag. Naturvidens.*, 79: 50–126.

Brooks, R. R., 1983. *Biological Methods of Prospecting for Minerals*. Wiley, New York.

Brooks, R. R., Trow, J. M. and Bølviken, B., 1979. Biogeochemical anomalies in Fennoscandia; a study of copper, lead and nickel in *Melandrium dioicum* and *Viscaria alpina*. *J. Geochem. Explor.*, 11: 73–87.

Brundin, N, 1939. *Method of locating metals and minerals in the ground*. U.S. Pat. 2158980.

Carter, S., Proctor, J. and Slingsby, D. R., 1986. Ecological studies on the Keen of Hamar serpentine, Shetland. *J. Ecol.* (in press).

Clapham, A. R., Tutin, T. G. and Warburg, E. F., 1981. *Excursion Flora of the British Isles,*. 3rd ed. Cambridge University Press, Cambridge.

Coombe, D. E. and Frost, L. C., 1956a. The heaths of the Cornish serpentine. *J. Ecol.*, 44: 226–256.

Coombe, D. E. and Frost, L. C., 1956b. The nature and origin of the soils of the Cornish serpentine. *J. Ecol.*, 44: 605–615.

Dahl, O., 1912. Botaniske undersøkelse i Helgeland. 1. *Kong. Nork. Videns. Sels.*, 1911: 1–221.

Druce, G. C., 1922. *Flora Zetlandica.* Buncle, Arbroath (Scotland).

Ernst, W., 1976. *Prodrome of the European Plant Communities* (R. Tüxen, ed) *R.3 Violetea calaminariea.* Cramer, Vaduz (Liechtenstein).

Ferreira, R. E. C., 1959. Some disjunctions between calciphilous and basiphilous plants. I Field data. *Trans. Proc. Bot. Soc. Edinb.*, 39: 399–421.

Halliday, G., 1960. *Studies on Arenaria ciliata and Minuartia verna Complexes.* PhD Thesis, University of Cambridge.

Heslop, R. E. F. and Bown, C. J., 1969. *The soils of Candacraig and Glenbuchat.* Macauley Inst., Aberdeen.

Hunter, J. G. and Vergnano, O., 1952. Trace element toxicities in oat plants. *Ann. Appl. Biol.*, 40: 761–777.

Johnston, W. R. and Proctor,J., 1977. Metal concentrations in plants and soils from two British serpentine sites. *Pl. Soil*, 46: 275–278.

Johnston, W. R. and Proctor, J., 1979. Ecological studies on the Lime Hill serpentine, Scotland. *Trans. Bot. Soc. Edinb.*, 43: 145–150.

Johnston, W. R. and Proctor, J., 1980. Ecological studies on Meikle Kilrannoch serpentines. *Trans. Bot. Soc. Edinb.*, 43: 207–215.

Jørgensen, P. M., 1974. Flora and vegetation in magnesium silicate area in Høle Southwest Norway. *Arb. Univ. Bergen, Mat.—Naturvidens.* 1973. Ser. 1:1–63.

Knaben, G., 1952. Botanical investigations in the middle districts of Norway. *Arb. Univ. Bergen, Naturvidens Rekke.*, 1950, 8; 1–117.

Kotilainen, M. J., 1921. *Asplenium adulterinum* Milde loydetty Suomesta. *Medd. Soc. F. Fl. Fenn.*, 46, Helsingfors.

Kotilainen, M. J., 1944. Kasvit erikoislaatuisen substraatin indikaatoreina. *Soc. Scient. Fenn. Vsk.*, 22: 1–18.

Kotilainen, M. J. and Seivala, O., 1954. Observations on serpentine flora at Sunnmøre. *Nytt. Mag. Bot.*, 3: 139–145.

Lag, J. and Bølviken, B., 1977. Natural heavy metal poisoning of soils and vegetation: an exploration tool in glacial terrain. *Trans. Inst. Min. Metall.*, Sec. B, 86: 173–180.

Lee, J., Brooks, R. R., Reeves, R. D. and Boswell, C. R., 1975. Soil factors controlling a New Zealand serpentine flora. *Pl. Soil*, 42: 153–160.

Lounamaa, J., 1956. Trace elements in plants growing wild on different rocks in Finland. *Ann. Bot. Soc. Vanamo*, 29: 1–196.

Lounamaa, J. and Vuokko, S., 1978. Kasvit kallioperän indikaattoreina Lapissa. *Acta Lappon. Fenn.*, No.10; 122–128.

Marrs, R. H. and Proctor, J., 1978. Chemical and ecological studies of heath plants over soils of the Lizard Peninsula, Cornwall. *J. Ecol.*, 66: 417–432.

Marrs, R. H. and Proctor, J., 1979. Vegetation and soil studies of the enclosed heaths of the Lizard Peninsula, Cornwall. *Vegetatio*, 41: 121–128.

Marshall, J. K., 1959. *Vegetation of Serpentine of Meikle Kilrannoch.* BSc Hons. Thesis, St Andrews University.

Mikkola, E., 1938. Ultramäksisten kivilajien vaikutus kasvillisuuteen Lapissa. *Luonnen Ystäva*, 42; 21–27.

Nordhagen, R., 1936. Versuch einer neuen Einteilung der subalpinen-alpinen Vegetation Norwegens. *Arb. Bergen Mus. 1936, Naturvidens Rekke,* 7.

Nordhagen, R., 1966. Remarks on the serpentine-sorrel *Rumex acetosa* subsp. *serpentinicola* (Rune) Nordhagen, and its distribution in Norway. *Blyttia*, 24: 286–294.

Proctor, J. and Johnston, W. R., 1977. *Lychnis alpina* L. in Britain. *Watsonia*, 11: 199–204.

Proctor, J. and Woodell, S. R. J., 1971. The plant ecology of serpentine. I Serpentine vegetation of England and Scotland. *J. Ecol.*, 59: 375–395.

Rintanen, T., 1968. The distribution of fjeld plants in eastern Lapland. *Ann. Bot. Fenn.*, 5: 225–305.

Rune, O., 1953. Plant life on serpentine and related rocks in the north of Sweden. *Acta Phytogeogr. Suecica,* 31: 1–139.

Rune, O., 1954. *Arenaria humifusa* on serpentine in Scandinavia. *Nytt. Mag. Bot.,* 3: 183–196.

Shewry, P. R. and Peterson, P. J., 1975. Calcium and magnesium in plants and soil from a serpentine area in Unst, Shetland. *J. Appl. Ecol.,* 12: 381–391.

Shewry, P. R. and Peterson, P. J., 1976. Distribution of chromium and nickel in plants from serpentine and other sites. *J. Ecol.,* 64: 195–212.

Slingsby, D. R., and Brown, D. H., 1977. Nickel in British serpentine soils. *J. Ecol.,* 65: 597–618.

Spence, D. H. N., 1957. Studies on the vegetation of Shetland. I—The serpentine debris vegetation in Unst. *J. Ecol.,* 45: 917–945.

Spence, D. H. N., 1958. The flora of Unst, Shetland, in relation to the geology. *Trans. Bot. Soc. Edinb.,* 37: 163–173.

Spence, D. H. N., 1969. *Cover-abundance list for related community types on serpentine and other rocks in Scotland.* Unpub. Rep., St. Andrews University.

Spence, D. H. N., 1970. Scottish serpentine vegetation. *Oikos,* 21: 22–31.

Spence, D. H. N. and Millar, E. A., 1963. An experimental study of the infertility of a Shetland serpentine soil. *J. Ecol.,* 51: 333–343.

Svenonius, F., 1883. Am olivinstens och serpentin förekomsten i Norrland. *Geol. Forh. Stockholm Forh,* 6: 342–369.

Takkala, K. and Seaward, M. R. D., 1978. Lichens of the Niinivaara serpentinite region, E. Finland. *Mem. Soc. Fauna Fenn.,* 54: 59–63.

Vogt, T., 1942. Geokjemisk og geobotanisk malmeleting. II *Viscaria alpina* (L.) G. Don som "kisplante". *Kong. Norsk. Videns. Sels.,* 15: 5–8.

Vuokko, S., 1978. Lapin ultraemäksisten alueiden kasvilllisuus, 82: 131–134.

West, W., 1912. Notes on the flora of Shetland with some ecological observations. *J. Bot. Lond.* 50: 265–275, 297–306.

Williams, W. T. and Lambert, J. M., 1959. Multivariate methods in plant ecology. I Association analysis in plant communities. *J. Ecol.,* 47: 83–101.

Williams, W. T. and Lambert, J. M., 1961. Multivariate methods in plant ecology. II Inverse Association analysis. *J. Ecol.,* 49: 717–729.

Wilson, M. J. and Berrow, M. L., 1978. The mineralogy and heavy metal content of some serpentine soils in northeast Scotland. *Chem. Erde,* 37: 181–205.

Chapter 14

CENTRAL AND SOUTHERN EUROPE

14.1 GEOLOGY AND TECTONICS

Europe may be divided tectonically into four main divisions which have been described by Ager (1980) as: Eo-Europa, Palaeo-Europa, Meso-Europa and Neo-Europa (Fig. 14.1).

Eo-Europa is the old Precambrian complex of Europe, the Fennoscandian Shield with a small section in the Northwest Highlands of Scotland. Palaeo-Europa has already been mentioned in Chapter 13 and encompasses the Caledonides of Northwest Europe stretching from the Scottish Highlands through Scandinavia.

Meso-Europa occupies much of the middle part of Europe and is characterised by flat-lying Mesozoic and Tertiary sediments resting on strongly folded rocks up to late Palaeozoic age. The dominant folding is of Variscan (Hercynian) age which started in the early Carboniferous and lasted until the late Triassic before leading into the next orogeny. The serpentine outcrops of Cornwall discussed in the previous chapter form part of this structure.

Neo-Europa constitutes the alpine fold belts of Southern Europe with the main folding and thrusting having occurred in the late Cretaceous to mid-Tertiary Period. This division of Europe stretches from the Betic Cordillera in southern Spain, through the Italian Peninsula, Alps, Carpathians, Dinaric Alps and Pindus mountains, and then to the Caucasus Range in Southern Russia. Neo-Europa is divided tectonically from the North African Plate in the south and from the Eurasian Plate in the northeast. Most of the extensive ultramafic outcrops of Europe (see Fig. 14.2) are found within Neo-Europa where compression from the North African Plate caused folding of increasing intensity up to about 35 million years ago. At this time the main alpine orogeny resulted in the piling up as overfolds and thrust plates, of sediments formed 570 m.y. ago, sediments which had already been folded in previous orogenies. The main mountain ranges resulting from this pressure from the south are curved convex to the north and include the Carpathians and Pyrenees which had already been folded in Variscan times.

The largest areas of contiguous serpentine outcrops are found in the Balkan Peninsula, particularly in Bosnia, Albania and Northern Greece where they form dark-coloured mountains (hence the name Montenegro = Crnagora in Serbian). In Yugoslavia the region is sometimes known as the Serbian Ophiolitic Zone.

Ultramafic rocks are also found in Meso-Europa though these are not as numerous or as extensive in area as those of Neo-Europa. They are found in the extreme west of the Iberian Peninsula, the Massif Central of France, and skirt the Alpine ophiolites, outcropping in Northern Bavaria, Hungary, Czechoslovakia, the Harz, and Poland.

14.2 THE IBERIAN PENINSULA

14.2.1 Geology

The Iberian Peninsula may be divided into two main regions geologically and tectonically. The first of these is the Iberian Massif which forms part of one of the Variscan Fold Belts extending over most of Western Europe (Meso-Europa). The older rocks outcrop in Northwest Spain and Northeast Portugal. To the south the Iberian Massif is cut off by the Betic Cordillera the most westerly part of the Mediterranean Ophiolitic Belt.

Serpentine rocks outcrop in Northwest Spain near La Coruña (Site 1 in Fig. 14.2) where

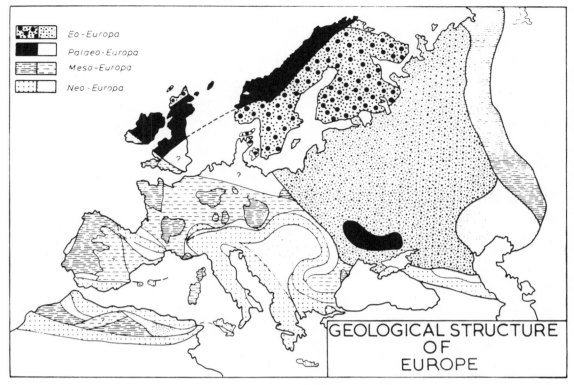

Fig. 14.1 The tectonic divisions of Europe.
Source: Ager (1980).

they form a circle around this city and pass through Santiago de Compostella reaching the sea again at Cabo Ortegal. The belt surrounds a dome of mica schist. The ultramafic rocks are part of a complex of mainly basic rocks (gabbros, norites, amphibolites and eclogites). The geology of this region is shown in Fig. 14.3.

Ultramafic rocks are also found in Northeast Portugal (Site 2 in Fig. 14.2) some 200 km to the southeast of La Coruña. They are scattered in small pockets in the Bragança area and are also part of the Iberian Massif. The geology of this region has been described by Ferreira (1965) and by Cotelo Neiva (1948) who interpreted the eruptive massif of Bragança-Vinhais as a batholith denuded by erosion and surrounded by amphibolites which give it the form of a vast cuvette in which about 60 ultramafic outcrops occur among the amphibolites. The ultramafic rocks of Bragança-Vinhais are shown in Fig. 14.4. The ultramafites in this area are represented by dunites, lherzolites, bragancaites, amphibolites and asbestosic peridotites which are heavily serpentinized.

The ultramafic rocks of Northern Portugal differ in a number of respects from ultramafites elsewhere. The most obvious difference lies in the very high magnesium content (typically 35% MgO) due to high concentrations of enstatite and forsterite. The sodium content is likewise quite high (1–2% Na_2O) due to the calcic-alkalic nature of the original magma. The nickel and chromium contents (0.75% and 12.4% respectively—as oxides) are likewise very high.

The third occurrence of serpentine in the Iberian Peninsula is by far the largest in area and is found in southeast Spain near Malaga (Site 3 in Fig. 14.2) in the Sierra Bermeja ("bermeja" means vermilion in Spanish and refers to the colour of the iron-rich rocks of the area south of Ronda). The geology of this region is shown in Fig. 14.5 and has been summarized by Gonzalez (1975) as follows: the ultramafites of Tertiary origin are surrounded by sediments and are invaded by strings of acid rocks. The structure can be considered as a vast

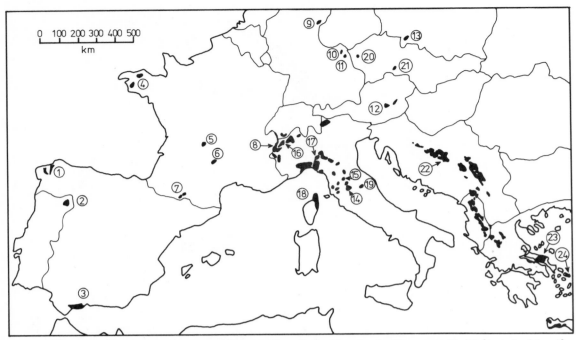

Fig. 14.2   Serpentine outcrops of Europe. Key: 1—La Coruña, 2—Bragança, 3—Malaga, 4—Massif Armoricain, 5—Aveyron, 6—Haute-Vienne, 7—Ste Béat, 8—Val d'Ayas, 9—Harz, 10—Grötschenreuth, 11—Wurlitz, 12—Kraubath, 13—Zabkowicz, 14—Impruneta, 15—Monte Ferrato, 16—Val d'Aosta, 17—Bobbio, 18—Corsica, 19—San Stefano, 20—Marianske Lazne, 21—Mohelno, 22—Gostovic, 23—Mantoudi (Euboa), 24—Tinos.

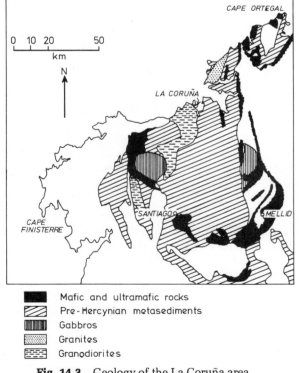

Fig. 14.3   Geology of the La Coruña area.
Source: Guitian Ojea and Lopez Lopez (1980).

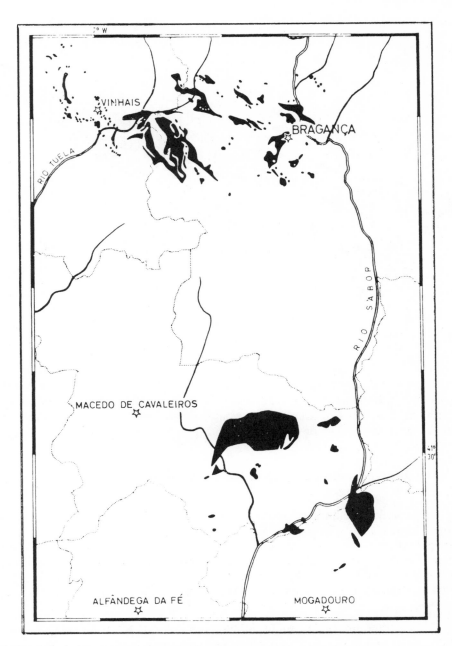

Fig. 14.4   Serpentine outcrops in the Vinhais—Bragança region of Northeast Portugal. Scale 1:400,000.
Source: Pinto da Silva (1970).

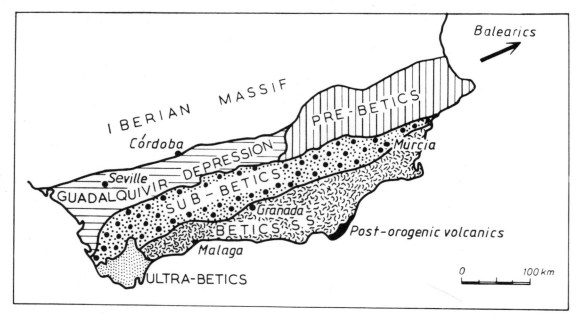

Fig. 14.5 The geology of the Malaga area.
Source: Ager (1980).

batholith elevated at the surface by orogenic movements. Gneisses represent the residue of the upper surface of the batholith. The peridotites are heavily serpentinized and contain abundant iron oxides. Cambrian calcareous sediments are also found together with argillaceous sandstones of Eocene age and form the upper part of the Valley of Sierra de Carratraca.

14.2.2 Soils and Vegetation of Serpentine at La Coruña

Soils

The soils of ultramafic rocks of La Coruña have been studied by Guitian Ojea and Lopez Lopez (1980). They are largely derived from the group of basic lopoliths near Cape Ortegal where there are numerous serpentine outcrops (Fig. 14.3). The soils are deficient in organic matter and strongly saturated with exchangeable magnesium. Total magnesium (as MgO) is as high as 16% in the C horizons where nickel and chromium are in the range 900–4000 and 700–5300 μg/g respectively. The Ca/Mg mole quotient was in the range 0.01–0.4.

Vegetation

The serpentine vegetation of the Iberian Peninsula has been studied by many workers (Table 14.1) and in the La Coruña area has been described by Bellot Rodriguez (1966) and Fraga Vila (1975) who found that the following plants were abundant over ultramafites: *Melandrium pratense, Carex flacca, C. panicea, Calluna vulgaris, Erica scoparia, Agrostis canina, Festuca rubra, Scilla autumnalis, Plantago carinata, P. lanceolata* var. *lanuginosa, P. serpentina, P. coronopus, Sesamoides canescens,* and *Filipendula vulgaris.*

A further group of plants shows metamorphoses compared with plants from other areas on non-ultramafic substrates. These are: *Tuberaria globularifolia, Scorzonera hispanica, Avena bromoides* and *Armeria duriaei.*

Species such as *Calluna vulgaris, Agrostis canina, Festuca rubra* and *Plantago* spp. are characteristic of Scottish serpentine sites much further north. The general physiognomy of the vegetation is also strongly reminiscent of the serpentine heaths of Cornwall and Southwest France. A view of typical serpentine vegetation at Mellid near La Coruña is

TABLE 14.1   Papers Which Refer to Serpentine Vegetation in Southern Europe

Albania	Ernst (1974); Markgraf (1925, 1932)
Austria	Eggler (1954, 1955, 1963); Ernst (1974); Hayek (1923); Johannes (1984); Kretschmer (1931); Lämmermayr (1926, 1927, 1928a,b, 1930, 1934); Maurer (1966); Nevole (1926); Sasse (1979b)
Czechoslovakia	Dvorak (1935); Ernst (1974); Müller-Stoll and Miloslav (1984); Novak (1928, 1937); Schüstler (1920); Suza (1919, 1921, 1927a,b, 1928, 1930); Zlatnik (1928a,b)
France	Duvigneaud (1966); Le Gendre (1919); Sasse (1979b)
Germany	Dahl (1912, 1915); Ernst (1974); Gauckler (1954); Johannes (1984); Krapfenbauer (1967); Sasse (1979b)
Greece	Babalonas (1983, 1984a,b); Babalonas and Papanicolaou (1984); Babalonas et al. (1984); Boydell (1921); Karataglis et al. (1982); Krause (1962); Krause and Klement (1962); Krause et al. (1963); Papanicolaou et al. (1983); Rechinger (1942, 1943, 1947, 1950, 1961); Turrill (1929)
Hungary	Soo (1934); Zolyomi (1936)
Italy	Amidei (1841); Bargoni (1943); Becherer (1969); Fiori (1919); Fiori and Pampanini (1914); Gismondi (1953); Martino and Orsini (1969); Messeri (1936); Negodi (1941); Pampanini (1903); Pavarino (1912, 1914, 1918); Pichi-Sermolli (1948); Rigotti (1930); Sasse (1979b); Verger (1979, 1982, 1983); Vergnano (1953, 1958); Vergnano Gambi et al. (1979, 1982); Vergnano Gambi and Cardini (1967); Vergnano Gambi and Gabbrielli (1979, 1981)
Yugoslavia	Krause and Klement (1958); Krause and Ludwig (1956, 1957); Novak (1928); Pancic (1859); Pavlovic (1953, 1955, 1962, 1964); Ritter-Studnicka (1956, 1963, 1964, 1970); Ritter-Studnicka and Klement (1968)
Poland	Sarosiek (1964); Sarosiek and Sadowska (1961)
Portugal	Menezes de Sequeira (1969); Pinto da Silva (1964, 1970, 1981)
Spain	Bello Rodriguez (1966); Ceballos Vicioso (1933); Fraga Vila (1975); Gonzalez (1975); Lopez Lopez and Guitian Ojea (1981); Palacios (1936); Rivas Goday (1969, 1972, 1973); Rivas Martinez et al. (1973)

shown in Plate 14.1a. The serpentine heath in the foreground contrasts sharply with the rich agricultural land in the background. Recently, Guitian Ojea (pers. comm.) has identified a new serpentinicolous species of *Centaurea* (*C. borjae*) from this area. A possibly new serpentine-endemic subspecies of *Alyssum serpyllifolium* also supplied by him, contained 1.15% nickel and is clearly of hyperaccumulator status (Chapter 8 and Section 14.2.5 of this chapter).

14.2.3   Soils and Vegetation and of Serpentine in Northeast Portugal

Soils

The serpentine soils of northeast Portugal have been studied by Menezes de Sequeira (1969) and by Pinto da Silva (1970). The soils are classified as lithosols and humic lithosols and their main characteristics are: the high abundance of small pebbles, the dark reddish colour strongly reminiscent of laterites in tropical zones, the low abundance of calcium, potassium and sodium, and the high concentrations of nickel, chromium, cobalt, iron and exchangeable magnesium. The serpentine soils of Trás-os-Montes ("Beyond the Mountains") province are therefore typical of many such soils elsewhere.

Vegetation

Numbers of species. The serpentine vegetation of Trás-os-Montes has been described by Menezes de Sequeira (1969) and Pinto da Silva (1964, 1970, 1981). Pinto da Silva (1970) reported a total of 409 species comprising 29% of the total of all plants growing in the province. This percentage is comparable to the 25% recorded by Rune (1953) for the much more impoverished vegetation of northern Sweden. The Portuguese serpentine flora contains a high number of taxa considered as serpentinicolous though only a few are truly endemic to the Portuguese serpentines. A total of 55 endemics is given in Table 14.2. This table also includes serpentinimorphoses and the overall total of all species is surprisingly high when the relatively small area of serpentine is considered (80 km^2).

TABLE 14.2   Characteristic Plants of the Trás-os-Montes Serpentine Areas of Portugal

Cheilanthes marantae	*Pteridium aquilinum*	*Asplenium cuneifolium*
Quercus ilex	*Quercus suber*	*Arenaria tetraquetra*
subsp. *rotundifolia*	*Spergularia purpurea*	subsp. *fontiqueri*
Silene legionensis	var. *congesta*	*Dianthus marizii*
Alyssum pintodasilvae	*Ionopsidium abulense*	*Iberis linifolia*
Reseda virgata	*Sesamoides canescens*	var. *serpentinicola*
Umbilicus rupestris	*Genista hystrix*	*Trifolium bocconei*
var. *violaceus*	var. *villosa*	*Trifolium cherleri*
Trifolium strictum	*Anthyllis sampaiana*	*Lotus tenuis*
var. *minus*	*Astragalus macrorhizus*	var. *serpentinicola*
Eryngium tenue	*Seseli peixoteanum*	*Armeria eriophylla*
var. *pumilum*	*Armeria langei*	*Armeria langei*
Convolvulus arvensis	subsp. *langei*	subsp. *daveaui*
var. *parviflorus*	*Linaria aeruginea*	*Plantago radicata*
Jasione crispa	var. *simplex*	var. *radicata*
subsp. *serpentinicola*	*Santolina semidentata*	*Tragopogon crocifolius*
Scorzonera hispanica	*Podospermum tenuifolium*	var. *serpentinicola*
subsp. *asphodeloides*	*Phleum bertolonii*	*Agrostis castellana*
Molineria laevis	*Periballia involucrata*	*Trisetaria ovata*
Gaudinia fragilis	*Koeleria crassipes*	*Dactylis glomerata*
var. *violacea*	*Festuca ovina*	subsp. *hispanica*
Micropyrum tenellum	subsp. *brigantina*	*Aegilops ovata*
var. *tenellum*	*Taeniatherum*	subsp. *ovata*
Allium gaditanum	caputmedusae	*Allium sphaerocephalon*
var. *exiguum*	subsp. *crinitum*	var. *pallidum*
Scilla autumnalis	*Allium vineale*	
var. *deflexoscaposa*	var. *minus*	

After: Pinto da Silva (1970)

Family representation on serpentine. Rune (1953) has reported the preponderance of the Caryophyllaceae among the serpentine plants of northern Sweden. In Portugal however, the Caryophyllaceae are much less important due perhaps to the paucity of numbers of taxa in this family in the surrounding vegetation which should be considered as the source for these serpentine taxa. Table 14.3 gives the percentage distribution of 15 plant families on and off serpentine in the Trás-os-Montes region of Portugal. The table shows the relative importance of the Fabaceae and Brassicaceae which have a much higher percentage not only in Portugal compared with Sweden but also in comparison with the surrounding non-serpentinitic Portuguese flora. The Asteraceae are likewise better represented on serpentine though the Ericaceae have a low percentage.

The poor representation of the Brassicaceae in northeast Portugal is somewhat misleading. Although this family contains only 12 taxa (2.9%) on serpentine compared with 55 (3.8%) in the surrounding flora on non-ultramafites, the list does include the well-known *Alyssum pintodasilvae* (see Chapter 8 and Dudley, 1986a) which was only the third hyperaccumulator of nickel to be discovered (i.e. after *A. bertolonii* and *A. murale*). The high nickel content of this taxon (ca. 1% in dried leaves), was first discovered by Menezes de Sequeira (1969) and was later investigated by Brooks and Radford (1978), Dudley (1986a), and Brooks et al. (1981a). *A. pintodasilvae* is an extremely common plant on Portuguese serpentines and is illustrated in Plate 14.2.

TABLE 14.3 Numbers and Percentages of Members of Plant Families of Serpentine Vegetation of Trás-os-Montes, Portugal Compared with Adjacent Non-ultramafic Areas.

Family	Ultramafic areas		Non ultramafic areas	
	#	%	#	%
Polypodiaceae	11	2.7	16	1.1
Caryophyllaceae	32	7.8	64	4.4
Ranunculaceae	6	1.5	36	2.5
Brassicaceae	12	2.9	55	3.8
Rosaceae	9	2.2	52	3.6
Fabaceae	48	11.7	123	8.6
Apiaceae	12	2.9	52	3.6
Ericaceae	3	0.7	10	0.7
Lamiaceae	10	2.4	40	2.7
Scrophulariaceae	15	3.7	56	3.9
Astetaceae	52	12.7	140	9.8
Poaceae	68	16.6	125	8.8
Cyperaceae	11	2.7	26	1.8
Liliaceae	15	3.7	42	2.9
Other families	105	25.6	585	41.1
Total	409	99.8	1422	99.3

Source: Pinto da Silva (1970)

Life form spectra. The Raunkiaer life form spectrum of the serpentine flora of Trás-os-Montes is shown in Table 14.4 and is compared with spectra from other parts of Europe including the serpentines of the Upper Tiber Valley in Tuscany (Pichi-Sermolli, 1948) and elsewhere in the Iberian Peninsula. The life form spectrum of Portuguese serpentine plants is very similar to that of vegetation of non-serpentine rocks from western Italy (Argentario) and is typical of a Mediterranean climate. By contrast the serpentine flora of Tuscany is deficient in therophytes (Table 14.4) and has been classified by Pichi-Sermolli as belonging to the sub-montane element. The life form spectra for Spain and Portugal show that the floristics of the Iberian Peninsula may be considered as a single unit.

Serpentinimorphosis. Serpentinimorphosis as defined by Rune (1953) may be described as morphological changes in the member species of vegetation of serpentine areas which enable individual taxa to be distinguished from their close relatives off serpentine, whether or not these serpentinimorphoses have been classified as separate species, subspecies or varieties.

Table 14.5 lists serpentinophytes of Trás-os-Montes showing morphological changes. The most common indication of serpentinimorphosis is glaucescence found in 63% of the species listed. Clearly stenophyllism, nanism and plagiotropism are also important morphological changes. Macrorrhizism does not feature as a very important indication, as only 27% of the plants showed this character, though it was evident in 38% of the therophytes.

From Table 14.5 it will be noted that a number of serpentinimorphoses in northeast Portugal are also identical with those found in the Upper Tiber Valley.

TABLE 14.4 Life Form Spectra of Portuguese and Italian Floras on Serpentine and on Other Substrates

Flora	Alt.	No. of species	Ph	Ch	H	G	Th
SERPENTINE FLORAS							
Trás-os-Montes (Port.)	500 m	409	8	8	33	10	41
Upper Tiber (Italy)	700 m	405	11	9	40	14	26
NON-SERPENTINE FLORAS							
Whole of Portugal	—	2696	11	7	49		33
Argentario (Italy)	0	866	12	6	29	11	42
Balkan Peninsula	—	6995	7	15	45	12	21
Friuli (N.E. Italy)	sea level	850	8	4	43	15	30
submontane	0–400 m	1161	9	5	52	13	21
montane	400 m	1083	9	7	59	11	14
subalpine	1600 m	551	5	14	67	9	6
alpine	2000 m	395	3	17	71	5	4

Ph = phanerophytes, Ch = chamaephytes, H = hemicryptophytes, G = geophytes, Th = therophytes.
Sources: Pinto da Silva (1970), Pichi-Sermolli (1948)

TABLE 14.5 Serpentinimorphoses Common to Both the Trás-os-Montes and Tuscan Serpentines

Trás-os-Montes (Portugal)	Upper Tiber Valley (Tuscany)
Alyssum pintodasilvae	*Alyssum bertolonii*
Anthyllis sampaiana	*Anthyllis dillenii* subsp. *tricolor*
Astragalus macrorhizus	*Astragalus monspessulanus*
Armeria eriophylla	*Armeria denticulata*
Armeria langei subsp. *langei*	*Plantago holosteum*
Armeria langei subsp. *daveaui*	*Festuca ovina* var. *glauca*
Plantago radicata var. *radicata*	*Aegilops ovata* var. *glauca*
Festuca ovina subsp. *brigantina*	
Aegilops ovata subsp. *nana*	

Source: Pinto da Silva (1970)

Plate 13.4   (a) Above: *Minuartia verna* subsp *gerardi* growing on serpentine at Kynance Cove, Cornwall.
Photo by A. J. M. Baker.
(b) Below: Serpentine barren at Junstern Klumpen, Sweden. The line of trees in the background marks the boundary.
Photo by W. R. Lauder.

Plate 14.1 (a) Above: Serpentine heath at Mellid near La Coruña, Northwest Spain. The heath in the foreground contrasts sharply with the rich farmland in the background.
Photo by F. F. Guitian Ojea.
(b) Below: *Alyssum murale* meadow over serpentine at Mt Voras Northern Greece. The background (also on serpentine) shows a *Quercus frainetto* woodland.
Photo by D. Babalonas.

Plate 14.1   (c) Above: *Linum elegans* over serpentine at 1000 m on Mt Vourinos.
Photo by D. Babalonas.
(d) Below: Contact zone between serpentine and limestone at Kandili, Euboa. The ochre-coloured
serpentine has a sparse cover of *Erica verticillata*.
Photo by W. Krause.

Plate 14.2 *Alyssum pintodasilvae* in full flower over serpentine in northeast Portugal. Photo by A. R. Pinto da Silva.

Phytogeographic character of the serpentine flora of Trás-os-Montes. The flora of the serpentines of northeast Portugal is of especial interest because of its geographical position at the western rim of the Mediterranean region and at the junction between the Atlantic and plateau climatic environments. The various floral elements contributing to the Portuguese serpentine flora are recorded in Table 14.6. The predominant floral element is still Mediterranean and is even stronger than that of the Upper Tiber Valley in Tuscany. Endemic taxa are also much more numerous (22% compared with only 3%).

In the vicinity of the Portuguese serpentine region, the Central European element contributes 52% to the total compared with only 30% from the Mediterranean element. The effect of serpentine is, however, to reverse this order.

TABLE 14.6 Phytogeographic Spectra of the Serpentine Floras of Trás-os-Montes and the Upper Tiber Valley

	Percentage	
Element	Trás-os-Montes	Upper Tiber
Eurosiberian-boreal American	21	38
Mediterranean	43	42
Endemic	22	3
Pluriregional and cosmopolitan	14	17

Sources: Pinto da Silva (1970), Pichi-Sermolli (1948)

Plant communities on serpentine in Portugal. The serpentine vegetation of Portugal has been divided by Pinto da Silva (1970) into 8 phytosociological units. Those of gently-sloping or level terrain have been incorporated by Ernst (1974) into a single Association; Armerio-Arenarietum fontiqueri, of the Armerion eriophyllae Alliance within the Thero-Brachypodietea Class. Character species of the Association are: *Arenaria tetraquetra, Dianthus marizii, Alyssum pintodasilvae, Seseli peixoteanum, Armeria eriophylla, Jasione crispa* and *Reseda virgata.*

Disjunctions in the Portuguese serpentine flora. Disjunction is a characteristic of many serpentine floras throughout the world, notably in boreal regions as has already been noted in Chapters 11 and 13 for the Gaspé Peninsula, Scotland and Fennoscandia. In warmer climates such as that of the Iberian Peninsula, disjunctions are less apparent but have indeed been reported by Pinto da Silva (1970) for taxa such as *Armeria langei* subsp. *langei,* and subsp. *daveaui, Silene legionensis, Ionopsidium abulense, Reseda virgata, Astragalus macrorhizus,* and *Plantago radicata.* The latter has two varieties, var. *monticola* and var. *radicata* which may well represent the same taxon at disjunct occurrences. All of the above disjunctions involve cases where the plants are confined to serpentine in Portugal but are found on other rocks to the north in more unfavourable climates.

14.2.4 Soils and Vegetation of Serpentines of Southeast Spain

Soils

The soils overlying serpentine are red limonite-rich soils and lithosols. They are in general fairly humic and have a good water-retention capacity. The pH is usually quite high (7.0) and the soils contain elevated quantities of chromium and nickel. Hoyos de Castro (1960) has presented analytical data for major elements in two profiles of limonitic ultramafic soils from Serrania de Ronda. The most notable feature of the soils is the loss of MgO during the soil-forming process. There is also a fairly strong loss of silica and an accumulation of Fe_2O_3 and Al_2O_3, particularly in clay minerals. The same author showed that the parent rock contained about 50% serpentine, 20% olivine and 20% amphibole. Gonzalez (1975) has reported 0.3% nickel, 0.02% chromium and 0.01% cobalt in these parent rocks.

Vegetation

The serpentine vegetation of southeast Spain has been studied by Palacios (1936), Rivas Goday (1969, 1972, 1973), Caballos Viciosa (1933), Rivas Martinez et al. (1973) and Gonzalez (1975). A provisional list of serpentine plants compiled from these workers is shown in Table 14.7 and includes some 38 taxa of which 6 are endemic to serpentines only, and 8 are endemic to both serpentine and dolomite.

The main phytosociological Association of the serpentinicolous flora of southeast Spain is the Asperulo-Staehelminetum baeticae and is the ubiquitous shrub community covering much of the peridotites of the Sierra Bermeja. It contains most of the endemic plants of these ultramafites and includes a number of acidicolous plants such as *Adenocarpus telonensis*, *Lavandula stoechas*, *Inula odora* etc. The Association is extremely homogeneous and local variation is very slight. The cover is more-or-less dense with a preponderance of chamaephytes. This community represents the first stage in the degradation of the climax vegetation which has all but been destroyed and in which the only trees are species of *Pinus* such as *P. pinea*, *P. pinaster*, and *P. halepensis* recolonising previously-cultivated terrain. It is interesting to record that *P. halepensis* is the dominant tree on serpentine several thousand kilometres to the east on Euboa in the Aegean, while *P. pinea* and *P. pinaster* are typical trees of the Tuscan serpentines.

Rivas Martinez et al. (1973) have also described a serpentine plant community dominated by *Iberis fontqueri* (Brassicaceae), and *Arenaria capillipes* (Caryophyllaceae). Character species of the Association are *Pistorinia breviflora*, *Silene lasiostyla*, *Arenaria retusa*, *Catapodium salzmanni*, and *Omphalodes brassicifolia*.

TABLE 14.7 Serpentine Vegetation of Southeast Spain

PLANTS FOUND ON SERPENTINE ONLY

Cerastium gibraltaricum	Teucrium reverchonii*
Centaurea carratracensis*	Saxifraga gemmulosa
Cheilanthes marantae	Dianthus boisseri
Galium viridiflorum*	Serratula baetica
Linum suffruticosum	Digitalis laciniata
subsp. carratracensis*	Staehelina baetica*
Genista lanuginosa*	Linaria rossmaessleri
Scorzonera baetica	Armeria colorata*
Cephalaria boetica	Phlomis × composita var. carratracensis
Iberis fontqueri	Arenaria capillipes

PLANTS CONFINED TO SERPENTINE AND DOLOMITE

Arenaria retusa*	Catapodium salzmanni
Linaria saturejoides*	Omphalodes brassicifolia
Silene psammitis subsp. lasiostyla	Alyssum malacitanum*
Asperula asperrima	Bunium macuca
Centaurea prolongi*	Digitalis laciniata var. laciniata*
Crambe filiformis var. granatense	Linaria anticaria var. angustifolia
Echium albicans*	Ulex parviflorus subsp. linkii
Linaria demavendica	Ulex baeticus*

* endemic species
Sources: Rivas Goday (1969, 1972, 1973), Gonzalez (1975)

14.2.5 Biogeochemical Investigations on Serpentine Vegetation of the Iberian Peninsula

There have been relatively few biogeochemical investigations on the flora of the serpentines of the Iberian Peninsula. Most of the work has been centred around the chemical composition of the various serpentinicolous morphological forms of the ubiquitous *Alyssum serpyllifolium* such as *A. pintodasilvae* from Trás-os-Montes (Menezes de Sequeira, 1969; Brooks and Radford, 1978; Dudley, 1986a), *A. malacitanum* from Sierra Bermeja (Brooks et al. 1981a; Dudley, 1986b), and a form from La Coruña which at present has not been recognised as being a distinct taxon. In their work on *A. malacitanum,* Shaw (1980) and Brooks et al. (1981a,b) determined 5 elements in a number of specimens of this genus and found a very high mean nickel content (2.08%) in dried leaves. The Ca/Mg mole quotient was a high 2.70 and parallels similar behaviour for *Alyssum argenteum* in the Alps of Central Europe. This may well be a mechanism for tolerating the low calcium content of serpentine; i.e., inordinate uptake of this element compared with magnesium which is much more abundant in the soil.

Biogeochemical work has also been carried out by Lopez Lopez and Guitian Ojea (1981) who have determined copper, nickel, chromium, calcium and magnesium in leaves of several *bodenvag* taxa growing on and off serpentine near La Coruña. As might have been expected the plants growing over serpentine had much higher levels of nickel, chromium and cobalt than those on non-ultramafic substrates.

14.3 CONTINENTAL FRANCE

14.3.1 Geology

Serpentine outcrops at 4 main regions in continental France. The first of these is in the Massif Armoricain of Brittany (Site 4 in Fig. 14.2) where the ultramafites are very similar to those of the Lizard Peninsula in Cornwall. Both outcrops are part of the so-called Central Variscides (Ager, 1980) of Meso-Europa (Fig. 14.1) in which orogeny started in the early Carboniferous and reached its maximum in the Permian. This Variscan orogeny is sometimes known as the Hercynian.

The second region of serpentine outcrops in continental France is in the *Departements* of Haute-Vienne and Aveyron (sites 5 and 6 of Fig. 14.2) in the Massif Central of Southwest France where the occurrences are also of Variscan origin. In Haute-Vienne the ultramafites cover about 20 km^2 in a series of outcrops of which only about 15 are large enough to carry a characteristic serpentine vegetation at sites near La Flotte and La Roche l'Abeille.

In the *Departement* of Aveyron, the best known of the serpentine outcrops are those of the Massif de la Bessenoits in which the Puy de Voll near Firmi is characteristically bare of vegetation. The Massif de la Cau, another important outcrop, occupies about 2 km^2 a few kilometres north of Puy de Voll.

The third region of continental France in which ultramafic outcrops occur is in the Pyrenees near St Béat and Bagnère de Luchon. Lake Lherz nearby, is the type locality for lherzolite.

The fourth serpentine occurrence in France is found in the southeast of the country in the Alps of Neo-Europa near the Val d'Isère close to the Italian border. The rocks are known locally as "roches vertes" (Nicolas, 1966), the green colour being due principally to the presence of serpentine. These rocks however also contain prasinites and metamorphic gabbros which are the chief components of the ophiolites of the area. The main occurrence of ultramafic rocks in this region is, however, across the border in Valle d'Aosta in the Vallée d'Ayas and the vegetation of this region is therefore discussed under Italy below.

14.3.2 Vegetation and Soils of Serpentines of the Massif Central

Vegetation units and soils

The serpentine vegetation of the Massif Central in the *Departements* of Haute-Vienne and Aveyron has been studied by Le Gendre (1919) and Duvigneaud (1966). The latter work is the more detailed of the two and is the main source material for the following short account. The soils of the region (Sasse, 1979a) are modified by the Atlantic climate. In contrast to the skeletal juvenile soils of many serpentine areas, these French soils have an appreciable clay content and have a red or red-brown texture, often with an appreciable organic component. The level of available calcium is also higher than would be expected for this type of soil and is typically in the range 12–43 meq./100 g soil. The same is true for exchangeable potassium (0.1–0.4 meq./100 g). Nickel and cobalt concentrations in the soils are typically 100 and 200 μg/g respectively as reported by Mouchoux (1961) for soils from the Puy de Voll. The main vegetation units recognized by Duvigneaud (1966) are summarized in Table 14.8.

TABLE 14.8 Plant Communities on Serpentine in the Massif Central, France

Description	Species
A — Pteridophytis of crevices	*Asplenium cuneifolium* *Notholaena marantae*
B — Pioneers of humic pockets in serpentine	*Sedum reflexum* *Scleranthus perennis*
C — Grassland on gravelly soils	*Festuca longifolia* *Koeleria vallesiana* *Armeria plantaginea*
D — Grassland on mature limonitic soils	*Brachypodium sp.* *Filipendula vulgaris*
E — Heaths on leached impoverished soils	*Erica vagans* *Ulex nanus* *Genista pilosa*
F — Forest on leached soils	*Quercus robur* *Castanea sativa* *Pteridium aquilinum*
G — Thorny thickets	*Prunus spinosa* *Rubus* spp.

After: Duvigneaud (1966)

Endemic species

Several species are locally confined to serpentine in the Massif Central. These are summarized in Table 14.9. Some of these taxa such as *Notholaena marantae,* a Mediterranean plant, have a disjunct appearance on serpentine to the north of their range whereas further south they are not confined to serpentine. A parallel phenomenon has been observed for species from the serpentines of eastern America which exist only on serpentine at localities close to the sites of maximum advance of the ice during the last glaciation. Among the other serpentine endemic taxa recorded in Table 14.9, few are endemic at the specific level and they are mainly serpentinimorphoses of non-serpentine taxa.

Affinities with other serpentine floras

The serpentine flora of the Massif Central is strongly reminiscent of that of the Lizard Peninsula (See Chapter 13). Communities and species common to both regions are a xerophytic *Festuca* grassland, a mesophytic *Brachypodium pinnatum* grassland, an *Erica vagans* heath, and a *Molinia caerulea* meadow. Pairs of closely related taxa in both regions (Cornwall first) are: *Koeleria gracilis* and *K. vallesiana, Armeria maritima* and *A. plantaginea, Sedum anglicum* and *S. reflexum.*

The serpentine flora of the Massif Central has also certain affinities with that of La Coruña in northwest Spain (see above) and with that of the d'Arguenos lherzolite massif in the Pyrenees where a *Molinia caerulea* and *Erica vagans* heath has become established.

In common with the serpentine floras of Cornwall and La Coruña, the serpentine vegetation of the Massif Central is not typically serpentinitic in its physiognomy. The reason, as has been observed in Cornwall, is probably the presence of a thick layer of humus in these soils which effectively insulates the plants from the full influence of the ultramafic substrate.

TABLE 14.9 Endemic or Locally-endemic Plants of the Serpentines of the Massif Central, France

Agrostis canina var. *decipiens**	*Agrostis rupestris*
Allium ochroleucum	*Armeria sabulosa* var. *serpentini**
*Asplenium adulterinum**	*Asplenium cuneifolium**
Asplenium septentrionale var. *nana**	*Astrocarpus purparescens*
Biscutella laevigata subsp. *lamottei**	*Centaurea decipiens*
Dianthus monspessulanus	*Erica vagans*
Euphorbia flavicoma subsp. *costeana**	*Galium viridulum*
Koeleria setacea	*Notholaena marantae*
Pimpinella saxifraga var. *dissectifolia*	*Sagina patula*
Sanguisorba officinalis var. *serpentini**	*Scleranthus biennis*
Sedum albescens	*Sedum telephium*
Serratula tinctoria	*Silene rupicola*
Spergularia rubra subsp. *serpentini**	*Spiraea filipendula*
Thymus serpyllum var. *serpentini**	

*locally endemic.
After: Duvigneaud (1966)

14.3.3 Biogeochemical Studies on French Serpentine Plants

Biogeochemical investigations on French serpentine plants have been carried out by Duvigneaud (1966) and Sasse (1979b). The former determined potassium, calcium, magnesium, nitrogen and phosphorus in several serpentinicolous plants from the Massif Central outcrops. The maximum uptake of nutrients was found in *Silene inflata.* The serpentinophytes were all characterised by a low uptake of all of the nutrients. Ca/Mg mole quotients were in most cases well below unity and ranged from 0.17 in *Vincetoxicum officinale* to 1.38 in *Calluna vulgaris.* The higher value for *C. vulgaris* was probably not so much due to inordinate uptake of calcium but rather was caused by the thick humus layer of the A horizon shielding the plant from the effects of serpentine in the C horizon. In this respect there is a pronounced similarity with *C. vulgaris* in the heaths of Cornwall (Chapter 13).

Sasse (1979b) determined Ni, Cr, Co, Ca, Mg, K, Na, Fe, Mn, Zn, Cu and P in a number of characteristic serpentine plants from the same region. No unusual accumulation of nickel was noted in any taxon (see Chapter 8) and chromium levels were invariably much lower than those for nickel. Although the data presented by Sasse (1979b) are not appreciably different from what would normally be expected for serpentine plants, they do represent a fairly comprehensive listing of taxa found on the French ultramafic outcrops.

Finally, mention should be made of the work of Reeves and Brooks (1983a) who determined zinc and nickel in European species of *Thlaspi* (including *Noccaea*—see Fig. 8.6).

They found that *N. firmiensis* from Aveyron contained over 1.6% nickel and is clearly of hyperaccumulator status. Similarly high nickel values were found in *T. rotundifolium* growing just inside the Italian border in the Val d'Ayas (Valle d'Aosta). The same taxon is, however, found in the much less widespread serpentine occurrences on the French side of the border. Although *T. rotundifolium* may once have been removed from the Val d'Ayas by glacial advances in the Quaternary and then retreated to lower altitudes, it has since apparently recolonised its former sites after recession of the glaciers.

14.4 CENTRAL EUROPE

14.4.1 Geology

There are several small outcrops of ultramafic rocks in Germany in the Harz Mountains (Site 9 in Fig. 14.2), and in the Fichtelgebirge in northeast Bavaria near the Czech border at Grötschenreuth and Wurlitz (sites 10 and 11). The most important serpentine occurrences in Austria are near Kraubath and constitute the largest contiguous areas of ultramafites in Central Europe (Site 12).

The Harz Massif is about 90 km long and 30 km wide and can be divided into three main sections: the Upper Harz, Middle Harz and Lower Harz. Serpentine outcrops are found in a small area of the Upper Harz in the Harz gabbros of the Upper Harz Diabase Belt (Oberharzer Diabaszug) near Clausthal, the mediaeval mining centre of the Harz. The region is the type locality for harzburgite. The Harz itself is part of Meso-Europa and was formed during the Variscan orogeny.

The serpentine outcrops in northeast Bavaria are located in Pre-Tertiary basic and ultramafic rocks at the western extremity of the Bohemian Massif, another product of the Variscan orogeny. Isolated serpentine occurrences are also found in Bohemia just across the border and in southwest Moravia (see below).

The ultramafic outcrop at Kraubath lies within the Eastern Alps of Neo-Europa. It is part of a massif some 14 km long and with a mean width of 2 km. A brief description of the geology of the area has been given by Johannes (1984). The body is composed mainly of serpentinized dunites, pyroxenites and other ultramafic rocks. Chrome mining was carried out here during the period 1855–1881 and also during World War I.

Serpentine outcrops are also found in southern Poland at Szklana Gora in the Bohemian Massif (site 13 in Fig. 14.2) and in southern Hungary.

14.4.2 Serpentine Vegetation

The Harz

Because the serpentine outcrops of the Harz are individually very small in area, there is little characteristic serpentine vegetation. However Johannes (1984) and Pape (1978) have described the vegetation of the region which is covered by the ubiquitous *Picea abies* and *Pinus sylvestris* with an understorey of *Calluna vulgaris* in the more open areas. Although there has been little or no description of serpentine vegetation in the region, the Harz has been the scene of an extremely original and thorough biogeochemical investigation (see below).

Northeast Bavaria

The serpentine vegetation of northeast Bavaria has been described by Gauckler (1954), Ernst (1974) and Sasse (1979b). There are significant areas of this type of plant cover on the serpentine terraces of Wurlitz. The main community here is the Diantho gratianopolitanae—Armerietum serpentini Association originally described by Gauckler (1954) and modified by Ernst (1974). It is the poorest in species of all of the Associations of the Asplenio serpentini-Festucion glaucae Alliance. Its main characteristics as outlined by Ernst (1974) are shown in

Table 14.10. It may be appropriate at this stage to make some general observations on the serpentine communities of Central and Southern Europe. They all belong to the Violetea calaminariae Class (as do the serpentine plants of Northwest Europe—see Chapter 13) within which the Order Halacsyetalia sendtneri includes three Alliances : Asplenio serpentini-Festucion glaucae (southeastern part of Central Europe), Polgonion albanicae (central Bosnia), and Potentillon visianii (eastern Bosnia, Serbia, Macedonia, and Albania). The Diantho gratianopolitanae Association occurs only intermittently in the Grötschenreuth area where it is sometimes replaced with *Pinus sylvestris* over the less phytotoxic soils.

TABLE 14.10 The Diantho gratianopolitanae—Armerietum serpentini Association of Northeast Bavaria

Height above sea level	530 m
Percentage cover	75–90
Character species of the Association	*Armeria maritima* var. *serpentinii*, *Dianthus gratianopolitanus*
Character species of the Alliance (Asplenio-Festucion)	*Festuca cinerea*
Character species of the Order (Halacsyetalia)	*Asplenium adiantum-nigrum* subsp. *serpentini*
Character species of the Class (Violetea calaminariae)	*Silene cucubalus*
Companion species	*Thesium alpinum, Potentilla verna, Thymus pulegioides, Arenaria serpyllifolia, Sedum acre, Rumex acetosella, Galium verum, Hedwigia ciliata, Cephaloziella starkei, Cladonia rangiformis, C. chlorophaea, C. mitis, Cornicularia aculeata, Cetraria islandica, Polytrichum pilosum, Ceratodon purpureus, Centaurea scabiosa, Polytrichum juniperinum*

After: Ernst (1974)

Kraubath

The serpentine vegetation of Kraubath has been described by Eggler (1955) who has outlined a number of plant communities of this type. The typical Association of serpentine itself is Festucetum glaucae—longifoliae gulsenense which has been classified by Ernst (1974) as a Subassociation of Diantho carthusianori—Festucetum cinereae with character species: *Festuca cinerea, Dianthus carthusianorum, Euphorbia cyparissias* and *Allium montanum*. Differentials of the Subassociation are *Erysimum sylvestre, Armeria maritima* subsp. *elongata*, and *Carex humilis*.

As described by Eggler (1955), the vegetation of crevices in the serpentine belongs to the Asplenietum serpentini gulsenense Association which has been incorporated by Ernst (1974) into the Diantho carthusianorum—Festucion cinereae Association.

In soils with a lower nickel content, the above Association is replaced with a scanty community of *Pinus sylvestris* with *Erica herbacea* in the understorey.

Space does not permit a description of serpentine vegetation of other parts of Austria and the reader is referred to Ernst (1974) for a further discussion of these.

Poland

The vegetation of the serpentine areas of Polish Silesia at Szklana Mountain near Zabkowic has been described by Sarosiek (1964) and later by Sulej et al. (1970) who used serpentine soil to carry out pot trials on a number of crop plants and vegetables. The vegetation cover is primarily *Pinus sylvestris* with stands of *Betula verrucosa*, *Salix caprea* and *Larix europaea*. The ground storey is dominated by *Trifolium arvense*, *Tussilago farfara*, and *Achillea millefolium*.

Czechoslovakia

The serpentine vegetation of Czechoslovakia has been described by a number of workers at various locations such as Marianske Lazne (site 20 in Fig. 14.2) in western Bohemia (Suza, 1927a), Mohelno in southwest Moravia (Suza, 1919, 1921, 1927b), and Raskov (Schüstler, 1920). The latter studied the serpentine-endemic fern *Asplenium adulterinum* and its intermediates with *A. viride*. Perhaps one of the best known endemic plants of the Czech ultramafites is *Cerastium alsinifolium* described by Novak (1928), and which is found at Mariankse Lazne. Serpentine vegetation at this site has recently been described by Müller-Stoll and Miloslav (1984). They have recognized four distinct Associations at the site which are associated with the Asplenietum serpentini Association in rock crevices.

The serpentine outcrop at Mohelno has a particularly rich flora described by Zlatnik (1928). The Asplenio serpentini—Seslerietum calcariae Association belongs to the Halacsyetalia Order and Asplenio—Festucion Alliance and has as its Association character species : *Sesleria varia*, *Armeria maritima*, *Biscutella laevigata* and *Dianthus pontederae*. A heliophile variant of this Association known as Euphorbio sequierianae—Festucetum, has *Carex humilis* as its differential. Character species of this variant are: *Festuca cinerea*, *Euphorbia sequieriana*, *Stipa capillata*, *S. pulcherrima* subsp. *mediterranea*, *Hieracium echioides* and *Allium flavum*. For a full listing of companion species for both of these Associations see Ernst (1974).

Hungary

Phytosociological studies of the vegetation of Hungarian serpentines have been carried out by Soo (1934) and Zolyomi (1936) but because of limitations of space are not discussed further in this book.

14.4.3 Biogeochemical Studies

The Harz

Perhaps the most important biogeochemical studies ever carried out in Europe are those of Pape (1978, 1981) and Johannes (1984). Pape (1978) initiated a comprehensive programme involving the analysis of a very large number of vegetation samples from *Picea abies* (needles), *Calluna vulgaris* (leaves) and *Juniperus communis* (needles). The specimens were taken from plants growing over a wide range of rock types in the Upper Harz area and were analysed for 23 elements (Li, Na, K, Rb, Mg, Ca, Sr, Ba, Al, P, Ti, V, Cr, Mn, Fe, Co, Ni, Cu, Zn, Mo, Cd, B and Pb). Geometric means of all elemental concentrations were calculated and the values were arranged in 13 concentration classes (6 below the mean, 1 equal to the mean and 6 above it: i.e., −6 to +6). Class 0 corresponded to the mean value over all rock types. The concentration classes were determined on the basis of a scale of 10, 10−1/loge, 10−2/loge, etc. for values below 0, and 10+1/loge, 10+2/loge etc. for values above the mean value. Hence a typical range of concentrations values for a given plant could be; 2.51, 3.16, 3.98, 5.01, 6.31, 7.94, 10 (class 0), 12.3, 14.6, 16.9, 19.2, 21.5, 23.8%.

From the data for the 23 elements, elemental associations were derived from a comparison of isoconcentration contours for each element in each of three species and a statistical correlation with each of the other elements. The data were then plotted on a map which showed a marked similarity with the geological map. This work shows the potential of the biogeochemical method for geological mapping particularly today, when multielement analysis with techniques such as plasma emission spectrometry (ICP) is commonplace, speedy and inexpensive.

Similar studies to the above have also been carried out by Johannes (1984) but are not described fully because they did not include serpentine vegetation. Basically, however, the technique involved plotting maps for individual species for each element rather than preparing a multielement map.

Northeast Bavaria

Biogeochemical work on plants from Grötschenreuth (Plate 14.3a) and Wurlitz in northeast Bavaria has been carried out by Sasse (1979b). He determined Ni, Cr, Co, Ca, Mg, K, Na, Fe, Mn, Zn, Cu and P in *Asplenium cuneifolium* (Plate 14.6b), *Dianthus gratianopolitanus*, *Armeria elongata* subsp. *serpentinii* and *Silene vulgaris*. The characteristic plant of this Association, *D. gratianopolitanus*, contained the highest nickel content (61 μg/g in dried leaves) and had a low Ca/Mg mole quotient (0.54).

Kraubath

As part of a study which also involved the Harz region, Johannes (1984) determined 23 elements in samples of plant ash from *Pinus sylvestris* growing over serpentine at Kraubath. He reported a mean of 132 μg/g nickel, 21 μg/g chromium and 6.75% magnesium for the samples. The same species growing over basic rocks in the Harz region gave values of 73, 9 and 2.53 respectively. In *Calluna vulgaris* the nickel contents were 188 and 105 μg/g respectively and for chromium were 15 and 13 μg/g. Magnesium gave respective values of 12.1 and 2.6%.

Sasse (1979b) determined 12 elements in serpentine plants from Kraubath. The species analysed included: *Asplenium cuneifolium*, *Cheilanthes marantae*, *Festuca cinerea*, *Alyssum montanum*, *Armeria elongata* subsp. *elongata*, *Silene vulgaris* and *Erica herbacea*. The highest nickel content was found in *Alyssum montanum* (52 μg/g) which also had by far the highest Ca/Mg mole quotient (0.9). This high value was due to the relatively high calcium content (5.36%) of the dried leaves. The high nickel content of *Alyssum* species of Section Odontarrhena growing over serpentine has already been discussed in Chapter 8. Although *A. montanum* does not belong to section Odontarrhena, the nickel concentration reported was high for any non-accumulator growing over serpentine.

Hyperaccumulation of nickel was found by Reeves and Brooks (1983a) for specimens of *Thlaspi goesingense* from Bruck an der Mur (near Kraubath). On serpentine the taxon contained over 1% nickel in dried leaves and also showed hyperaccumulation of zinc (2000 μg/g).

14.5 ITALY AND CORSICA

14.5.1 Geology

There are numerous serpentine outcrops in northern and northwestern Italy in the Appennine range and in the alpine zones of Piedmont and Valle d'Aosta. Geologically all the Italian serpentine occurrences lie within Neo-Europa (Fig. 14.1). The northern Appennines cover the old Italian provinces of Tuscany, Liguria, Umbria and Latium. The ultramafic rocks within the Appennines consist of a suite of pillow lavas, serpentinites and associated rocks of Jurassic age which decrease in size and abundance towards the northeast. The most striking mountains of serpentine can be seen along the coast road south of Livorno but to the northeast, the mountains become blocks and the blocks, pebbles. The ophiolites can be taken as being a wedge of ocean floor material thrust up from the Tyrrhenian Sea which lies to the west. The best-known serpentine areas of Tuscany are in the Impruneta (site 14 in Fig. 14.2), the Upper Tiber Valley, and at Monte Ferrato (site 15) near Florence.

The main serpentine occurrences outside the Appennines are located on the Italian side of the French border in the Northeast in the Valle d'Aosta (site 16 in Fig. 14.2). These are also part of Neo-Europa. Important ultramafic outcrops are also found in Corsica (site 18) in a Variscan extension of Meso-European rocks of the Iberian Massif. An important ophiolitic belt extends here from Cape Corse to Insecca in the southeast of the island.

14.5.2 An Introduction to the Serpentine Vegetation of Italy and Corsica

Corsica

Very little work has been done on the serpentine vegetation of Corsica, and I will merely recapitulate some of the findings of a previous chapter (Chapter 8) in which it was reported that Corsica is the home of two *Alyssum* species which hyperaccumulate nickel, *A. corsicum* and *A. robertianum*. The latter is the only one of the two which was originally endemic to Corsica but the former (Fig. 8.7) became established on a few hectares at the outskirts of Bastia as a result of having been transported from western Anatolia in a shipment of grain where it was present as weed seed. This occurred during the 14th century by courtesy of the Venetian traders. It was only a few years ago that the true origin of *Alyssum corsicum* was discovered.

Italy

It seems that the Italian serpentine vegetation was the first to be studied anywhere on earth. The work began in the 16th century when Caesalpino (1583) reported the presence of an "alyson" (*Alyssum bertolonii*) in the "black stones" of the Upper Tiber Valley. In more modern times the first detailed studies of the flora were by Amidei (1841) who was followed by a succession of numerous other Italian botanists who investigated the serpentine flora of Monte Ferrato, Impruneta, Alta Val Tiberina, Val di Cecina, Elba, and Montignosa (Pampanini, 1912; Fiori, 1920; Messeri, 1936; Corti, 1940; Pichi-Sermolli, 1936, 1948). Some areas in the northern Appennines were also studied as, for example, in Liguria (Martino and Orsino, 1969), Emilia (Pampanini, 1903; Pavarino, 1914, 1915, 1918; Negodi, 1941), and Prealpi near Turin (Mussa, 1937). Far less work has been carried out in the Alpine districts of Italy in Val d'Aosta, though Vaccari (1903) performed some early studies in this region.

By far the most detailed study of any Italian serpentine vegetation is the often-quoted paper by Pichi-Sermolli (1948) which to southern Europe was as important as that of Rune (1953) was to Fennoscandia. The Italian work ascribed the general infertility of Tuscan serpentine soils to their dark colour (absorbing much heat in summer), high stone and sand content (leading to overdrainage and xeric conditions), the low Ca/Mg quotient, and deficiency of calcium.

The intensity of study of Italian serpentine plants is due not only to the "headstart" provided by the classical botanists but also to the strong interest in this subject centred in the University of Florence which is conveniently located near some of the most important outcrops, and at which centre, Pichi-Sermolli's work was based, thus establishing a tradition which has been maintained with constant vigour by O. Vergnano Gambi and her co-workers.

14.5.3 The Serpentine Vegetation of Tuscany and Liguria

Plant communities

Ernst (1974) has proposed a plant Association for Tuscan serpentine areas, Alyssetum bertolonii, which contains two Subassociations, *Plantago holosteum* and *Centaurea paniculata*. This Association is within the Class Violetea calaminariae, Order Halacsyetalia and Alliance Asplenio-Festucion. It is one of three Alliances within the Order and its essentials are shown in Table 14.11. The list of companions includes most of the characteristic serpentine plants of the region.

The tree layer of the Appenninian serpentines is dominated (as elsewhere in the world) by species of pine. Plate 14.4a shows a sparse stand of *Pinus pinea* and *Pinus pinaster* over

TABLE 14.11 The Alyssetum bertolonii Association of Tuscan Serpentines

		Subassociations	
		A	B
Character species of the Association	Alyssum bertolonii	5	5
Differentials of Subassociation A	Plantago holosteum	5	—
	Juniperus oxycedrus	4	—
Differentials of Subassociation B	Centaurea paniculata	—	5
	Euphorbia nicaeensis	—	3
Character species of the Alliance	Festuca cinerea	5	5
Character species of the Order	Asplenium adiantum-nigrum subsp. serpentini	2	1
	Stachys recta	3	1
	Notholaena marantae	2	1
Character species of the Class	Silene cucubalus	2	1
Companions	Helichrysum italicum	5	5
	Thymus striatus	5	4
	Galium lucidum	5	3
	Genista januensis	5	2
	Stipa pulcherrima subsp. mediterranea	5	1
	Bromus erectus	5	1
	Hieracium piloselloides	4	4
	Sanguisorba minor	4	3
	Trinia glauca	4	2
	Centaurea jacea	4	1
	Picris hieracioides	4	1
	Cerastium semidecandrum	—	4
	Dianthus virgineus	3	4
	Aira capillaris	3	3
	Minuartia laricifolia	3	3
	Reichardia picroides	3	3
	Sedum rupestre	3	2
	Carlina corymbosa	3	2
	Silene paradoxa	3	2
	Artemisia alba	3	1
	Echium vulgare	3	1
	Cerastium campanulatum	3	1
	Carex caryophyllea	3	1
	Herniaria glabra	1	3
	Lactuca viminea	3	—
	Stachys hyssopifolia	3	—
	Hippocrepis comosa	3	—
	Knautia illyrica	3	—
	Ceterach officinarum	2	2
	Armeria denticulata	2	3
	Linum trigynum	2	1
	Dactylis glomerata	2	1
	Dorycnium hirsutum	2	—
	Arenaria serpyllifolia	2	—

		Subassociations	
		A	B
Companions (cont.)	Gastridium lendigerum	2	—
	Cuscuta epithymum	2	—
	Rubus ulmifolius	2	—
	Prunella laciniata	2	—
	Allium sphaerocephalon	2	—
	Danthonia calycina	2	—
	Carex humilis	2	—
	Antherium liliago	2	—
	Hieracium pilosella	—	2
	Crepis setosa	—	2
	Allium vineale	—	2
	Jasione montana	—	2
	Cistus salvifolius	—	2
	Inula viscosa	1	1
	Vincetoxicum officinale	1	1
	Euphorbia exigua	1	2
	Filago germanica	1	1
	Convolvulus cantabrica	1	1
	Potentilla recta	1	1
	Anthyllis vulneraria	1	1

Note: numerical values are relative abundances where "1" is rare and "5" is common.
After: Ernst (1974)

TABLE 14.12   Typical Serpentine Plants of the Upper Tiber Valley

TYPICAL SERPENTINOPHYTES

Alyssum bertolonii	Armeria denticulata
Stachys recta subsp. labiosa	Silene cucubalus subsp. vulgaris
Campanula glomerata subsp. hispida	Tanacetum corymbosum var. achillea
Festuca ovina subsp. eu-ovina	Vulpia myuros
Aegilops ovata	Ranunculus arvensis var. spinosus
Galium tricorne var. genuinum	Knautia purpurea var. illyrica
Thymus striatus var. ophioliticus	

PREFERENTIAL SERPENTINOPHYTES

Asplenium adiantum-nigrum subsp. cuneifolium	Potentilla hirta var. laeta
	Festuca ovina subsp. eu-ovina
Leucanthemum crassifolium	Cerastium campanulatum subsp. typicum

RELIC SPECIES

Notholaena marantae	Knautia purpurea var. illyrica
Minuartia laricifolia subsp. diomedis	Cirsium pannonicum
Rosa spinosissima	Scorzonera austriaca
Potentilla tormentilla var. dacica	Stipa pennata var. pulcherrima
Cytisus nigricans var. sericeus	Stipa pennata var. tirsa
Cytisus hirsutus var. scepusiensis	Poa concinna
Daphne cneorum	Carex montana
Plantago holosteum	Carex humilis
Plantago argentea	

After: Pichi-Sermolli (1948)

ultramafites in the Impruneta region of Tuscany. The shrub layer shows *Juniperus oxycedrus* subsp. *macrocarpa*. An interesting feature of the Liguria region at Monte Nero (black mountain), is a relic stand of *Abies alba* (Plate 14.4b).

Life form spectra

The life form spectrum of the Tuscan serpentine flora has been shown above in Table 14.4 in comparison with the Portuguese serpentinophytes. It was concluded by Pichi-Sermolli (1948) that the Tuscan serpentine flora has the life form spectrum of a sub-mediterranean type with some affinities with the Euro-Central Asiatic flora. There is a noteworthy paucity of species compared with Argentario situated on non-ultramafic soils on the west coast nearby (see Table 14.4).

Serpentinicolous plants

A list of characteristic serpentinicolous plants from the Upper Tiber Valley is given in Table 14.12. The plants are divided into *typical*, *preferential* and *relict* serpentinophytes (i.e. plants whose last refuge is on serpentine). Within the first category is the well-known *Alyssum bertolonii* (Plate 14.5a) which was the first serpentine-endemic plant ever reported (Caesalpino, 1583) and also had the distinction of being the first hyperaccumulator of nickel to be discovered (Minguzzi and Vergnano, 1948). It is clearly allied to *A. argenteum*, another hyperaccumulator confined to serpentine in Piedmont and Valle d'Aosta. *A. bertolonii* has been divided into three subspecies of which subsp. *bertolonii* is found in Tuscany and subsp. *rigidum* and subsp. *scutarinum* grow in Albania. Another typical plant of the serpentine outcrops of the Ligurian Appennines is *Minuartia laricifolia* subsp. *ophiolitica* shown in Plate 14.5b.

Among the preferential species on the Tuscan serpentines are the ubiquitous *Asplenium adiantum-nigrum* subsp. *cuneifolium* and *Festuca ovina* subsp. *eu-ovina*, which has its type locality on serpentine at Monte Ferrato. A typical relict species is *Abies alba*, found also in Liguria.

The origin of the Tuscan serpentine flora

The phytogeography of the serpentine vegetation of Tuscany is shown in Table 14.13 which shows the predominant importance of the Mediterranean element which accounts for 33% of the total. There is also a significant input from the Eurasian element. The number of endemics is, however, quite small for a flora in the warm temperate zone which occupies terrain never previously glaciated.

Endemic species reported by Pichi-Sermolli (1948) include *Asplenium adiantum-nigrum* subsp. *cuneifolium*, *Silene cucubalus* var. *zlatiborensis*, *Alyssum bertolonii* subsp. *bertolonii*, *Armeria denticulata*, *Stachys recta* var. *ophiolitica* and var. *serpentina*, *Campanula glomerata* var. *serpentinicola*, and *Leucanthemum vulgare* subsp. *crassifolium*. A few other taxa are restricted to serpentine elsewhere in Tuscany though not in the Upper Tiber Valley.

14.5.4 Serpentine Vegetation of the Valle d'Aosta

A detailed description of the soils and serpentine vegetation of the Valle d'Aosta has been given by Verger (1979, 1982, 1983). In his earlier paper, Verger studied plant communities growing over serpentine talus and debris. The large boulders at the bottom of the scree slopes were colonised by *Thlaspi rotundifolium* and *Oxyria digyna*. On the finer scree upslope, the plant community belonged to the Thlaspietum rotundifolii Association with its character species *Thlaspi rotundifolium*, *Cerastium latifolium* and *Festuca rupicaprina*. On the more level slopes, the character of the Thlaspietum Association regresses. *T. rotundifolium* becomes rare, *C. latifolium* disappears and *Arabis alpina* becomes a common constituent of a *Festuca pumila* grassland with strong representation of xerophile and heliophile plants such

TABLE 14.13 Floral Elements of the Tuscan Serpentine Flora

Element	Percentage
Mediterranean	33
Eurasian	17
Euro-Central Asian	11
Ubiquitous	9
Mediterranean-Anatolian	7
Montane Central Mediterranean	6
Central Mediterranean-Central European	6
Eurosiberian	3
Endemic	3
Ruderal species	2
Mediterranean-Atlantic	1
Alpine	0.2

Source: Pichi-Sermolli (1948)

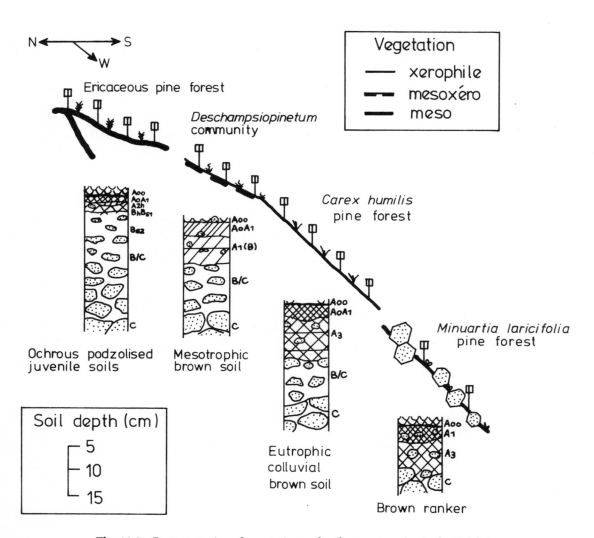

Fig. 14.6   Representation of vegetation and soils on serpentine in the Val d'Ayas.
Source: Verger (1982).

as *Minuartia verna, Saxifraga aizoon, Helianthemum alpestre, Thymus polytrichus, Sesleria caerulea* and *Carex sempervirens*.

Verger (1982) has also studied the serpentine vegetation of the Val d'Ayas and has recognized vegetation communities in the ground storey below a *Pinus sylvestris* woodland. These are of 4 main types depending on the slope and nature of the soils. The soil-vegetation sequence is illustrated in Fig. 14.6 and in Table 14.14. It is clear that the vegetation is influenced not only by slope but also by the pH of the soil, a typical acidiphilous heath being found on more level ground on the summit where the pH is quite low. Character species of these acid soils are *Calluna vulgaris* and *Genista germanica*. The same worker (Verger, 1983), has recognised a Caricetum fimbriatae Association on brown hypermagnesian soils overlying serpentine in the Valle d'Aosta.

TABLE 14.14 Plant Communities of the Shrub/Herb Layer on Serpentine below The *Pinus sylvestris* Woodland of the Valle d'Aosta

Description	Community			
	Minuartia debris vegetation	*Carex* scrub	*Deschampsia* grassland	Ericaceous heath
Character	xerophile	xerophile	meso-xerophile	mesophile
Type of soil	brown ranker	mesotrophic brown	eutrophic colluvial brown	podzol
pH of A hor.	5.86	4.70	5.90	4.85
% organic (A)	27.3	16.9	23.8	27.1
Constituent species	*Deschampsia flexuosa*	*Deschampsia flexuosa*	*Deschampsia flexuosa*	*Deschampsia flexuosa*
	Minuartia laricifolia	*Minuartia laricifolia*	*Minuartia laricifolia*	*Calluna vulgaris*
	Silene nutans	*Carex humilis*	*Veronica officinalis*	*Genista germanica*
	Thlaspi alpinum	*Festuca hervieri*	*Festuca lemanii*	*Vaccinium myrtillus*
	Laserpitium latifolium	*Dianthus sylvestris*	*Saponaria ocymioides*	*Vaccinium vitis-idaea*
	Hippocrepis comosa	*Euphorbia cyparissias*	*Phyteuma betonicaefolium*	*Juniperus nana*
	Hieracium bifidum	*Laserpitium siler*		
	Centaurea alpestris			

After: Verger (1982)

14.5.5 Biogeochemical Studies of Italian Serpentine Vegetation

Tuscany and Liguria

Sasse (1979a,b) has studied the concentrations of Ni, Cr, Co, Ca, Mg, and K in serpentine soils and plants from San Stefano in Tuscany (site 19 in Fig. 14.2), Impruneta and Monte Ferrato. He also analysed characteristic plants of the Alyssetum bertolonii Association. His data and other values from Vergnano Gambi and Gabbrielli (1979) and Vergnano Gambi et al. (1982) are given in Table 14.15 and show a number of significant features. The first of these is hyperaccumulation of nickel by *Alyssum argentum* and *A. bertolonii* reported by Minguzzi and Vergnano (1948) and Brooks and Radford (1978). It is noteworthy that the Ca/Mg mole quotient in both taxa greatly exceeds that of any other species encountered. This high value is entirely due to excess uptake of calcium rather than restriction of magnesium and has also been reported for many other hyperaccumulators such as in the case of *Hybanthus floribundus* from Western Australia (Severne, 1974). None of the other Tuscan or Ligurian plants showed hyperaccumulation of nickel.

TABLE 14.15 Elemental Concentrations in Dried Plant Leaves and Soils from Serpentine Areas in Tuscany and Liguria.

Location	Species or Soil	Ni(μg/g)	Cr(μg/g)	Co(μg/g)	Ca(%)	Mg(%)	Ca/Mg*
Bo (17)	Total soil	2300	1700	190	—	—	—
St (19)	Total soil	1368	644	112	0.24	13.89	0.01
	Extractable fraction	7	3	2	0.08	0.17	0.28
Im (14)	Total soil	1935	1185	167	0.37	14.80	0.02
	Extractable fraction	15	2	1	0.12	0.22	0.33
Fe (15)	Total soil	1805	1060	144	1.25	15.38	0.05
	Extractable fraction	11	1	1	0.14	0.23	0.36
Br	Alyssum argenteum	5646	22	6	4.83	0.23	12.60
St	Alyssum bertolonii	5665	11	50	2.54	0.57	2.67
Im		13098	11	36	2.49	0.71	2.10
Fe		11269	5	59	2.65	0.81	1.96
St	Armeria denticulata	20	11	3	0.40	0.71	0.34
Fe		18	5	4	0.54	0.60	0.54
St	Asplenium cuneifolium	26	6	3	0.55	0.52	0.63
Im	Centaurea paniculata	120	—	—	—	—	—
Bo	Cerastium exile	52	34	6	0.32	0.64	0.30
Im		53	34	6	0.25	0.12	1.25
Fe		71	41	6	0.34	1.38	1.48
St	Cheilanthes marantae	37	11	3	0.56	0.28	1.20
Im		35	4	5	0.37	0.13	1.71
Fe		32	6	3	0.32	0.22	0.87
Im	Euphorbia prostrata	115	3	12	1.17	0.87	0.80
Fe		54	1	6	0.57	0.81	0.42
Fe	Festuca cinerea	12	6	3	0.18	0.08	1.35
Fe	Festuca glauca	17	3	5	0.05	0.16	0.19
St	Helichrysum italicum	20	6	3	0.63	0.34	1.11
Fe		21	6	4	0.63	0.44	0.86
Bo	Minuartia ophiolitica	12	3	6	0.63	0.30	1.26
		35	14	6	1.16	0.53	1.31
St	Plantago holosteum	18	6	3	0.46	0.52	0.53
Im		27	6	4	0.67	0.61	0.65
Fe	Scorzonera stenophylla	41	14	6	0.57	1.02	0.33
Fe	Stachys serpentina	24	3	5	0.43	0.30	0.86
Fe	Stipa pulcherrima	6	2	5	0.05	0.17	0.18
Im	Thymus ophioliticus	35	7	6	1.16	0.56	1.24
Fe		29	7	6	0.83	0.55	0.90

Note: numerals in parentheses refer to locations in Fig. 14.2.
Bo = Bobbio, Fe = Monte Ferrato, Im = Impruneta, St = San Stefano
* mole quotient
Sources: Sasse (1979a, b), Vergnano Gambi et al. (1982), Vergnano Gambi and Gabbrielli (1979)

Plate 14.3 (a) Above: Serpentine vegetation at Grötschenreuth, Bavaria.
Photo by F. Sasse.
(b) Below: *Pinus nigra* woodland over serpentine near Gostovic in Bosnia.
Photo by W. Krause.

Plate 14.4 (a) Above: *Pinus Pinea* and *P. pinaster* over serpentine in the Impruneta region of Tuscany. Photo by R. Gabbrielli.
(b) Below: Relic stand of *Abies alba* over serpentine at Monte Nero (black mountain) in the Emilian Appennines in Liguria, Italy.
Photo by M. Guido and C. Montanari.

Plate 14.5 (a) Above: The hyperaccumulator *Alyssum bertolonii* growing over serpentine in the Impruneta region of Tuscany.
Photo by R. Gabbrielli.
(b) Below: A cushion of *Minuartia laricifolia* subsp. *ophiolitica* growing over serpentine at Monte Aioua in the Ligurian Appennines.
Photo by M. Guido and C. Montanari.

Plate 14.6 (a) Above: *Halacsya sendtneri* growing over lightly-weathered serpentine in the Gostovic region of Bosnia. Photo by W. Krause. (b) Below: *Asplenium cuneifolium* over serpentine from the Schwesnitztal in Bavaria. Photo by F. Sasse.

Valle d'Aosta

Vergnano Gambi et al. (1982) and Vergnano Gambi and Gabbrielli (1979, 1981) have determined several elements in serpentine plants from the Valle d'Aosta region of the Italian Alps. The plants were obtained from moraines in the Val d'Ayas below the Verra glacier. Analytical data for these plants are shown in Table 14.16. It is immediately noticeable that the list contains seven taxa that hyperaccumulate nickel of which the following had not been previously recorded as having such a character: *Cardamine resedifolia, Linaria alpina, Luzula lutea, Minuartia laricifolia, Saxifraga aizoon,* and *Trifolium pallescens.* Hyperaccumulation of nickel by *Thlaspi rotundifolium* was originally discovered by Vergnano Gambi (1979) and was also observed by Reeves and Brooks (1983a) who reported 1300–18300 $\mu g/g$ nickel in dried leaves of specimens from Val de Cogne, Zermatt and Val d'Ayas. This taxon and its varieties have one of the greatest tolerances of any species towards heavy metals. For example, *T. rotundifolium* subsp. *cepaeifolium* from Cave del Predil in northern Italy is also a hyperaccumulator of lead (up to 8200 $\mu g/g$ in dried leaves), and can contain up to 17300 $\mu g/g$ (1.73%) zinc (Reeves and Brooks, 1983b).

The unusual hyperaccumulation of nickel by seven taxa in this alpine moraine appears to be due to the high nickel availability in the substrate. Vergnano Gambi et al. (1982) reported that 165 $\mu g/g$ of the soil concentration was soluble in 2.5% acetic acid compared with only 88 $\mu g/g$ for nickel in soil from the Impruneta. For chromium the respective values were 6 and 2 $\mu g/g$. The above authors suggested that the plants of the high alpine serpentine regions (2500 m) were able to tolerate such high concentrations of metals in their leaves because of the short growing season which allowed them to shed their metallic burden much sooner than serpentine plants at lower altitudes.

TABLE 14.16 Elemental Concentrations in Dry Plant Leaves and Soils from the Moraine (2500 m) below the Verra Glacier, Valle d'Aosta, Italy

Species	Maximum			Mean		
	Ni($\mu g/g$)	Cr($\mu g/g$)	Co($\mu g/g$)	Ca(%)	Mg(%)	Ca/Mg*
Cardamine resedifolia	2370	16	45	1.77	1.00	1.06
Cerastium latifolium	968	196	20	0.38	0.27	0.84
Linaria alpina	2625	9	23	1.07	1.37	0.46
Luzula lutea	2401	6	30	1.18	1.24	0.95
Minuartia laricifolia	1910	53	22	0.50	0.80	0.38
Plantago serpentina	212	6	6	0.59	0.48	0.74
Salix myrsinites	912	74	40	0.85	0.89	0.57
Saxifraga aizoon	3840	8	76	1.23	2.25	0.33
Saxifraga autumnalis	106	28	6	1.62	1.76	0.55
Silene vulgaris	359	30	14	0.96	0.89	0.65
Thlaspi rotundifolium	23790	43	743	0.85	0.51	1.00
Trifolium pallescens	1550	15	27	1.54	2.61	0.36
Trisetum distichophyllum	425	77	16	0.22	0.28	0.47
Moraine soil (total)	1711	2327	179	2.99	15.80	0.11
Moraine soil (extractable)	165	6	12			

* mole quotient
Note: the soil extract was carried out with 2.5% acetic acid.
After: Vergnano Gambi et al. (1982) and Vergnano Gambi (1981)

14.6. YUGOSLAVIA AND ALBANIA

14.6.1 Geology

Perhaps the most extensive areas of contiguous ultramafic outcrops in Europe are in the Balkan Peninsula, particularly in Yugoslavia and Albania. These serpentines occur along the Neo-European Dinaric Alps (Dinarides) which are divided into several tectonic zones extending in a northwest—southeast direction. Most of the ophiolites are found in the Serbian Zone (Ager, 1980) which extends from Banju Lake in the north to the Neogene Basin near Pec where it passes into the vast ophiolitic Mirata Massif occupying most of Albania. This ophiolitic body, sometimes known as the Serbian Ophiolitic Zone, is separated from the Adriatic by the vast limestone Karst Zone which occupies most of western Yugoslavia and even extends as a narrower belt into western Albania. The Dinarides lead into the Hellenides which begin in northern Albania and continue into the Greek Peninsula.

Although Albania is one of the smallest, poorest and least-known countries in Europe, it is the world's third biggest producer of chrome. The local name for Albania is "Shqiperi" which means "eagles country" and which aptly reflects its rugged nature and remoteness. An excellent account of the geology of Albania and its mineralization has been given by Rabchevsky (1985) who has described how the mountains rise abruptly from the coastal lowlands to an altitude of over 2600 m in the steep N-S-trending escarpment of the Central Uplands. The rivers are small and swift and generally flow in an east-west direction along major faults.

The Albanian Dinaric Alps were uplifted during the Tertiary. The western zone is characterised by a sedimentary sequence with thick formations of flysch and molasse. The ultramafic rocks are found mainly in the Eastern Internal Albanides (Fig. 14.7), and extensive chrome deposits are found in the Mirdita Ophiolitic Complex and occur in either olivine- or bronzite-rich rocks or serpentinites derived from them. A west-east geological section through the southern Albanides is given in Fig. 14.8 and bears some resemblance to almost any other west-east section northwards as far as the northern Adriatic.

14.6.2 The Halacsya sendtneri Phytosociological Order

The serpentine vegetation of Yugoslavia and Albania is one of the richest warm-temperate floras of this type found anywhere in the world. It was an early "happy hunting ground" for the famous classical botanists of the Austro-hungarian Empire such as Pancic (1859), and later by other pioneering botanists such as W. Krause, F. Markgraf, and A. Baldacci. Sadly, one of the most interesting countries botanically, Albania, has until recently been "off limits" to foreign botanists and we have had to rely on early work such as that of Markgraf (1925, 1932) for our understanding of the flora.

Before looking at the serpentine flora of Yugoslavia and Albania, it will be appropriate to make some mention of the ubiquitous shrub *Halacsya sendtneri* which is a truly serpentine-endemic taxon distributed in a large part of the Balkan Peninsula, but especially in Bosnia. The ecology of *H. sendtneri* has been described by Johnston (1953) and Krause and Ludwig (1956) who pointed out that it is not only monotypic but has no relative anywhere on earth from which it might have been derived. It is therefore a true relic species. The plant (Plate 14.6a) sends up numerous shoots bearing yellow flowers resembling *Echium*. It tends to colonise steep cliffs and rocky sites where it favours heavily-weathered crevices wbich have a sufficient accumulation of soil. In such locations, the plant has minimal competition from other more vigorous plants.

Because it is such a characteristic plant of Balkan serpentines, *H. sendtneri* has been described as the character species of the Halacsyetalia phytosociological Order which encompasses the geographically-separated Alliances Asplenio serpentini—Festucion glaucae (Austria and Czechoslovakia), Polygonion albanicae (Middle Bosnia), and Potentillon visianii (Eastern Bosnia, Serbia, Macedonia, and Albania). The Polygonion

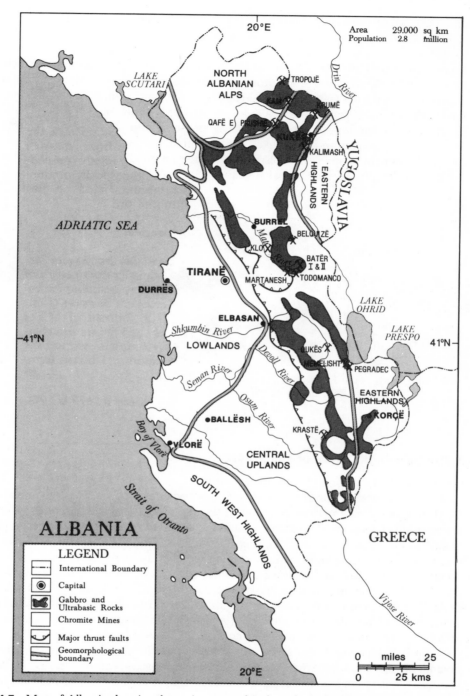

Fig. 14.7 Map of Albania showing the main geographical, geological and geomorphological features. Source: Rabchevsky (1985).

albanicae Alliance encompasses five Associations of which only two, Halacsyo—Seselietum rigidae and Carex humilis—Halacsyo sendtneri actually contain *H. sendtneri*, though it is extremely abundant in both Associations. The percentage cover of this heliophile Association is only about 10–30%. Character species of the Halacsyo—Seselietum rigidae Association are *Seseli rigidum*, *Sesleria latifolia* and *Silene staticifolia*, of which only the first two are character taxa for the Carex humilis—Halacsyo sendtneri community. A number of character species of the Order Halacsyetalia are present along with *H. sendtneri*. They include the ubiquitous *Asplenium adiantum-nigrum* subsp. *serpentini*, *Notholaena marantae*, *Stachys recta* subsp. *baldacci* and the nickel hyperaccumulator *Alyssum murale*. A very long list (> 60) of companion species (see Ernst, 1974) gives a good indication of the composition of the serpentine flora of the Central Balkans.

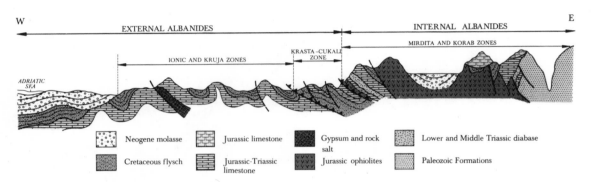

Fig. 14.8   A west-east geological section through the southern Albanides. Source: Rabchevsky (1985).

14.6.3 The Serpentine Flora of Yugoslavia

The variability of the serpentine flora of Bosnia

The serpentine vegetation of Bosnia has been described by many botanists (see Table 14.1). Ritter-Studnicka (1956) has studied the ecology of Bosnian serpentine floras and has shown how quickly the serpentine vegetation can modify under the influence of physical and chemical changes in the soil. This is illustrated in Table 14.17 which shows the steady decrease of base saturation with increasing weathering of the serpentine soil. The poorly-weathered soil supports the normal basiphile serpentine, but as the bases are washed out of the soil, the vegetation pattern changes through woodland to an acidiphilous heath over podzolic soils, a community reminiscent of the Cornish and French serpentine heathlands. In many parts of Bosnia the whole gamut of vegetation changes can be observed on quite a small area and gives a good series of contrasts.

Over lightly-weathered serpentine soils, the usual vegetation is a carpet dominated by chamaephytes such as *Erica carnea*, *Cytisus austriacus* var. *maezeius*, *C. hirsutus*, *C. supinus*, *Genista januensis*, *Dorycnium herbaceum*, *Alyssum murale*, and various species of *Thymus* and *Sedum*.

Several alpine species colonise Bosnian serpentine at altitudes well below their usual distribution on non-serpentine soils. For example, in the serpentine gorges of Gostovic near Ozren (Fig. 14.9), the following alpine plants occur at altitudes of only 200–500 m: *Carduus carduelis*, *Centaurea triumfetti* subsp. *adscendens*, *Cerastium lanigerum* var. *silvaticum*, *Doronicum austriacum*, *Euphorbia montenegrina*, *Hieracium transsilvanicum*, *Rosa pendulina*, *Rubus hirtus*, *Hypochoeris illyrica*, *Rhamnus fallax*, *Silene bosniaca*, and *Thlaspi jankae*.

TABLE 14.17 Serpentine Communities in Bosnia Related to the Physical and Mineralogical Characteristics of the Soil

Locality	Soil characteristics			% Base Sat.	Community
	Sand %	Sand-clay %	Clay %		
Tirilovac	24.60	1.96	25.56	92.66	Serpentine-endemic pioneer plants
Volujak, Ozren	28.60	2.60	31.20	91.67	*Pinus nigra* woodland
Svatovac	26.60	4.88	30.48	83.99	*Pinus nigra* woodland
Bokavici	17.15	4.23	21.38	80.22	*P. sylvestris* woodland
Poljanatal, Ozren	16.00	4.55	20.55	77.86	*Quercus petraea, Carpinus betulus, Fagus sylvatica*
Tirilovac (podsol)	6.60	10.40	16.00	35.00	*Calluna vulgaris* heath

After: Ritter-Studnicka (1956)

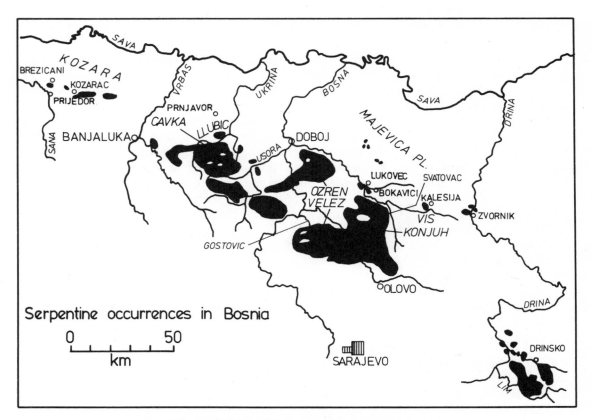

Fig. 14.9 Map of serpentine occurrences in Bosnia.
Source: Ritter-Studnicka (1970b).

Plant communities of Bosnian serpentines

The extremely variable nature of the vegetation cover of Bosnian serpentines has been investigated not only by Ritter-Studnicka (1956) but also by Krause and Ludwig (1957). They identified the following 5 units in this flora:

1—Illyric sub-mediterranean—*Pinus nigra/Quercus petraea* forest.

2—Illyric sub-mediterranean—*Fraxinus ornus/Ostrya carpinifolia* woodland.

3—Central European low montane—*Quercus petraea/Carpinus betulus* mixed forest.

4—Central European montane—*Abies alba/Fagus sylvatica* woodland.

5—Subalpine—*Sesleria rigida* mats.

There are about a dozen serpentine-endemic plants in the Gostovic area (site 22—Fig. 14.2 and Fig. 14.9). Their distribution among different plant communities is shown in Table 14.18. The fern *Notholaena marantae* is only serpentine-endemic at the northern end of its range. At Gostovic it is therefore not a true endemic. The serpentinophytes are confined to open or lightly-wooded steep slopes or cliffs. There is some doubt as to whether this is because of the physical properties of the soils or whether it is an edaphic factor which disappears in mature forest soils and podsols. The seven truly serpentine-endemic taxa listed in Table 14.18, comprise only 1.9% of the 363 species recorded over serpentine by Krause and Ludwig (1956) in the Gostovic region. This is very similar to the 2% recorded by Pichi-Sermolli for the Upper Tiver Valley where he found a total of 405 species growing over serpentine.

The relationship between vegetation and the chemical and physical properties of Serbian serpentine soils

The relationship between the chemical and physical properties of serpentine soils and vegetation in the Gostovic region has also been studied by Krause and Ludwig (1956). Their data are shown in Table 14.19. The pH values are near 7.0 in lightly-weathered serpentine soils and fall to 5.5 in mature forest soils, though this is not as low as in some soils. The constant movement downslope of serpentine boulders allows the weathered products of these boulders to maintain the pH at a higher level than would normally be the case.

The acidity of the soils as measured by titration with sodium hydroxide, shows a steady gradation from lightly-weathered original soils through mature forest soils with a southern exposure, to mature soils in shady locations. The vegetation changes for the same sequence of soils are from a *Satureja thymifolia* debris flora through an oak-blackpine (*Pinus nigra*) woodland with an ericaceous ground storey, to a beech woodland in the most acid soils. *Pinus nigra* (Plate 14.3b) is the characteristic tree of the serpentines of the northern and central Balkans. It has its counterpart in *P. halepensis* in Portugal and Euboa Island. The Ca/Mg quotient in the Balkan soils does not change very much in the base-acid sequence, thus indicating that parameters other than an adverse Ca/Mg balance are controlling factors for the serpentine vegetation.

14.6.4 The Serpentine Vegetation of Albania

The serpentine vegetation of Albania has been thoroughly described by K. H. Rechinger and by Markgraf (1932). The latter work was so thorough that it left little room for a successor, which is fortunate because of the current difficulties of visiting that country.

The particular charm of the Albanian flora lies in the two basically dissimilar aspects which it presents to the observer. To the north of the country there is an essentially Central European plant cover, at least at the higher altitudes, whereas in the south, Mediterranean elements cover the entire terrain, even on the highest mountain tops.

Ultramafic rocks cover a large part of the surface of Albania and have a very charac-

TABLE 14.18   Distribution of Serpentinicolous Plants among Serpentine Communities of the Gostovic Area, Bosnia

Species	A	B	C	D	E	F	G	H	I	J
Halacsya sendtneri	5	—	—	—	—	—	—	—	—	—
Stachys recta var. *chrysophaea*	5	5	1	3	1	—	—	—	—	—
Potentilla australis subsp. *malyana*	5	3	3	4	1	—	—	—	—	—
Asplenium adiantum-nigrum subsp. serpentini	1	3	3	1	2	1	—	1	—	—
Viola beckiana	2	3	5	1	—	—	1	—	—	—
Notholaena marantae	—	1	1	—	—	2	—	—	—	—
Asplenium adulterinum	—	—	—	—	—	—	—	—	1	—
Sesleria latifolia var. *serpentica*	4	4	2	1	2	1	1	—	—	—
Cytisus austriacus	3	—	—	2	—	—	—	1	1	—
Cerastium moesiacum var. *silvaticum*	—	—	3	—	2	1	—	—	—	—
Centaurea smolinensis	—	1	3	—	—	—	1	—	—	—
Chrysanthemum leucanthemum subsp. montanum	—	—	2	—	—	—	—	—	—	—

Note: numerical values are relative abundances.

A = *Carex humilis—Halacsya sendtneri* community; B = serpentine fern—black pine woodland; C = *Sesleria rigida—Viola beckiana* mat; D = *Bromus erectus—Euphorbia montana* community; E = *Cotinus* scree community; F = *Notholaena—Myosotis suaveolens* scree community; G = *Erica*—oak—black pine woodland; H = *Asarum*—oak woodland; I = *Vaccinium*—spruce—beech woodland; J = oak—beech woodland.

After: Krause and Ludwig (1956)

TABLE 14.19   Serpentine Vegetation Communities of the Gostovic-Zlatibor Region of Bosnia and their Relation to Properties of the Supporting Soils

	A	B	C	D	E	F	G	H	I	J	K	L	M	N
Soil type	Original		South-facing mature					Mature in shade				Water-sat.		
pH	7.1	7.0	6.5	6.3	6.2	6.1	6.3	6.1	5.5	5.0	5.8	7.0	6.2	6.1
Titratable acid*	3.7	—	—	13.7	14.4	16.0	13.4	22.5	—	21.4	24.0	—	—	—
K_2O (μg/g)	60	50	60	60	60	110	260	120	90	100	180	70	150	180
Ca (meq./100 g)	1.25	3.10	1.55	1.85	1.80	1.00	1.55	2.05	1.40	1.95	2.60	3.05	1.05	0.85
Mg (meq./100 g)	5.33	7.95	8.44	9.00	8.58	12.6	10.9	14.5	7.56	3.25	9.7	10.6	17.4	18.2

* Ml of 0.1M NaOH for 50 g soil. Meq. refers to exchangeable ions extracted with 1% ammonium chloride.

Communities: A = *Satureja thymifolia* scree community; B = *Poa badensis* meadow; C = *Alyssum murale* scree community; D = *Bromus erectus—Euphorbia montenegrina* rocky community; E = *Erica*—oak—black pine woodland; F—as E; G = *Asaram* oak woodland; H = *Vaccinium*—spruce—beech woodland; I = as H; J = as H; K = oak—beech coppice—woodland; L = meadows in stream valleys; M = damp *Agrostis* meadow; N = *Agrostis* meadow dampened by streams.

Source: Krause and Ludwig (1957)

teristic flora, dominated in the tree layer by *Pinus nigra* which in Albania is confined to serpentine though further north in Yugoslavia it can be found on non-ultramafic substrates.

Another typical coloniser of serpentine is a herb community dominated by the polymorphic *Alyssum murale*, a hyperaccumulator of nickel (Chapter 8), and component of Section Odontarrhena of the genus which is said to have its centre of phylogenetic development in Albania.

Characteristic serpentine plants

Markgraf (1932) has listed a number of species characteristic of serpentine in Albania. They are shown in Table 14.20 and include 28 taxa endemic only to serpentine in Albania but not elsewhere. A further 18 species are endemic to serpentine in the Balkan Peninsula and 11 are *bodenvag* taxa. The list shows *Halacsya sendtneri* as endemic to Albania but as is now known it has a much wider distribution, albeit confined to serpentine.

TABLE 14.20 Serpentine Plants of Albania

<table>
<tr><td colspan="2" align="center">SERPENTINE ENDEMIC</td></tr>
<tr><td>On serpentine everywhere</td><td>Only on Albanian serpentine</td></tr>
<tr><td>Asplenium adiantum-nigrum subsp. serpentini</td><td>Pinus nigra</td></tr>
<tr><td>Notholaena marantae</td><td>Brachypodium ramosum</td></tr>
<tr><td>Narthecium scardicum</td><td>Carex macrolepis</td></tr>
<tr><td>Gypsophila spergulifolia var. serbica</td><td>Luzula spicata</td></tr>
<tr><td>Alyssum balcanicum</td><td>Aristolochia pallida</td></tr>
<tr><td>Alyssum bertolonii subsp. rigidum</td><td>Genista radiata</td></tr>
<tr><td>Alyssum smolikanum</td><td>Dorycnium germanicum</td></tr>
<tr><td>Ptilotrichum baldacci</td><td>Linum tauricum var. serbicum</td></tr>
<tr><td>Ptilotrichum baldacci var. markgrafii</td><td>Buxus sempervirens</td></tr>
<tr><td>Sedum serpentini</td><td>Hypericum grisebachii</td></tr>
<tr><td>Potentilla visiani</td><td>Daphne blagayana</td></tr>
<tr><td>Cytisus pseudoprocumbens</td><td>Erica carnea</td></tr>
<tr><td>Genista hassertiana var. glabrata</td><td>Onosma taurica</td></tr>
<tr><td>Genista csikii</td><td>Calamintha patavina</td></tr>
<tr><td>Linum tauricum var. albanicum</td><td>Verbascum longifolium</td></tr>
<tr><td>Haplophyllum albanicum</td><td>Pinguicula hirtiflora</td></tr>
<tr><td>Polygala maior var. pindica</td><td>Campanula tymphaea</td></tr>
<tr><td>Fumana bonapartei</td><td>Chrysanthemum larvatum</td></tr>
<tr><td>Viola dukadjinica</td><td>Gentiana nopcsae</td></tr>
<tr><td></td><td>Moltkia doefleri</td></tr>
<tr><td></td><td>Halacsya sendtneri</td></tr>
<tr><td></td><td>Thymus lykae</td></tr>
<tr><td></td><td>Veronica andrasovskyi</td></tr>
<tr><td></td><td>Orobanche nowackiana</td></tr>
<tr><td></td><td>Plantago carinata</td></tr>
<tr><td></td><td>Plantago media var. pindica</td></tr>
<tr><td></td><td>Aster albanicus</td></tr>
<tr><td></td><td>Scorzonera rhodantha</td></tr>
<tr><td colspan="2" align="center">BODENVAG SPECIES</td></tr>
<tr><td>Pinus peuce</td><td>Daphne oleoides</td></tr>
<tr><td>Minuartia baldacci</td><td>Soldanella pindicola var. dimoniei</td></tr>
<tr><td>Silene quadridentata subsp. albanica</td><td>Forsythia europaea</td></tr>
<tr><td>Cardamine glauca</td><td>Stachys recta subsp. baldacci</td></tr>
<tr><td>Trifolium pilczii</td><td>Carlina acanthifolia</td></tr>
<tr><td>Euphorbia glabriflota</td><td></td></tr>
</table>

After: Markgraf (1932)

Markgraf (1932) observed many serpentinimorphoses among the serpentine plants and also noted that some taxa endemic to serpentine in Albania were also found over calcareous rocks in other countries. Examples of such distributions are afforded by: *Pinus nigra*, *Genista radiata*, *Dorycnium germanicum*, *Daphne blagayana* and *Erica carnea* which in Albania never leave ultramafites even if calcareous rocks are adjacent. A further group of plants tolerates both ultramafic and calcareous rocks and is referred to by Markgraf as "lime-tolerant serpentine plants". Other *bodenvag* species such as *Euphorbia glabriflora* and *Forsythia europaea* grow on slates if not on serpentine.

Some of the Albanian serpentine-endemic plants are in fact found not only on chalk elsewhere but are exclusive to it. This is in spite of the very low calcium content of Albanian ultramafic rocks.

The serpentine vegetation gives Albania a certain character, particularly the presence of large forests of *Pinus nigra*, a species which in other Balkan countries has a limited distribution. In the steeper mountainous terrain, the *Pinus nigra* woodland is replaced by the chamaephytic *Alyssum* community on coarse rocky slopes. This community is shown in Table 14.21. The same table shows the *Artemisia* community over the same substrate. This includes the well-known *Halacsya sendtneri*.

TABLE 14.21 The *Alyssum* and *Artemisia* Communities of Serpentine Scree in Albania

ALYSSUM COMMUNITY

Shrubs

Alyssum balcanicum	Alyssum bertolonii
Genista hassertiana var. glabrata	Euphorbia glabriflora
Buxus sempervirens	Ptilotrichum baldacci
Fumana bonapartei	

Perennial herbs

Dorycnium germanicum	Linum tauricum var. albanicum
Onosma taurica	Calamintha patavina
Polygala nicaeensis	Silene vulgaris
Thesium divaricatum	Linaria peleponnesiaca
Salvia ringens var. macedonica	Notholaena marantae
Minuartia garckeana	Potentilla hirta var. laeta
Haplophyllum albanicum	Plantago carinata
Sedum serpentini	Rumex scutatus
Hippocrepis glauca	Silene serbica
Potentilla micrantha	Brachypodium ramosum
Herniaria parnassica	

Therophytes

Arenaria serpyllifolia	Cardamine glauca

Grasses

Stipa pulcherrima

ARTEMISIA COMMUNITY

Shrubs

Artemisia camphorata var. canescens	Asperula flaccida
Satureja montana	Genista hassertiana var. glabrata
Euphorbia glabriflora	

Perennial herbs

Ferulago galbanifera	Saponaria depressa var. maior
Podanthum canescens	Halacsya sendtneri
Galium lucidum	Carlina acanthifolia

After: Markgraf (1932)

The origin of the Albanian serpentine flora

The floral elements of the entire Albanian flora including its serpentinicolous component have been depicted by Markgraf (1932) and are shown in Fig. 14.10. Since a large part of the Albanian flora is found on serpentine, the scheme shown in Fig. 14.11 applies equally well to this type of flora. The most sriking feature is the decline in importance of the Central European element going from north to south. The figure clearly shows that Albania is an intermediate zone in the transition from the Central European serpentine flora to the mainly Mediterranean type of the Greek Peninsula. It is this intermediate character which has fascinated botanists for the past 100 years.

14.7 GREECE

14.7.1 Geology

The Dinarides of Neo-Europa merge into the Hellenides of the Greek Peninsula. The Hellenides can be divided into a number of tectonic zones of which the most important are: the Serbo-macedonian Massif, and the Vardar, Pelagonian, Subpelagonian, Pindus and Ionian Zones (Ager, 1980). These divisions are shown in Fig. 14.11. The Serbo-macedonian Massif consists of metamorphic rocks originally affected by the Variscan Orogeny but later folded and thrust westward during the much later Neo-European Alpine orogeny. It is a rugged bare terrain with abundant (mainly sulphide) mineralization, and extends through Macedonia to the island of Lesbos in the eastern Aegean. Serpentine outcrops at several places in the Massif.

Further west, the Vardar Zone passes through the city of Thessaloniki (Salonika) and contains some ophiolitic bands with serpentine outcrops.

The Pelagonian Zone is not clearly correlated with structures further north in Yugoslavia and Albania. The basement consists of granite and gneisses overlain with a metamorphic Palaeozoic succession. The zone passes in a southeast direction east of the Pindus mountains and through Euboa and the Cyclades. Important ultramafic outcrops occur in the islands of Euboa and Tinos.

The Subpelagonian Zone is the great ophiolitic belt of the Hellenides and is one of the major sutures of Europe. It is a direct continuation of the Serbian Zone of the Dinarides, with which it shares some common features. Serpentine is well exposed in the Katara pass east of Ionannina. The ophiolites of the Subpelagonian zone are found in a belt some 600 km long and 40 km wide. The Pindus Zone further to the west forms the high Pindus mountains and branches out in the south to include most of the Peleponnese. It is extremely complex geologically and contains some serpentine, though not on the scale of the Subpelagonian Zone.

The most westerly Ionian Zone is entirely sedimentary in origin and has numerous outcrops of calcareous rocks strongly reminiscent of the west coasts of Albania and Yugoslavia. The location of ultramafic outcrops in Greece is shown in Fig. 14.12.

14.7.2 The Serpentine Flora of Greece

Northwest Greece

Despite the very large proportion of the Greek Peninsula covered by ultramafic rocks, it is surprising that until recently, little had been done on the serpentine flora of these outcrops. Although classical works on the flora of Greece (e.g., Rechinger, 1942) carry a listing of many serpentinicolous taxa (particularly in Euboa), little effort has been devoted to a specific serpentine flora covering the whole country, particularly in the northwest where so many important ultramafic outcrops are located. Recently however, the situation has changed by the initiation of a "Mountain Flora of Greece" project in 1979 which had as its aim, the

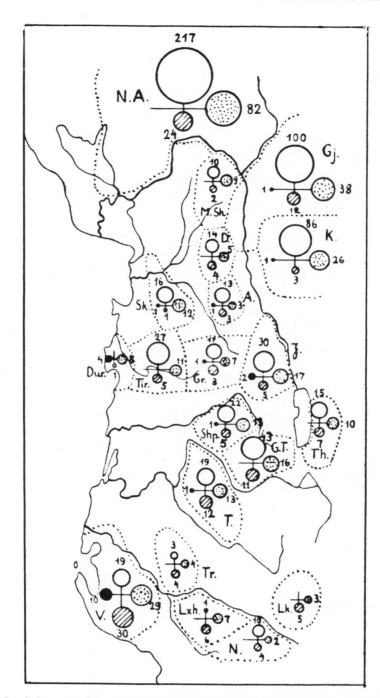

Fig. 14.10 Floral elements of the vegetation of Albania indicating numbers of species in the northern (open circles), eastern (dotted circles), southern (hatched circles), and western (solid circles) elements. Key: NA = North Albanian Alps, Gj = Gjaliqa, K = Korab, M.Sh = Mnela and Mal i Shenjit, D = Deja and Kunora, A = Mal i Alamanit, Sk = Skanderbeg Mt, Dur = Durazzo, Tir = Tirana with Mal i Dajtit, Gr. = Mal me Grope, J = Jablanica Mts, T = Tomor, V = Valona, Tr = Trebeshinj, Lxh = Lunxherrie Mts, N = Nemercka, Lk = Leskovik.
Source: Markgraf (1932).

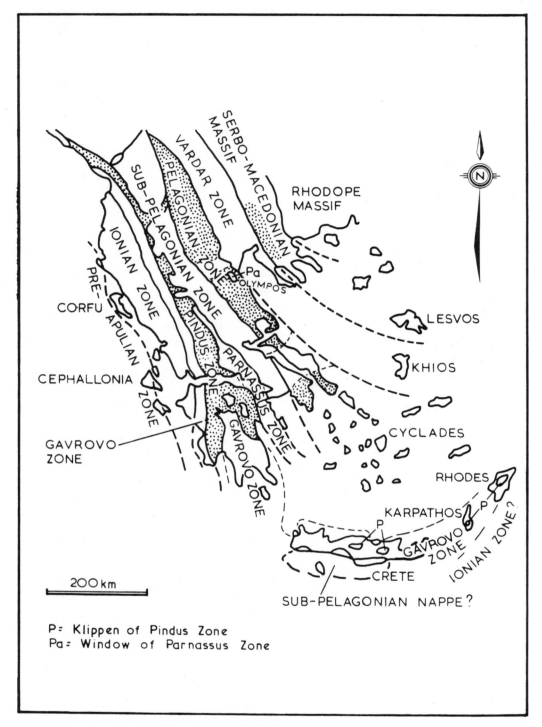

Fig. 14.11 Tectonic zones of Greece.
Source: Ager (1980).

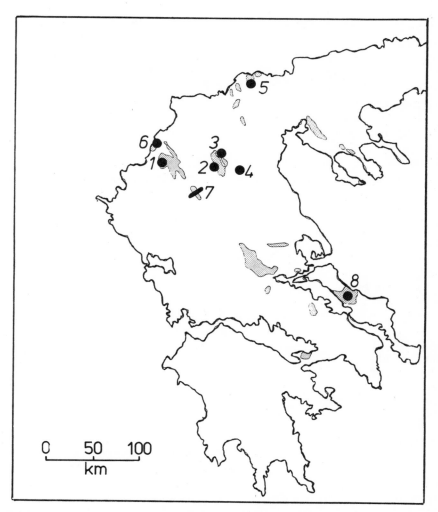

Fig. 14.12   Serpentine outcrops in Greece. 1—Mt Smolikas, 2—Mt Vourinos, 3—Kteni, 4—Pr. Servia, 5—Mt Voras, 6—Mt Grammos, 7—Katara Pass, 8—Euboa Island.

mapping of plant species above 1500 m in the whole of the country. This altitude covers most of the Greek serpentines (outside Euboa). As reported by Papanicolaou et al. (1983), the vascular flora of Greece has about 6000 species of which 1400 are found above 1500 m. Of these about 250 are endemic to this country and are nearly all found on limestone or serpentine.

The serpentine flora of northwest Greece extends into Albania and is characterised by extensive scree fields and a flora relatively poor in taxa but rich in endemics. Papanicolaou et al. (1983), Babalonas (1983, 1984a,b), and Babalonas and Papanicolaou (1984) have listed 26 serpentine-endemic taxa from the Greek mainland (excluding Euboa). These are recorded in Table 14.22. The table shows the high incidence of endemism on Mt Smolikas where 18 of the endemics are found. It is also to be noted that 9 of these are confined to a single mountain. Although only 9 endemics have been reported from Mt Vourinos, this area has received very little attention until recently and is a favourable site for future discoveries. Plate 14.1c shows *Linum elegans* growing on serpentine at 1000 m on this mountain.

Phytosociological studies on the serpentine flora of the Voras Mts (site #5 in Fig. 14.12) were carried out by Babalonas (1984). In the submontane area (ca. 500 m), there are two main communities. The first of these is a deciduous forest of the Quercion frainetto Alliance. Most of the non-serpentine areas at this altitude are covered with a *Fagus sylvatica* woodland whioh is absent on serpentine where it is replaced by the oak forest. The main components of this latter community are *Quercus pubescens* (dominant), *Q. frainetto, Q. dalechampii, Carpinus orientalis, Fraxinus ornus* and *Cornus mas*. The shrub layer is dominated by *Juniperus communis*.

In places where fire damage and other human activities have removed the oak woodland, or where edaphic conditions are too stringent, a highly characteristic *Alyssum*

TABLE 14.22   Serpentine-endemic Plants of the Greek Mountains Found Above 1500 m.

Species	Main distribution																				
	1	2	3	4	5	6	7	8	9	10	11	12	13	14	15	16	17	18	19	20	21
1 *Thesium vlachorum*	X																				
2 *Minuartia baldacci*		X	X	X	X	X	X	X	X												
3 *Cerastium vourinense* subsp. *rechingeri*		X			X	X				X											
4 *Silene radicosa*		X			X	X	X		X	X	X		X	X	X						
5 *S. schwarzenbergeri*	X		X	X	X	X	X				X	X				X	X	X	X		
6 *S. pindicola*	X	X			X		X				X		X		X		X				
7 *S. haussknechtii*					X	X					X		X			X	X				
8 *Saponaria sicula* subsp. *intermedia*		X					X	X	X	X						X					
9 *Dianthus degenii*	X	X			X	X	X												X	X	X
10 *Thlaspi epirotum*					X		X					X									
11 *T. pindicum*		X	X			X	X			X						X	X				
12 *Euphorbia glabriflora*	X	X			X	X	X	X	X	X						X					
13 *Viola albanica*	X				X		X	X				X									
14 *V. dukadjinica*					X	X	X						X		X						
15 *V. declinata* var. *epirota*	X						X				X	X		X							
16 *Campanula hawkinsiana*							X			X							X	X			
17 *Inula serpentinica*										X											
18 *Centaurea vlachorum*																		X			
19 *Fritillaria epirotica*							X														
20 *Iris falcata*										X											
21 *Armeria maritima* subsp. *smolikana*							X														
22 *Cephalaria smolikanum*							X														
23 *Medicago prostrata*										X											
24 *Ligusticum lucidum*																					X
25 *Alyssum smolikanum*							X														
26 *A. vourinense*										X											
TOTAL	7	7	2	2	10	7	19	6	3	10	2	5	1	6	1	4	3	8	4	2	1

1—Mt Grammos, 2—Katara Pass, 3—Traghoptera, 4—Kambos Despothi, 5—Milea, 6—Pirostia, 7—Mt Smolikas, 8—Bouchetsi, 9—Lefkasia, 10—Mt Vourinos, 11—Mitsikeli, 12—Aspra Litharia, 13—Papignon, 14—Mavrouvoumi, 15—Fleka, 16—Vasilitsa, 17—Oxia, 18—Zigos, 19—Aftia, 20—Tsouka Rossa, 21—Mt Voras.
After: Papanicolaou et al. (1983).

murale meadow makes its appearance. Plate 14.1b shows a typical example of such a community. The trees in the background are part of the oak forest. Krause et al. (1963) have described similar *Alyssum* meadows in Southern Europe composed of *A. murale* (Bosnia and Serbia), *A. euboeum* (Euboa), *A. balcanicum* (Albania) and *A. bertolonii* (Tuscany). *A. murale* is particularly polymorphic with its numerous phenotypes, meadows etc.

Studies of the Greek mountain flora are still continuing and it seems certain that new serpentinicolous taxa will be identified in the near future, particularly at the subspecific and varietal ranks, and will provide exciting research material for many years to come.

Euboa

One of the most thorough investigations of the serpentine flora of a specific region was carried out on the island of Euboa by Krause et al. (1963) who described the floristics, ecology and phytosociology of the vegetation of the Mantoudi area to the north of the island. The flora of this region had been previously described by Rechinger (1961) as part of a survey of the whole island. A map of the area studied by Krause et al. (1963) is shown in Fig. 14.13. The Kandili and Mavrovouni mountains are composed primarily of ultramafites interspersed with limestones. The east coast between Mantoudi and Pili is also primarily ultramafic in structure though there are deposits of magnesite here and there. The serpentine hills of Mantoudi are covered with rusty soils (Krause, 1962; Krause et al. 1963) known as red loam or rusty loam and are usually at least 30 cm deep. The pH of these soils varies from 5.2 to 6.8 depending on the geomorphology, plant cover and aspect. The Ca/Mg mole quotient is extremely low and averages about 0.20. There is virtually no agricultural activity in the ultramafic areas between Mantoudi, Pili and Kymasi. Plate 14.1d shows the contrast

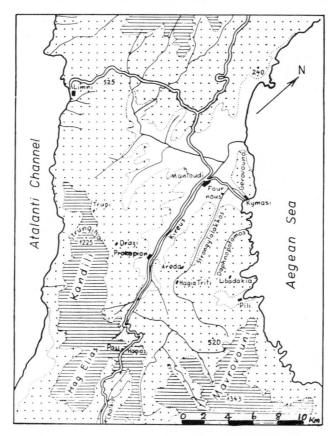

Fig. 14.13   Map of Mantoudi area of Euboa Island.

between serpentine and limestone at Kandili and illustrates very well the characteristic ochrous colour of the ultramafic soil which has a sparse cover of *Erica verticillata*.

Krause et al.(1963) described a large number of plant communities growing over serpentine on Euboa. Space does not permit a full listing of these Associations. However, their names, environments and character species are given in Table 14.23. The list of character species contains most of the serpentine-endemic taxa of Euboa. In his review of the entire flora of this island, Rechinger (1950) listed 32 endemics including a genus (*Leptoplax*), 22 species and 9 varieties. This was later raised to 48 taxa (Rechinger, 1961) including 37 species, 7 subspecies, and 4 varieties. However 23 of these are calciphile species and only 11 are serpentinophytes. The later work by Krause et al. (1963) raised the total of serpentine-endemic taxa to 26, all of which are shown in Table 14.22.

TABLE 14.23 The Distribution of Serpentine Plants of Euboa among Environments and Plant Communities

Environment	Community	Species
On original soils		
1. Rocks with flowing water	Adiantion	*Pinguicula hirtiflora* (a)
2. River sands	*Nerium oleander— Tamarix tetrandra*	*Leptoplax emarginata* (b) *Alyssum murale* (c)
3. River border by cliff faces	*Agropyretum juncei mediterraneum*	*Alyssum praecox* (e)
4. Rocky river banks affected by fire	Crithmo-Staticion	*Euphorbia deflexa* (d) *Aethionema graecum* (d)
Serpentine red loam		
5. Rocks of the highest mountain peaks	*Malcolmia scyria— Alyssum praecox*	*Alyssum euboeum* (a) *Alkanna graeca* (b) *Cheilanthes marantae* (c) *Thymus teucrioides* var. candilicus (d) *Alyssum praecox* (e) *Thymus atticus* (e)
6. Rocks in depressions	*Stachys cretica— Alyssum euboeum*	*Alyssum euboeum* (a) *Onosma euboica* (a) *Centaurea ebenoides* (a) *Fumana pinatzii* (a) *Leptoplax emarginata* (b) *Cheilanthes marantae* (c) *Dorycnium pentaphyllum* (c) *Thymus teucrioides* (d) var. candilicus (d) *Alyssum praecox* (e) *Thymus atticus* (e) *Linum elegans* (e) *Pennisetum orientale* (e)
7. Deep soils in hills	*Erica verticillata— Pinus halepensis*	*Alyssum euboeum* (a) *Onosma euboica* (a) *Centaurea ebenoides* (a) *Ferulago serpentinica* (a) *Scorzonera serpentinica* (a) *Leptoplax emarginata* (b)

Plate 14.6 (c) Above: *Pinus halepensis* over serpentine at Mantoudi, Euboa. The flowering shrub is *Fraxinus ornus*. Photo by W. Krause. (d) Below: *Alyssum euboeum* growing over nickeliferous mine tailings on an access road to a magnesite mine in Euboa. Photo by W. Krause.

Plate 15.1 (a) Above: *Sclerorhachys platyrhacis,* a serpentine-endemic Composite from the Robat Safid region of Northeast Iran.
(b) Below: *Eremurus spectabilis* subsp. *spectabilis,* a serpentinicolous plant from the Safid Robat area of Northeast Iran.
Photos by K. R. Rechinger.

Environment	Community	Species
7. Deep soils in hills	*Erica verticillata— Pinus halepensis*	*Dorycnium pentaphyllum* (c) *Plantago holosteum* (c) *Thymus teucrioides* var. *candilicus* (d) *Thymus atticus* (e) *Linum elegans* (e) *Polygala nicaeensis* subsp. *graeca* (e)
8. Well grassed plains near sites 5–7	*Crepis neglecta— Aira elegans*	*Alyssum euboeum* (a) *Alkanna graeca* (c) *Alyssum murale* (c)
Brown loam and brown earth		
9. Deep soils of lower slopes	*Quercus ilex— Arbutus andrachne*	*Alyssum euboeum* (a) *Leptoplax emarginata* (b)
10. Terraces of stream valleys above water table	*Myrtus communis— Pinus halepensis*	*Leptoplax emarginata* (b) *Centaurea thracica* (e)
11. Flooding areas of large streams	*Dracunculus vulgaris— Platanus orientalis*	*Leptoplax emarginata* (b) *Alyssum murale* (c)
12. Untilled fields near sites 10 and 11	*Alyssum murale— Pteridium aquilinum*	*Leptoplax emarginata* (b) *Alyssum murale* (c)

a = strictly serpentine endemic, b = serpentine endemic in the whole region, c = widely distributed and *bodenstets* or *bodenvag*, d = serpentine forms of a widely distributed species, (e) *bodenvag* in the whole region but *bodenstets* at Mantoudi.
Source: Krause et al. (1963)

The western Mediterranean origin of the serpentine flora of Euboa is indicated by the presence of such characteristic plant communities such as Quercion ilicis and Isoetion. The vegetation cover is also unusual in the extensive development of woodland and the high proportion of Balkan Submediterranean or montane species.

The vegetation of Euboa may be summarized by a number of its characteristics as follows:

1—The main components of the flora are *Pinus halepensis* (Plate 14.6c) and *Erica verticillata*.

2—Endemic species are numerically at least equal to those of the richest European serpentine floras.

3—Semi-ruderal *Alyssum* floras have a relatively large areal representation.

4—The rock communities are related to those of Central European and Central Balkan serpentine floras. Examples of this are the ferns *Cheilanthes marantae* and *Asplenium silesiacum*.

5—Junco—Molinietea sedge communities are established in small bogs.

6—The serpentines of the region support plants which have a more northerly distribution on other rock types or occur at higher altitudes on them. This disjunction is typically of serpentine floras elsewhere (see Chapter 13) where competitive pressure restricts some plants either to the edaphically-harsh environment of ultramafites, or the climatically-harsh environment of more northerly regions.

7—Where magnesite occurs amid the serpentine, its vegetation communities are typically serpentinicolous. However where a significant amount of limestone starts to appear, colonisation by plants from non-ultramafic "fertile" soils commences. The serpentine nature of magnesite floras is demonstrated in Plate 14.6d which shows the development of *Alyssum euboeum* over nickeliferous ore tailings on an access road to a magnesite mine in Euboa.

8—The *Isoetes durieui—I. histrix* community on Euboa parallels the isolated occurrence of *I. histrix* on serpentine in Cornwall.

Chromio Kazani

The serpentine region of Chromio Kazani (site 23 in Fig. 14.2) is situated in western Macedonia near the Skoumtsa chrome mines in the middle of an ophiolitic belt where there are sharp vegetational changes across the geological boundary. In the course of geobotanical and biogeochemical studies in this area, Karataglis et al. (1982) have described the principal components of a serpentine community over soils with an extremely high nickel and chromium content (4400 and 88000 μg/g respectively). A list of these species is given in Table 14.24. It will be noted that few if any of these plants are common to Euboa about 200 km further south. *Alyssum euboeum* has been replaced at Chromio Kazani by *A. murale* which is very common over serpentine in Macedonia, Albania and Serbia. Floral elements of this Macedonian serpentine site are largely derived from the central Balkan region rather than from the eastern Mediterranean. The relative richness of this serpentine flora is indicated by the recognition of 36 taxa in a 40 m^2 quadrat.

TABLE 14.24 Serpentine Vegetation in a 40 m^2 Quadrat at Chromio Kazani, Northern Greece

Quercus pubescens	*Juniperus oxycedrus*
Buxus sempervirens	*Melica ciliata*
Koeleria macrantha	*Hypericum rumeliacum*
Fumana bonapartei	*Thymus teucrioides*
Convolvolus boissieri subsp. *compactus*	*Festuca* sp.
Draba lasiocarpa	*Alyssum montanum* subsp. *montanum*
Sedum sartorianum	*Thlaspi praecox*
Carex humilis	*Minuartia verna*
Anthemis orientalis	*Bromus racemosus*
Linum austriacum	*Helianthemum nummularium*
Acinos alpinus	*Teucrium montanum*
Aethionema saxatile	*Iris* sp.
Sedum caespitosum	*Medicago* sp.
Hieracium sp.	*Poa perconcinna*
Centaurea sp.	*Alyssum* sp.
Chrysopogon gryllus	*Veronica austriaca*
Rumex acetosella	*Stachys scardica*
Scorzonera sp.	*Armeria canescens*

Source: Karataglis et al. (1982)

14.7.3 Biogeochemical Work on Greek Serpentine Plants

We have already discussed (Chapter 8) the biogeochemistry of a number of hyperaccumulators of nickel, all of which were in the family Brassicaceae. Many of these unusual plants were found in Greece (Reeves and Brooks, 1983a; Reeves et al. 1980, 1982). Data for nickel in Greek Brassicaceae are given in Table 14.25 and do not include *Alyssum* since this has been discussed by Brooks and Radford (1978). The table also includes zinc data because many of the Crucifers are able to hyperaccumulate this element as well as nickel. It is noteworthy that *Thlaspi goesingense* is also found in Austria near Kraubath and elsewhere in serpentine as well as in the Pindus Range (Mt Traghoptera).

The hyperaccumulation of zinc by *Thlaspi* species is of particular interest following the discovery of this character in *T. calaminare* growing on calamine ore in Western Germany. None of the species listed in Table 14.24 was in fact growing on a zinc-rich substrate, and it appears that inordinate uptake of both nickel and zinc is a character of several genera, particularly in the Brassicaceae.

Karataglis et al. (1982) have determined the elemental content of *Buxus sempervirens* in connection with their study of the serpentine vegetation of Chromio Kazani (see above). Although they did not find elevated levels of nickel or chromium in the leaves of this plant (45 and 7 μg/g respectively), they observed a quite high Ca/Mg mole quotient (1.34) whereas that of the soil was only 0.10. They proposed that selective uptake of calcium was a mechanism whereby this taxon was able to colonise serpentine substrates.

Babalonas et al. (1984) determined Ca, Mg, Ni and 7 other elements in serpentine plants from Mt Voras (site #5 in Fig. 14.12). The plants selected were: *Stachys germanica*, *Silene fabarioides*, *S. sp.*, *Verbascum glandulosum*, *Scrophularia canina* subsp. *canina*, *Alyssum murale*, *Lactuca viminea* subsp. *ramosissima*, and *Rumex scutatus*. Fig. 14.14 summarizes data for Ca, Mg, and Ni concentrations in roots, shoots, leaves and seeds of each of these species and clearly shows the extraordinary ability of *Alyssum murale* to hyperaccumulate nickel compared with the other taxa. There is also an inverse relationship between Ca and Mg for many species.

TABLE 14.25 Nickel and Zinc Concentrations in Brassicaceae from Serpentine Areas of Greece and Other Parts of the Balkan Peninsula

Species	Location	No.	Concentrations (μg/g in dry matter) Nickel	Zinc
Bornmuellera baldacci				
subsp. *baldacci*	Mt Smolikas (Greece)	6	6670-21300	
subsp. *markgrafii*	Kamja (Albania)	1	27300	
subsp. *rechingeri*	Pindus Mts (Greece)	4	6480-12000	
B. tymphaea	Pindus Mts (Greece)	9	1590-31200	
B. × *petri*	Mt Livadhi (Greece)	2	3420-11400	
Noccaea boeotica	Pindus Mts (Greece)	2	303-23400	3120
N. tymphaea	Pindus Mts (Greece)	2	8140-11800	2500
Peltaria emarginata	Pindus Mts (Greece)	17	4800-34400	
Thlaspi bulbosum	Patras (Greece)	1	2000	10000
T. epirotum	Pindus Mts (Greece)	1	2500	2000
T. goesingense	Pindus Mts (Greece)	1	15000	2000
T. graecum	Pindus Mts (Greece)	1	13000	1500

Note: values for zinc are means.
Sources: Reeves et al. (1980, 1983), Reeves and Brooks (1983).

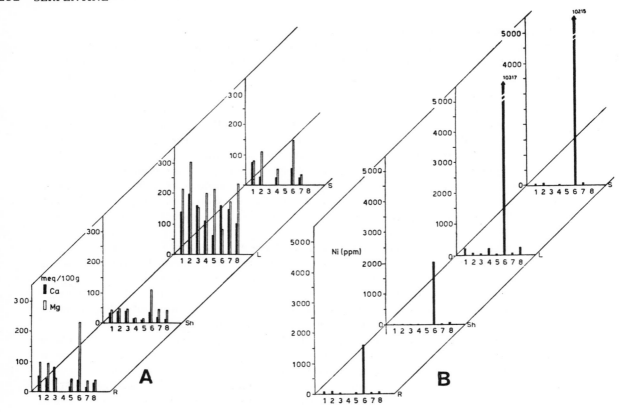

Fig. 14.14 The Ca, Mg, and Ni content of different organs of eight plant species from Mt Voras. 1—*Stachys germanica*, 2—*Silene fabarioides*, 3—*Silene sp.*, 4—*Verbascum glandulosum*, 5—*Scrophularia canina* subsp. *canina*, 6—*Alyssum murale*, 7—*Lactuca viminea* subsp. *ramosissima*, 8—*Rumex scutatus*. R = root, Sh = shoot, L = leaves, S = seeds.
Source: Babalonas et al. (1984).

14.8 A SUMMARY OF SERPENTINE PLANT COMMUNITIES OVER THE WHOLE OF EUROPE

A useful listing by Krause et al. (1963) shown in Table 14.26, relates serpentine plant communities to ecological and edaphic conditions throughout Europe following a southeasterly trend from Shetland to Euboa. The communities represented in the first 7 columns of the table are the building blocks for the representative serpentine floras of most parts of Europe. To these must be added taxa which occupy alpine niches in other rock types but descend to lower altitudes to colonise serpentine. In some cases these plants form their own communities as for example the *Sesleria rigida*—*Viola beckiana* carpet, or comprise individual plants such as *Lychnis alpina* or *Silene acaulis* in Scandinavia (Rune, 1953), *Saxifraga rosacea* in Northeast Bavaria (Gauckler, 1954), or *Poa alpina* subsp. *parnassica* and *Euphorbia deflexa* on Euboa (Krause et al. 1963). Other communities are restricted to southern Europe and have their richest displays on serpentine such as the *Alyssum* communities of the Balkan Peninsula and Italy, and the *Quercus*—*Fagus* woodland (column 9 of Table 14.25) of southeast Europe. Columns 10 and 11 of the table show the dominance of therophyte meadows and hard-leaved species.

Within the sequence of plant communities from Shetland to Euboa there is a trend to increasing endemism along the southeast-trending line. At Shetland there is only one taxon said to be endemic to serpentine in the region, and in Central Europe there are perhaps 2–5 of such species. In Albania, Markgraf (1932) estimated that there were about 20–30 serpentine-

TABLE 14.26   A Summary of Plant Communities over European Serpentines

Region	Plant Communities										
	1	2	3	4	5	6	7	8	9	10	11
Shetland	AN	AV	CE	CF	MS	—	—	—	—	—	—
Scandinavia	AN	AV	CV	JF	MS	—	—	—	—	—	—
Cornwall	—	—	EU	FO	EM	IH	—	—	—	—	—
Bohemia	AS	AS	VP	FA	CS	—	—	—	—	—	—
North Bavaria	—	AS	CP/EP	FG	ASM	—	—	—	—	—	—
S. Moravia (Mohelno)	—	AS	—	FG	—	—	—	—	—	—	—
Austria (Gurhofgraben)	AS	AS	—	FG	—	—	—	—	—	—	—
Austria (Steiermark)	—	AS	PEP	FG	FAR	—	CT	—	—	—	—
Bosnia (Gostovic)	CC	HS	OE	FS	MC	NC	CT	AM	QC	—	—
Serbia (Zlatibor)	SC	HS	PN	PP/FS	MD	—	—	AM	QS	—	—
Albania	CC	HS	EB	SF	—	—	PH	ABC	QSF	—	—
Tuscany	AS/AB	AS	EJ	PO	MH	—	AD	AB	QP	CA	—
Euboa (Greece)	—	SA	EH	—	HJ	IH/ID	PH/AD	AE	DP	CA	MQ

KEY TO PHYSICAL AND VEGETATIONAL ENVIRONMENTS
1. Tundra on unstable talus slopes
2. Chasmophytes on dry rocky slopes
3. Shrubby heath below pine forest on mature soils with climax vegetation
4. Grassy heath below pine forest on mature soils with climax vegetation
5. Damp meadows over marshlands
6. Carpets of dwarf rushes over gleyed soils
7. Basiphile mosses over irrigated rocks
8. *Alyssum* meadow among ruderal vegetation
9. Oak-beech woodland in eutrophic stations
10. Helianthemetalia communities over Mediterranean therophytic pastures
11. Quercetalia ilicis communities in Mediterranean hard-leaved woodland.

PLANT COMMUNITIES

AB — *Alyssum bertolonii* scree community
AE — *Alyssum euboeum/murale* scree flora
AS — *Asplenietum serpentini* Association
ABC — *Alyssum balcanicum* scree flora

CA — *Crepis neglecta-Aira elegans*
CD — *Campylium stellata-Drepanocladus* sp.
CF — *Carex flacca-Festuca ovina*
CS — *Carex caespitosa*
CV — *Calluna vulgaris*
EB — *Erica carnea-Pinus nigra*
EJ — *Erica scoparia-Juniperus oxycedrus*
EP — Erico-Pinetum Association
FA — *Festuca duriuscula-Anthericum ramosum*
FO — *Calluna vulgaris-Festuca ovina*
FAR — *Festuca arundinacea*
HS — *Halacsyo sendtneri* Association
IH — *Isoetes histrix*
MC — *Molinia-Carex paniculata*

MH — *Molinia-Holoschoenus-Schoenus*
MS — *Molinia-Schoenus nigricans*
OE — Orneto-Ericion serpentinicum All.
PN — Pinetum nigrae-Silvestris ericosum
PP — *Poa molinieri-Plantago carinata*

AD — Adiantetum Association
AN — Arenarion norvegicae Alliance
AV — Asplenion viridis subarcticum All.
ASM — Asplenietum serpentini moliniosum Association

CC — *Cotinus coggyria-Satureja* scree
CE — *Calluna-Erica cinerea*

CP — Calluno-Pinetum Association
CT — Cratoneurium community
DP — *Dracunculus vulgaris-Platanus*
EH — *Erica verticillata-Pinus halepensis*
EM — *Erica vagans-Molinia-Schoenus*
EU — *Erica vagans-Ulex europaeus*
FG — Festucetum glaucae Association

FS — *Festuca sulcata*
HJ — *Holoschoenus-Schoenus-Juncus*
ID — *Isoetes durieui*
JF — *Juncus trifidus-Festuca ovina*
MD — Molinia-Deschampsietum Association

MQ — *Myrtus-Pinus halepensis-Quercus*
NC — Nanocyperion-Cynodon meadows
PH — *Pinguicula hirtiflora*
PO — *Pinus pinaster-Ovina*
QC — Querceto-Carpinetum croaticum Association

PLANT COMMUNITIES

QP — *Quercus cerris—Q. pubescens*

QSF — Quercetum sessiliflora-Fagetum
       Association

SC — *Scrophularia* cf. *canina* scree flora

VP — Vaccinio-Picetalia woodland

QS — Quercetum sessiliflora Association

SA — *Stachys cretica-Alyssum euboeum*

SF — *Sesleria nitida-Festuca violacea* mat

After: Krause et al. (1963).

endemic taxa in the vast ultramafic areas. In the much smaller serpentine occurrences of Bosnia, Krause and Ludwig (1957) determined 12 serpentinophytes of which 7 seemed to be confined to this type of substrate. In Euboa there are perhaps 10–20 serpentine endemics. The above figures are, however, uncertain because the tally will always depend on whether the line is drawn at the specific, subspecific, or varietal level, and there is always a great deal of controversy about whether a given taxon is a true subspecies or variety or not. Nevertheless there is an unmistakable trend to increasing endemism along that southeast-trending line running from Shetland to Euboa.

The serpentine vegetation of Europe is easily the most thoroughly studied of anywhere on earth, so that this chapter has had, of necessity, to skim superficially over the surface. Even so, parts of Europe's serpentine vegetation remain only lightly touched by the botanist and ecologist, particularly in the Balkan Peninsula, parts of which such as Albania, remain inaccessible to the botanist. Another problem is the fact that so much of the European work is not in English and unless the student of this flora has a good command of Spanish, French, German, and Italian, it will remain virtually a closed book to him. It is hoped that this chapter will have given some insight into the rich, and varied serpentine vegetation of Europe and will serve to stimulate further work in this field.

REFERENCES

Ager, D. V., 1980. *The Geology of Europe*. McGraw Hill, London.

Amidei, G., 1841. Specie di piante osservati nei terreni serpentinosi. *Atti 3rd Riunione Degli Scienziati Italiani*, 523.

Babalonas, D., 1983. Neue Fundorte fur seltene Pflanzen in Nordgriechenland. *Ann. Musei Goulandris*, 6; 17–25.

Babalonas, D., 1984a. Zur Kenntnis der Flora und Vegetation auf Serpentin-Standorte Nordgriechenlands. I—Serpentinvegetation im Voras-Gebirge. *Fedd. Rep.*, 95: 687–697.

Babalonas, D., 1984b. *Armeria maritima* subsp. *smolikana*, ein neues Taxon aus NW-Griechenland. *Willdenowia*, 14: 61–64.

Babalonas, D., Karataglis, S. and Kabassakalis, V., 1984. The ecology of plant populations growing on serpentine soils. III Some plant species from North Greece in relation to the serpentine problem. *Phyton (Austria)*, 24; 225–238.

Bargoni, I., 1943. Osservazioni fenologiche sulle serpentine dell'Impruneta (Firenze). *Nuov. G. Bot. Ital.*, 50: 232–251

Becherer, A., 1969. Serpentinfarne der Tessin und der italienischen Granzgebieten. *Bauhinia*, 4: 65–66.

Bellot Rodriguez, F., 1966. La vegetacion de Galicia. *An. Inst. Bot. A.J. Cavanilles*, 24: 5–306.

Brooks, R. R. and Radford, C. C., 1978. Nickel accumulation by European species of the genus *Alyssum*. *Proc. Roy. Soc. Lond. Sec.*B, 200: 217–224.

Brooks, R. R., Shaw, S. and Asensi Marfil, A., 1981a. Some observations on the ecology, metal uptake and nickel tolerance of *Alyssum serpyllifolium* subspecies from the Iberian Peninsula. *Vegetatio*, 45: 183–188.

Brooks, R. R., Shaw, S. and Asensi Marfil, A., 1981b. The chemical form and physiological function of nickel in some Iberian *Alyssum* species. *Physiol. Plant.*, 51: 167–170.

Boydell, H. C., 1921. The magnesite deposits of Euboa, Greece. *Econ. Geol.*, 16: 507–523.

Caesalpino, A., 1583. *De Plantis Libri,* v.16. Florentiae, 369.

Ceballos, L. and Viciosa, C., 1933. *Estudio de la Vegetacion y Flora Forestal de la Provincia de Malaga.* La Monclea, Madrid.

Corti, R., 1940. Appunti sulla vegetazione dell'Isola d'Elba. *Nuov. G. Bot. Ital.*, 47: 494–504.

Cotelo Neiva, J. M., 1948. *Rochas e minerios da vegetação Bragança-Vinhais.* Relat. Serv. For. Min. 14.

Dahl, O., 1912. Botaniske undersøkelser i Helgeland. 1. *Kong. Norsk. Videns. Selsk.*, 1911: 1–221.

Dahl, O., 1915. Botaniske undersøkelser i Helgeland. 2. *Kong. Norsk. Videns. Selsk.*, 1914: 1–178.

Dudley, T. R., 1986a. A new nickelophilous species of *Alyssum* (Cruciferae) from Portugal. *Alyssum pintodasilvae* T. R. Dudley, sp. nov. *Fedd. Rep.*, 97: 135–138.

Dudley, T. R., 1986b. A nickel hyperaccumulating species of *Alyssum* (Cruciferae) from Spain: *Alyssum malacitanum* (Rivas Goday) T. R. Dudley, comb. et stat. nov. *Fedd. Rep.*, 97: 139–142.

Duvigneaud, P., 1966. Note sur la biogéochimie des serpentinites du soud-ouest de la France. *Bull. Soc. Roy. Bot. Belg.*, 99: 271–329.

Dvorak, R., 1935. Nanismi plantarum in stepposis ad substratum serpentiniaceum prope Mohelno in Moravia. *Arch. Natur- Heimatschutz. Mähr. Lande* 5a: 1–152.

Eggler, J., 1954. Vegetationsaufnahmen und Bodenuntersuchungen von Serpentingebieten bei Kirchdorf in der Steiermark und bei Bernstein in Burgenland. *Mitt. Naturw. Ver. Steierm.*, 84: 25–37.

Eggler, J., 1955. Ein beitrag zu Serpentinvegetation in der Gulsen bei Kraubath in Obersteiermark. *Mitt. Naturw. Ver. Steierm.*, 85: 27–72.

Eggler, J., 1963. Bemerkungen zu Serpentinvegetation in der Gulsen und auf der Kirchkogel bei Pernegg in Steiermark. *Mitt. Naturw. Ver. Steierm.*, 93: 49–54.

Ernst, W., 1974. *Schwermetallvegetation der Erde.* Fischer, Stuttgart.

Ferreira, M. R., 1965. Geologia i petrologia da região de Rebordelo-Vinhais. *Revist. Fac. Cienc. Univ. Coimbra,* 36: 1–287.

Fiori, A., 1919. Contribuzione alla flora dei serpentini del Pavese. *Bol. Soc. Bot. Ital.*, 1919: 39–40.

Fiori, A. and Pampanini, R., 1914. La flora dei serpentini della Toscana. II Confronti tra la flora del M. Ferrato (serpentino) e quella della Calvana (calcare alberose). *Nuov. G. Bot. Ital.*, 21: 216–240.

Fraga Vila, M. I., 1975. *Estudio Floristico de las Gandares de Mellid.* Trab. Licent. Faculdad Cienc., Univ. de Santiago de Compostela.

Gauckler, H., 1954. Serpentinvegetation in Nordbayern. *Ber. Bäyer. Bot. Ges.*, 30: 19–26.

Gismondi, A., 1953. Intorno ad una particulare fitocenosi commune al Ferrini serpentinosi ed al calcare dolomitice in Liguria. *Atti Accad. Ligure Sci. e Lett.*, 9: 240–241.

Gonzalez, G. L., 1975. Contribucion al estudio floristico y fitosociologico de Sierra de Aguas. *Acta. Bot. Malacitana,* 1: 81–205.

Guitian Ojea, F. F. and Lopez Lopez, M. I., 1980. Suelos de la zona humeda española. X. Suelos sobre serpentinas. *An. Edaf. Agrobiol.* 39: 403–415.

Hayek. A., 1923. Pflanzengeographie von Steiermark. *Mitt. Naturw. Ver. Steierm.*, 59: 1–209.

Hoyos de Castro, A., 1960. La genèse du sol sur roches basiques. *Trans. 7th Int. Congr. Soil. Sci.*, 4: 413–417.

Johannes, D., 1984. *Biogeochemische Untersuchungen im Nordwestlichen Harz und dem Angrenzenden Vorland.* Doc. Thesis, Tech. Univ.; Clausthal.

Johnston, I. M., 1953. Studies in the Boraginaceae. *J. Arn. Arbor.*, 34: 258–299.

Karataglis, S., Babalonas, D. and Kabasakalis, B., 1982. The ecology of plant populations growing on serpentine soils. II Ca/Mg ratio and the Cr, Fe, Ni, Co concentrations as development factors of *Buxus sempervirens* L. *Phyton (Austria),* 22: 317–327.

Krapfenbauer, A., 1967. Eine autoökologische Studie eines Serpentinstandortes im Dunkelsteinerwald und ein Gefassversuch mit *Pinus sylvestris* und *Pinus nigra* var. *austriaca* auf Serpentinböden. *Zbl. Ges. Forstw.*, 84: 207–230.

Krause, W., 1962. Zur Kenntnis der Flora und Vegetation auf Serpentinstandorten des Balkans. 4. Mikropräparate von Serpentinböden aus Griechenland. *Z. Pfl.-ernähr. Düng. Bodenk.*, 99: 97–107.

Krause, W. and Klement, O., 1958. Uber die Felsflechten zweier jugoslawischer Serpentingebiete. *Vegetatio*, 8: 1–17.

Krause, W. and Ludwig, W., 1956. Zur Kenntnis der Flora und Vegetation auf Serpentinstandorte des Balkans. 1. *Halacsya sendtneri. Ber. Dt. Bot. Ges.*, 49: 417–428.

Krause, W. and Ludwig, W., 1957. Zur Kenntnis der Flora und Vegetation auf Serpentinstandorte des Balkans. 2. Pflanzengesellschaften und Standorte im Gostovic Gebiet (Bosnien). *Flora*, 145: 78–131.

Krause, W., Ludwig, W. and Seidel, F., 1963. Zur Kenntnis der Flora und Vegetation auf Serpentinstandorten des Balkans. 6. Vegetationstudien in der Umgebung von Mantoudi. *Bot. Jb.*, 82: 337–403.

Kretschmar, L., 1931. Die Pflanzengeographie auf Serpentin in Gurhofgraben bei Melk. *Verh. Zoo-bot. Ges. Wien*, 80: 163–208.

Lämmermayr, L., 1926. Materialen zur Systematik und Okologie der Serpentinflora. I. Neue Beitrage zur Kenntnis der Flora steierischer Serpentine. *Sitz. Ber. Akad. Wiss. Wien. Math. -Nat. Kl. I*, 135: 361–407.

Lämmermayr, L., 1927. Serpentinpflanzen—eine kritische ökologische Studie. *Sitz. Ber. Akad. Wiss., Math. -Nat. Kl. I*, 136: 25–69.

Lämmermayr, L., 1928a. Weitere Beiträge zur Flora der Magnesit- und Serpentinböden. *Sitz Ber. Akad. Wiss. Wien Math. -Nat. Kl. I*, 137: 55–99.

Lämmermayr, L., 1928b. Vierte Beitrag zur Okologie der Flora auf Serpentin und Magnesitböden. *Sitz. Ber. Akad. Wiss. Wien, Math. -Nat. Kl. I*, 137: 825–859.

Lämmermayr, L., 1930. Neue floristische Ergebnisse der Begehung steirischer Magnesit- und Serpentinlager. *Verh. Zool. -Bot. Ges. Wien.*, 80: 83–93.

Lämmermayr, L., 1934. Ubereinstimmung und Unterschiede in der Pflanzendecke über Serpentin und Magnesit. *Mitt. Naturw. Ver. Steierm.*, 71: 41–62.

Le Gendre, C., 1919. Flore des terrains de serpentine de la Haute-Vienne. *Bull. Géogr. Bot.*, 29: 19–34.

Lopez Lopez, M. I. and Guitian Ojea, F., 1981. Suelos de la zone humeda española. X Suelos sobre serpentina. 2. Oligoelementos y relacion Ca/Mg en suelos y vegetacion. *An. Edaf. Agrobiol.*, 40: 1–10.

Markgraf, F., 1925. Botanische Reiseeindrücke aus Albanien. *Repert. Beih.* 36: 60–82.

Markgraf, F., 1932. Pflanzengeographie von Albanien. *Bibliotheca Bot.*, 105: 1–132.

Martino, E. and Orsini, F., 1969. Flora e vegetazione delle Valli dei Torrenti Acquabona. Scorza e Lerca. *Webbia*, 23: 397–511.

Maurer, W., 1966. Flora und Vegetation des Serpentingebietes bei Kirchdorf in Steiermark. *Mitt. Zoo.—Bot. Landmus. Joanneum (Graz)*, 24: 13–76.

Menezes de Sequeira, E., 1969. Toxicity and movement of heavy metals in serpentine soils (North-eastern Portugal). *Agron. Lusit.*, 30: 113–154.

Messeri, A., 1936. Richerche sulla vegetazione dei dintorni di Firenze. La vegetazione delle rocce ofiolitiche di Monte Ferrato. *Nuov. G. Bot. Ital.*, 40; 277–372.

Minguzzi, C. and Vergnano, O., 1948. Il contenuto di nichel nelle ceneri di *Alyssum bertolonii* Desv. *Atti. Soc. Tosc. Sci. Nat. Mem.*, 55: 49–77.

Müller-Stoll, W. R. and Miloslav, T., 1984. Asplenietum serpentini and its contact communities in the serpentine complex in Slavkovsky Les near Marianske Lazne in western Bohemia (Czechoslovakia)-(in Ger.). *Fedd. Rep.*, 25; 97–119.

Mussa, E., 1937. Squardo alle vegetazione del Monte Musine (Val di Susa). *Nuov. G. Bot. Ital.*, 44: 715–730.

Negodi, G., 1941. Studi sulle vegetazione dell'Appennino Emiliano e della pianura adiacente. II. La flora e la vegetazione dei serpentini di Varana. *Ann. Bot.*, 22: 117–142.

Nicolas, A., 1966. *Etude Pétrochimique des Roches-vertes et de leurs Minéraux entre Dora Maira et Grand Paradis.* Thèse,. Fac. Sci., Grenoble.

Novak, F. A., 1928. Quelques remarques relatives au problème de la végétation sur les terrains serpentiniques. *Preslia*, 6: 42–71.

Novak, F. A., 1937. Kretena a vegetace hadcovych pud. *Archiv. Svazu Pro Cochram Prirodi a Domoviny v Zemi Moravskolezske*, 1: 113–160.

Palacios, M. L., 1936. Algunas observaciones geobotanicas en la Serrania de Ronde. *Bot. Soc. Esp. Hist. Nat.*, 36: 39–46.

Pampanini, R., 1903. Essai sur la géographie botanique des Alpes et en particulier des Alpes sud-orientales. *Mém. Soc. Frib. Sci. Nat. Sér. Géol. Géogr.*, 8: 1–213.

Pampanini, R., 1912. *La Flora dei Serpentini della Toscana.* Montignosa.

Pancic, J., 1859. Die Flora der Serpentinberge in Mittelserbien. *Verh. Zoo. Bot. Ges. Wien*, 9: 139–150.

Papanicolaou, K., Babalonas, D. and Kokkini, S. 1983. Distribution patterns of some Greek mountain endemic plants in relation to geological substrate. *Flora (Jena)*, 174; 405–437.

Pape, H., 1978. *Entwicklung einer Geochemischen Kartiermethode fur Lagerstättenprospektion, Umweltforschung und Landesplanung auf der Grundlage von Multielementuntersuchungen an Pflanzenaschen.* Doc. Thesis, Tech. Univ. Clausthal.

Pape, H., 1981. *Development of a Geochemical Mapping Method for the Prospecting Deposits, Environmental Research and Regional Planning on the Basis of Multielement Investigations of Plant Ashes.* Borntraeger, Berlin.

Pavarino, G. L., 1912. Intorno alla flora del serpentino nel'Appennino Bobbiese. Contribuzione prima. *Att. Ist. Univ. Lab. Crittogam. Pavia*, 12: 21–56.

Pavarino, G. L., 1914. Intorno alla flora del calcare e del serpentino nell'Appennino Bobbiese. Contribuzione seconda. *Att. Ist. Bot. Univ. Lab. Crittogam. Pavia*, 14: 19–42.

Pavarino, G. L., 1918. Intorno alla flora del calcare e del serpentino nell'Appennino Bobbiese. Contribuzione terza. *Att. Ist. Bot. Univ. Lab. Crittogam. Pavia*, 15: 89–108.

Pavlovic, Z., 1953. Prilog poznavanju serpentinske flore Ozren planine kod Sjenice (I). *Bull. Mus. Hist. Nat. Pays Serbe Sér.B*, 5–6: 3–19.

Pavlovic, Z., 1955. Prilog poznavanju serpentinske flore i vegetacije Ozrena kod Sjenice (II). *Bull. Mus. Hist. Nat. Pays Serbe Sér.B*, 7: 1–45.

Pavlovic, Z., 1962. Karakteristioni elementi serpentinske flore Srbije. *Glasn. Muz. Drust. Slov.*, 18: 3–18.

Pavlovic, Z., 1964. Borove sume nea serpentinima Srbije. *Glasn. Muz. Drust. Slov.*, 19.

Pichi-Sermolli, R., 1936. Osservazione sulle principali morfosi delle piante del serpentini. *Nuov. G. Bot. Ital.*, 43: 461–474.

Pichi-Sermolli, R., 1948. Flora e vegetazione delle serpentine e delle altre ofioliti dell'Alta Valle del Tevere (Toscana). *Webbia*, 6; 1–380.

Pinto da Silva A. R., 1964. *Os habitats serpentinicos e o seu racional aproveitamento agrario.* Colloq. "Aportacion de las Investigaciones Ecologicas y Agricolas a la Lucha del Mundo Contra el Hambre". Madrid, 1–40.

Pinto da Silva, A. R., 1970. A flora e a vegetação das areas ultrabasicas do Nordeste Transmontano. *Agron. Lusit.*, 30: 175–364.

Pinto da Silva, A. R., 1981. Mais algumas plantas serpentinicolas do Nordeste Transmontano. *Bol. Soc. Brot.*, 54; 239–247.

Rechinger, K. H., 1942. *Ostliche Agäische Inseln.* Vegetationsbilder 26.

Rechinger, K. H., 1943. *Flora Aegaea. Flora der Halbinseln des Agäisches Meeres.* Denkschr. Akad. Wiss. Wien, Math. -Naturwiss., 105.

Rechinger, K. H., 1947. Der Polymorphismus in der ägäischen Flora. *Ost. Bot. Z.*, 94; 152–234.

Rechinger, K. H., 1950. Grundzüge der Pflanzenverbreitung in der Aegäis. *Vegetatio*, 2: 35–119.

Rechinger, K. H., 1961. Die flora von Euboa. *Bot. Jb.*, 80: 294–465.

Reeves, R. D. and Brooks, R. R., 1983a. European species of *Thlaspi* L. (Cruciferae) as indicators of nickel and zinc. *J. Geochem. Explor.*, 18: 275–282.

Reeves, R. D. and Brooks, R. R., 1983b. Hyperaccumulation of lead and zinc by two metallophytes from a mining area of Central Europe. *Environ. Pollut. Ser.A*, 31: 277–287.

Reeves, R. D., Brooks, R. R. and Dudley, T. R., 1983. Uptake of nickel by species of *Alyssum, Bornmuellera* and other genera of Old World Tribus Alyssae. *Taxon*, 32: 184–192.

Reeves, R. D., Brooks, R. R. and Press, J. R., 1980. Nickel accumulation by species of *Peltaria* Jacq. (Cruciferae). *Taxon*, 29: 629–633, 1980.

Rigotto, H., 1930. Significato fitogeografico delle florule dei serpentini submontani in Piemonte. *Atti Congr. Geograf. Ital.*, 11: 72–74.

Ritter-Studnicka, H., 1956. Beitrag zur Okologie der Serpentinflora in Bosnien. *Vegetatio*, 7: 89–98.

Ritter-Studicka, H., 1963. Biljni pokrov na serpeninimau Bosne. *Godisnjak. Biol. Inst. Sarajevo*, 16: 91–204.

Ritter-Studnicka, H., 1964. Anatomske razlike izmedju biljaka sa serpentinske dolomitno i krecnjacsko podloga. *Godisnjak. Biol. Inst. Sarajevo*, 17: 72–74.

Ritter-Studnicka, H., 1970a. Die Flora der Serpentinvorkommen in Bosnien. *Bibl. Bot.*, 130: 1–100.

Ritter-Studnicka, H., 1970b. Die Vegetation der Serpentinvorkommen in Bosnien. *Vegetatio*, 21; 75–156.

Ritter-Studnicka, H. and Klement, O., 1968. On lichen species and their associations on serpentine in Bosnia. *Ost. Bot. Z.*, 115: 93–99.

Rivas Goday, S., 1969. Flora serpentinicola española. Nota primiera. *An. Real. Acad. Farm. Madr.*, 35: 297–304.

Rivas Goday, S., 1972. Flora serpentinicola española. Nota secunda. *An. Real. Acad. Farm. Madr.*, 38: 459.

Rivas Goday, S., 1973. Plantas serpentinicolas y dolomiticas del sur de España. *Bol. Soc. Brot.*, 47: 161–178.

Rivas Martinez, S. and Izco, J. and Costa, M., 1973. *Asplenium cuneifolium* Viv. en Sierra Bermeja (Malaga). *Trab. Dep. Bot. Fisiol. Veg.*, 6: 23–30.

Rune, O. 1953. Plant life on serpentine and related rocks in the north of Sweden. *Acta Phytogeogr. Suec.*, 31: 1–139.

Sarosiek, J., 1964. Ecological analysis of some plants growing on serpentine soil in Lower Silesia (in Pol.). *Monograph. Bot.*, 18: 1–105.

Sarosiek, J. and Sadowska, A., 1961. Ekologia roslin gleb serpentynowych. *Wiad. Bot.*, 5: 73–86.

Sasse, F., 1979a. Untersuchungen an Serpentinstandorten in Frankreich, Italien, Osterreich und der Bundesrepublik Deutschland. I Bodenanalysen. *Flora*, 168: 379–395.

Sasse, F., 1979b. Untersuchungen an Serpentinstandorten in Frankreich, Italien, Osterreich und der Bundesrepublik Deutschland. II Pflanzenanalysen. *Flora*, 168: 578–594.

Schüstler, F., 1920. Slezinnik prostredni (*Asplenium adulterinum* Milde) a jeho systematicky vyznam. *Veda Prirodni*, 1: 167–171.

Severne, B. C., 1974. Nickel accumulation in *Hybanthus. Nature*, 248: 807–808.

Shaw, S., 1980. *Some Observations on the Ecology and Phytochemistry of Nickel-accumulating Alyssum species from the Iberian Peninsula.* MSc Thesis, Massey University, Palmerston North, New Zealand.

Soo, R. von, 1934. Vasmegyi szociologiae es florisztikai novenyfoldrajzahoz. *Vasi Szemli, Folia Sabariensia (Dunantuli Szemle)*, 1: 105–134.

Sulej, J., Slesak, E., Leonowicz-Babiak, K. and Buczek, J. Tentative explanation of dwarfish growth of plants on serpentine soil (in Pol.). *Acta Soc. Bot. Pol.*, 39: 405–419.

Suza, J., 1919. *Rinodina oveina* var. *mongeotioides* (Nyl.) Zahlbr. na Morave. *Sbor. Klubu Prirodovedeckoho y Brne*, 2; 11–15.

Suza, J., 1921. Xerothermni kvetena podkladu serpentinovych na dolmin toku Jihlavky. *Cas. Morav. Zemsk. Mus.*, 20; 1–32.

Suza, J., 1927a. Prirodni reservace u Mohelno. *Priroda*, 20: 239–244.

Suza, J., 1927b. Nova rostlina moravska. *Priroda*, 20.

Suza, J., 1928. Guide géobotanique pour le terrain serpentineux pres de Mohelno dans la Moravie du sud-ouest (Tchécoslovaquie). *Rozpr. Cesk. Akad. Ved. Umeni*, 37: 1–116.

Suza, J., 1930. Vergleichen der Studien über die Flechtflora der Serpentine (Mohelno, Gurhof und Kraubath)—(in Czech.). *Sbor. Prirod. Spol. Mor. Ostrave*, 6: 231–256.

Turrill, W. B., 1929. *The Plant Life of the Balkan Peninsula. A Phytogeographic Study.* Clarendon Press, Oxford.

Vaccari, L., 1903. La flore de la serpentine, du calcaire et du gneiss dans les Alpes Graies Orientales. *Bull. Soc. Flore Valdôt.*, 2: 32–75.

Verger, J. P., 1979. Origine du sol sur prasinites et serpentinites sous végétation pionnière en climat alpin (Val d'Aosta). *Doc. Cartogr. Ecol.*, 21: 127–138.

Verger, J. P., 1982. L'étage montagnard sylvicole sur serpentinites en Vallée d'Ayas (Val d'Aosta). *Doc. Cartogr. Ecol.*, 25: 51–66.

Verger, J. P., 1983. Contribution à la connaissance d'un groupement alpin climacique original sur serpentines; le Caricetum fimbriatae. Phytosociologie et pédologie. *C. Rend. Acad. Sci. Paris. Sér.III*, 296: 775–778.

Vergnano, O., 1953. L'azione fisiologica del nichel sulle piante de un terreno serpentinoso. *Nuov. G. Bot. Ital.*, 40: 109–183.

Vergnano, O., 1958. Il contenuto di elementi inorganici delle piante delle formazione ofiolitica dell'Impruneta (Firenze). *Nuov. G. Bot. Ital.*, 65: 133–162.

Vergnano Gambi, O., Brooks, R. R. and Radford, C. C., 1979. L'accumulo di nichel nelle specie italiane del genere *Alyssum*. *Webbia*, 33: 269–277.

Vergnano Gambi, O., Gabbrielli, R. and Pancaro, L., 1982. Nickel, chromium, and cobalt in plants from Italian serpentine areas. *Acta Oecol. Oecol. Plant.*, 3: 291–306.

Vergnano Gambi, O. and Cardini, F., 1967. Il contenuto di rame e di altri microelementi in alcune piante della zona mineraria di Montecatini val di Cecina (Livorno). *G. Bot. Ital.*, 101: 63–65.

Vergnano Gambi, O. and Gabbrielli, R., 1979. Ecophysiological and geochemical aspects of nickel, chromium and cobalt accumulation in the vegetation of some Italian ophiolitic outcrops. *Ofioliti*, 4; 199–208.

Vergnano Gambi, O. and Gabbrielli, R., 1981. La composizione minerale delle vegetazione degli affioramenti ofiolitici dell'Alta Valle di Ayas. *Rev. Valdôt. Hist. Nat.*, 35: 51–61.

Zlatnik, A., 1928a. Etudes écologiques et sociologiques sur le *Sesleria caerulea* et le Seslerion calcariae en Tchécoslovaquie. *Trav. Soc. Roy. Sci. Bohême Cl. Sci.*, 8.

Zlatnik, A., 1928b. Les association végétales et les sols du terrain serpentineux près de Mohelno. *Bull. Int. Acad. Tchéque Sci.*, 29: 333–337.

Zolyomi, B., 1936. Ubersicht der Felsenvegetation in der pannonischen Florenprovinz und den nordwestlich angrenzenden Gebieten. *Ann. Mus. Nat. Hist. Hungary*, 30: 136–174.

Chapter 15

CONTINENTAL ASIA

15.1 GEOLOGY AND TECTONICS

An overview of the tectonics of the Eurasian continent has been given by Derry (1980). A glance at the map of Eurasia shows the vast mountain chain of Urals. This was formed about 400 m.y. ago when the European and Asian Plates, formerly separated by ocean floor, collided and remained fused together to form the Eurasian Plate. Along this suture, the Urals form a long ophiolitic belt stretching from just north of the Aral Sea to the Arctic Ocean and into the long islands of Novaya Zemlya (Fig. 15.1).

Tectonic disturbances resulting from movement along the Eurasian and African Plates were particularly active during the Tertiary at the time of the Alpine orogeny in Southern Europe. The compression of Arabia on Eurasia resulted in Anatolia being squeezed westward about 15 m.y. ago, a movement which is still continuing today and is responsible for most of the earthquake activity in Turkey.

The folding which produced the Urals was followed by a folding in southern Russia during the Hercynian (Variscan) which terminated about 275 m.y. ago. This was followed by an outpouring of basic lavas in east-central Siberia which formed the so-called "Siberian Traps" consisting of bedded tuffs near the base, and basalt flows near the top. Related intrusive sills and dykes are interlayered within the volcanic trap rocks.

The geology and tectonics of the southern part of the Asian portion of the Eurasian Plate are much more complex than in the northern part. More than 200 m.y. ago, India and Sri Lanka were attached to the southeast part of what is now the African continent. The Indian section broke away shortly after and drifted north to strike the southern part of the Eurasian Plate about 50 m.y. ago. In the subsequent folding, the Himalayas were formed and the Tibetan Plateau was raised to about 5000 m.

About 75 m.y. ago, great basaltic flows occurred in western India and are known as the "Deccan Traps". The vulcanism continued into the early Tertiary.

The Indian Subcontinent is continuing its northward movement and is largely responsible for extensive tectonic activity in the Himalayas and in the People's Republic of China. The Altyn Tagh Fault and its extension, the Gansu Fault in North China, constitute the greatest active continental strike slip plate anywhere in the world. Of the 22 greatest earthquakes in the world between 1897 and 1955, seven occurred in China.

In the later stages of tectonic movement, the Arabian Plate separated from the African Plate along the Red Sea portion of the Great Rift Valley, pushed against the Eurasian Plate and plunged under it.

Apart from the Urals, ophiolitic belts in the rest of Asia are found mainly in Anatolia, Iran and Oman. In the latter territory, the Semail Ophiolitic Belt occupies a large part of the country and has a surface expression of 30,000 km². It is one of the world's largest exposures of ancient oceanic crust. It forms part of the "Periarabian Ophiolitic Crescent" which can be followed westward from Oman through Neyriz Kermanshah in Iran, along the Turkish-Iranian border fold belt and finally into Hatay vilayet of southern Turkey.

Elsewhere in continental Asia, ultramafic outcrops are found mainly along the line of the Himalayas and down the Irrawaddy river basin in Burma. Sporadic occurrences are also found along the Altyn Tagh Fault and Gansu Thrust in China.

Fig. 15.1 Map of Western Siberia. 1—Noril'sk, 2—Tannu Tuva, 3—Aktyubinsk, 4—Mts Rai-Iz and Slantsevaya, 5—Lake Turgojak. Ultramafic rocks are shown as solid areas.

15.2 RUSSIA IN ASIA

15.2.1 Geological Introduction

Although sporadic occurrences of ultramafic rocks are found in many regions of Russia such as in the Caucasus and in southern Siberia, the main outcrops are found in the vast ophiolitic belt of the Ural mountains (Fig. 15.1). The western Urals are characterized by thick Palaeozoic post-orogenic sediments which are separated from the eastern Urals by the main Uralian fault (Ager, 1980) which runs the whole length of the main range. Just to the east of this fault there is a great belt of ocean floor ophiolites continuous in the north and intermittent in the south. These and accompanying volcanics are overlain by thick Palaeozoic eugeosynclinal successions which pass upwards into transitional sediments.

The Urals are the treasure house of Russia with extensive ores of iron, manganese, copper, nickel, chromium and platinum. This region accounts for about one third of the world's annual production of chrome. Indeed, in the 18th century it was the only source of supply after Johann Gottlob Lehman first described "Siberian Red Lead" (lead chromate) which he obtained from the Beresof Mines near Ekaterinburg (Sverdlovsk).

Although there are few extensive outcrops of ultramafic rocks in the Soviet Union outside the Urals, nickel sulphide mineralization does occur at Noril'sk (site #1 in Fig. 15.1), and in Tannu Tuva near the joint borders of the Soviet Union, Mongolia and China's Xinjiang Province (site 2). The deposits are usually Ni/Fe sulphides with some copper and are regarded as being formed from the segregation of a sulphide melt from magma at an early stage of crystallization.

15.2.2 The Serpentine Vegetation of Russia

In spite of the pre-eminence of the Soviet Union in the field of biological methods of prospecting (Malyuga, 1964; Kovalevsky, 1979), very little of this work has been devoted to a thorough study of the phytosociology and floristics of serpentine vegetation as such (see Table 15.1 for a list of workers in these fields). The student of the serpentine vegetation of Russia does not have source material available which covers the subject with the same coverage and depth as for example the classical work of Rune (1953) on the Fennoscandian plants, or that of Pichi-Sermolli (1948) on the serpentine flora of Tuscany. Perhaps the best-known Russian work on the subject, is a paper by Igoshina (1966) describing the serpentine plants of Mt Rai-Iz (site #4 in Fig. 15.1) in the Polar Urals. The vast majority of the Soviet work is biogeochemical rather than geobotanical, though serpentinimorphosis has sometimes been studied in connection with its application to mineral exploration. An example of this is the work of Storozheva (1954) who observed abnormal and chlorotic forms of *Pulsatilla patens*, *Avena desertorum* and *Linosyris villosa* over nickel-rich soils in the southern Urals.

Malyuga (1964) described a serpentine vegetation community in the Aktyubinsk region (Fig. 15.2 and site #3 of Fig. 15.1) in the southern Urals. These plants included *Gypsophila patrinii* and the endemic species *Matthiola fragrans*, *Silene suffrutescens*, *Anabasis cretacea*, *Berteroa spathulata*, and *Alyssum tortuosum* growing on soils containing 3500 μg/g nickel, and which replaced the normal *Festuca rupicola*, *Stipa capillata* and *S. lessingiana* community of non-mineralized soils.

Plant communities over serpentine among the larch forests of the southern Urals near Chelyabinsk have been studied by Iljinsky (1936) who described such vegetation in the neighbourhood of Lake Turgojak (site #5 in Fig. 15.1) in the Ilmen Range. The vegetation is a mixture of pine, larch and heath dominated by the ubiquitous *Pinus sylvestris* (Scotch Pine) a common coloniser of serpentine in Central Europe. Iljinsky (1936) described the community as a "*Pinus sylvestris—Larix sibirica—Cytisus ruthenicus—Myrtillus niger, Calmagrostis arundinacea*" Association. Character species of this Association are the following: *Pinus sylvestris*, *Larix sibirica*, *Cytisus ruthenicus*, *Myrtillus niger*, *Calamagrostis arundinacea*, *Digitalis ambigua*, *Orobus vernus*, *Ramischia secunda*, *Vaccinium vitis-idaea*, and *Rubus*

TABLE 15.1 Papers which Describe Serpentine Vegetation of Continental Asia

India	Banerjee (1972), Roy (1974)
Oman	Mandaville (1977)
Russia	Igoshina (1966), Iljinsky (1936), Kovalevsky (1979), Malyuga (1954, 1966), Paribok and Alekseeva-Popova (1966), Storozheva (1954)
Turkey	Akman (1973a, b, c, d, e, f), Brooks et al. (1979), Davis et al (1965), Dudley (1964)

saxatilis. This Association belongs to the Pineto-cytision uralense Alliance. Iljinsky (1936) has assigned it to the Rubetalia saxatilis Order.

A "serpentine" vegetation exists in the Tannu-Ola range of Tannu Tuva (site #2) in southern Siberia near the border with Mongolia and Xingkiang Province of China. Although the nickel was derived primarily from ultramafic rocks, the presence of copper has modified the vegetation to such an extent that it is now more typically a "copper flora" than one influenced by serpentine alone. This is shown by the presence of *Gypsophila patrinii* which is known chiefly as a copper indicator (Makarova, 1960; Malyuga and Petrunina, 1961; Malyuga; 1964). The presence of nickel is indicated by the occurrence of the hyperaccumulator *Alyssum biovulatum*, a widespread plant extending from Europe through Siberia to Alaska where it is known as *A. americanum*. Other indicators of nickel are *Silene jenissensis* and *Potentilla bifurca* which are found in the *Caragana spinosa*—*C. arborescens* steppe community. The northern slopes of the Mountain Range (0.7% copper and 0.9% nickel) carry a sparse vegetation community with mainly chlorotic, dwarf forms of the *Larix sibirica*—*Betula verrucosa* woodland which is common in the region.

The work of Igoshina (1966) on serpentine vegetation of the Polar Urals is a useful starting point for the understanding of the vegetation cover of Russian serpentines. Igoshina compared the vegetation of the ultramafic Mt Rai-Iz (1100 m) with that of the adjacent Mt Slantsevaya (Schist Mt) with a similar elevation (950 m) and aspect. These mountains form part of the Sobsky Range which has a length of about 20 km and maximum width of 7 km (site 4 in Fig. 15.1). Mt Rai-Iz carries only about 50% of the number of species found on Mt Slantsevaya, but among these are many taxa which are rare or entirely absent on other non-ultramafic terrain of similar latitude and elevation. Examples of such serpentinicolous species are: *Arabis septentrionalis*, *Cochlearia arctica*, *Alyssum biovulatum*, *Minuartia rubella*, *Cerastium arvense*, *Dianthus repens*, *Armeria maritima*, *Linum boreale*, *Koeleria asiatica*, and *Asplenium viride* as well as a number of *bodenvag* species such as *Minuartia arctica*, *Silene acaulis*, *Cerastium regelii*, *Deschampsia brevifolia*, *Carex saxatilis* and the moss *Racomitrium lanuginosum*. Igoshina considered that *Arabis septentrionalis* is a particularly good indicator of serpentine in the Polar Urals. It is also interesting to note that *Cerastium arvense* is not only endemic to serpentine in the northern Urals but also to serpentine on the east coast of North America (see Chapter 11).

The base of Mt Rai-iz is covered with sparse stands of *Larix sibirica* among the boulder trains of the first 200 m of the mountain. In the 200–500 m zone, the surface is covered with low subarctic tundra interspersed with low boreal shrubs. The next zone (500–1000 m) is characterized by south-facing boulder slopes covered with *Racomitrium lanuginosum* with occasional stunted specimens of *Salix reptans*. The slopes of the north faces are virtually devoid of vegetation. At the flat summit of Mt Rai-iz (1100 m), the stony terrain is also nearly completely barren apart from occasional areas of *Deschampsia brevifolia* interspersed with lichens in the more sheltered sites.

On comparing the vegetation of Mts Rai-iz and Slantsevaya, Igoshina (1966) recorded only 91 species of higher plants in the former, compared with 216 on Mt Slantsevaya. Not only are there far fewer taxa on the serpentine but there are significant differences in the distribution of families as is shown in Table 15.2. One of the most notable of these differences is the dominance of the Caryophyllaceae (13.2% compared with 5.6%) over the ultramafic substrate, as has also been observed by Rune (1953) for the serpentine plants of Fennoscandia.

TABLE 15.2 A Summary of the Floristics of the Vegetation of Ultramafic Mt Rai-Iz in the Polar Urals and of the Nearby Schistose Mt Slantsevaya.

	Mt Rai-Iz	Mt Slantsevaya
Total number of taxa	91	216
Total number of genera	60	122
Total number of families	30	44
Cyperaceae	14	21
Caryophyllaceae	12	12
Poaceae	9	19
Saxifragaceae	8	13
Juncaceae	4	8
Salicaceae	4	9
Scrophulariaceae	4	10
Asteraceae	4	15
Ranunculaceae	3	9
Brassicaceae	3	13
Rosaceae	3	17
Ericaceae	3	0

After: Igoshina (1966)

15.2.3 Biogeochemical Prospecting over Serpentine in Russia

The Polar Urals

Russia is the home of biogeochemical prospecting (Malyuga, 1964; Kovalevsky , 1979) which followed the original pioneering work of Tkalich (1938). Kovalevsky (1979) estimated that 460 biogeochemical papers had been published in the Soviet Union in the period 1938–1970 of which over half had appeared in the last 5 years of this time span. Today there are probably over 1000 Russian papers on the subject, though of these, very few have been concerned with the chemical analysis of vegetation without consideration of the applications to mineral exploration. Nevertheless, a paper by Paribok and Alekseeva-Popova (1966) contained concentration data on trace elements in serpentine vegetation of Mt Rai-Iz (see Igoshina, 1966 above) with a view to using the information to understand the "serpentine problem" (see Chapter 4). These workers determined 14 elements in 5 trees, 11 herbs, 1 moss and 4 lichens from the serpentine of Mt Rai-iz.

Table 15.3 summarizes the data of Paribok and Alekseeva-Popova (1966). None of the species is endemic to serpentine and the levels of nickel and chromium are typical for most of the pan-boreal taxa growing over ultramafic substrates. Ca/Mg quotients are normal for serpentine plants (< 0.40) and exceed 1.00 for species growing over sediments nearby (presumably at Mt Slantsevaya—see above). Paribok and Alekseeva-Popova (1966) concluded that the high nickel and chromium content of the soil, coupled with the low Ca/Mg quotient was mainly responsible for the general infertility of the soils of Mt Rai-iz.

The Southern Urals

As indicated by the reviews of Malyuga (1964) and Kovalevsky (1976), most of the biogeochemical prospecting over ultramafic rocks has been carried out in the southern Urals

Plate 15.2 (a) Above: Serpentine barren at Welipatanwila, Sri Lanka. The terrain is heavily serpentinized and almost completely devoid of vegetation except for scattered specimens of *Evolvulus alsinoides*.
(b) Below: serpentine vegetation at Uda Walawe, Sri Lanka. The grass is a serpentine-endemic variety of *Cymbopogon flexuosus* interspersed with shrubs of *Morinda tinctoria*.
Photos by the author.

Plate 16.1 (a) Above: *Picea glehni* forest on Mt Shiratori, Hokkaido.
(b) Below: Scree slopes on Mt Yupari, Hokkaido.
Photos by S. Nosaka.

TABLE 15.3 Mean Elemental Concentrations (µg/g dry weight) in Aerial Parts of Plants Growing over Serpentine in the Polar Urals at Mt Rai-Iz Compared with Plants from the Nearby Schistose Mt Slantsevaya.

Plant Type	Species	Rock	Ni	Cr	Ca	Mg	Ca/Mg*
Trees	Larix sibirica	Serp.	40	10	3700	6600	0.33
		Schist	30	<10	13300	5500	1.45
Shrubs	Betula nana, Dryas octopetala, Ledum decumbens, Salix arctica, Vaccinium uliginosum	Serp.	130	5	9200	13800	0.40
		Schist	20	<5	15000	6900	1.31
Cushion plants	Minuartia arctica, Saxifraga spinulosa, Silene acaulis	Serp.	100	37	4300	—	—
		Schist	9	2	16500	—	—
Herbs	Lagotis minor, Oxyria digyna, Oxytropis sordida, Pachypleurum alpinum, Polygonum bistorta, Rumex arifolius, Saxifraga hirculus	Serp.	90	8	3700	13300	0.17
		Schist	7	<1	11300	6500	1.04
Sedges	Carex ensifolia subsp. arctisibirica, Eriophorum angustifolium, E. vaginatum	Serp.	37	4	2000	6000	0.20
		Schist	10	<1	6200	3800	1.00
Lichens	Alectoria ochroleuca, Cetraria cucullata, C. islandica, Cladonia alpestris	Serp.	200	105	—	—	—
		Schist	20	9	—	—	—
Rocks		Serp.	4000	4000	5000	100000	0.03
		Schist	60	300	10000	5000	0.12

* mole quotients
After: Paribok and Alekseeva-Popova (1966)

(see also Aleskovsy et al. 1959; Biske, 1972; Ivanova et al. 1974; Maiorov (1969); Skarlina Ufimtseva et al. 1976).

Malyuga (1964) has reported biogeochemical studies over the Kimpersaisky ultramafic region in the southern Urals near Aktyubinsk (Figs. 15.1 and 15.2). The soils of the area are of the chestnut and light chestnut type with a tendency to be heavy in texture. They overlie recent and ancient clays and loams. The Kimpersaisky Complex (Fig. 15.2) is covered with a grass community of Festuca sulcata, Stipa capillata and Agropyron sibiricum. On serpentine outcrops, the common species are Anabasis cretacea, Silene suffrutescens, Gypsophila patrinii, Bertoroa sp. and Alyssum tortuosum. The latter has been reported by Malyuga (1964) as containing 1000 µg/g nickel in its dried leaves and is of hyperaccumulator status (see Chapter 8).

In the Taiketkensky nickel deposit, Malyuga (1964) sampled endemic forms of Pulsatilla patens and Linosyris villosa across the ore body and analysed them for nickel, cobalt and copper. The Ni/Co quotient was particularly useful in delineating the ore body. The use of quotients rather than absolute values helped to minimize the occurrence of false anomalies caused by different physical conditions of the soil.

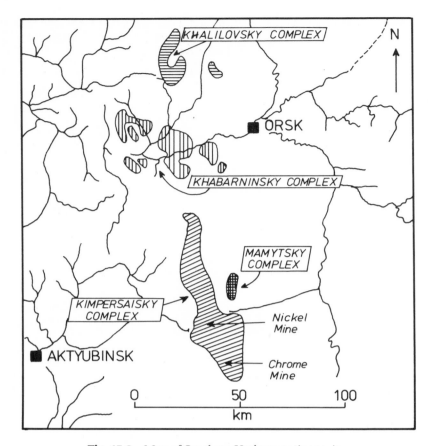

Fig. 15.2   Map of Southern Ural serpentine region.

In the Chugaevsky nickel deposit (Fig. 15.3), Malyuga (1964) used *Linosyris villosa* in a biogeochemical survey across the ore body and observed an extremely close relationship between nickel in plant material and the content of the same element in the soil. The mean Ni/Co quotient in this species was 12 and was about ten times the value for background sites.

In the Kimpersaisky region (Fig. 15.4), Malyuga (1964) carried out a biogeochemical survey over a chromite deposit using *Stipa* sp. as the sampling medium. The chromium content of the plant material accurately reflected the distance of the ore body below the surface and did so more closely than did the analysis of the soil.

Tannu Tuva

The vegetation of the Tannu Tuva nickel/copper province has already been mentioned above, and Malyuga (1964) has carried out biogeochemical investigations in this area. The pattern of nickel uptake is however disturbed by concomitant accumulation of copper which is to some extent antagonistic to nickel in plant physiology. Plants sampled across the Cu/Co/Ni ore body were: *Pulsatilla turczaninovii, Larix sibirica, Iris flavissima, Cotoneaster uniflorus, Vicia cracca, Artemisia frigida, Linum sibiricum, Capsella bursetapastoris,* and *Scutellaria grandiflora.* There was a close relationship between cobalt in plants and soils in a transect across the ore body, with consequent implications for successful biogeochemical prospecting. This is shown in Fig. 15.5.

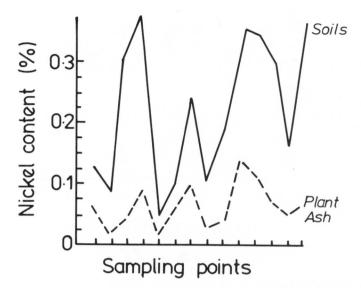

one of our famous labels

Fig. 15.3   Correlation of nickel concentrations in soils and in plant ash of *Linosyris villosa* from the Chugaevsky nickel deposit at the Kimpersaisky serpentine region of the Southern Urals.
Source: Malyuga (1964). Copyright Plenum Publishing Corp. Reprinted by permission

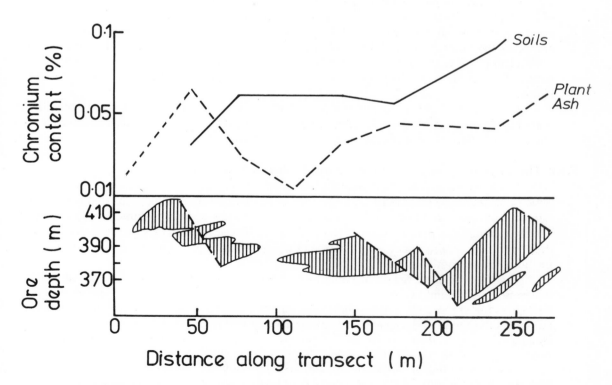

Fig. 15.4   Distribution of chromium in soils and plant ash as a function of the ore depth in the Kimpersaisky serpentine region of the Southern Urals.
Source: Maiyuga (1964). Copyright Plenum Publishing Corp. Reprinted by permission

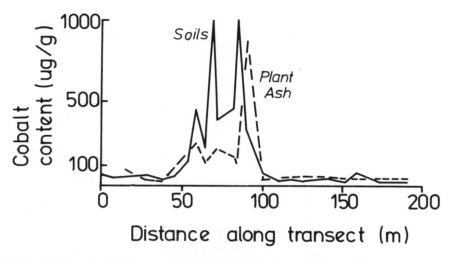

Fig. 15.5 Correlation of cobalt concentrations in soils and plant ash (mean of several taxa) over an ore deposit in Tannu Tuva.
Source: Malyuga (1964). Copyright Plenum Publishing Corp. Reprinted by permission

15.3 ANATOLIA

15.3.1 Geology and Topography

Asiatic Turkey (Anatolia) covers nearly 250,000 km² and consists of a plateau rising steadily towards the east and bounded to the north and south by steep mountain ranges—part of the Alpine-Himalayan system. East of the Antitaurus chain, the southern boundary range curves round in an arc to the mountain mass of Kurdistan in southeast Anatolia and embraces the outer plateau of Mesopotamia which is really the northern extension of the Syrian Desert. In western Anatolia the plateau falls gradually to sea level and terminates in a series of promontories which face the islands of the Aegean such as the Sporades and Khios.

There are widespread serpentine occurrences in Anatolia (Fig. 15.6) among which the ophiolitic complex of southern Anatolia (Hatay—site 1 in Fig. 15.6) extends through Iran into Oman and is part of the Periarabian Crescent (Coleman, 1977).

15.3.2 The Phytogeography of the Serpentine Vegetation of Anatolia

The serpentine flora of Anatolia closely resembles the surrounding vegetation from which it is derived. The flora of Turkey (Davis et al., 1965) is exceedingly rich and is of great interest because it is the meeting place of three phytogeographic regions: Euro-Siberian, Mediterranean, and Irano-Turanian (see Fig. 10.1). These regions can be recognized from their different vegetational aspects reflecting differences in climate and in floristics, including endemism.

The Euro-Siberian region of Anatolia extends along the Black Sea littoral in the north where relatively humid climatic conditions result in a typically mesophytic vegetation with deciduous forest being the normal climax community. The Euro-Siberian region is sometimes known as the Euxine Province. The western parts of this region (Paphlagonia and Bithynia) show a progressive decrease in the Euxine species and at the same time an infiltration of Balkan and Central European elements.

The Mediterranean vegetation extends along the Mediterranean littoral of Anatolia from The Dardanelles to the Amanus Mts near the Syrian border. The transition to the Irano-Turanian flora is relatively abrupt in southern Anatolia but more gradual in the west. A shrub association known as "macchie" (Fr. = maquis) dominates much of the Mediterranean

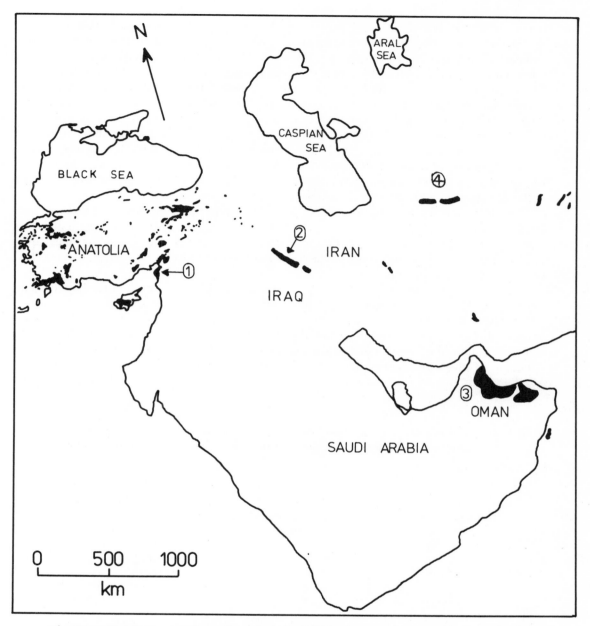

Fig. 15.6 Distribution of ultramafic rocks in the Middle East. 1—Amanus Mts, Anatolia; 2—Nayriz-Kermanshah, Iran; 3—Semail Ophiolitic Belt, Oman; 4—Kuh-i-Chaghatai, Iran.

regions of Turkey below 1000 m. However, over deeper soils, forests prevail. Above 1000 m the Mediterranean vegetation is largely dominated by conifers such as *Pinus nigra* subsp. *pallasiana,* particularly over serpentine. The taxon therefore resembles its close relative *P. nigra* which is common over, or endemic to, ultramafites in much of the Balkan Peninsula. *Pinus nigra* and subsp. *pallasiana* are particularly abundant in zones transitional between the Mediterranean and Irano-Turanian regions. Above the tree line, the serpentine vegetation is dominated by various cushion communities.

The Irano-Turanian phytogeographic region is by far the largest in Anatolia and is mainly confined to the central regions of the eastern part of the territory. It is part of a very much larger phytogeographic region extending southwards to Palestine and eastwards to Mongolia. Treeless steppes are dominant in Central Anatolia and are largely colonized by *Artemisia* spp. and closely resemble the steppes of southern Siberia.

Endemism is widespread through the Anatolian flora (serpentine and otherwise) and is about 20%—an extremely high figure for a territory not isolated from others by extensive oceans. The largest number of endemic species occurs in the Irano-Turanian and Mediterranean regions. Endemism tends to be most apparent in regions encompassing the junctions of phytogeographic provinces.

The genus *Alyssum* is a particularly good example of endemism in Anatolia where it appears to have its maximum centre of diversity and multiplicity of species (Brooks et al., 1979). This genus contains at least 33 taxa endemic to serpentine in one taxonomic section alone (Odontarrhena) and the subject has already been discussed to some extent in Chapter 8. The distribution of serpentine endemic species among the three phytogeographic regions of Anatolia is given in Table 15.4. The highest number of endemics is found in the Mediterranean province which is much smaller in area than the Irano-Turenian part of the

TABLE 15.4 Distribution of *Alyssum* Species of Section Odontarrhena, among the Phytogeographic Regions of the Anatolian and E. Aegean Serpentine Flora

Mediterranean Region	Irano-Turanian Region	Euxine Region
A. corsicum*	A. masmenaeum*	A. callichroum*
A. syriacum*	A. davisianum*	A. longistylum
A. discolor*	A. constellatum*	A. tortuosum
A. oxycarpum*	A. callichroum*	A. gehamense
A. callichroum*	A. eriophyllum*	A. borzaeanum
A. cypricum*	A. longistylum	A. sibiricum
A. hubermorathi*	A. pateri	A. murale*
A. sibiricum	A. borzaeanum	A. peltarioides
A. condensatum	A. sibiricum	subsp. *virgatiforme*
A. murale*	A. condensatum	
A. cassium*	A. filiforme	
A. cicilicum*	A. anatolicum*	
A. crenulatum*	A. haussknechtii	
A. giosnanum*	A. murale*	
A. pterocarpum*	A. floribundum*	
A. floribundum*	A. trapeziforme*	
A. caricum*	A. peltarioides	
A. pinifolium*	subsp. *peltarioides*	
A. samariferum*	subsp. *virgatiforme*	
A. dubertretii*	A. virgatum*	
A. lesbiacum*	A. samariferum*	
A. peltarioides		

* hyperaccumulator of nickel

territory. The distribution of *Alyssum* species in Subsection Samarifera of Section Odontarrhena has been given in Fig. 6.2 of Chapter 6. The pattern is of a single non-hyperaccumulator of nickel (*A. peltarioides*) surrounding enclaves of other hyperaccumulating taxa from the same subsection. The latter have presumably been derived from the much more widespread serpentine-intolerant *A. peltarioides* and demonstrate the mechanism of the evolution of tolerance to ultramafic substrates. A similar pattern is shown for *A. subspinosum* as a non-serpentine parent for serpentine-tolerant taxa within Subsection Compressa.

Because of the vastness of the Turkish flora, and because of the lack of studies orientated specifically to serpentine floras in this country, it is not feasible to give an in-depth survey which also has wide coverage of Anatolia. However, an excellent survey of the flora of the Amanus Mountains has been given by Akman (1973a,b,c,d,e,f) and is the source material for the following section.

15.3.3 The Serpentine Vegetation of the Amanus Mountains

The Environment

The Amanus Mountains of Hatay Province of southern Anatolia constitute a NE-SW continuation of the Antitaurus Chain of mountains. The mean maximum altitude is 1500–2000 m commencing at Cape Hinzer and extending northwards to Gavur and to the Haruniye Hills (see Fig. 15.7). The massif is about 85 km long and has a mean width of 20–25 km. It was formed in the Miocene and is essentially a horst bounded by the Hatay-Golbasi depression in the east and by the Haruniye-Osmaniye and Dortyol-Iskenderum plain in the west.

The eastern and western limits of the Amanus Mountains are intruded with ultramafic rocks of the ophiolites of the Periarabian Crescent. The central part of the mountain chain is covered mainly by calcareous rocks, schists, quartzites and greywackes. The climate is typically Mediterranean with dry summers and wet cool winters. The annual precipitation (1000 mm) is relatively high for this region and despite the altitude, mean winter temperatures are well above freezing (Akman, 1973d).

Soil Types

Akman (1973e) has recognized 5 main types of soil in the Amanus mountains. These are: eroded soils on limestones, red Mediterranean soils, brown calcareous soils, brown forest soils, and leached brown soils. Only the brown forest soils are typical of ultramafic substrates and are found principally beneath *Pinus brutia* woodland. These soils have an organic-rich A horizon about 4 cm in depth overlying a 40 cm horizon which has a reddish-brown colour. The sand content rises to typically 40–60%, clays 20–30% and limonite 50–60%. The superficial organic layer is just thick enough to shield the smaller plants from the full unfavourable edaphic effects of serpentine. The general physiognomy of the serpentine vegetation is therefore not significantly different from that of other vegetation communities in this region, since xeromorphism (mainly shown here by hard-leaved plants) is as much a characteristic of Mediterranean floras as it is of serpentine communities.

The Character of the Serpentine Flora of the Amanus Mountains

The serpentine flora of the Amanus Mountains is derived largely from the surrounding pool of Mediterranean plants, disjunctions being nowhere very evident. The percentage distribution of the various plant families in this serpentine community is given in Table 15.5. In comparison with the corresponding flora in Europe, the most obvious differences are the high proportion of Fabaceae and Brassicaceae and the relative insignificance of the Caryophyllaceae. This is entirely due to the nature of the source pool from the surrounding non-serpentine taxa which is typically Mediterranean with its high proportion of Fabaceae. Among the serpentine-endemic Brassicaceae (Akman, 1973b) are several *Alyssum* species including the nickel hyperaccumulators *A. cassium*, *A. constellatum*, *A. oxycarpum*, and *A.*

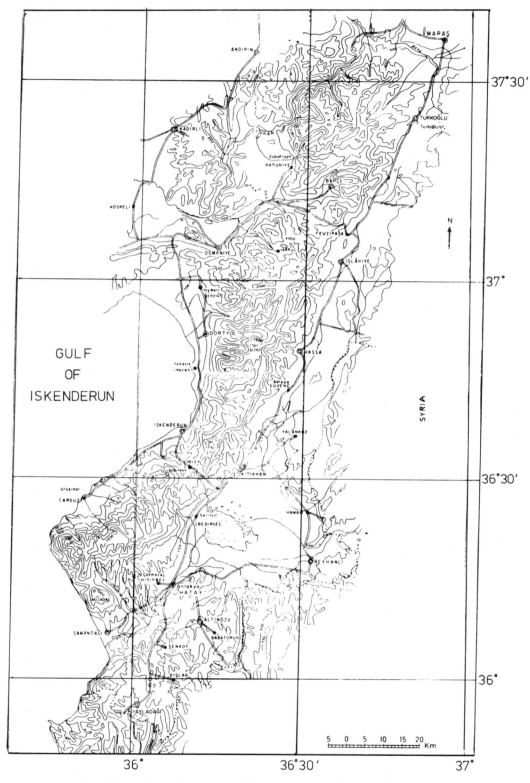

Fig. 15.7 Map of the Amanus Mountains of Southern Anatolia.
Source: Akman (1973a).

samariferum (Brooks et al. 1979) plus a number of *Thlaspi* species which are also hyperaccumulators (*T. austroamanicus*, *T. elegans*, and *T. oxyceras*). Almost all of these plants are found in the more open areas amid the forests of *Pinus brutia* and *P. nigra*.

The origin of the serpentine flora of the Amanus Mountains is given in Table 15.6. It is appropriate at this stage to compare the floral elements of this vegetation with those of the serpentine vegetation of northeast Portugal and the Upper Tiber in Tuscany (Table 14.6). The most obvious difference is the strong Mediterranean element in the Turkish flora. This is not surprising because of the relative isolation of the Amanus Range from other phytogeographic regions. There is also the factor that the region does not suffer the same climatic extremes of Tuscany and northeast Portugal.

TABLE 15.5 Distribution of Taxa Among Plant Families in the Serpentine Flora of the Amanus Mts of Southern Anatolia

Family	Percentage
Fabaceae	14.3
Asteraceae	8.3
Lamiaceae	8.3
Poaceae	5.5
Brassicaceae	5.0
Apiaceae	4.0
Liliaceae	4.0
Rosaceae	3.6
Rubiaceae	3.1
Caryophyllaceae	3.0
Boraginaceae	3.0
Orchidaceae	2.5
Hypericaceae	2.0
Ranunculaceae	2.0
Other	3.4

After: Akman (1973e)

TABLE 15.6 Phytogeographic Spectrum of the Serpentine Vegetation of the Amanus Mts in Southern Anatolia

Floral element	Percentage
Mediterranean	57.0
Eurasian	12.0
European	5.0
Palaeotemperate	5.0
Endemic	3.0
Irano-Turanian	2.5
Pluriregional	2.5
Boreal	2.0
Palaeo-subtropical	2.0
Cosmopolitan	2.0
Turkish	1.5

Vegetation Communities of Serpentine in the Amanus Mountains

Vegetation communities in the serpentine areas of the Amanus Mountains have been described by Akman (1973f) who has recognized two vegetation assemblages. The first of these is a *Ptosimopappus bracteatus* community found only on ultramafic rocks at altitudes of 0–1000 m. It consists primarily of perennial herbs growing over soils 15–40 cm deep. The soil is only slightly eroded, has 1–4% organic matter and contains coarse gravel and stones amounting to 9–25% of the volume. The pH is typically in the range 5.6 to 7.5. Data pertaining to this community are shown in Table 15.7.

The second vegetation community over serpentine in the Amanus Mountains is the widespread *Pinus brutia* woodland (Table 15.7) dominated by this conifer and also by *Quercus infectoria*. It is found in the 0–1000 m altitude range and grows not only on ultramafic rocks but also on types other than quartzites or greywackes. The pH of these soils is in the range 6.5 to 8.0 with a mean of 7.0.

Pinus brutia woodland is to serpentine in Amanus what *P. nigra* is to ultramafites in the Balkans. The former species is very characteristic of serpentine but is not confined to it. The vegetation cover is not dense and many of the characteristic serpentine-endemic herbs and perennials of the lower storey occur on rocky outcrops amid the more open parts of the woodland. There are other communities which also occur sporadically on serpentine in the Amanus Mountains and mention should therefore be made of the *Pinus nigra* subsp. *pallasiana* woodland. This tree is not serpentine endemic but forms extensive woodland on and off serpentine in the Anatolian Plateau at elevations above 1000 m. In the Amanus Mountains, it occurs in the 1100–1600 m interval particularly on north-facing slopes such as in the Zorkun region.

Pinus nigra subsp. *pallasiana* is not confined to serpentine, and sometimes grows on calcareous rocks. It also favours quartzite to a considerable degree where it is found over shallow skeletal soils. It appears to favour the same ecological niches as *P. brutia* but at a much higher altitude where it replaces the latter since it is more tolerant of the harsher climatic conditions.

15.4 IRAN

15.4.1 Introduction

There is no source material for an evaluation of the serpentine flora of Iran *per se*. However K. H. Rechinger f., is still in the process of writing a flora of Iran which will be complete in a year or so, and he has been kind enough to give me advance information on this subject which is the source material for this subsection.

Ultramafic rocks outcrop at many locations in Iran. The largest of these is in the Neyriz-Kermanshah region to the southwest of the country (site #2 in Fig. 15.6). Another important ultramafic region is in northeast Iran near the Soviet and Afghan borders along the Alburz Mountains (site #4 in Fig. 15.6). The geology of this area has been described by Fisher (1968). The main outcrop is at Kuh-i-Chaghatai and is about 160 km long and 24 km wide. The northern boundary of this body consists of Eocene tuffaceous volcanic rocks. Further east is another ultramafic complex known as the "Coloured Melange", an assemblage of shales, limestones, vesicular lavas and serpentine. Both ultramafic bodies consist of low hills rising to 1600–1800 metres above the surrounding high plateau.

15.4.2 The Serpentine Vegetation

The serpentine vegetation of the Robat Safid area in the "Coloured Melange" of northern Iran has been studied by K. H. Rechinger in his expeditions of 1937 and 1948. From the brief notes supplied by him, it appears that the terrain is exceedingly bare and completely devoid of trees or shrubs. The commonest serpentinicolous plants are the Asteraceous

TABLE 15.7 Plant Communities over Ultramafic Rocks in the Amanus Mts of Southern Anatolia

Ptosimopappus heath	Pinus brutia woodland	Pinus nigra var pallasiana woodland
Ptosimopappus bracteatus 5	Pinus brutia 5	Pinus nigra var. pallasiana 5
Erica verticillata 5	Quercus infectoria 4	Pteridium aquilinum 2
Serratula cerinthifolia 4	Pistacia terebinthus 2	Fragaria vesca 2
Dorycnium pentaphyllum subsp. haussknechtii 2	Cotinus coggytia 3	Chrysanthemum cicilicum 1
Peucedanum ruthenicum 3	Arbutus unedo 3	Trifolium davisii 1
Salvia aramiensis 2	Phillyria media 2	Doronicum caucasicum 1
Polygala supina 2	Daphne sericea 2	Rubus tomentosus 1
Genista antiochia 2	Spartium junceum 3	Lathyrus laxiflorus 1
Centaurea cataonica 1	Calycotome villosa 1	Sorbus torminalis 1
Prunella vulgaris 1	Gonocytisus pterocladus 1	Dorycnium graecum 1
Prunella orientalis 1	Rhamnus punctatus 2	Thlaspi oxyceras 1
	Cistus salvifolius 2	Genista lydia 2
	Cytisopsis dorycniifolia 1	Juniperus oxycedrus var. oxycedrus 2
	Eryngium falcatum 2	Centaurea cheiracantha 2
	Asparagus acutifolius 3	Alyssum cassium 1
	Myrtus communis 2	Veronica pectinata 2
	Cistus creticus 2	
	Smilax aspera 2	
	Dactylis glomerata 2	
	Ruscus aculeatus 3	
	Euphorbia macrostegia 2	
	Origanum laevigatum 1	
	Coronilla emeroides 2	
	Vicia tenuifolia var. stenophylla 3	
	Alyssum cassium 3	
	A. samariferum 2	
	Glycarrhiza flavescens 2	
	Thlaspi austroamanicus 1	
	Alyssum constellatum 1	
	A. murale 1	
	A. oxycarpum 1	
	Thlaspi elegans 2	
	T. oxyceras 1	

Numerals refer to relative abundances where "5" is very abundant.
After: Akman (1973f)

Sclerorhachys platyrhachis (Plate 15.1a), and *Jurinea pungens* (endemic) and the *bodenvag Eremurus spectabilis* subsp. *spectabilis* (Plate 19.1b). Other serpentinicolous plants including 13 endemics are listed in Table 15.8. The present political problems in Iran (and in neighbouring Afghanistan which has important ultramafic outcrops with serpentine endemics such as *Paracaryum serpentinicum*) preclude the possibility of botanical exploration by westerners in the immediate future, so that the notes of K. H. Rechinger are of great importance. There is no doubt that the serpentine flora of Iran is both rich and poorly studied and it is to be hoped that the political problems in that part of the world will be solved in the near future so that renewed botanical exploration may continue.

TABLE 15.8   Plants of the Serpentine Outcrops of Northern Iran

Serpentine endemics	Bodenvag species
Cousinia bienerti	*Cousinia afghanica*
C. chrysandra	*Echinops villosissimus*
C. heliantha	*Eremurus spectabilis* subsp.
C. sabzevarensis	spectabilis
C. trachyphyllaria	
Diaphanoptera khorasanica	
Jurinea pungens	
*Lomatopodium staurophyllum**	
Onobrychis amoena subsp. *meshkedensis*	
*Prangos serpentinica**	
Sclerorhachys platyrhachis	
Scorzonera microcalathia	
Silene gertraudiae	

* found also on gypsum several hundred km to the west.
Source: K. H. Rechinger (per. commn.)

15.5 OMAN

15.5.1 Geology

The Semail Ophiolitic Belt (site #3 of Fig. 15.6) of Oman is one of the great ultramafic complexes of the world. The highest point of the Oman Mountains is Jabal-al-Akhdar which rises to 3050 m. The mountain range consists of a core of Mesozoic sediments, in part metamorphosed, uplifted and folded in Oligocene and Miocene times. There are great superimposed masses of igneous rocks and ophiolitic nappes.

15.5.2 Serpentine Vegetation

Although associated with the very arid Arabian Peninsula, the rainfall in the Jabal-al-Akhdar region is relatively high (ca. 400 mm) and has permitted a relatively luxuriant vegetation to be established including even a type of forest.

Mandaville (1977) has described the vegetation of Jabal-al-Akhdar but his observations will be given only brief mention because he made virtually no notes on the geology of the area, and it is probable that most of the observations were made over limestone rather than over serpentine. A very brief checklist of plant communities is given in Table 15.9. The serpentine vegetation will clearly have evolved from the surrounding plant communities listed in this table. The ophiolites of the Oman highlands will provide rich dividends for future botanical expeditions interested in the virtually unknown serpentine flora of this region.

15.6 INDIA AND SRI LANKA

15.6.1 Geology

Although there are extensive areas of ultramafic rocks which follow the line of the Himalayas and descend down the Irrawaddy river basin into the Bay of Bengal (Fig. 15.8), the Indian part of this ophiolitic belt is of such high altitude that it has virtually no vegetation cover. Elsewhere in India ultramafic rocks are limited in area except in the Sukinda area of Orissa state south of Calcutta near the east coast (Site #1 in Fig. 15.8). These ultramafites are covered with a thick layer of laterite due to serpentinization of the dunites under tropical conditions, and are currently a source of both nickel and chrome ore. The rocks are found within the khandalite-charnockite suite of the Brahmani Valley granulites and also within the

TABLE 15.9   Plant Communities of the Jabal-al-Akhdar in the Oman Mountains

Vegetation zone	Altitude (m)	Dominant species
Desert parkland	0–600	*Acacia tortilis*
Mountain wadis	350–1050	*Zizyphus spinachristi* *Acacia* sp. *Ficus salicifolia*
Euphorbia larica shrubland	450–1350	*Euphorbia larica* *Gaillonia* sp.
Reptonia-Olia woodland	1350–2300	*Reptonia mascatensis* *Olea africana*
Juniper summit community	2300–3050	*Juniperus macropoda* *Cymbopogon* sp.

Source: Mandaville (1977)

low-grade metamorphites of the iron ore stage. According to Banerjee (1972), the ultramafites of Sukinda are ophiolites of the Alpine type.

Until fairly recently it was supposed that there were no occurrences of ultramafic rocks in Sri Lanka; however, Dissanayake and Van Riel (1978) discovered rocks of this type located along what they suggested was a Precambrian suture zone between two plate boundaries (the Vijayan and Highland Group). The ultramafic outcrops of Sri Lanka are also shown in Fig. 15.8. Apart from the serpentine occurrences at Uda Walawe (site #2 in Fig. 15.8) and, Welipatanwila (site #3), the boundary between the Vijayan and Highland rocks is also the site of a very large zone of copper/iron mineralization near Trincomalee on the northeast coast of the island.

15.6.2 The Serpentine Vegetation of India

Roy (1974) has studied the serpentine vegetation of the Sukinda Valley, Orissa State, India. The humid forest of the non-serpentinitic rocks consists of large trees such as *Shorea robusta* (sal), *Terminalia tomentosa* (asan) and *Pterocarpus marsupia* (piasal). In the transition to serpentine, the *Shorea* and *Pterocarpus* disappear and the *Terminalia* becomes stunted, forming a dense shrubby community with *Combretum decandrum* (atandi), and *Mallotus velutina* (khakra). Roy (1974) noted that this community was always associated with ores containing >0.4% nickel below the soils. These ores were found in the depth interval of 10–20 m and this work clearly illustrated that the vegetation cover was an indication of ore below the surface.

In biogeochemical work, Roy (1974) determined nickel concentrations in many of the plants of the area. Nickel levels in dried leaves of *Combretum decandrum* were up to 200 μg/g over the ore body and had a minimum level of about 50 μg/g away from the mineralization. Because of the wide distribution of this taxon on and off serpentine, Roy (1974) concluded that it would be suitable for biogeochemical prospecting.

Banerjee (1972) also carried out biogeochemical prospecting at Sukinda. He determined the Ni, Cr, and Co content of both sal and asan and found a good contrast between the nickel content of sal trees growing on and off ultramafites. He suggested that *Shorea robusta* would be useful in biogeochemical prospecting for nickel below the laterite which covers both ultramafic and non-ultramafic rocks in the Sukinda area.

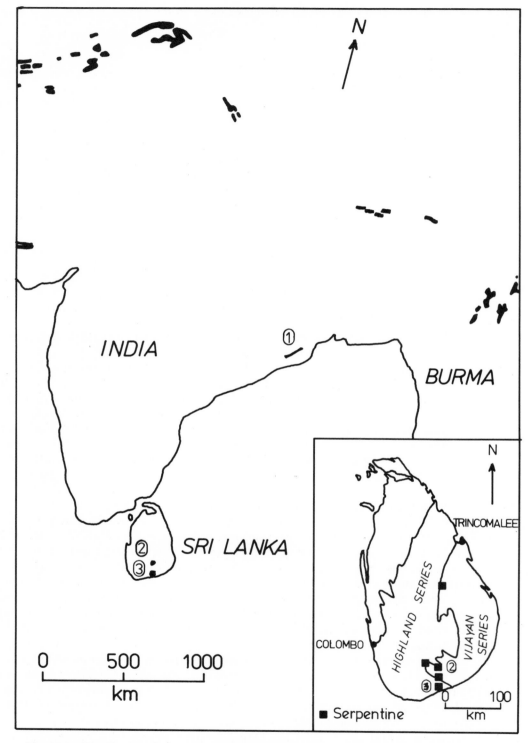

Fig. 15.8 Distribution of ultramafic rocks in Southern Asia. 1—Sukinda Valley, India; 2—Uda Walawe, Sri Lanka; 3—Welipatanwila, Sri Lanka.

15.6.3 The Serpentine Vegetation of Sri Lanka

Although the serpentine outcrops of Sri Lanka are very small, they do carry a characteristic vegetation. At Welipatanwila (Plate 15.2a) the heavily-laterised ultramafites are almost completely devoid of vegetation except for a scattering of a small blue-flowered herb, *Evolvulus alsinoides*. The boundary of the serpentine is marked by low thorn bushes interspersed with *Opuntia* spp.

Another interesting serpentine outcrop in Sri Lanka is at Uda Walawe (Plate 15.2b). The terrain is covered with a thin cover of a serpentine-endemic grass *Cymbopogon flexuosus* var. interspersed with low bushes of *Morinda tinctoria*.

The serpentine vegetation of Sri Lanka, like that of India, has not been studied very extensively, but in both cases the floras are somewhat impoverished as regards numbers of species and do not hold the same potential for future botanical research as other Asian serpentine floras, particularly those of the offshore islands of Southeast Asia.

REFERENCES

Ager, D. V., 1980. *The Geology of Europe*. McGraw-Hill, London.

Akman, Y., 1973a. Contribution à l'étude la flore les montagnes de l'Amanus, I. *Commn. Fac. Sci. Univ. Ankara Sér. C*, 17: 1–19.

Akman, Y., 1973b. Contribution à l'étude la flore les montagnes de l'Amanus, II. *Commn. Fac. Sci. Univ. Ankara Sér. C*, 21–42.

Akman, Y., Contribution à l'étude de la flore les montagnes de l'Amanus, III. *Commn. Fac. Sci. Univ. Ankara Sér. C*, 43–70.

Akman, Y., 1973d. Aperçu préliminaire sur les conditions phytoécologiques de la chaîne de l'Amanus dans la région du Hatay I. *Commn. Fac. Sci. Univ. Ankara Sér. C*, 75–98.

Akman, Y., 1973e. Aperçu préliminaire sur les conditions phytoécologiques de la chaîne de l'Amanus dans la région du Hatay II. *Commn. Fac. Sci. Univ. Ankara Sér. C.*, 99–135.

Akman, Y., 1973f. Aperçu préliminaire sur les conditions phytoécologiques de la chaîne de l'Amanus dans la région du Hatay III. *Commn. Fac. Sci. Univ. Ankara Sér. C.*, 137–164.

Aleskovsky, V. E., Mokhov, A. A. and Spirov, V. N., 1959. Integrated biogeochemical methods of prospecting for nickel in the Kola Peninsula (in Russ.). *Geokhimiya*, #3: 266–272.

Banerjee, P. K., 1972. Geology and geochemistry of the Sukinda ultramafic field, Cuttack District, Orissa. *Mem. Geol. Surv. India*, 103: 11–19.

Biske, G. S., 1972. On the perspectives of biogeochemical prospecting in the Baltic territories. *Trudy Geol. Karelian Auton. SSR*, 13: 109–115.

Brooks, R. R., Morrison, R. S., Reeves, R. D., Dudley, T. R. and Akman, Y., 1979. Hyperaccumulation of nickel by *Alyssum* Linnaeus (Cruciferae). *Proc. Roy. Soc. Lond. Sec.B*, 203: 387–403.

Coleman, R. G., 1977. *Ophiolites*. Springer, New York.

Davis, P. H. et al. Eds. 1965. *The Flora of Turkey* Vol.1., Univ. Edinb. Press, Edinburgh.

Derry, D. R., 1980. *World Atlas of Geology and Mineral Deposits*. Mining Journal Books, London.

Dissanayake, C. B. and Van Riel, B. J., 1978. Petrology and geochemistry of a recently discovered nickeliferous serpentinite from Sri Lanka. *Geol. Soc. India J.*, 19: 464–471.

Dudley, T. R., 1964. Synopsis of the genus *Alyssum*. *J. Arn. Arb.*, 45: 358–373.

Fisher, W. B., 1968. *The Cambridge History of Iran*, V.1. Cambridge University Press, Cambridge.

Igoshina, K. N., 1966. Specificity of the flora and vegetation of ultramafic rocks in the Polar Urals (in Russ.). *Bot. Zhur.*, 51: 322–338.

Iljinsky, A. P., 1936. Zur Phytocoenologie der Lärchenwalder des Ilmengebirges (Sud-Ural). *Ber. Schweiz. Bot. Ges.*, 46: 85–93.

Ivanova, A. M., Kulikov, Y. C. and Egerova, I. S., 1974. *Geochemical Landscapes of the Yano-Indigirsky Region* (in Russ.). Nedra Press, Moscow.

Kovalevsky, A. L., 1976. *Biogeochemical Methods of Prospecting for Deposits of Non-ferrous Metals* (in Russ.). Ministerstvo Geologii, Moscow.

Kovalevsky, A. L., 1979. *Biogeochemical Exploration for Mineral Deposits*. Amerind Pub. Co. New Delhi.

Maiorov, N. F., 1969. The upwards migration of nickel and copper in the formation of salt aureoles under conditions of marine deposition (in Russ.). *Zapiski Leningr. Gorn. In-Ta.* 56: 63–72.

Makarova, A. I., 1960. Biogeochemical investigations on polymetallic deposits (in Russ.). *Geokhimiya,* #7: 624–633.

Malyuga, D. P., 1954. Experiments with the use of the biogeochemical method for exploration of ore deposits in the Southern Urals (in Russ.). *Trudy Biogeokhim. Lab.,* 10; 28–59.

Malyuga, D. P., 1964. *Biogeochemical Prospecting for Minerals*. Consultants Bureau, New York.

Malyuga, D. P. and Petrunina, N. S., 1961. Biogeochemical investigations in the Tuvinsky Autonomous Oblast. *Geokhimiya,* #3: 258–267.

Mandaville, J., 1977. Plants. In, *Scientific Results of the Oman Flora and Fauna Survey 1975.* J. Oman Stud. Spec. Rep. #1: 229–267.

Paribok, T. A. and Alekseeva-Popova, N. V., 1966. The content of some chemical elements in the wild plants of the Polar Urals as related to the problem of the serpentine vegetation (in Russ.). *Bot. Zhur.,* 51: 339–353.

Pichi-Sermolli, R., 1948. Flore e vegetazione delle serpentine e delle altre ofioliti dell'alta valle del Tevere (Toscana). *Webbia,* 6: 1–380.

Roy, S., 1974. Geobotany in the exploration of nickel in the ultramafics of the Sukinda Valley, Orissa. *Q. J. Geol. Min. Metall. Soc. India,* 46: 251–256.

Rune, S., 1953. Plant life on serpentine and related rocks in the north of Sweden. *Acta Phytogeogr. Suec.,* 31: 1–139.

Skarlygina-Ufimtseva, M. D., Chernyakhov, V. and Berezkina, G. A., 1976. *Biogeochemical Characteristics of Chalcopyrite Deposits in the Southern Urals* (in Russ.). SUN Press, Leningrad.

Storozheva, M. M., 1954. Teratological phenomena in *Pulsatilla patens* under the conditions of a nickel ore field (in Russ.). *Trudy Biogeokhim. Lab.,* 10: 64–75.

Tkalich, S. M., 1938. Experience in the investigation of plants as indicators in geological exploration and prospecting (in Russ.). *Vest. Dal'nevost. Fil. Akad. Nauk SSR,* 32: 3–25.

Plate 16.2   (a) Above left: *Hypericum tatewakii* var. *nigropunctatum* on scree at Mt Bodzu, Hokkaido.
(b) Above right: *Viola yubariana* on scree at Mt Yupari, Hokkaido.
(c) Below left: *Primula yuparensis* on Mt Yupari, Hokkaido.
(d) Below right: *Saussurea chionophylla*, Mt Yupari, Hokkaido.
Photos by S. Nosaka.

Plate 16.3 (a) Above left: *Polygonum hayachinense* on serpentine at Mt Hayachine.
(b) Above right: *Leontopodium hayachinense* on serpentine at Mt Hayachine.
(c) Below left: *Primula macrocarpa* on serpentine at Mt Hayachine
(d) Below right: *Draba japonica* on serpentine scree at Mt Hayachine.
Photos by N. Doi.

Chapter 16
JAPAN

16.1 GEOLOGY AND TECTONICS

The whole of the Japanese Archipelago is traversed by a southwest-northeast train of ultramafites forming part of the Circumpacific Ophiolitic Belt. The basement of much of the islands is Permian, but there are extensive areas of volcanic rocks including terrestrial volcanics and older metamorphosed sedimentary rocks.

About 50 m.y. ago, the volcanics and sedimentary lenses that had accumulated were involved in a period of folding and granitic instrusions producing the metamorphic rocks known as "green tuff". This was followed by a period of subsidence and intense volcanic activity for a period of 10 m.y. starting 23 m.y. ago, an activity which, on a reduced scale, has continued over the last 10 m.y.

In general terms, the Japanese islands can be said to occupy the eastern border of the Eurasian continental shelf and represent a position where the Pacific Plate creeps slowly under the Eurasian Plate after a long transmission from the east (Numata, 1974). The resultant upheaval has given rise to several mountain ranges and numerous volcanoes.

The ultramafic rocks of Japan have been described by Susuki (1952) and are found along two southwest-northeast-trending belts in Kyushu, Shikoku and central and southern Honshu (Fig. 16.1) where the occurrences are somewhat sporadic. The more northerly of the two belts begins near Fukuoka in Kyushu, follows the backbone of the Japan Alps somewhat inland from the coast of the Sea of Japan, and extends as far as Nagano where it joins the more southerly belt which begins in southern Kyushu and passes through the centre of Shikoku before entering Honshu. The combined belt continues northwards through the Mt Hayachine ultramafic complex (the most extensive in Honshu), passes under the sea and reappears in southern Hokkaido near Mt Apoi where it continues to the northern tip of the island.

It is not possible to give an overall geological description of all the serpentine areas of Japan, because of the pronounced variability of the various regions. However the geology of Mt Yupari in central Hokkaido is typical of the ultramafites of the central and northern part of the island, has some affinity with parts of Honshu, and is portrayed in Fig. 16.2. According to Nosaka (1974), the upper elevations of Mt Yupari consist of metamorphic rocks of the Yubaridake Group, comprising phyllitic and schistose rock of Pre-Cretaceous age. Ultramafites, particularly serpentinites, occur as large masses on the western side of the backbone ridge and as smaller masses along the tectonic line of the eastern side.

16.2 HISTORICAL INTRODUCTION TO THE SERPENTINE VEGETATION OF JAPAN

It is particularly fitting that the serpentine vegetation of Japan be accorded a separate chapter in this book because of its extreme richness and diversity. The flora of Japan is part of the Sino-Japanese phytogeographic region (Fig. 10.1) and the serpentine flora is largely derived from this source apart from a few notable disjunctions.

The amount of work carried out by Japanese botanists on the serpentine flora of that country is very great. The first work on serpentine plants of Japan has been accredited to T. Yoshinaga who in 1914 published a paper on the serpentinophytes of Tosa Province. Later Nishida (1918, 1919) described the serpentinicolous flora of Mt Yupari (site #7 in Fig. 16.1) in Hokkaido. This was followed by detailed work on Mt Apoi (site #12) by Tatewaki (1928).

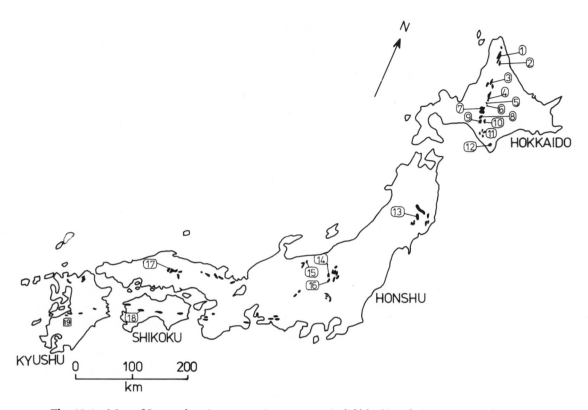

Fig. 16.1   Map of Japan showing serpentine outcrops (solid black) and sites mentioned in text. 1—Toikambetsu, 2—Tokiwa, 3—Mt Bodzu, 4—Kamuikotan, 5—Furano, 6—Yamabe, 7—Mt Yupari, 8—Iwachishi, 9—Mts Iwanai and Nukabira, 10—Mt Porojiri, 11—Shidzunai, 12—Mt Apoi, 13—Mt Hayachine, 14—Mt Shibutsu, 15—Mt Shirouma, 16—Mt Tanigawa, 17—Hinokami, 18—Mts Kigashi-Akaishi and Nishi-Akaishi, 19—Tanoura.

Following the enforced hiatus in botanical research resulting from World War II, the post-war years gave birth to accelerated research in this field as evidenced by the number of papers recorded in Table 16.1. Particular mention should be made of the work of Ohba (1968, 1969) who carried out the first phytosociological work on Japanese plants, and of a series of papers by Toyokuni (1955, 1956a,b,c, 1957a,b, 1958, 1960a,b, 1982) in which he described most of the serpentine floras of Hokkaido. He divided the serpentine plants of Japan into 3 main classes:

A—ultrabasicosaxicolous,

B—ultrabasic rock—indifferent,

C—accidental

with various subdivisions. The system is shown in Table 16.2 and is to some extent based on that of Rune (1953). Although the Toyokuni system has a nomenclature which appears clumsy in the English translation, and is not likely to find a great deal of support among western botanists and plant sociologists, it will be used below in a description of the Japanese serpentine flora to avoid confusion.

The vastness and diversity of the Japanese serpentine flora is perhaps only surpassed by those of Cuba (see Chapter 12) and the Malay Archipelago (Chapter 18). This has insured a continuing interest in the subject by many Japanese botanists such as Nosaka (1974) who has written an excellent and detailed description of many of the features of the serpentine vegetation of a single mountain (Mt Yupari) in Hokkaido.

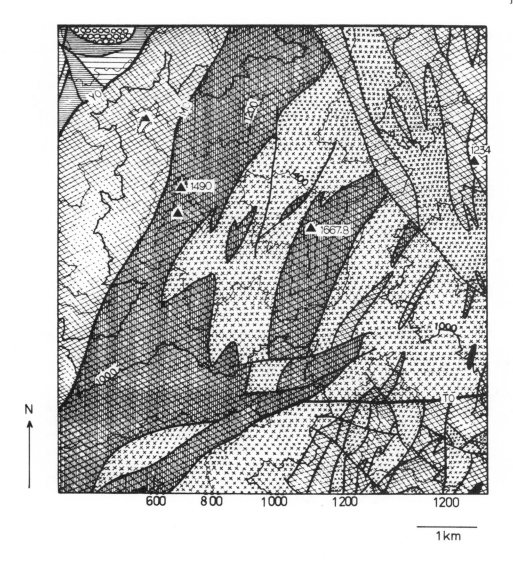

N

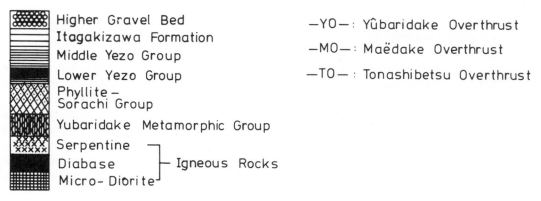

Fig. 16.2 The geology of Mt Yupari in central Hokkaido.
Source: Nosaka (1974).

TABLE 16.1 Papers Which Describe Japanese Serpentine Plants

HOKKAIDO

Inagaki et al. (1966, 1967, 1968, 1969), Ishizuka (1974), Ishizuka et al. (1982), Kawano (1971), Kitamura (1956, 1957), Nishida (1918, 1919), Nosaka (1960a,b, 1961a,b, 1962, 1971, 1974), Ohba (1968, 1969), Takeda (1913), Tatewaki (1928, 1963), Toyokuni (1955, 1956a,b,c, 1957a,b, 1958, 1960a,b, 1982), Watanabe (1957, 1971)

HONSHU

Ishizuka (1974), Ishizuka et al. (1982), Kikuchi and Komidzunai (1961), Kitamura (1950, 1952a,b), Kitamura and Momotani (1952), Kitamura et al. (1953), Nagano et al. (1966), Ohba (1968, 1969), Saito et al. (1977), Taniguti (1958)

KYUSHU

Yamanaka (1967)

SHIKOKU

Kitamura and Murata (1952), Yamagata et al. (1960), Yamanaka (1952, 1954, 1955, 1958, 1959)

TABLE 16.2 The Classification of Japanese Serpentine Plants According to Toyokuni (1955)

A—ultrabasicosaxicolous (occurring more frequently on serpentine than elsewhere)			
I—ultrabasicosaxophytes		II—relics (UR)	III—ubiquists (UU)
Typical (TU)	Preferential (PU)	Plants which occur disjunctively on serpentine and are isolated from related plants occuring a long distance away.	Plants which are not morphologically distinct or isolated from ubiquitous plants of the surroundings
Confined to serpentine	Preferring serpentine		

B—ultrabasic rock indifferent (plants which occur on serpentine to the same extent as on the surrounding non-serpentinitic substrates)

C—ultrabasic rock accidental (plants which occur accidentally on serpentine)

16.3 A BROAD OVERVIEW OF THE JAPANESE SERPENTINE FLORA

The Japanese Islands have an extremely varied flora (serpentine and otherwise) due to a number of unique, geological, hydrological and climatic features of the archipelago. The first of these is the very wide range of latitude (24° to 46°N) which is covered, and which provides temperatures ranging from +40° to −40°C. The second factor is the pronounced altitudinal effects resulting from the numerous mountain ranges in all four of the main islands culminating in the Japan Alps with several peaks with an altitude of over 3000 m, so that even a single small region can provide vegetation ranging from subtropical to subarctic.

Three other factors contribute to the diversity and richness of the Japanese flora of which the first is the more-than-adequate precipitation which lies in the range 800–3000 mm with a mean of 1740 mm. There are hence no arid regions in Japan.

The next factor which influences the Japanese flora is the complicated pattern of cold and warm ocean currents surrounding the islands (Fig. 16.3). The most prominent of these is the warm Japan Current (Kuro-shio) which passes in a northwest direction along the south

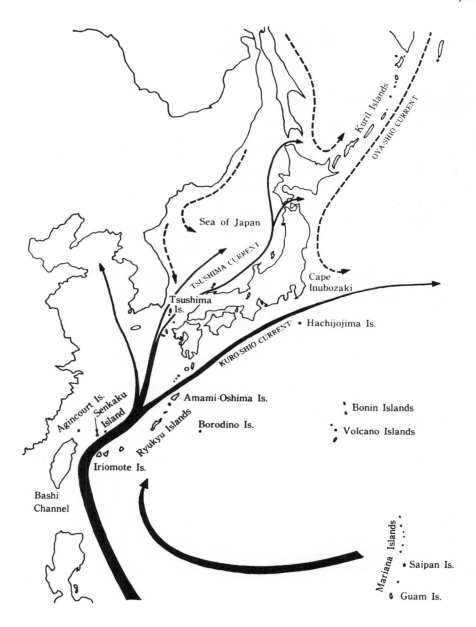

Fig. 16.3 Ocean currents which influence the climate of Japan.
Source: Numata (1974).

coasts of Kyushu, Shikoku and Honshu before branching to the east at Cape Inubozaki. A branch of the same current passes through the Straits of Tsushima and along the west coast of Honshu (Tsushima Current) before petering out as it passes through the Soya Strait between Sakhalin and Hokkaido. Another branch of this current passes through the strait dividing Hokkaido and Honshu and joins the cold Chishima (Oya-shio) Current which flows southwards from the Kuriles and cools the east coast of Hokkaido. At the confluence of the two currents near Mt Apoi in Hokkaido, extensive summer fogs are produced and have a pronounced effect on the vegetation. The Chishima current continues southwards along the northeast coast of Honshu before being deflected eastwards at Cape Inubozaki.

The last factor which accounts for the diversity and richness of the Japanese flora, one of the richest of any north-temperate zone, is that the polar ice cap during the Ice Ages of the Pleistocene was asymmetric about the present North Pole and had its centre in southern Greenland, so that although the ice cap descended into lower latitudes in Europe and North America, its position in Asia, and particularly East Asia, remained as it is today. Since vegetation was not eliminated in Japan by the advancing ice caps, there has been ample time in this country for the plant diversity and high degree of endemism to continue to develop without the hiatus experienced elsewhere. The Japanese serpentine flora is therefore more similar to that of the Mediterranean, at least as far as endemism and diversity are concerned, than it is to American or Eurasian serpentine floras of similar latitude.

Basically four principal vegetation types have been recognized in Japan (Numata, 1974): subtropical, warm temperate, cool temperate, and subarctic. These range with altitude and latitude, though subarctic plants are not evident in Kyushu because the elevations are not high enough in this subtropical zone.

The life form spectra of the Japanese plants are also influenced to some extent by the much higher snowfall on the coastal and inland districts facing the Sea of Japan where snow can remain on the ground for 4–6 months during the winter period, thus shortening the growing period of the plants. Because most ultramafic exposures in Japan are found at higher altitudes (>1000 m) the serpentine vegetation of that country tends to be found in the so-called "alpine deserts". Ishizuka (1974) has described 5 representative mountainous serpentine regions of Japan with their associated floras. These are as follows; Mt Apoi (southern Hokkaido), Mt Yupari (central Hokkaido), Mt Hayachine (northern Honshu), Mts Shibutsu and Tanigawa (central Honshu), and Mt Shirouma (central Honshu). Mt Apoi contains by far the greatest number of endemic species as will be detailed later.

16.4 THE PHYTOSOCIOLOGY OF THE JAPANESE SERPENTINE FLORA

Phytosociological classification of the Japanese serpentine flora has been carried out by Ohba (1968) whose work has also been described by Ernst (1974). Ohba assigned Japanese serpentine plants to the Order Minuartietalia vernae japonicae within which he recognized 2 Alliances and 6 Associations. These are shown schematically in Fig. 16.4 and the data are summarized in Table 16.3 together with their geographical locations and character species. Minuartietalia vernae japonicae corresponds partly to the Thlaspietea rotundifolii Order of the European Alps.

The Drabo-Arenarion katoanae Alliance is found in Hokkaido and north and central Honshu. The normal Pinus Pumila—Betula ermanii forest on non-serpentine substrates gives way to a herbaceous community dominated by Arenaria katoana and Draba japonica. Within this Alliance there are 5 Associations beginning with Violetum yubarianae and its character species Viola yubariana found on the western to northwestern slopes of Mts Yupari and Tottabetsu in Hokkaido. The same slopes support the Saussuretum chionophyllae Association with Saussurea chionophylla as the character species and Lagotis glauca, Saxifraga laciniata, Stellaria japonica, Carex stenantha and Campanula chamissonis as differentials.

The third Association within Drabo-Arenarion is known as Arenarietum katoanae and is found on Mt Apoi in southern Hokkaido, floristically one of the richest serpentine mountains in Japan. This Association with its character species Aruncus dioicus is really only a species-poor development of Sanguisorbo—Minuartietum vernae japonicae which is found further south on Mt Hayachine in northern Honshu. Character species of the latter Association are: Sanguisorba obtusa, Aruncus dioicus, Polygonum hayachinense, and Calamagrostis deschampsioides.

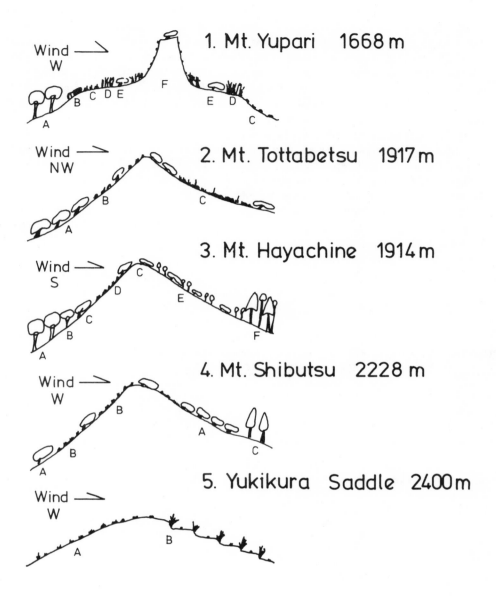

Fig. 16.4 Schematic representation of serpentine plant communities in Japan.
1—Yubari, A = *Betula ermanii* forest; B = *Viola yubariana* community; C = Saussaretum chionaphyllae; D = *Allium schoenoprasum—Deschampsia caespitosa* meadow; E = *Pinus pumila* scrub; F = summit flora.
2—Tottabetsu, A = Vaccinio-Pinetum pumilae; B = Saussuretum chionophyllae; C = flora of snow valleys.
3—Hayachine, A = *Fagus crenata* woodland; B = *Betula ermanii* woodland; C = Vaccinio-Pinetum pumilae; D = Sanguisorbo-Minuartietum vernae japonicum, E mixed community of *Pinus pumila* and *Tsuga diversifolia*; F = *Thujopsis dolabolata* woodland.
4—Shibutsu, A = Vaccinio-Pinetum pumilae; B = Leontopodetum fauriei angustifolii; C = *Thuja standishii* woodland.
5—Yukikura Saddle, A = Cerasteo-Minuartietum vernae japonicae; B = *Sanguisorba stipulata—Calamagrostis longiseta* community.
Source: Ohba (1968).

Further south, the fifth Association of the Drabo-Arenarion Alliance, Leontopodietum fauriei appears on Mts Shibutsu and Tanigawa. Character species of this Association are: *Leontopodium fauriei* var. *angustifolium* and *Erigeron thunbergii* var. *heterotrichus*.

The second Alliance within Minuartietalia vernae japonicae is Cerasteo-Minuartion vernae japonicae whose single Association of the same name replaces Drabo-Arenarion katoanae still further south on Mt Shirouma. Character species of the Association and Alliance are *Minuartia verna* subsp. *japonica*, *Cerastium schizopetalum* var. *bifidum*, *Arabis serrata*, and *Dianthus superbus* var. *amoenus*.

The serpentines of Mts Higashi-Akaishi and Nishi on Shikoku support the Spiraeon blumei—sikokualpinae Alliance and its Association of the same name (Yamanaka, 1955). This Alliance has not been assigned officially to the Minuartietalia vernae japonicae Order. It is found primarily on dry serpentine soils at altitudes of 1500–1700 m on both mountains and is dominated by its character species *Spiraea sikokualpina*. The shrub layer of this community includes *Abelia serrata* var. *luchwardii* and the herb layers includes *Carex blepharicarpa*, *C. chrysolepis*, and *C. alterniflora* as well as the grass *Miscanthus oligostachyus*.

TABLE 16.3   The Phytosociology of the Japanese Serpentine Flora

Community	Alt. (m)	Character species	Site
Ass.: Cerasteo-Minuartietum vernae japonicae	2000–2800	*Arabis serrata*, *Cerastium schizopetalum* var. *bifidum*, *Dianthus superbus* *Minuartia verna* subsp. *japonica*	A
Alliance: *Drabo-Arenarion katoanae*		*Draba japonica*	
Ass. 1: Violetum yubarianae	1400–1920	*Viola yubariana*	B
Ass. 2: Saussuretum chionophyllae	1400–1920	*Saussurea chionophylla*	B, CD
Ass. 3: Arenarietum katoanae	700	*Arenaria katoana*, *Draba japonica*	D
Ass. 4: Sanguisorbo-Minuartietum vernae japonicae	1500–1800	*Sanguisorba obtusa*, *Aruncus dioicus*, *Polygonum hayachinense* *Calamagrostis deschampsioides*	E
Ass. 5: Leontopodietum fauriei angustifolium	1550–2000	*Leontopodium fauriei* var. *angustifolium* *Erigeron thunbergii*	F, G
Order: not assigned			
Alliance: Spiraeon blumei-sikokualpinae	1540–1670	*Spiraea sikokualpina*	H, I
Ass.: Spiraeetum sikokualpinae	1540–1670	*Spiraea sikokualpina*	H, I

A—Mt Shirouma, B—Mt Yupari, C—Mt Tottabetsu, D—Mt Apoi, F —Mt Hayachine, F—Mt Tanigawa, G—Mt Shibutsu, H—Mt Higashi-Akaishi, I —Mt Nishi.
After: Ohba (1968)

16.5 THE SERPENTINE VEGETATION OF SPECIFIC REGIONS OF JAPAN

16.5.1 Hokkaido

The serpentine vegetation of Hokkaido has been described by many Japanese botanists (see Table 16.1) but perhaps the most extensive of these studies is a series of nine papers by Toyokuni (1955–1960) describing the serpentine flora of 12 mountainous districts in the provinces of Teshio, Ishikari, Iburi and Hidaka. The ultramafic rocks occur mainly in the Kamuikotan Complex which follows tectonic lines and in the metamorphic zone of the Hidaka Range (Suzuki, 1952). The following descriptions of the vegetation of serpentine sites follow in a north-south sequence.

Teshio Province

The vegetation of the main serpentine outcrops in Teshio Province in northern Hokkaido (sites 1 and 2 in Fig. 16.1) has been described by Toyokuni (1955, 1956a) and by Kitamura (1957). One of the more interesting localities floristically is the Nuppromapporo Valley, whose river is a tributary of the Teshio. In the forest the dominant tree is *Picea glehni* (Plate 16.1a) mixed with *Abies sachalinensis, Taxus cuspidata* and deciduous trees such as *Betula platyphylla* var. *japonicae, B. ermanii, Alnus maximowiczii, Quercus mongolica* var. *grosseserrata, Prunus maximowiczii, Sorbus commixta, S. sambucifolia, Euonymus macropterus,* and *Viburnum furcatum.* In the alpine region, the dominant shrub is *Pinus pumila.* A remarkable serpentine relic is *Japonolirion osense* var. *saitoi* which is found only in the Nappromapporo Valley and on Mt Shibutsu in central Honshu. The genus is monotypic and related somewhat to the *Helonias* of eastern North America. Serpentino-morphic forms in the area include *Primula takedana* a dwarf and crassulescent relative of *P. jessoana* subsp. *pubescens,* and the stenophyllic *Picris hieracioides* subsp. *jessoensis,* and *Achillea ptarmica* subsp. *macrocephala.*

Ishikari Province excepting Mt Yupari

The serpentine vegetation of Ishikari Province excepting Mt Yupari (sites 3–6 in Fig. 16.1) has been described by Toyokuni (1956a). The ultramafites are found predominantly on Mts Bodzu and Uryu-gun and rise to about 700 m above the young sediments at the foothills.

The forested area of Mt Bodzu is dominated by *Pinus pumila* and *Picea glehni* with broadleaf trees such as *Betula ermanii, Quercus mongolica* var. *grosseserrata, Prunus nipponica* and *Acer tschonoskii.* The herb and shrub layers comprise *Osmunda cinnamonea* var. *fokiensis, O. japonica, Lycopodium serratum* var. *thunbergii, Vaccinium smallii, Rosa acicularis* and many others. Serpentine-endemic plants of this mountain are *Adenophora pereskiaefolia* var. *uryuensis, Crepis gymnopus* and *Picris hieracioides* subsp. *jessoensis.*

Inagaki et al. (1966, 1967, 1968, 1969a,b) have studied the flora of serpentine areas of north and central Hokkaido. In the course of this work, they recognized the following 12 taxa as being serpentine-endemic or relic species (appropriate site locations of Fig. 16.1 are given in parentheses): *Quercus mongolica* var. *grosseserrata* (3), *Geranium erianthum glabriusculum* (2,3), *Tithymalus sieboldianus* var. *montanus* (3), *Euonymus alatus* var. *kakurensis* (3), *Hypericum tatewakii* var. *nigropunctatum* (3) (Plate 16.2a), *Viola sachalinensis* var. *alpina* (2,3), *Primula takedana* (2,3), *Adenophora pereskiaefolia* var. *uryuensis* (3), *Achillea ptarmica* subsp. *macrocephala* (2,3), *Anaphalis alpicola* (2,3), *Picris hieracioides* subsp. *jessoensis* (2,3), and *Crepis gymnopus* (2,3).

Mt Yupari (Ishikari Province)

With the possible exception of Mt Apoi, Mt Yupari carries one of the richest serpentine floras of any mountain in Japan. Its floristics have been studied by several workers including Toyokuni (1956b) and Nosaka (1974). The former recognized some 16 serpentine-endemic taxa on Mt Yupari of which 8 are endemic to that mountain alone.

The work by Nosaka (1974) covers the whole of the phanerogamic flora of Mt Yupari. He listed 535 species in 315 genera and 91 families of which about 60 taxa were from the serpentine scree and talus slopes in the upper altitudes of the the mountain.

The vegetation of Mt Yupari can be divided into three main zones: the mixed forest (<900 m), the *Betula ermanii* forest (900–1300 m), and the alpine (mainly serpentinic) zone. The vegetation of the latter is dominated by thickets of *Pinus pumila* on the more level ground. Among these thickets are the following ligneous plants: *Picea glehni, Juniperus communis* var. *sibirica, Berberis amurensis* var. *japonica, Aruncus dioicus, Sanguisorba tenuifolia* var. *alba, Hypericum erectum, Rhododendron dauricum* and *R. fauriae* var. *roseum.*

The most typically serpentinicolous plants are found on the serpentine screes and talus slopes in the alpine region of Mt Yupari (Plate 16.1b). Using the classification system of Toyokuni (1955) as shown in Table 16.2, these plants are distributed as follows:

(i) Typical ultrabasicosaxophytes (TU); *Viola sachalinensis* var. *alpina, V. yubariana* (endemic—Plate 16.2c), *Primula yuparenais* (endemic—Plate 16.2b), *Veronica schmidtiana* var. *yezoalpina, Lagotis glauca* subsp. *takedana* (endemic), *Adenophora pereskiaefolia* var. *yamadae, Erigeron thunbergii* subsp. *glabratus* f. *haruoi* (endemic), *Saussurea riederi* subsp. *yezoensis* f. *yuparensis* (endemic), *Taraxacum yuparense, Deschampsia caespitosa* subsp. *levis* (endemic), *Hierochloë pluriflora, Allium maximowiczii* var. *shibutsuense.*

(ii) Preferential ultrabasicosaxophytes (PU); *Tithymalus sieboldianus* var. *montanus, Angelica stenoloba.*

(iii) Ultrabasicosaxicolous relics (UR); *Arenaria katoana, Draba japonica, Crepis gymnopus, Saussurea chionophylla* (Plate 16.2d).

(iv) Ultrabasicosaxicolous ubiquists (UU); *Aconitum yuparense, Ranunculus acris* var. *nipponicus* f. *yuparensis, Berberis amurensis* var. *japonica, Minuartia verna* subsp. *japonica, Thlaspi japonicum, Thymus quinquecostatus* var. *ibukiensis.*

(v) Ultrabasic indifferent and accidental plants. About 30 species belong to this category but for the sake of brevity are not listed. See Nosaka (1974) for the full listing.

Among the plants listed above are several which are endemic to Mt Yupari alone. These are: *Viola yubariana, Primula yuparensis, Lagotis glauca* subsp. *takedana, Deschampsia caespitosa* subsp. *levis, Erigeron thunbergii* subsp. *glabratus* form. *haruoi,* and *Saussurea riederi* var. *yezoensis yuparensis.* The last two taxa are not distinct at the varietal level and are probably only serpantinomorphoses.

A very good example of serpentinomorphosis is provided by the various leaf forms of the serpentinicolous subspecies of *Potentilla matsumurae* (Fig. 16.5) as reported by Toyokuni (1957b).

Nosaka (1974) reported a further 7 taxa endemic to serpentine on Mt Yupari but which occur elsewhere in Hokkaido, sometimes off ultramafites. These are: *Aconitum yuparense, Angelica stenoloba, Gentianella yuparensis, Crepis gymnopus, Saussurea chionophylla, Taraxacum yuparense* and *Hierochloë pluriflora.*

Iburi Province

The only sizeable ultramafic areas in Iburi Province (site 8 in Fig. 16.1) are at Iwachishi where the mountain rises to 741 m and was once a source of chrome ore. According to Toyokuni (1956b), the mountain is covered with mixed forest including *Picea yezoensis, Alnus tinctoria* var. *velutina,* and *Magnolia obovata.* The only serpentine-endemic plant found in this area is *Taraxacum yuparense.*

Fig. 16.5 Leaf forms of subspecies and varieties of *Potentilla matsumurae*. 1–4 subsp. *apoiensis* (Mt Apoi); 5,6 subsp. *matsumurae* var. *yupariensis* (Mt Yupari); 7, ditto Mt Taisetsu; 8, subsp. *matsumurae* var. *matsumurae* (Mt Yotei); 9, ditto Mt Shokambetsu; 10, ditto Mt Muineshiri, 11, ditto Mt Rakko. Source: Toyokuni (1957b).

Hidaka Province

Hidaka Province includes a number of important serpentine occurrences including those on Mts Iwanai and Mt Nukabira (site 9 in Fig. 16.1), Mt Porojiri (site 10), Shidzunai (site 11), and the very important Mt Apoi (site 12) with its rich and remarkable flora. Serpentinicolous plants at site 9 include *Angelica stenoloba* and *Callianthemum miyabeanum*.

The region of Mts Porojiri and Tottabetsu (site 10) contains extensive areas of ultramafic rocks. The serpentine-endemic *Saussurea chionophylla* (character species of the Sausseretum chionophyllae Association) is present on Mt. Tottabetsu.

The area near Shidzunai (site 11) has not yet been studied botanically; however, by contrast, Mt Apoi (site 12) has probably been studied by more botanists than any other serpentine site in Japan, because of its ready accessibility and rich flora. The richness of the flora is caused by the convergence of the warm Tsushima Current with the cold Oya-Shio Current from the Kuriles, causing extensive fog in summer and hence lowering the treeline and allowing an alpine vegetation (characteristically serpentinicolous) to occupy a much greater areal extent than it would otherwise have done.

The ultramafites of Mt Apoi are primarily peridotitic and are not as heavily serpentinized as those of the Kamuikotan Complex further north. The mountain is an ellipse with major and minor axes of 15 and 12 km. The serpentine vegetation of Mt Apoi (810 m) was originally described by Tatewaki (1928) and later by Tatewaki (1963), Toyokuni (1957a) and Kitamura (1956). According to the latter, this flora is one of the most distinct among the serpentine communities of Japan. In the deciduous forest (1–200 m), *Quercus*, *Rhododendron*, *Fraxinus*, *Sorbus*, *Viburnum*, and *Berberis* are abundant. This is a common feature of many serpentine floras at lower altitudes in Japan.

In the coniferous forest (200–600 m), *Picea glehni*, *Abies sachalinensis*, and *Pinus parviflora* are dominant and are accompanied by some of the above deciduous trees. As compared with other regions of similar latitude, the tree line terminates at low altitudes (500–600

m) compared with 1000–1500 m. For example, *Pinus pumila* of the alpine region can occur at 500 m on Mt Apoi or even at 300 m after fire has destroyed the natural vegetation.

There are some remarkable serpentine relics on Mt Apoi. Examples of these with the location of related species in parentheses, are as follows: *Hypochoeris crepidioides* (*H. maculata* in the Euro-Siberian region), *Callianthemum miyabeanum* (*C. insigne* in North Korea; and *C. hondoense* in central Honshu), *Crepis gymnopus* (*C. praemorsa* in Siberia), *Rhamnus ishidae* (*R. alnifolia* in North America), *Betula apoiensis* (*B. fruticosa* in Siberia), *Viola hidakana,* and *Primula hidakana.*

There are many serpentinomorphoses on Mt Apoi which are characterized by stenophyllism, glabrism, nanism, lucency (lustrous leaves), and crassulescence. Examples of these are: *Angelica stenoloba* (stenophyllism), *Arenaria katoana* var. *lanceolata* (stenophyllism), *Aster dubius* subsp. *glabratus* var. *angustifolia* (stenophyllism, glabrism), *Potentilla matsumurae* subsp. *yuparensis* (glabrism, lucency, and stenophyllism), *Aruncus subrotundus* (lucency, crassulescence), *Bupleurum yezoense* (stenophyllism), *Viola sachalinensis* var. *alpina* (nanism, lucency, crassulescence, *Allium schoenoprasum* var. *yezomonticola* (nanism), *Tofieldia nutans* var. *kondoi* (stenophyllism), *Veronica yezoalpina* f. *exigua* (stenophyllism, nanism).

Table 16.4 lists 22 taxa endemic to serpentine on Mt Apoi of which 14 are endemic to that mountain alone. The same table gives lists of serpentine species for all of the major serpentine regions of Japan.

TABLE 16.4 Typical Serpentine Plants of Japan

Species	Site # in Fig. 16.1	Outside distn. (site #)	Status
HOKKAIDO			
Achillea ptarmica subsp. *macrocephala*	1–4	none	E
Aconitum yuparense var. *itoseiyanum*	1,2	none	E
Adenophora pereskiaefolia var. *uryuensis*	3,7	none	E
Allium maximowiczii var. *shibutsuense*	1,2,7	14	E
Anaphalis alpicola	2,3	none	E
Angelica stenoloba	7–12	none	P
Arenaria katoana	7	13,14	R
A. katoana var. *lanceolata*	12	none	E
Aruncus dioicus var. *subrotundus*	12	none	E
Betula apoiensis	12	none	E
Bupleurum nipponicum var. *yezoense*	12	none	E
Callianthemum miyabeanum	9,12	none	R
Cirsium kamtschaticum var. *opoiense*	1,2,12	none	E
Crepis gymnopus	1–3,7,12	none	R
Deschampsia caespitosa subsp. *levis*	7	none	E
Draba japonica	7	13	R
Erigeron thunbergii subsp. *glabratus*			
f. *haruoi*	7	none	E
var. *glabratum*	12	none	E
Eriocaulon perplexum	12	none	E
Euonymus alatus var. *kakurensis*	3	none	E
Geranium erianthum var. *glabriusculum*	3	none	E
Hypericum samaniense	12	none	E
H. tatewakii var. *nigropunctatum*	2	none	E
Hypochoeris crepidioides	12	none	E
Lagotis glauca subsp. *takedana*	7	none	E
Pieris hieracioides subsp. *jessoensis*	1–3	none	E
Potentilla matsumurae subsp. *apoiensis*	7,12	none	E

Species	Site # in Fig. 16.1	Outside distn. (site #)	Status
Primula farinosa subsp. *fauriei*	12	none	E
P. hidakana	9–12	none	R
P. takedana	1,2	none	R
P. yuparensis	7	none	E
Quercus mongolica var. *grosseserrata*	2,3	none	E
Rhamnus ishidae	7,12	none	R
Saussurea chionophylla	7	none	E
S. riederi subsp. *kudoana*	12	none	E
S. riederi var. *yezoensis* f. *yuparensis*	7	none	E
Silene repens	12	none	E
Taraxacum yuparense	7,8	none	E
Tithymalus sieboldianus var. *montanus*	1,2,7,12	none	P
Tofieldia nutans var. *kondoi*	12	none	E
Viola hidakana	12	none	P
V. sachalinensis var. *alpina*	1–7,9–12	none	E
V. yubariana	7	none	E
HONSHU			
Allium maximowiczii var. *shibutsuense*	14	7	E
Arenaria katoana	13,14	7	R
Aruncus astilboides	13	none	E
Bistorta hayachinensis	13	none	E
Calamagrostis deschampsioides var. *hayachinensis*	13	none	E
Cerastium schizopetalum var. *bifidum*	15	none	E
Dianthus superbus var. *amoenus*	15	none	E
Draba japonica	13	7	R
Erigeron thunbergii var. *heterotrichus*	14,16	none	E
Leontopodium fauriei var. *angustifolium*	14,16	none	E
L. hayachinense	13	none	E
Lonicera linderifolia	13	none	E
Minuartia verna subsp. *japonica*	13	none	E
Platanthera hyperborea	15	none	E
Polygonum hayachinense	13	W. China	E
Primula macrocarpa	13	none	E
Sanguisorba obtusa	13	none	E
SHIKOKU			
Adenophora triphylla var. *puellaris* f. *albiflora*	18	none	E
Berberis amurensis var. *brevifolia*	18	none	E
Lonicera mochidzukiana var. *filiformis*	18	none	E
Prunus incisa var. *kinkiensis*	18	none	E
Spiraea sikokualpina	18	none	E
Vaccinium vitisidea var. *minus*	18	none	E
KYUSHU			
Pinus densiflora	19	common	P

NB—Site numbers are as in Fig. 16.1.
E = serpentine endemic at least at the specified site, R = relic, P = preferential serpentinophyte.

16.5.2 Honshu

The volume of work on the serpentine vegetation of Honshu is much less than that reported from Hokkaido. The most important regions of such vegetation in Honshu are at Mts Hayachine (site 13 in Fig. 16.1), Shibutsu (site 14), Shirouma (site 15) and Tanigawa (site 16). The serpentine flora of each of these regions will now be described.

Mt Hayachine

Mt Hayachine rises to an altitude of 1913 m amid the Kitakami Mts of northern Honshu and is the site of several ultramafic outcrops in the area. This serpentine mountain has already been portrayed in Plate 1.1. The serpentine vegetation forms part of the Sanguisorba—Minuartietum vernae japonicae Association (see Table 16.3) which has been described by Ohba (1968) and Kitamura (1952b). The character species of the Order is Minuartia verna subsp. japonica* (the asterisk here and below signifies serpentine-endemic), and characters of the Association are Sanguisorba obtusa, Aruncus dioicus, Polygonum hayachinense* (Plate 16.3a) and Calamagrostis deschampsioides. Differentials of the Association are Leontopodium hayachinense* (Plate 16.3b), Primula macrocarpa* (Plate 16.3c), Aletris foliata, Calamagrostis sachalinensis, Carex doenitzii, Anaphalis margariticea and Bistorta hayachinensis*. Companions of the Sanguisorba Association include: Festuca ovina, Dianthus superbus subsp. speciosus, Thymus quinquecostatus, Parnassia palustris, Tilingia tachiroei, Viola biflora, Ixeris dentata, Aquilegia flabellata, Potentilla matsumurae var., Carex sabynensis, and Hypericum kamtschaticum.

A detailed description of the serpentine vegetation of Mt Hayachine has been given by Ishizuka et al. (1982) who studied the alpine vegetation above the tree line (1200 m at its lowest point). The normal tree line in this region is at about 2200 m which is well above the summit of Mt Hayachine and clearly shows the influence of the ultramafic substrate upon the vegetation (Plate 16.4a). The forest vegetation below 1200 m has been described by Saito et al. (1977) but some of this zone is not on serpentine so that little more will be said about it beyond mentioning a relic stand of Picea glehni which has its southernmost location on this mountain, a species not encountered again until the serpentine massifs of Hokkaido.

Ishizuka et al. (1982) described five major vegetation habitat types in the alpine zone of Mt Hayachine. Within these habitats, there were 21 types of plant community. Space limitations preclude a listing of all of the serpentinicolous plants of Mt Hayachine and the endemic taxa have already been listed in Table 16.4. However, Table 16.5 summarizes the distribution of several categories of serpentinicolous plants among the vegetation communities of this mountain.

It will be noted from Table 16.5 that only 3 of the species listed are confined to the forested areas of Mt Hayachine. In the alpine zone the endemics are most often found on windy rocky sites with maximum exposure. Some endemic plants such as Sanguisorba obtusa and Aruncus astilboides are extensively distributed through various types of vegetation community whereas others such as Picea glehni, Androsace chamaejasme subsp. lehmanniana, Phyllodoce caerulea and Carex capillaris are found only in one or two locations. Most of these taxa are relics with disjunct distributions in the Sino-Japanese floristic region. Species such as Draba japonica (Plate 16.3d) are confined to only one vegetation type though fairly abundant in such communities.

Mts Shibutsu and Tanigawa

The serpentine vegetation of Mts Shibutsu and Tanigawa (sites 14 and 16) is prominent in the 1550–2000 m interval and has been studied by Kitamura (1952a), and Ohba (1968). Among the serpentinicolous plants listed by the former are: Allium schoenoprasum var. shibutsuense, Arenaria katoana, Aster dubius subsp. glabratus var. angustifolius, Leontopodium fauriei var. angustifolium, Berberis amurensis var. brevifolia, Ixeris dentata var. kimurana, Arnica unalascensis, Cirsium okamotoi, and Erigeron thunbergii var.

TABLE 16.5 Distribution of Serpentinicolous Plants in the Alpine Zone of Mt Hayachine, Northern Honshu.

Species	Type	Vegetation habitat						
		A	B	C	D	E	F	G
Leontopodium hayachinense	en	1	3	2	1	4	3	—
Aruncus astilboides	en	1	5	—	3	1	1	3
Sanguisorba obtusa	en	1	4	—	3	4	2	3
Polygonum hayachinense	en	1	1	1	4	1	1	—
Calamagrostis deschampsioides var. hayachinensis	en	—	—	—	4	—	—	—
Primula macrocarpa	en-s	1	3	1	2	3	—	—
Draba japonica	se-sl	—	—	—	4	—	—	—
Arenaria katoana	se-rt	1	2	1	—	—	—	—
Minuartia verna subsp. japonica	se-s, rt	—	2	—	5	1	1	—
Poa hayachinensis	se-s, sl	1	—	—	—	—	—	5
Saussurea riederi subsp. yezoensis	sl	1	3	—	2	1	—	2
Artemisia arctica subsp. sachalinensis	sl-s	1	—	3	—	—	—	—
Weigela middendorffiana	sl-s	—	—	—	—	—	—	1
Bryanthus gmelinii	sl-s	—	—	2	—	—	—	1
Geranium erianthum	sl-s	—	—	1	—	—	—	1
Chiogenes hispidula var. japonica	nl	1	—	—	—	—	—	—
Anaphalis alpicola	rt	—	—	—	—	—	—	1
Tilingia tachiroei	rt	1	4	—	2	1	1	—
Campanula dasyantha	rt-s	1	—	1	—	—	—	—
Swertia perennis var. cuspidata	rt-s	1	5	1	—	1	2	3
Lloydia serotina	rt-s	—	3	3	—	5	4	1

A—alpine scrub, B—windward grasslands, C—dwarf shrub heath, D—scree vegetation, E—vegetation of rock crevices, F—vegetation of rock ledges, G—snow-bed vegetation.
Numerals indicate frequencies in each class.
The plant categories are as follows: en = endemic to Mt. Hayachine alone; en-s = endemic to the Kitakami Mts.; se = taxa restricted to serpentine in central and northern Japan; se-s = serpentinicolous plants not restricted to ultramafic rocks; sl = species normally found on Hokkaido but with a disjunct appearance on Mt. Hayachine; sl-s = as sl but with a few occurrences in northern Honshu; nl = species whose normal range is south of Mt. Hayachine; rt = species more common in Hokkaido and central Honshu but confined to Mt. Hayachine in northern Honshu.; rt-s = as rt but with a few occurrences in northern Honshu.
Source: Ishizuka et al. (1982).

heterotrichus. Of these, L. fauriei var. and E. thunbergii var. are endemic to the area and are character species for the Leontopodietum fauriei Association (Table 16.3).

Differentials of the above Association are: Adenophora nikoensis, Potentilla togashii, Euphrasia insignis, Angelica acutiloba, and Thalictrum minus. The character species of the Order, Minuartia verna subsp. japonica, is present on the rocky slopes. Numerous companions of the Association include: Festuca ovina, Dianthus superbus subsp. speciosus, Thymus quinquecostatus, Parnassia palustris. Allium schoenoprasum, Tilingia tachiroei, Viola biflora, Angelica stenoloba, Primula modesta, Ixeris dentata, Festuca rubra, Seseli coreanum, Agrostis borealis, Pedicularis verticillata, Racomitrium lanuginosum, Carex blepharicarpa, Cladonia nipponica, and C. rangiferina. It is interesting to note the occurrence of Racomitrium lanuginosum, a moss associated with serpentine throughout the boreal areas of North America and Eurasia.

Mt Shirouma

Serpentine vegetation is found at 2000–2800 m on Mt Shirouma which is situated close to the coastline of the Sea of Japan and which is somewhat different climatically from locations further east where the snowfall is not as great. Most of the serpentine plants of this mountain belong to the Cerasteo-Minuartietum vernae japonicae Association which includes the character species of the Order (Ohba, 1968). Differentials of the Association are: *Minuartia hondoensis. Eritrichium nipponicum,* and *Deschampsia caespitosa.* Companion species include *Festuca ovina, Dianthus superbus* var. *speciosus, Thymus quinquecostatus, Tilingia tachiroi, Viola crassa, Festuca rubra,* and *Seseli coreanum.* Serpentine-endemic species are: *Dianthus superbus* var. *amoenus* and *Platanthera hyperborea.* The latter is endemic to serpentine only on Mt Shirouma, and is common off serpentine elsewhere.

16.5.3 Shikoku

Mt Higashi-Akaishi is situated in eastern Ehime prefecture on the island of Shikoku. It rises to 1707 m and consists mainly of dunite and serpentinite. The serpentine flora is very rich and has been described by Yamanaka (1952, 1955, 1958, 1959). In his last paper, Yamanaka listed 422 taxa on this mountain representing 88 families, and 269 genera. The lower slopes are covered by a coniferous forest dominated by *Chamaecyparis obtusa, Thuja standishii, Pinus pentaphylla* var. *himekomatsu* and *Tsuga* spp. At higher altitudes there are thickets dominated by the serpentine-endemic *Spiraea sikokualpina* (Plate 16.4b). In the rocky and gravelly locations on ultramafic rocks, there are several relic and serpentinicolous plants. These are listed in Table 16.6 which shows six taxa endemic to serpentine on Shikoku. There are also several relics such as *Rosa nipponensis* and *Pinus koraiensis.*

TABLE 16.6   Serpentinicolous Plants of Mt Higashi-Akaishi, Shikoku, Japan.

Species	Status
Adenophora triphylla var. *puellaris* f. *albiflora*	Endemic to serpentine on Shikoku
Berberis amurensis var. *brevifolia*	Endemic to serpentine on Shikoku
Carex duvaliana	Bodenvag, often on serpentine
Chamaecyparis obtusa	Bodenvag, often on serpentine
Euphrasia microphylla	Bodenvag, often on serpentine
Gymnocarpum jessoense	Endemic to serpentine and limestone
Lonicera mochidzukiana var. *filiformis*	Endemic to serpentine on Shikoku
Pinus koraiensis	Relic, disjunctive on serpentine
P. pentaphylla var. *himekomatsu*	Abundant on serpentine
Prunus incisa var. *kinkiensis*	Endemic to serpentine on Shikoku
Rosa nipponensis	Relic, disjunctive on serpentine
Saussurea nipponica subsp. *sikokiana*	Bodenvag, often on serpentine
Spiraea sikokualpina	Endemic to serpentine to Shikoku
Thuja standishii	Abundant on serpentine and limestone
Vaccinium vitisidaea subsp. *minus*	Common on serpentine in Shikoku

After: Yamanaka (1959).

16.5.4 Kyushu

Yamanaka (1967) has described the serpentine vegetation of Kyushu. The location described is a lowland site at Tanoura, Kumamoto prefecture and is dominated with a thin cover of *Pinus densiflora.* Although this author has listed 55 species within the serpentine community, he gives no indication as to which of the taxa are endemic to serpentine. However *Pinus densiflora* is a common colonizer of serpentine elsewhere in Japan, particularly on Shikoku where it forms a sparse cover over an undergrowth of *Arundinaria pygmaea.*

Plate 16.4 (a) Above: Aerial view of Mt Hayachine. The tree line descends to 1200 m at its lowest point (elsewhere in the region it is at 2200 m). This clearly shows the effect of the ultramafic rocks upon the vegetation. Note the scree slopes on the mountain.
Photo by the National Trust of Japan.
(b) Below: Impoverished pine community on serpentine on the southern slopes of Mt Higashi-Akaishi, Shikoku. The serpentine-endemic *Spiraea sikokualpina* is found in the undergrowth.
Photo by T. Yamanaka.

Pyroxenite a
Olivine-pyrox

Serpentinite

Granite

Plate 17.1 Aerial photograph of the Great Dyke south of Mtoroshanga Pass showing central area of treed pyroxenite and parallel bands of grass-covered serpentine. There are also broad serpentine bands on both sides of the central pyroxenites and patches of Brachystegia-Julbernardia woodland on granitic soils to the left and away from the dyke.
Photograph by courtesy of the Surveyor General, Harare, Zimbabwe.

16.6 DISJUNCTIONS IN JAPANESE SERPENTINE PLANTS

Several serpentine relics show interesting disjunctions in Japan. Examples of such disjunctions have been given by Nosaka (1974) and include *Arenaria katoana* (Fig. 16.6a) and *Draba japonica* (Fig. 16.6b). The former is found in Hokkaido in the Hidaka Range (Mts Tottabetsu and Apoi) and in Honshu at Mts Hayachine and Shibutsu. *D. japonica* is found at Mts Tottabetsu, Kittatottabetsu and Hayachine.

Carex capillaris (Fig. 16.7) is a holoarctic species widespread in Sakhalin, eastern Siberia, and the Kuriles and has its southernmost occurrence on serpentine at Mt Hayachine. A similar disjunct distribution occurs for *Platanthera hyperborea* on serpentine at Mt Shirouma (Fig. 16.1 site #15).

The occurrence of taxa endemic to serpentine only at the southernmost extent of their distribution is found commonly elsewhere in the world, particularly in Northwest Europe, where for example (Chapter 13), *Arenaria norvegica* is found only on serpentine in central Scandinavia (Rune, 1953) and in Shetland.

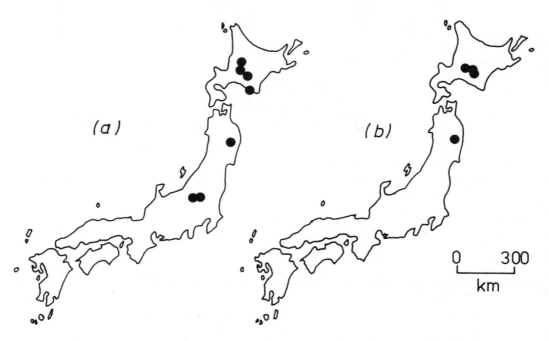

Fig. 16.6 Disjunctive distribution of (a) *Arenaria katoana* and (b) *Draba japonica* in Japan. All sites are on serpentine.
Source: Nosaka (1974).

16.7 THE COMPOSITION AND ORIGIN OF THE SERPENTINE FLORA OF JAPAN

The distribution of plant species by families in the flora (mainly serpentine) of Mt Yupari in Hokkaido is shown in Table 16.7 and illustrates the relatively high importance of the Rosaceae, Asteraceae and Cyperaceae.

The data in Table 16.8 show the origin of the alpine flora of Mt Yupari and indicate that the flora of Hokkaido has close affinities with that of Honshu, followed in order of decreasing importance by the Kuriles and Sakhalin. The flora clearly belongs to the Sino-Japanese floral region (Good, 1974).

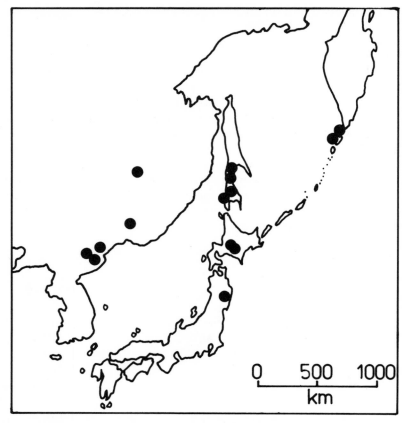

Fig. 16.7   Disjunctive distribution of *Carex capillaris*. The Japanese sites are on serpentine. Source: Nosaka (1974).

TABLE 16.7   Distribution of Species by Families in the Mainly Serpentinicolous Flora of Mt Yupari

Family	Percentage of total
Rosaceae	7.2
Cyperaceae	6.9
Asteraceae	6.7
Poaceae	5.4
Ericaceae	5.2
Liliaceae	4.8
Ranunculaceae	4.3
Orchidaceae	3.6
Saxifragaceae	3.6
Apiaceae	3.4
Polygonaceae	2.4
Lamiaceae	1.9
Scrophulariaceae	1.9
Other	42.7

After: Nosaka (1974)

TABLE 16.8 Floral Elements in the Alpine (mainly serpentinicolous) Flora of Mt. Yupari

Common to	Percentage of total
Honshu	81.3
Kuriles	62.9
North and central Honshu	60.7
Sakhalin	52.9
Central and North Kuriles	42.2
Korea	27.5
Manchuria	27.5
Kamchatka	25.5
North America	23.9
Siberia	23.1
China	13.5
Europe	7.2

After: Nosaka (1974)

16.8 BIOGEOCHEMICAL STUDIES ON JAPANESE SERPENTINE PLANTS

Although research on biogeochemical prospecting for minerals had its beginnings in Scandinavia (Brundin, 1939), Russia (Tkalich, 1938), and Canada (Warren and Howatson, 1947), pioneering work in this field has also been carried out in Japan, following the studies on manganese uptake by plants (Kimura and Murakami, 1950; Yamagata and Yamagata, 1957). Later, Yamagata et al. (1960) extended the work to include biogeochemical exploration in the serpentine areas of Honshu in the Hinokami mining district of Tottori Prefecture in the western part of the island (site 17 in Fig. 16.1). The serpentine of Mt Inazumi contains numerous chrome deposits which have been worked sporadically for many years. The soil, which is rich in clay and is of a reddish colour, contains typically 2500–6500 μg/g chromium in the sequence of the A to the C horizon, where corresponding values for nickel are 750–2500 μg/g and for cobalt are 700–800 μg/g.

The vegetation of the serpentines of the Hinokami district is not physiognomically very different from that of the surrounding flora. The tree layer is dominated by *Quercus crispula* and *Q. serrata*, though other woody species such as the deciduous *Clethra barbinervis*, *Deutzia crenata*, *Cynoxylon japonica*, *Castanea crenata*, and *Lindera umbellata* are common. Other species observed by Yamagata et al. (1960) were: *Hydrangea serrata*, *Ilex pedunculosa*, *Rhus japonica*, *Pieris japonica*, *Carpinus tschonoskii*, *Lonia neziki*, *Magnolia salicifolia*, and *Lindera obtusiloba*. It is noteworthy that none of the plants analysed by these workers was known to be serpentine-endemic, though the possibility that they were previously-undescribed serpentinomorphoses cannot be ruled out.

The concentrations in plants and the plant/soil quotients for each of 5 elements as determined by Yamagata et al. (1960) are given in Table 16.9. The approximate constancy of the plant/soil concentration values for several species led to the conclusion that a number of plants could be used for biogeochemical prospecting for nickel and chromium in this mining district. Yamagata and Murakami (1958) also noticed the extraordinarily high uptake of cobalt by *Clethra barbinervis* relative to the other species investigated. Mean Ni/Co quotients were 0.38 for this species (dry weight basis) compared with 7.1–20.7 for the others. The original data had been expressed on an ash-weight basis (i.e. 661 μg/g cobalt and 140 μg/g nickel) but even on a dry weight basis, the resultant cobalt concentration of 66 μg/g is well above that normally encountered in serpentine flora elsewhere. For example, although Brooks and Yang (1984) reported 115 μg/g cobalt in dried leaves of the nickel hyperaccumulator *Pearsonia metallifera* (1.14 % nickel) from the Great Dyke, Zimbabwe, none of the other

19 serpentine-endemic taxa contained more than 20 μg/g cobalt in its dried leaves. There are of course many plants which hyperaccumulate cobalt (>1000 μg/g) from the copper/cobalt deposits of Central Africa (Brooks and Malaisse, 1985), but none of these ores is derived from ultramafic rocks. The only taxa which seem to have a behaviour analogous to that of *Clethra barbinervis*, are species of *Nyssa* such as *N. sinensis* and *N. sylvatica* which according to Brooks et al. (1977) can contain up to 120 and 530 μg/g cobalt respectively, even when growing over soils which do not have inordinately high levels of this element. The true significance of *Clethra barbinervis* as an accumulator of cobalt still remains to be established, but because of its widespread occurrence in Japan, it might conceivably be used to determine the cobalt status of Japanese soils as has been done by Kubota et al. (1960) for American soils using *Nyssa sylvatica*.

TABLE 16.9 Concentrations in Plants (μg/g dry weight) and Plant/Soil Quotients for Five Elements in the Serpentine Vegetation of the Hinokami Mining District of Western Honshu

Species	n	Fe Conc.	Fe P/S	Ni Conc.	Ni P/S	Co Conc.	Co P/S	Mn Conc.	Mn P/S	Cr Conc.	Cr P/S
Clethra barbinervis	17	55	0.001	14.0	0.016	66.0	0.137	812	0.608	2.4	0.001
Castanea crenata	24	85	0.002	3.2	0.006	0.4	0.002	1110	1.214	1.8	0.005
Cynoxylon japonica	24	69	0.002	2.5	0.006	0.2	0.001	68	0.056	1.2	0.001
Deutzia crenata	26	79	0.003	2.4	0.004	0.5	0.004	127	0.152	3.1	0.002
Lindera umbellata	11	70	0.001	2.7	0.005	0.4	0.002	348	0.278	4.4	0.003
Quercus crispula	69	61	0.001	4.2	0.007	0.3	0.001	808	0.776	1.7	0.004
Mean (excl. Clethra)		68	0.002	3.3	0.006	0.3	0.002	635	0.612	2.1	0.003

P/S = Plant/soil quotient
After: Yamagata et al. (1960). Reprinted by permission of Pergamon Press—copyright 1960.

REFERENCES

Brooks, R. R. and Malaisse, F., 1985. *The Heavy-metal Tolerant Flora of Southcentral Africa—a Multidisciplinary Approach.* Balkema, Rotterdam.

Brooks, R. R., McCleave, J. A. and Schofield, E. K., 1977. Cobalt and nickel uptake by the Nyssaceae. *Taxon* 26: 197–201.

Brooks, R. R. and Yang, X. H., 1984. Elemental levels and relationships in the endemic flora of the Great Dyke, Zimbabwe, and their significance as controlling factors for this flora. *Taxon,* 33: 392–399.

Brundin, N., 1939. *Method of locating minerals in the ground.* U.S. Pat. 2158980.

Ernst, W., 1974. *Schwermetallvegetation der Erde.* Fischer, Stuttgart.

Good, L., 1974. *The Geography of the Flowering Plants,* 4th ed. Longman, London.

Inagaki, K., Toyokuni, H., Matsunaga, K., Horochi, S., Chida, M., Yamaguchi, M., Kobayashi, T., Hanzawa, M., Kita, S. and Odajima, T., 1966. On the flora of ultrabasic rock areas in central and northern Hokkaido Japan (Part 1). *J. Hokk. Gakugei Univ. Sec.IIB,* 16: 99–113.

Idem. 1967. Same title (Part 2). ibid. 18: 16–23.

Idem. 1968a. Same title (Part 3). ibid. 19: 20–26.

Idem. 1968b. Same title (Part 4). ibid. 19: 79–81.

Idem. 1969. Same title (Part 5). ibid. 20: 16–19.

Ishizuka, K., 1974. Mountain vegetation. In (M. Numata ed.) *The Flora and Vegetation of Japan.* Kodansha-Elsevier, Tokyo-Amsterdam.

Ishizuka, K., Saito, K., Komizunai, M. and Chiba, T., 1982. Alpine vegetation of Mt Hayachine in the Kitakami Mountains, Northeast Japan. *Saito Ho-on Kai Mus. Res. Bull.,* #50: 1–22.

Kawano, S., 1971. Studies on the alpine flora of Hokkaido, Japan. I. Phytogeography. *J. Coll. Lib. Arts Toyama Univ. Nat. Sci.,* 4: 13–96.

Kikuchi, M. and Komidzunai, L., 1961. *Flora of Mt Hayachine and the adjacent mountains, Province Rikuchu in N. Hondo.* Soc. Kaminishi-Sci. Educ. Tono.

Kimura, K. and Murakami, Y., 1950. Geochemical prospecting by the use of vegetation. *Proc. Symp. on Geochemistry and Analytical Chemistry.* Japan. Chem. Soc.

Kitamura, S., 1950. Adaptation and isolation on the serpentine areas (in Jap.). *Acta Phytotax. Geobot.,* 12: 178–185.

Kitamura, S., 1952a. Serpentine flora of Mt Shibutsu, Prov. Kodzuke, Japan (in Jap.). *Acta Phytotax. Geobot.,* 14: 174–176.

Kitamura, S., 1952b. Serpentine flora of Mt Hayachine, Prov. Rikuchi, Japan (in Jap.). *Acta Phytotax. Geobot.,* 14: 177–180.

Kitamura, S., 1956. Serpentine flora of Mt Apoi, Prov. Hidaka, Hokkaido (in Jap.). *Acta Phytotax. Geobot.,* 16; 143–148.

Kitamura, S., 1957. Serpentine flora of Nuppromapporo Valley a branch of Teshio River, Hokkaido (in Jap.). *Acta Phytotax. Geobot.,* 17: 41–45.

Kitamura, S. and Momotani, Y., 1952. Serpentine flora of island Sugashima, Prov. Shima, Japan (in Jap.). *Acta Phytotax. Geobot.,* 14: 118–119.

Kitamura, S., Murata, G. and Torii, K., 1953. Serpentine flora of Mikawa Province (in Jap.). *Acta Phytotax. Geobot.,* 15: 1–3.

Kubota, J., Lazar, V. A. and Beeson, K.C., 1960. The study of cobalt status of soils in Arkansas and Louisiana using the blackgum as indicator plant. *Soil Sci. Proc.,* 24: 527–528.

Nagano, H., Shibuichi, H. and Tajino, T., 1966. On the serpentine vegetation of Mt Kamafuse, Chichibu Dist. central Japan. *Bull. Chichibu Mus. Nat. Hist.,* 13: 7–17.

Nishida, S., 1918. On the distribution of plants in the Yubari mountain range. *Trans. Sapporo Nat. Hist. Soc.,* 7: 71–92.

Nishida, S., 1919. Same title, ibid., 7: 138–177.

Nosaka, S., 1960a. A preliminary report on the phanerogam flora of Mt Yupari, Prov. Ishikari, Hokkaido. *J. Geobot.* 8: 102–105.

Nosaka, S., 1960b. Same title, ibid., 9: 14–17, 42–45.

Nosaka, S., 1961a. Same title, ibid., 9: 88–94.

Nosaka, S., 1961b. Same title, ibid., 10: 23–25, 59–61.

Nosaka, S., 1962. Same title, ibid., 10: 111–112.

Nosaka, S., 1971. A new subspecies of *Sedum pluricaule* from Mt Yupari, Prov. Ishikari, Hokkaido, together with a comment on allied species. *J. Jap. Bot.,* 46: 167–172.

Nosaka, S., The phanerogam flora of Mt Yupari, Prov. Ishikari, Hokkaido, Japan. *J. Fac. Sci. Hokk. Univ. Ser.V (botany)* 9: 55–300.

Numata, M. (ed.), 1974. *The Flora and Vegetation of Japan.* Kodansha-Elsevier, Tokyo-Amsterdam.

Ohba, T., 1968. Uber die Serpentinpflanzengesellschaften der alpinen Stufe Japans. *Bull. Kanagawa Pref. Mus.,* 1(1): 37–64.

Ohba, T., 1969. Eine pflanzensoziologische Gliederung über die Wüstenpflanzengesellschaften auf alpinen Stufen Japans. *Bull. Kanagawa Pref. Mus.,* 1(2): 23–70.

Rune, O., 1953. Plant life on serpentines and related rocks in the north of Sweden. *Acta Phytogeogr. Suecica,* 31; 1–139.

Saito, K., Ishizuka, K., Chiba, T. and Komizunai, M., 1977. Forest vegetation on Mt Hayachine in the Kitakami Mountains, Northeastern Japan. *Saito Ho-on Kai Mus. Res. Bull.*, #45: 39–55.

Suzuki, J. 1952. Ultrabasic rocks and associated ore deposits of Hokkaido Japan. *J. Fac. Sci. Hokk. Univ. Ser.IV*, 8: 175–210.

Takeda, H., 1913. Notes on the Japanese primulas. *Notes. Roy. Bot. Gard. Edinb.*, 8: 94.

Taniguti, M., 1958. Phytosociological study of serpentine area of Mt Asama, Mie Pref. (in Jap.). *Acta Phytotax. Geobot.*, 17: 122–127.

Tatewaki, M., 1928. The Vegetation of Mt Apoi, Prov. Hidaka, Hokkaido, Japan.

Tatewaki, M., 1963. Alpine plants in Hokkaido. *Sci. Rep. Tokohu Univ. Ser.IV (biology)*: 29: 165–188.

Tkalich, S. M., 1938. Experience on the investigation of plants as indicators in geological exploration and prospecting (in Russ.). *Vest. Dal'ne Vost. Fil. Akad. Nauk SSSR*, 32; 3–25.

Toyokuni, H., 1955. On the ultrabasicosaxicolous flora of Hokkaido, Japan (1). *Hokuriku J. Bot.*, 4: 97–101.

Toyokuni, H., 1956a. Same title (2). ibid., 5: 1–12.

Toyokuni, H., 1956b. Same title (3). ibid., 5: 81–84.

Toyokuni, H., 1956c. Same title (4). ibid., 5: 115–116.

Toyokuni, H., 1957a. Same title (5). ibid., 6: 17–20

Toyokuni, H., 1957b. Same title (6). ibid., 6: 63–67.

Toyokuni, H., 1958. Same title (7). ibid., 7: 37–38.

Toyokuni, H., 1960a. Same title (8). ibid., 8: 10–13.

Toyokuni, H., 1960b. Same title (9). ibid., 9: 38–41.

Toyokuni, H., 1982. An outline of the ultrabasicosaxicolous flora of Hokkaido, Japan. *J. Fac. Lib. Arts Shinshu Univ. Nat. Sci.*, #16; 99–106.

Warren, H. V. and Howatson, C. H., 1947. Biogeochemical prospecting for copper and zinc. *Bull. Geol. Soc. Amer.*, 58: 803–820.

Watanabe, S., 1957. Notes on the alpine flora of the Hidaka Range, Hokkaido, Japan. *Acta Phytotax. Geobot.*, 17: 23–30.

Watanabe, S., 1971. Phytogeographical studies of the alpine plants on the Hidaka-Yupari Ranges, Hokkaido. *Mem. Nat. Sci. Mus. Tokyo*, 4: 95–124.

Yamagata, N. and Murakami, Y., 1958. A cobalt-accumulating plant, *Clethra barbinervis* Sieb. et Zucc. *Nature Lond.*, 181: 1808–1809.

Yamagata, N. and Yamagata, T., 1957. Fundamental studies on the biogeochemical prospecting for minerals. *Bull. Chem. Soc. Japan.*, 30: 900–904.

Yamagata, N., Murakami, Y. and Torii, T., 1960. Biogeochemical investigations in serpentine-chromite ore district. *Geochim. Cosmochim. Acta*, 18: 23–35.

Yamanaka, T., 1952. Studies in the vegetation and the flora on serpentine. *Res. Rep. Kochi Univ.*, 1: 1–8.

Yamanaka, T., 1954. Sociological studies on the serpentine vegetation. III. The vegetation of Mt Shiraga, Kochi Pref. (in Jap). *Bull. Fac. Educ. Kochi Univ.*, 5: 47–53.

Yamanaka, T., 1955. Sociologiocal studies on the serpentine vegetation. IV. The vegetation on Mt Higashi-akaishi, Ehime Pref. (in Jap.). *Bull. Fac. Educ. Kochi Univ.*, 8: 49–57.

Yamanaka, T., 1958. Sociological studies on the serpentine vegetation. VI. On the communities of *Spiraea* in Tokoshima/Shikoku and Ehime Pref. (in Jap.). *Bull. Fac. Educ. Kochi Univ.*, 10: 71–76.

Yamanaka, T., 1959. Serpentine flora of Mt Higashi-akaishi, Shikoku, Japan. *Acta Phytotax. Geobot.*, 18: 80–97.

Yamanaka, T., 1967. The serpentine vegetation of Tanoura, Kunamote Pref., Kyushu. *Acta Phytotax. Geobot.*, 22: 192–194.

Chapter 17

AFRICA

17.1 GEOLOGY AND TECTONICS

Africa is one of the oldest and tectonically most stable of all the continents. Folding of any age later than Precambrian is rare and is restricted to the young rocks (90–50 m.y. ago) of the Atlas Range in the North (Derry, 1980).

The African continent consists of about a dozen cratons which moved relative to each other in late Precambrian times causing folding of the sediments or volcanics between them. In some cases, such as the Zimbabwe craton, the usual circular structure of these bodies is clearly visible on the map.

There are two intrusions in southern Africa which are of great significance for the deposition of ultramafic rocks. The first of these is the intrusion of the Great Dyke (site 1 in Fig. 17.1) which bisects Zimbabwe along a north-south line of some 500 km and which carries some of the world's greatest deposits of chrome and asbestos.

The second important intrusion in southern Africa is the Bushveld Igneous Complex (site 2 in Fig. 17.1) which was formed about 1950 m.y. ago when it intruded into the older Precambrian gneisses north of Johannesburg. The surface area of the Complex is about 65,000 km^2 with basic and ultramafic rocks occupying the outer circumference of the circular structure and dipping down towards the centre which is granitic at the surface and forms part of a saucer fed from a central pipe. The Bushveld Complex carries in its ultramafic layers the largest world reserves of chrome and platinum metals accompanied by nickel and other base metals.

At a much later period (550 m.y. ago), an orogeny known as the Damaran, affected West Africa showing a sharp break near Accra in Ghana, along the line of the Volta River (site 3 in Fig. 17.1). Other outcrops occur at several places in Zimbabwe outside the Great Dyke such as in Zambia on the Zambezi River (site 4), at Tete in Mozambique (site 5) and in Morocco in the north in the Rif (site 6) facing the ultramafites of the Betic Cordillera near Malaga to which they were once joined.

There have been very few vegetation studies on any African serpentines apart from those of the Great Dyke, and this chapter will perforce have to be concerned mainly with the serpentine vegetation of Zimbabwe.

17.2 ZIMBABWE

17.2.1 Geology of the Great Dyke

A good summary of the geology of the Great Dyke (Fig. 17.2) has been given by Prendergast (1984):

> This huge intrusion (530 km long and up to 11 km wide) is not in fact a dyke at all. It is rather a line of four elongated mafic-ultramafic layered complexes arranged end to end. Although very different in size, they all have essentially similar structures and rock successions and were formed by the same processes.
>
> The rock succession common to all the complexes consists of two distinct portions. The *Ultramafic Sequence* is the lower and thicker portion and contains all the known chromium deposits. Overlying it is the *Mafic Sequence* which is now found only in the centre of each complex.

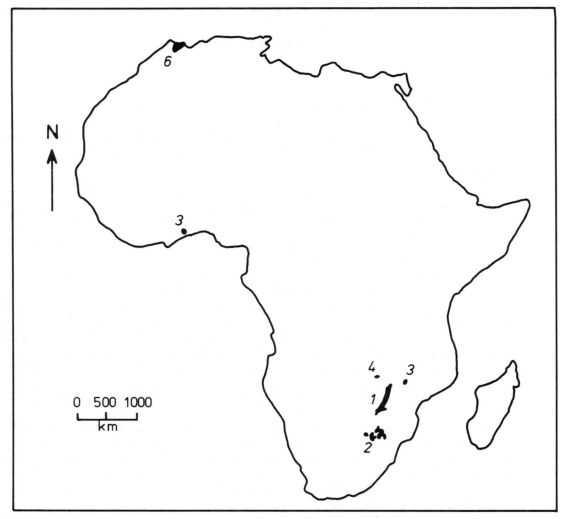

Fig. 17.1   Map of Africa Showing Ultramafic Outcrops (solid black): 1—Great Dyke, Zimbabwe, 2—Bushveld Igneous Complex, South Africa, 3—Anum Region, Ghana, 4—Zambezi Valley, Zambia, 5—Tete, Mozambique, 6—Rif, Morocco.

The *Ultramafic Sequence* is made up of a number of repeated cyclic layering units. Each complex unit commences with a thin chromite seam at or near the base and this is overlain, in turn, by a thick chromite-bearing dunite (or harzburgite) layer, and finally by a pyroxenite layer. Some of the cycles are apparently incomplete and lack either the basal chromite seam or the top pyroxenite. The thick pyroxenite layer that caps the *Ultramafic Sequence* in all four complexes contains an important platinum-bearing sulphide horizon.

Each cyclic unit is the product of fractional crystallisation of a cooling mafic magma during which layers of successively lower temperature forms of chromite, olivine and pyroxene were deposited in systematically varying proportions. New units commenced as fresh batches of magma entered the magma chamber and mixed with the old, a process which probably occurred many times. The origin of the Great Dyke is very similar to that of the Bushveld Igneous Complex and most other layered intrusions.

Although the layers were probably laid down flat, they later subsided along the middle. As a result, each complex now has a boat-like shape, with the layers

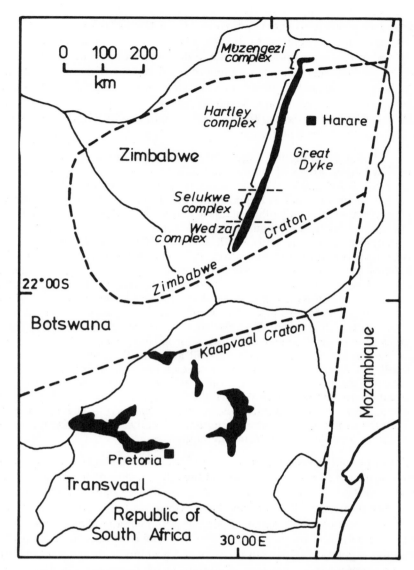

Fig. 17.2   Map of the Great Dyke and Bushveld Igneous Complex.
Source: Gruenewaldt (1983).

dipping inwards from the margins and the ends so that the seams form a series of shallow elongated basins overlaying one another.

The dunites (and to a much smaller extent, the harzburgites) are serpentinized to a depth of between 200–300 m below the surface. The serpentinite is soft and tends to distintegrate rapidly on exposure to air. At the surface and especially on the hills, circulating ground waters rich in silica and iron have recemented the serpentinite to a relatively hard form.

17.2.2 A Broad Overview of the Vegetation of the Great Dyke

The serpentine vegetation of the Great Dyke has been thoroughly described due largely to the work of one man, the late Hiram Wild, who carried out his studies over the period 1965–1975, while head of the Department of Botany at the University of Zimbabwe. A list of his papers on this subject is shown together with others, in Table 17.1. His works have also been summarized by Brooks and Malaisse (1985).

Wild (1978) has described the general appearance of the serpentine vegetation of the Great Dyke in the following terms:

> The general picture suggested by the appearance of the serpentine flora is that we have areas of maximum toxicity where only almost pure grassland survives. The grass cover is, especially on the stony hills, very poor, and succulent shrubs such as *Euphorbia wildii*, *E. memoralis* etc. together with a few geophytes, are the only other plants accompanying the grasses. The community is comparable with the 'open' serpentine communities of Kruckeberg (1954) who was dealing primarily with North American serpentine communities. This open type changes gradually into shrub or small tree savanna in which the woody species are few, e.g. *Diplorhynchus condylocarpon* subsp., *Faurea speciosa*, *Protea* spp. etc, with the grassy and other ground level vegetation unchanged. By streams, especially at the bottom of the steeper-sided valleys, riverine forest of *Syzygium*, *Olinia*, *Raphia* etc. occur with a herbaceous and shrubby layer beneath, which is presumably less subject to serpentine influence. The dominant grass species are *Loudetia simplex*, *Andropogon gayanus*, *Themeda triandra* and numerous species of *Aristida* as well as more than 40 other members of this family. A total of 316 angiosperm species has been recorded which implies an impoverished flora in comparison with the average Rhodesian (Zimbabwean) situation as pointed out by Wild (1965). The typical geological formation adjacent to the Great Dyke is granite whose sandy soils have a vegetation quite distinct from the serpentine, being predominantly *Brachystegia spiciformis—Julbernardia globifera* woodland with *Hyparrhena* grasses.

The contrast between the vegetation of the Great Dyke and its granitic surroundings is well demonstrated in Plate 17.1 which shows the portion of this structure just south of the Mtoroshanga Pass. There is a central area of wooded pyroxenite and parallel bands of grass-covered serpentine. Broad serpentine bands occur on both sides of the central pyroxenites and there are patches of *Brachystegia—Julbernardia* woodland on granitic soils to the left and away from the dyke. Various views of the Great Dyke are shown in Plate 17.2. The contrast between the vegetation of the ultramafites and granites is shown very clearly in Plate 17.2a which is a scene near Vanda Pass. The plant in the foreground is *Aloe ortholopha*.

TABLE 17.1 Papers Which Describe Serpentine Vegetation of Africa

Zimbabwe	South Africa	West Africa
Brooks and Malaisse (1985)	Werger (1978)	Woodell and Newton (1974)
Brooks and Yang (1984)		
Ernst (1974)		
Proctor and Craig (1978)		
Proctor et al. (1980)		
Thomas (1972)		
Thomas et al. (1977)		
Wild (1965, 1970, 1971, 1974a, 1974b, 1978)		

17.2.3 Endemism in the Flora of the Great Dyke

The Great Dyke falls naturally into two parts due to a large norite intrusion some 80 km long which separates the northern third from the southern (more arid) two thirds. Although Wild (1965) originally reported 20 species as being endemic to serpentine on the Great Dyke, this was later (Wild, 1978) reduced to 14 taxa of which seven were found in the north only, two in the south only, and five occurred overall. These endemic plants are listed in Table 17.2.

As has already been mentioned in Chapter 6, there is some evidence that the serpentinophytes of the Great Dyke are in the main palaeoendemics because of the absence of nearby source taxa from which they might have been derived. In some cases however, there are plants which are clearly neoendemic in status because of nearby residual biotypes on non-serpentinitic soils.

A special mention should be made of the nickel accumulator *Dicoma niccolifera* (Asteraceae—Wild 1971) which is virtually confined to serpentine, particularly on the Great Dyke. Wild (1970) has noted that this species is not only an accumulator of nickel but is also a nickel indicator since it seems to be associated with nickeliferous soils with high levels (8000 μg/g = 0.8%) of this element. *D. niccolifera* has also been reported from Zambia, though not in this case on nickeliferous soils. This taxon has some affinities with *D. macrocephala* and *D. schinzii*. The distribution of all three species is shown in Fig. 17.3. *D. niccolifera* occurs throughout Zimbabwe only on serpentine, whereas the other two taxa are found throughout much of southern Africa. As no readily discernable morphological differences have been observed between the Zimbabwean (serpentine) population of *D. niccolifera* and a small population off serpentine in Zambia, it seems that the serpentine plants represent the final stage of neoendemism where the populations will be classified as relict palaeoendemics once the Zambian biotypes have died out.

17.2.4 Plant Communities of the Great Dyke

Wild (1965) has recognized four main plant communities of the Great Dyke. These are as follows:

(1) *The Mvuradona-Darwendale Community*

This community occupies a well-developed serpentine ridge between Darwendale and Mvuradona in the northern part of the dyke. The community can be divided into five subgroups: (i) grassland, (ii) bush steppe, (iii) small tree steppe, (iv) riverine forest, and (v) *Raphia* groves.

(i) The grassland species include *Loudetia simplex*, *Andropogon gayanus*, *A. schirensis*, *Themeda triandra*, *Aristida canescens*, *A. hispidula*, *A. pardyi*, *A. scabrivalvis*, *A. submucronata*, *A. vestita*, *Brachiaria eruciformis*, *Cymbopogon excavatus*. *Diplachne biflora*, *Eragrostis denudata*, *E. lappula* var. *divaricata*, *E. patens*, *E. plana*. *Heteropogon contortus*, *Pogonarthria squarrosa*, *Schizachyrium semiberbe*, and *Trachypogon spicatus*. Succulents such as *Aloe ortholopha* and *Euphorbia monteiri* and *E. memoralis* (Plate 17.2b) sometimes form part of this community.

(ii) The bush steppe community resembles that of the grasslands above but with the addition of shrubs such as: *Protea welwitschii*, *P. angolensis*, *Securidaca longepedunculata* and *Vellozia equisetoides*. This community is shown in Plate 17.2c.

(iii) The small tree steppe community is similar to the above assemblages but with the addition of scattered small trees such as: *Combretum zeyheri*, *Faurea speciosa*, *F. saligna*, *Diplorhynchus condylocarpon*, *Pterocarpus angolensis*, *Albizia antunesiana*, *Heeria* sp. nov. (Wild, 1965), *Ximenia caffra*, *Tapiphyllum velutinum* and *Piliostigma thonningii*.

(iv) Riverine forest is found near perennial streams such as at the Mpinga Pass. Trees of this community include *Syzygium guineense*, *Bequartiodendron magalismontanum*, *Rapanea melanophloeos*, *Ilex mitis*, *Apodytes dimidiata* and *Olinia usambarensis*.

TABLE 17.2   Endemic Taxa from the Great Dyke, Zimbabwe

Species	Part of Dyke	Distribution
Aloe ortholopha	North	Mvuaradona—Mtoroshanga
Barleria molensis	South	Widespread
Dicoma niccolifera	North and south	Widespread
Euphorbia memoralis	North	Horseshoe—Mtoroshanga
E. wildii	North	Mvuaradona—Mpinga Pass
Leucas aggerestris	North	Just north of Maryland
L. hephaestis	North	Mvuaradona
Lotononis serpentinicola	North and south	Widespread
Ozoroa longepetiolata	North	Widespread
*Pearsonia metallifera**	North and south	Widespread
Rhus tenuipes	South	Widespread
*R. wildii**	North	Mpinga Pass—Noro Mine
Sutera fodina	North and south	Widespread
Vernonia accommodata	North and south	Widespread

* hyperaccumulators of nickel (see also Chapter 8).
After: Wild (1965).

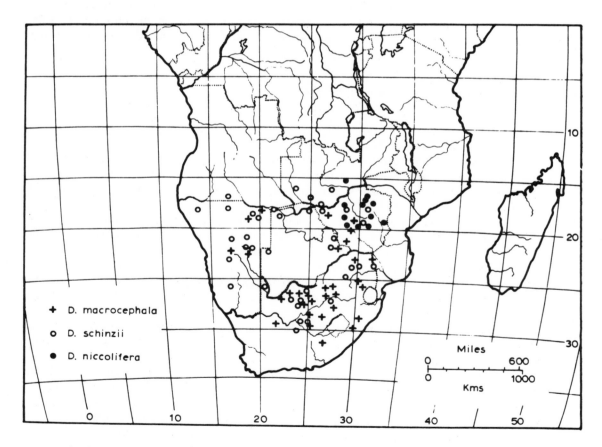

Fig. 17.3   Distribution of *Dicoma niccolifera*, *D. macrocephala* and *D. schinzii* in southern Africa.
Source: Wild (1971).

Sometimes the riverine forest includes species not normally found on serpentine such as *S. guineense*, *I. mitis* and *B. mahalismontanum*. *Brachystegia* woodland, normally associated with granites, can also be found sometimes over serpentine. Proctor and Craig (1978) examined this problem and came to the conclusion that in the case of riverine forest, the greater availability of water was able to counteract to some extent, the adverse effects of serpentine. The *Brachystegia* woodland on the ridges, however, was growing over soils with a lower exchangeable nickel content than those of the grassland plains and which were consequently less phytotoxic.

(v) The final subgroup of the Mvuradona-Darwendale community is the tall *Raphia ruffia* groves which occur in the Horseshoe area. These groves seem to be outliers of a once much greater distribution now confined mainly to West Africa and are probably serpentine relics remaining after gradual diminution of rainfall in southcentral Africa.

(2) The Darwendale-Hunyani Savanna Grassland

From Darwendale to the Hunyani River, the Great Dyke is a flat grassy plain with a few small wooded hills of pyroxenite (Plate 17.2d). The dominant grass is *Loudetia simplex* but the relatively more mesic conditions provide a niche for a number of other grasses more associated with swamps such as: *Fimbristylis complanata* and *Scirpus muricinux*.

(3) The Ngezi—Otto Mine communities of higher ground

The large norite intrusion stretches from just south of the Hunyani River to the Ngezi River. There are two subgroups in the community over this formation. The first is a grass steppe with principal grasses including: *Themeda triandra* (dominant), *Eragrostis superba*, *Pogonarthria squarrosa*, *Aristida canescens*, *A. barbicollis*, *A. scabrivalvis*, *Andropogon gayanus* var. *squamulatus*, *Cymbopogon excavatus* and *Schmidtia bulbosa*. A number of geophytes accompanies these grasses and includes: *Argyrolobium eylesii*, *Thamnosma rhodesica*, *Corchorus asplenifolius*, *Polygala hottentotta*, *Aptosimum lineare*, *Sutera brunnea*, *Walafrida angolensis*, *Helichrysum pachyrhizum*, *Convolvulus ocellatus* var. *plicinervius*, *Thesium* spp., *Gnidia capitata*, *Boophne disticha*, *Cyphostemma humile* subsp. *dolichopus*, *Tylosema fassoglensis*, *Euphorbia oatesii*, *Geigeria africana*, *Vellozia viscosa*, *Rhynchosia minima*, and *Vernonia accommodata*.

The second subgroup of the Ngezi—Otto Mine community is the shrub steppe which includes: *Rhus erosa*, *R. trifoliata*, *Euclea linearis*, *Mundulea sericea*, *Diplorhynchus condylocarpon*, *Bolusanthus speciosus*, *Acacia chariessa*, *Tarchonanthus camphoratus*, *Tapiphyllum velutinum*, *Croton gratissimus*, *Heeria reticulata*, *Zizyphus mucronata*, *Combretum apiculatum*, *C. hereroense*, and *Schrebera argyrotricha*.

(4) The Lundi River—Bannockburn savanna grasslands

In this part of the Great Dyke, the terrain consists of an elongated plain between granitic hills. Principal species are *Aristida hispidula*, *Brachiaria eruciformis*, *Setaria porphyrantha*, *Eragrostis superba* and *Themeda triandra* with *Scirpus muricinux* in wet places. In the very flat grassland the only woody vegetation is the occasional stunted bush of *Euclea linearis* or *Combretum hereroense*. On pyroxenite outcrops there is a shrubby cover of *Croton gratissimus*, *Combretum apiculatum*, *Tapiphyllum velutinum* and *Mundulea speciosa*. In the north of the Great Dyke, the dominant grass species is *Loudetia simplex* which is replaced further south by the more drought-resistant *Themeda triandra*.

17.2.5 Floristics of the Vegetation of the Great Dyke

There are pronounced phytogeographic differences between the northern and southern sections of the Great Dyke. These differences arise from the barrier to migration provided by the large norite instrusion. This situation has already been discussed in terms of the endemic species. 61 taxa of other serpentinicolous plants are reported only in the northern part and 20 in the south. The rest are distributed throughout.

Although Wild (1965) reported a total of 322 phanerogams in the 3000 km² of the Great Dyke, this total is far less than for example the 859 species found over a mere 400 km² of the Chimanimani Mts of eastern Zimbabwe on non-ultramafic substrates. The Great Dyke flora is clearly very impoverished. This is particularly evident for trees which are common on the surrounding granites but are virtually absent on the serpentines.

The percentage distribution of the various families of Zimbabwean plants has already been given in Table 6.3. It seems that the families with an unusually high percentage of species on serpentine in Zimbabwe are the Poaceae, Papilionaceae, Proteaceae, Polygalaceae, Euphorbiaceae, Combretaceae, Lamiaceae, Scrophulariaceae, Asteraceae, Convolvulaceae and Anacardiaceae.

17.2.6 Vegetation of Other Serpentine Sites in Zimbabwe

We are again indebted to H. Wild for a description of serpentine vegetation of Zimbabwe other than on the Great Dyke itself. In an important paper on this subject, Wild (1970) described the vegetation of 28 serpentine districts in Zimbabwe from Mtoroshanga in the north to Noel Mine in the south and from the Bubi district in the west to Umtali in the east. The main aim of his paper was to compare nickel floras with copper floras elsewhere in the country, however this in no way detracts from the contribution that this work makes to our understanding of the serpentine flora of Zimbabwe. To summarize briefly, Wild (1970) observed that nickel anomalies did not produce completely bare areas as did copper deposits. The graminoid zone often contains stunted trees in stands of more or less uniform height. The ecotonal zone with an abrupt change to trees of normal height is more narrow than with copper and there is a tendency for some nickel anomalies to have a swamp-like form though these do not lie along drainage lines. Pteridophytes are rare over Zimbabwean serpentines. The genera *Acacia*, *Aristida* and *Combretum* are widespread over both copper and nickel anomalies. The families Fabaceae, Poaceae and Asteraceae are likewise common over the ultramafites. The Proteaceae are very important also and are represented over serpentines by two species of *Faurea* and one of *Protea*. The following species, though not found exclusively on serpentine, can acts as indicators for this rock type: *Albizia amara*, *Barleria aromatica*, *Combretum molle*, *Dalbergia melanoxylon*, *Eminia antennulifera*, *Turraea nilotica*, *Pterocarpus rotundifolius* and *Allophylus africanus*. The most frequently occurring grasses are: *Loudetia simplex*, *Andropogon gayanus*, *Aristida leucophaea* and *Danthoniopsis intermedia*.

The species which occur most frequently on Zimbabwean serpentines (in order of decreasing abundance) are: *Diplorhynchus condylocarpon*, *Loudetia simplex*, *Andropogon gayanus*, *Combretum molle*, *C. apiculatum*, *Cymbopogon excavatus*, *Brachystegia boehmii*, *Combretum zeyheri*, *Julbernardia globifera*, *Themeda triandra*, *Aristida leucophaea*, and *Albizia amara*.

Further work on the vegetation of Zimbabwean serpentine soils has been reported by Wild (1974a) in which he related the flora of 13 sites with the chemical composition of the soils. The analyses were carried out on soil extracts (2.5% acetic acid) in which copper, chromium and nickel were determined as well as calcium/magnesium quotients. At the same time the degree of toxicity was determined by observing the presence or absence of trees in the vegetation as well as recording the actual species present at the site to see whether they were typically of a serpentine or heavy-metal type. The main objective was to see if nickel alone, in the absence of a low calcium/magnesium quotient, could create distinct vegetation anomalies. In the majority of cases, high nickel values were accompanied by low calcium/magnesium ratios and it was not possible to distinguish between the effects of these two variables. In a few cases however, where nickel was present and where the host rock was not typically serpentine and had a high calcium/magnesium ratio, pronounced anomalies were created by high nickel values alone. Examples of this were found at Kingston Hill near Wedza mountain and at Bare Bottom Hill near the Empress Mine.

In soils derived from serpentine soils such as actinolite schists, carbonate schists, pyroxenites and norites with high calcium/magnesium quotients but with low nickel levels, a well-developed non-anomalous vegetation community was developed.

Wild (1970) has listed a number of species which may be regarded as serpentinicolous on serpentine sites other than the Great Dyke. These are shown in Table 17.3. The list does not include numerous grasses such as *Andropogon gayanus*, *A. schirensis*, *A. schinzii*, *Cymbopogon excavatus*, *Trachypogon spicatus*, *Themeda triandra*, *Loudetia simplex* and *Heteropogon contortus*. These species are common on serpentine and other substrates throughout Zimbabwe.

TABLE 17.3 Serpentinicolous Plants of Serpentine Outcrops (excluding the Great Dyke) in Zimbabwe

Species	Comments
Albizia amara	Bodenvag but common on nickeliferous soils.
Barleria aromatica	Serpentine endemic. Common in eastern Zimbabwe and on Great Dyke.
Combretum molle	Characteristic plant of most serpentine occurrences.
Dalbergia melanoxylon	Common on serpentines but not on Great Dyke. Found on mafic as well as ultramafic rocks.
Dicoma niccolifera	Virtually endemic to serpentines. Accumulates nickel.
Eminia antennulifera	Characteristic plant of serpentines in northern Zimbabwe.
Faurea saligna	Widespread on serpentines.
F. speciosa	Widespread on serpentines.
Protea angolensis	Widespread on serpentines.
Pterocarpus rotundifolius	Common as dwarf form on serpentines.
Turraea nilotica	Common on mafic and ultramafic rocks.

After: Wild (1970).

17.3 SOUTH AFRICA

17.3.1 The Bushveld Igneous Complex

The serpentine occurrences of South Africa are found mainly in the Barberton Schist Belt and on the ultramafites of the Bushveld Igneous Complex in central Transvaal near Pretoria. The complex is famous for its chromium and platinum deposits (among the largest in the world) which have been described in numerous papers (e.g. Gruenewaldt, 1983). The overall area of this structure is about 65,000 km² though most of it is the granite basement or is composed of basic rather than ultrabasic rocks. The ultramafic rocks tend to have their surface expressions mainly along the outside rim of the circular structure. The rocks were formed about 2100 m.y. ago during widespread magmatic activity and were emplaced in the very stable Kaapvaal Craton which has protected it from folding until the present time.

The ultramafites of the Bushveld Igneous Complex are preserved in three separate areas in which the successions of rock types are broadly very similar although they differ considerably in detail. This led to the suggestion that although the magma giving rise to these rocks was emplaced as several cone-like intrusions that crystallised mainly in isolation, these were interconnected at times.

The extensive chromite and platinum deposits are confined essentially to the Critical Zone of the Rustenburg Layered Suite. They occur as layers varying in thickness from less than a centimetre to more than 2 m and can be continuous for up to a length of 100 m.

17.3.2 The Vegetation of the Bushveld Igneous Complex

In sharp contrast with the flora of the Great Dyke, there is virtually no literature of the serpentine vegetation of the equally-important Bushveld Igneous Complex. Floristically the zone belongs to the Sudano-Zambezian phytogeographic region as defined by Werger and Coetzee (1978) and more precisely to its Zambezian domain. Perhaps one of the more surprising feature of the flora of the Bushveld Complex is the abrupt phasing out of the Zimbabwean *Brachystegia-Julbernardia-Isoberlinia* woodland south of the Limpopo, perhaps due to frost. The Barberton-Lydenburg Centre at the eastern rim of the Bushveld Complex is a centre of endemism of genera such as *Euphorbia*, *Aloe*, *Stapelia* and *Euryops*, but it is doubtful whether this endemism results from the presence of ultramafic rocks in the area.

The dominant species of the central part of the Bushveld Igneous Complex is *Combretum apiculatum* which is however more typical of granites than of ultramafites. The literature of the serpentine vegetation of the Complex is extraordinarily sparse, particularly when it is compared with the relatively vast amount of information pertaining to the Great Dyke not much further north. In spite of this there is a local tradition that the "olivine plant" *Helichrysum fleckii* (= *H. pumilio* subsp. *fleckii*) shown in Plate 17.3a, is apparently an indicator of serpentine in this area.

A general view of the typical flora of ultramafic outcrops in parts of the Bushveld igneous complex is given in Plate 17.3d.

Observations on the serpentine flora of the Barberton area on the eastern fringe of the Bushveld Igneous Complex have been made by Balkwill (1985). Near Kaapsehoop east of Nelspruit, the serpentine is dominated by an undescribed *Sutera* which appears to be endemic to the area. This would of course be analogous to the serpentine-endemic *Sutera fodina* (Plate 17.3b) which grows on the Great Dyke and which is highly tolerant of nickel and chromium ore.

The presence of serpentine in the Barberton area is indicated by *Aloe marlothii* and an undescribed species of *Xerophyta* (Plate 17.3c) which gives a grey-green appearance to the whole hillside. Balkwill (1985) has collected a number of species from serpentine which appear to be undescribed. These include species of *Rhus*, *Berkheya* and *Dipcadi*.

There is no doubt that the South African serpentine flora has been very little studied and it seems certain that further research in this region will reap rich botanical dividends in the future.

17.4 PHYTOSOCIOLOGICAL STUDIES OF THE SERPENTINE FLORAS OF SOUTHERN AFRICA

The serpentine vegetation of southern Africa has been classified by Ernst (1974) into the Dicometum niccoliferae Association which forms part of the Indigofera-Loudetion Alliance of the Eragrostietea cupricolae Class. The character species of the Association is *Dicoma niccolifera* (see above). Companion species of the Association are shown in Table 17.4.

17.5 BIOGEOCHEMICAL STUDIES ON SERPENTINE PLANTS OF SOUTHERN AFRICA

Biogeochemical studies on the serpentine flora of southern Africa have been carried out by a number of workers such as Cole (1971) who studied the flora of the Empress copper/nickel deposits some 50 km west of Gatooma in Zimbabwe. Mineralization occurs within gabbro and amphibolite, though there is some serpentine nearby. The soils contain around 5000 $\mu g/g$ (0.5%) of both copper and nickel. An undescribed species of *Barleria* was observed to be confined to the ore body. It was found together with *Celosia trigyna* and a sparse cover of grasses. Leaves and twigs of *Dalbergia melanoxylon* and *Combretum*

Plate 17.2   (a) Above: View of Great Dyke near Vanda Pass looking to the woodland on granite in the background. The flowering plant is the serpentine-endemic *Aloe ortholopha*. Photo by A. I. Robertson. (b) Below: View of *Aloe ortholopha* (left) and *Euphorbia memoralis* (right) on the Great Dyke near Mtoroshanga Pass. Photo by A. I. Robertson.

Plate 17.2 (c) Above: View of grassland on the Great Dyke near Horseshoe. Photo by A. I. Robertson. (d) Below: View of the Great Dyke near Darwendale. The foreground and wooded hill on the right are pyroxenite. Photo by M. D. Prendergast.

Plate 17.3 (a) Above: The "Olivine Plant" *Helichrysum fleckii* which grows over ultramafic rocks of the Bushveld Igneous Complex. (b) Below: The serpentine-endemic *Sutera fodina* growing over chrome mine wastes on the Great Dyke. Photo by A. I. Robertson.

Plate 17.3 (c) Above: *Aloe marlothii* (small upright shrubs), a characteristic plant of the South African serpentines. The larger trees are pines. Photo by K. Balkwill. (d) Below: Serpentine vegetation over hortonolite dunite in the eastern Bushveld Igneous Complex. Photo by W. R. Lauder.

TABLE 17.4 The Dicometum niccoliferae Association

Character species of the Association: *Dicoma niccolifera*
Character species of the Alliance (Indigofera-Loudetion): *Loudetia flavida,*
  Indigofera setiflora, Aristida leucophaea, Fimbristylis exilis.
Character species of the Class (Eragrostietea cupricolae): *Loudetia simplex,*
  Eragrostis racemosa, Becium homblei.
Companions: *Diheteropogon amplectens, Themeda triandra, Brachiaria serrata,*
  Heteropogon contortus, Securidaca longepedunculata, Scilla benguellensis,
  Cymbopogon excavatus, Andropogon gayanus, Diplorhynchus condylocarpon,
  Blepharis acuminata, Albizia antunesiana, Combretum apiculatum, Thesium
  ssp., *Elephantorrhiza elephantina, Bulbostylis contexta, Tapiphyllum*
  velutinum, Dolichos schlechteri, Aristida barbicollis, Rhynchosia totta,
  Becium obovatum, Faurea speciosa, Lapeyrousia sandersonii.

After: Ernst (1974)

hereroense were sampled and analysed for copper and nickel. The levels of these two elements delineated the ore body more precisely than did the soils. Cole (1971) concluded that plant sampling was a most effective exploration technique in the savanna woodland environment.

A very thorough geobotanical/biogeochemical investigation on a copper/nickel deposit at Nkai, Zimbabwe has been carried out by Thomas et al. (1977). These workers used principal components statistical analysis to assess the relative importance of major environmental factors such as man-made disturbance, nutrients in the soil, and heavy metals in the soil, in controlling vegetation communities in various parts of the terrain. The authors used cluster analysis to define the vegetation communities. The work showed that the above three variables all had an influence on the vegetation distribution but that the effect on heavy metals was less than disturbance of the nutrient status of the soils. This excellent piece of work is perhaps one of the soundest statistically to emerge from southcentral Africa, but it must of course be remembered that statistics in themselves can never compensate for inadequate field work but they do form a very good basis for a proper quantitative and objective treatment of the original data.

In the same area at Nkai, a biogeochemical study by Thomas (1972) and Thomas et al. (1977) involved the use of twigs of 7 native shrubs and trees to attempt to detect a serpentine body beneath Kalahari sands south of the amphibolite body near Nkai. However the nickel content of the vegetation showed no relation to bedrock, perhaps because of the geochemical barrier presented by the sand.

Some mention should also be made of the work of Wild (1974b) who determined nickel and chromium in a number of serpentine plants from Zimbabwe. He reported extremely high levels of chromium in plants such as *Sutera fodina* (Plate 17.3b) which apparently contained about 2400 μg/g in dried leaves (estimated from the original data which has been reported on an ash weight basis), and 1500 μg/g in *Pearsonia metallifera*. This worker found high concentrations of chromium in the roots of both species and this seemed to indicate that the plants restricted uptake to some extent.

Brooks and Yang (1984) analysed 55 specimens of 20 serpentine-endemic plants from the Great Dyke and determined some 15 elements in them. The data confirmed the nickel-hyperaccumulator status of *Pearsonia metallifera* (see also Chapter 8) and identified an additional 3 hyperaccumulators which had not previously been so classified: *Blepharis acuminata, Merremia xanthophylla,* and *Rhus wildii. Dicoma niccolifera* did not seem to have the hyperaccumulator status originally assigned to it by Wild (1970). It is noteworthy that no taxon contained more than 98 μg/g chromium in spite of the high values obtained by

Wild (1974b). It seems highly likely that Wild's samples had been contaminated by wind-blown dust since they had been collected near the Noro chrome mine.

Perhaps the most important finding of this study (see also Chapter 4) was the highly significant inverse correlation between levels of magnesium in plants and the concentrations of the nutrients boron, cobalt, iron, manganese, phosphorus and sodium. This finding led Brooks and Yang (1984) to conclude that antagonism to nutrient uptake caused by high levels of magnesium in the plants was a major cause of the so-called "serpentine problem."

Proctor et al. (1980) have determined Ni, Cr, Co, Fe, Mg, Ca, K and Na in serpentine plants of Zimbabwe and in extracts of serpentine soils using various extractants. The plants were: *Andropogon gayanus, Combretum molle, Dicoma niccolifera* and *Ledebouria revoluta*. The extractable metal concentrations were compared with the total levels of these elements in plant material (i.e. bioassay) and were used to determine which extractants gave values for exchangeable metal concentrations which most closely approximated to the values obtained by bioassay. It was concluded that the proportion of nickel extracted with ammonium acetate gave the best indication of the available nickel. For other elements, ammonium acetate and acetic acid as extractants appeared to give approximately the same results.

Although the amount of biogeochemical prospecting work carried out in Zimbabwe is far greater than in South Africa or elsewhere in southern Africa, the volume of this work is still quite small. This is surprising in view of the fact that much of the region is covered with a thick blanket of Kalahari sand which does not reflect the true nature of bedrock. It is in such environments that biogeochemical prospecting should have its greatest potential as an indicator of mineralization at depth. Cole and her coworkers have carried out other geobotanical/biogeochemical work in southern Africa (Cole and Brown, 1976; Cole and Le Roex, 1978) but these studies did not involve serpentine vegetation. There is clearly a great need for further studies along such lines and it is to be hoped that at some time in the future, as much attention will be devoted to the serpentine vegetation of areas outside Zimbabwe, as has already been devoted to that latter country thanks to the efforts of the late Hiram Wild.

REFERENCES

Balkwill, K., 1985. Pers. commn.

Brooks, R. R. and Malaisse, F., 1985. *The Heavy Metal Tolerant Flora of Southcentral Africa—a Multidisciplinary Approach*. Balkema, Rotterdam.

Brooks, R. R. and Yang, X. H., 1984. Elemental levels and relationships in the endemic serpentine flora of the Great Dyke, Zimbabwe, and their significance as controlling factors for this flora. *Taxon, 33*: 392–399.

Cole, M. M., 1971. Biogeographical/geobotanical and biogeochemical investigations connected with exploration for nickel/copper ores in the hot wet summer/ dry winter savanna woodland environment. *J. S. Afr. Inst. Min. Metall.*, 1971; 199–209.

Cole, M. M. and Brown, R. C., 1976. The vegetation of the Ghanzi area of western Botswana. *J. Biogeogr., 3*: 169–196.

Cole, M. M. and Le Roex, H. D., 1978. The role of geobotany, biogeochemistry and geochemistry in mineral exploration in South West Africa and Botswana—A case history. *Trans. Geol. Soc. S. Afr., 81*: 277–317.

Derry, D. R., 1980. *World Atlas of Geology and Mineral Deposits*. Mining Journal Books, London.

Ernst, W., 1974. *Schwermetallvegetation der Erde*. Fischer, Stuttgart.

Gruenewaldt, G. von, 1983. Chromium deposits of the Bushveld Igneous Complex. *Chromium Review, #1*: 8–11.

Kruckeberg, A. R., 1954. The ecology of serpentine soils. 2. Plants species in relation to serpentine soils. *Ecology, 35*: 267–274.

Prendergast, M. D., 1984. Chromium deposits of Zimbabwe. *Chromium Review #2*: 5–9.

Proctor, J., Burrow, J. and Craig, G. C., 1980. Plant and soil chemical analyses from a range of Zimbabwean serpentine sites. *Kirkia,* 12: 127–139.

Proctor, J. and Craig, G. C., 1978. The occurrence of woodland and riverine forest on the serpentine of the Great Dyke. *Kirkia,* 11: 129–132.

Thomas, P. I., 1972. *Ecological and Biogeochemical Investigations at Nkai, Rhodesia.* M. Phil. Thesis, Univ. London.

Thomas, P. I., Walker, B. H. and Wild, H., 1977. Relation between vegetation and environment at an amphibolite outcrop near Nkai, Rhodesia. *Kirkia,* 10: 503–541.

Werger, M. J. A. and Coetzee, B. J., 1978. The Sudano-Zambezian Region. In (M. J. A. Werger ed.) *Biogeography and Ecology of Southern Africa,* V.1. Junk, The Hague.

Wild, H., 1965. The flora of the Great Dyke of Southern Rhodesia with special reference to the serpentine soils. *Kirkia,* 5: 49–86.

Wild, H., 1970. Geobotanical anomalies in Rhodesia. 3—The vegetation of nickel-bearing soils. *Kirkia,* 7, Suppl.: 1–62.

Wild, H., 1971. The taxonomy, ecology, and possible method of evolution of a metalliferous species of Dicoma Cass. (Compositae). *Mitt Bot. Staatssamml. München,* 10: 266–274.

Wild, H., 1974a. Variation in the serpentine flora of Rhodesia. *Kirkia,* 9: 209–232.

Wild, H., 1974b. Indigenous plants and chromium in Rhodesia. *Kirkia,* 9: 233–241.

Wild, H., 1978. The vegetation of heavy metal and other toxic soils. In (M. J. A. Werger ed.) *Biogeography and Ecology of Southern Africa.* Junk, The Hague.

Woodell, S. R. J. and Newton L. E., 1974. *The serpentine outcrop at Anum (Volta Region) in Ghana.* Unpub. Rep.

Chapter 18
THE MALAY ARCHIPELAGO

18.1 THE ENVIRONMENT

The Malay Archipelago (Malesia) stretches from Sumatra in the west to New Guinea and the Solomons in the east. It includes the Philippines in the north (Fig. 18.1) and has geological affinities with New Caledonia in the southeast though that island is not included in this chapter as it receives special consideration later. Geologically the Malay Archipelago is much younger (300 m.y.) than adjacent Australia (2500 m.y.). A broad description of the geology and tectonics of the area has been given by Derry (1980). Sections of the northern part of Malesia lie along a vast ophiolitic belt extending in a discontinuous line from New Caledonia, through New Guinea, Celebes, and Borneo to the Philippines and beyond. Ophiolites outcrop particularly along the Owen Stanley fault in New Guinea.

Volcanic activity has been, and is, very extensive in much of the region. The geology of Philippines is different from that of Indonesia. Earlier geological events had established a stable platform in Philippines by the end of the Permian (225 m.y.) when vulcanism and sedimentation had occurred alternately. Later the volcanic and sedimentary strata were involved in a period of folding and moderate metamorphism, followed by erosion and subsidence below sea level. Widespread island arc vulcanism commenced in the mid-Cretaceous (100 m.y.) and continued interspersed with sedimentation. On several occasions, ocean floor material (ophiolites) were thrust up on to the volcanics-sediments and were sometimes folded with them. A sizeable proportion of the Philippines Celebes Island is therefore composed of ultramafic rocks.

Somewhat idyllically, Woodman (1955) described the islands of the Malay Archipelago in the following terms:

> . . . 3000 islands strung along the Equator for 3000 miles . . . all sizes and shapes; small atolls built up by millions of coral polyps; island volcanoes; islands of undisturbed green jungle; islands where no foreigner has wandered and unknown to most Indonesians; islands that hug the coast of thickly-populated Java; a string of islands appearing like a row of distant steamers along the coast of Sumatra; hundreds of islands in the Moluccas famous for the spices and cloves and pepper which first attracted visitors from the western world; islands that are rich in tin; islands thickly covered with rubber trees; islands rich in oil. Throughout these islands and islets the sun always shines; there is no winter, no spring, no autumn, only a wet and dry season.

This description is romanticised, but gives an accurate description of the general environment of Malesia.

The land surface of Indonesia is about 1,900,000 km^2, that of the Philippines is 300,000 km^2, and Papua New Guinea adds a further 400,000 km^2 to the total.

Botanically and zoologically Malesia has been divided into two regions by "Wallace's Line" (Wallace, 1869) shown in Fig. 18.1. The western region includes the Philippines and has strong floristic and faunistic affinities with Southeast Asia, whereas the eastern portion has affinities with Australia. Wallace's Line separates Java, Sumatra, Bali, and Borneo (part of the Sunda Shelf once attached to the mainland of Asia) from the Sahul Shelf of which Aru Island and New Guinea are a part.

The Celebes and Moluccas form an intermediate zone. Wallace's Line had been originally defined on the basis of zoological considerations, but Zollinger's Line (Steenis, 1948) also shown in Fig. 18.1 is based on purely botanical data. This line places all the Sunda

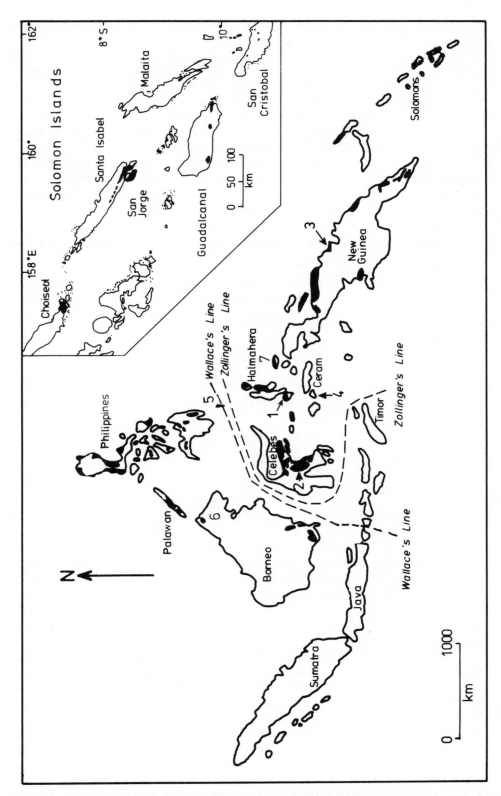

Fig. 18.1 Map of the Malay Archipelago showing distribution of ultramafic rocks (solid black areas). 1—Obi, 2—Soroako, 3—Jayapura, 4—Ambon, 5—Talaud Is., 6—Mt Kinabalu, 7—Waigeo I.

islands, Timor and the Philippines into the western part of the Archipelago, and places the Moluccas and Sulawesi into the eastern section.

Despite the division of the Malay Archipelago into eastern and western sections, the flora of the region is often considered as a single floristic unit—Malesia. Because of the extremaly rich floras of the islands of Malesia (over 10,000 phanerogams), and because of the extensive areas of ultramafic rocks in the Philippines, Celebes and New Guinea, there is a rich serpentine flora on all three of these islands. Although this flora is very rich, it has hardly been studied at all on the basis of its serpentine nature, and this is apparent from the very small number of papers describing serpentine floras in Malesia (Table 18.1). Those who wish to study this type of vegetation have perforce to seek out individual taxa in comprehensive listings of the entire vegetation of the area (e.g., *Flora Malesiana*) which do not necessarily identify serpentine plants as such. The serpentine plants of Malesia therefore represent a vast field which to date has hardly been touched at all.

TABLE 18.1 Papers which Describe Serpentine Vegetation of the Malay Archipelago

Territory	References
General for region	Brooks and Wither (1977), Whitmore (1975), Wither (1977), Wither and Brooks (1977).
Celebes	Meijers (1984)
New Guinea	Royen (1963)
Obi Island	Wither (1977)
Philippines	Podzorski et al. (1985), Santos Ynigo and Esguerra (1961)
Sabah	Dransfield (1982a, b), Meijer (1965, 1971), Proctor et al. (1983)
Solomon Islands	Whitmore (1969)
Talaud Islands	Lam (1927)

There are several reasons for the lack of information on the serpentinicolous plants of the Malay Archipelago. First of these is the fact that there is not the sharp physiognomic differentiation of serpentine floras as found in temperate zones. Often the only indication that the substrate is ultramafic, is afforded by differences in species composition rather than by overall morphological features of the plants. The vastness and relative inaccessibility of the serpentine flora has also been a deterrent to studies. Botanists of the late 19th and early 20th centuries, working in what was then the Dutch East Indies were seldom aware of the nature of the bedrock when making their collections and even if they were, did not give it the meticulous recording which is more common today.

The magnitude of the task of recording serpentine vegetation can best be illustrated by considering the east-central Celebes where virtually the entire flora of several hundred species is serpentine-tolerant if not serpentinicolous. The flora of this region must contain very many serpentinimorphoses distinct at the subspecific or varietal level, but it seems unrealistic to expect that these will ever be described to the extent that they have been (for example, in Southern Europe) where many more systematic botanists are active, and where all parts of the terrain (except perhaps Albania) are readily accessible by good road systems.

There is a final factor hindering research into the serpentine vegetation of Malesia. In the Philippines at least, and to some extent in New Guinea, plant collecting is unsafe because of bandits and guerrilla groups intent on opposing the government of the day. For example in the Philippines, which today has perhaps the richest potential for this type of research, the ultramafic areas (usually in mountainous terrain) are mainly controlled either by the left-wing New Peoples Army or by the Moslem insurgents of Mindanao. Virtually the only "peaceful" island carrying extensive areas of serpentine vegetation, is Palawan in southwest Philippines. How long even this island will remain accessible is open to doubt.

The need to study the serpentine vegetation of Malesia is an urgent one, not only because of growing insurgency in the region, but because of the steady destruction of the vegetation by mining interests (e.g., at Soroako in Celebes), timber felling, and slash-and-burn agriculture. By the time the insurgency problem has been settled, much of the virgin forest will have been destroyed. The botanist is therefore confronted with a situation which apparently has no solution.

Because of a lack of source material for a description of the serpentine vegetation of Malesia, this chapter is of necessity severely limited in extent and depth of coverage, but it will indicate the great potential for further research which this region possesses.

18.2 THE SERPENTINE VEGETATION

18.2.1 The Island of Obi

The island of Obi (site 1 in Fig. 18.1) lies just south of Halmahera and is part of the North Moluccas in Indonesia. It has an area of about 2000 km² and is heavily forested. It rises to about 1500 m with a small lowland area at the eastern end of the island. The coasts are fringed with mangrove swamps. The island yields timber, sago, rattan and resins such as copal and dammar. The latter is derived from extensive forests of *Agathis alba*, a gymnosperm.

About 10 years ago, a party of botanists from the Rijksherbarium at Leiden under the leadership of Dr. E. F. de Vogel collected plants over ultramafic rocks near the northwestern coast of the island at Jikodolong. A checklist of the plants collected by this expedition is given in Table 18.2. The plants included 57 species in 37 genera derived from a small area of ultramafic rocks. Among these plants were 3 species: *Myristica laurifolia*, var. *bifurcata*, *Planchonella oxyedra*, and *Trichospermum kjellbergii* which contained over 1000 μg/g (0.1%) nickel and were clearly of hyperaccumulator status (see also Chapter 8). The latter species also contained 350 μg/g cobalt, which is extremely high even for serpentine plants. Inordinate uptake of manganese (>2000 μg/g) was also recorded for *Psychotria longicauda* (2620 μg/g) and *Planchonella firma* (2200 μg/g).

There is no evidence that any of the taxa in Table 18.2 are serpentine endemic except perhaps *Trichospermum kjellbergii* which has been collected elsewhere in Malesia (e.g., Celebes), but always over ultramafic rocks. *Planchonella oxyedra* also appears to favour serpentine, and the plants from Obi might indeed be endemic serpentinomorphoses. Herbarium specimens of both taxa were obtained from Leiden and elsewhere and were analysed for nickel and cobalt (Wither and Brooks, 1977). The distribution and nickel content of 19 specimens of *P. oxyedra* and four of *T. kjellbergii* are shown in Fig. 18.2. Specimens containing >1000 μg/g nickel were clearly correlated with known ultramafic areas throughout Malesia. The specimen of *T. kjellbergii* from Celebes had been collected over the ultramafites at Malili near to the present nickel mining centre of Soroako (site 2 in Fig. 18.1). One of the specimens of *P. oxyedra* with anomalous nickel had been collected over ultramafites in the neigbourhood of Jayapura in Irian Jaya (site 3 in Fig. 18.1). However a specimen from Ambon (site 4) near Ceram (South Moluccas) was clearly growing on serpentine though this rock type had not previously been recorded from that particular site (Hoetemoeri). This study had shown that analysis of herbarium material of selected species could be used to identify specific rocks types or mineralization within these rocks, relying on herbarium material, without the necessity of even visiting the country concerned.

TABLE 18.2 Elemental Concentrations (μg/g) in Dried Leaves of the De Vogel Collection of Plants Collected over Serpentine from Obi Island, North Moluccas.

Species	Co	Ni	Mn
Agathis alba subsp. *corneensis*	<1	5	33
Alphitonia incana	2	35	712
Alyxia stellata	3	29	910
Bruguiera gymnorrhiza	<1	3	168
Buchanania amboinensis	<1	15	25
Casearia glabra	<1	36	81
Celtis paniculata	1	4	8
Cerbera manghas	1	6	39
Commersonia bartramia	<1	26	621
Cyathocalyx biovulatus	<1	<1	29
Decaspermum fruticosum	2	95	34
Dendrotrophe varians	5	34	407
Desmodium umbellatum	<1	5	60
Dianella nemorosa	1	2	488
Dillenia ovalifolia var. *sericea*	2	423	690
Elaeocarpus gjellerupi	3	16	295
Eugenia acutangula	6	28	111
Gahnia aspera	<1	9	121
Garcinia microphylla	<1	8	133
Gastonia papuana	31	40	1225
Gironniera subaequalis	<1	50	46
Gmelina lepidota	<1	6	720
Gnetum gnemon var. *domesticum*	2	113	415
Gomphandra mappioides	<1	6	43
Heritiera littoralis	1	7	12
Horsfieldia glabra	<1	20	136
H. roxburghii	3	3	68
Hydnophytum formicarum	19	412	118
Intsia palembanica	<1	6	8
Kibara macrophylla	<1	28	286
Knema tomentella	<1	1	111
Leptospermum flavescens	1	11	1310
Machaerina glomerata	26	276	345
Melastoma polyanthemum	<1	23	820
Mezzetia leptopoda	<1	25	295
Myristica laurifolia var. *bifurcata*	56	1110	889
Nepenthes maxima	7	65	191
N. mirabilis	1	17	390
N. reinwardtiana	9	66	380
Palaquium ridleyi	1	2	24
Parastemon versteeghii	<1	2	13
Piper caninum	2	4	40
Pittosporum ferrugineum	1	100	133
Planchonella firma	<1	3	2200
P. oxyedra	34	19600	110
Pseuderia foliosa	4	109	15
Psychotria longicauda	1	12	2620
Rapanea densiflora	<1	10	122
Rhodamnia cinerea	3	66	47
Scaevola oppositifolia	95	121	1790
Schizomeria serrata	262	590	1900
Smilax australis	2	57	53

Species	Co	Ni	Mn
Styphelia abnormis	6	63	108
Tetractomia obovata	2	59	520
Trichospermum kjellbergii	350	3770	1600
Vatica papuana	<1	5	224
Ventilago oblongifolia	<1	2	4

Source: Wither (1977)

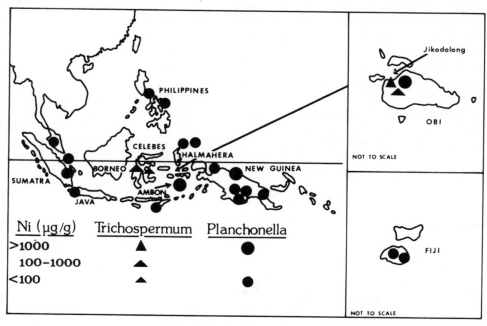

Fig. 18.2 Distribution of collection localities for herbarium specimens of *Planchonella* oxyedra and *Trichospermum kjellbergii* with anomalous concentrations of nickel.
Source: Wither and Brooks (1977).

18.2.2 Rinorea bengalensis

Brooks and Wither (1977) as the result of a herbarium survey of plants within the family Violaceae, found hyperaccumulation of nickel by *Rinorea bengalensis,* a serpentine-tolerant plant widespread in a broad arc encompassing Sri Lanka, the Malay Archipelago, New Guinea, The Solomons and Queensland. Their survey of the nickel and cobalt content of 89 specimens of this taxon showed that many of the collection localities corresponded with important serpentine occurrences throughout the area. This is shown in Fig. 18.3. The analytical data for cobalt and nickel are shown in Table 18.3 where they are arranged under the rock type of the substrate supporting the plants.

Rinorea bengalensis grows over a wide range of substrates and is a hyperaccumulator of nickel when growing over ultramafic rocks. Over these rocks, the Co/Ni quotient (ca. 0.01) is considerably lower than for plants growing over other rock types. This serves as an additional criterion for pinpointing ultramafic occurrences. It was invariably possible to identify ultramafic substrates by nickel levels exceeding 3000 μg/g in the plant material. Values above 1000 μg/g usually indicated this type of rock but there was some overlap with higher values corresponding to sedimentary substrates. Whereas plants growing over ultramafic rocks could almost always be differentiated from those over other rock types (i.e., by a combination of high nickel concentrations and low quotients), it was not possible to distinguish other substrates from each other by the nickel content of *R. bengalensis* alone.

In Fig. 18.3, the large circles represent known ultramafic areas except in the case of two sites (Nabire and Sorong in Irian Jaya—Indonesian New Guinea). The nickel contents of the plants collected at these sites were 1.75% and 1.20% respectively. These plants also had the low Co/Ni quotients of 0.003 and 0.002 and were therefore almost certainly growing over ultramafites. In the Nabire area the presence of serpentine rocks can be inferred from partially-surveyed sporadic undifferentiated mafic intrusives forming a long belt passing through Nabire. A similar conclusion can be made about the Sorong area. The main point of the findings is that geological inferences can be made by analysis of herbarium specimens collected many years ago in areas where geological surveys have been lacking or at best have been rudimentary. The chain of events ending at Nabire began with a collection of *R. bengalensis* by two Japanese botanists in 1940. The specimens found their way to the Arnold Arboretum at Harvard University, and fragments of them were analysed 37 years later in New Zealand by my research group in which no-one had ever visited New Guinea. In a later world-wide survey of the nickel and cobalt content of *Rinorea*, Brooks et al. (1977) identified another hyperaccumulator in this genus: *R. javanica* from Kalimantan (Borneo).

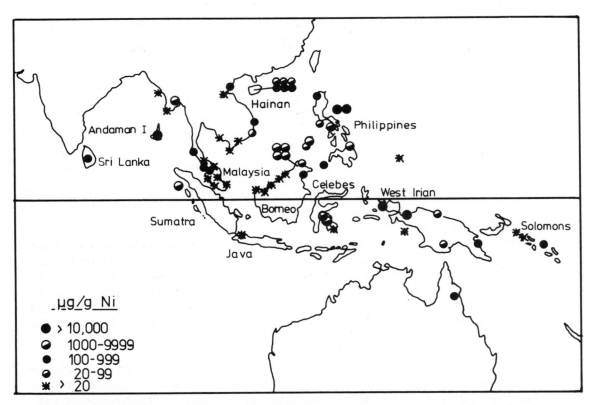

Fig. 18.3   Nickel concentrations (μg/g) in herbarium specimens of *Rinorea bengalensis*. Levels exceeding 10,000 μg/g in the dried plant material invariably indicated that the substrate was serpentinic.
Source: Brooks and Wither (1977).

TABLE 18.3   The Relationship between the Nickel and Cobalt Content (μg/g dry weight) of Rinorea bengalensis and the Nature of the Substrate.

Rock type	No.	Cobalt		Nickel		Co/Ni
		Mean	Range	Mean	Range	
Ultramafic	21	87	6–545	6860	836–17500	0.01
Limestone	12	12	1–33	113	2–560	0.11
Other sed.	14	75	3–290	674	3–3000	0.11
Basic	11	27	1–217	103	1–550	0.26
Acid	5	16	5–29	20	2–56	0.80
Unknown	26	38	1–300	177	1–2000	0.21
Overall	89	51	1–545	1810	1–17500	0.03

Source: Brooks and Wither (1977)

18.2.3 Celebes

Celebes (Sulawesi) is situated in the centre of the Malay Archipelago and has a particularly rich serpentine flora, partly because of its position at the boundary of two floristic regions along Wallace's and Zollinger's Lines, and partly because ultramafic rocks cover perhaps 20% of the 189,000 km² of this well-watered island. In spite of this rich flora, it remains virtually a closed book as far as its serpentine component is concerned, because so little effort has been expended in studying it.

With the development of mining activities at Soroako (site 2 in Fig. 18.1) however, the ultramafic areas have become more available and data are starting to accumulate. For information on the serpentine plants of east-central Celebes, I am indebted to Vogel (1985), Balgooy (1985) and Meijers (1984).

Physiognomically, the serpentine vegetation of the region around Lake Matano near where the mining activities are centred, is not very different from that of non-serpentinitic areas except that the undergrowth is less dense, and the dark red lateritic soil is visible beneath the forest litter. A common tree in the area is *Gymnostoma sumatrana* (Plates 18.1a and 18.2a) which sometimes forms almost pure stands, though mixed with *Metrosideros petiolata* and fringed with low thickets of *Kjellbergiodendron celebicum* (Plate 18.2a) at the shores of lakes or along the banks of rivers. Other species in more open areas amid the *G. sumatrana* forest are *Ostellia mesenterica, Mussaendopsis* sp. (Plate 18.1b), *Glochidion ultrabasicola, Deplanchea bancana* (Plate 18.1c), *Xanthostemon confertiflorum* (Plate 18.1d), *Macademia hildebrandii* and *Gluta papuana* (Plate 18.2b). The hyperaccumulator of nickel, *Trichospermum kjellbergii* is also found in the area.

The serpentine flora of Celebes is largely derived from surrounding non-serpentinitic source taxa and is predominantly of "western" (i.e., west of Wallace's and Zollinger's Lines) origin. Lam (1945) has calculated that "western" elements account for 65% of all phanerogams on the basis of systematic analysis of the origins of 440 species from Celebes. The breakdown of the source of this flora is given in Table 18.4. It is interesting to record that this proportion is exactly the same as for the fauna of Celebes (Lam, 1927, 1945). The largest source of "western elements" seems to be from Mindanao a Philippine island, which accounts for some 14.8% of the total.

18.2.4 The Talaud Islands

One of the first serpentine floras to be studied in the Malay Archipelago is located in the Talaud Islands (site #4 in Fig. 18.1). The survey was made by Lam (1927) who described a "plantengeografisch Dorado" (a plant geographical El Dorado).

The serpentinitic Mt Piapi (fire mountain) rises to about 500 m on the east coast of the main island near Karakelang. Although the rest of the island is covered with dense rainforest,

TABLE 18.4 Origin of the Serpentine Flora of Celebes Based on a Sample of 440 Phanerogams

Common to	No. of species	Percentage of total
Sundaland-Celebes	41	9.3
Sundaland-Philippines	40	9.1
Sundaland-Moluccas	9	2.0
Sundaland-Philippines-Moluccas	22	5.0
Sundaland-Lesser Sunda Islands	9	1.4
Java-Lesser Sunda Islands	17	3.9
Sumatra-Java	7	1.6
Java	8	1.8
Sumatra	2	0.5
Sumatra-Java-Philippines	5	1.1
Palawan	15	3.4
Borneo-Philippines	6	1.4
Philippines-Lesser Sunda Islands	4	0.9
Mindanao	65	14.8
Talaud-Phillippines	9	2.0
Talaud	12	2.7
Lesser Sunda Islands	9	2.0
Moluccas	31	7.0
New Guinea-Moluccas	32	7.3
New Guinea-Moluccas-Philippines	21	4.8
New Guinea-Moluccas-Borneo	4	0.9
New Guinea-Moluccas-Philippines-Borneo	18	4.1
New Guinea-Moluccas-Talaud	30	6.8
Australia-Lesser Sunda Islands-Java	1	0.2

Sundaland = the four main islands of the Greater Sundas—Java, Sumatra, Borneo and Celebes.

the summit of Mt Piapi carries an unusual xerophytic yellow-green scrub comprising grasses, scattered shrubs and small trees. It shows a sharp contrast with the surrounding 10 m tall rain forest, and has the appearance of an alpine flora even at 150 m altitude. The dominant grass is *Themeda gigantea* accompanied by abundant Cyperaceae and Orchidaceae with *Pandanus tectorius*. The small trees exhibit the typical "Krummholz" physiognomy of the classical serpentine localities of Japan and Europe, accompanied by leathery leaves and thickly entwined twigs.

Altogether Lam (1927) recorded 58 species of plants growing in the "alpine" zone of Mt Piapi. In descending order of importance these were in the families: Rubiaceae, Myrtaceae, Orchidaceae, Cyperaceae, Apocynaceae, Clusiaceae, Euphorbiaceae, Lauraceae, Loganiaceae, Loranthaceae, and Rutaceae. Of the 58 species, 10 (17%) were derived from alpine floral elements from all over Malesia including New Caledonia. Five undescribed species in the genera *Ilex, Fagraea, Eugenia, Leptospermum* and *Myrtus,* were probably endemic to this mountain. Lam's original paper seems to have excited very little interest since it appeared 60 years ago and it is to be hoped that other botanists will be tempted to follow in his footsteps and investigate this "El Dorado" of the remote Talaud Islands.

18.2.5 Sabah

Although the extensive serpentine outcrops of southern Borneo do not seem to have been investigated botanically, some work has been done on the ultramafites which outcrop in the vicinity of Mt Kinabalu in northern Sabah (site #5 in Fig. 18.1). This massif rises to 4100 m and is the highest point of the whole island. Mt Kinabalu which is part of the Palawan

Ophiolitic Belt (see Fig. 18.4), has an area of 500 km² and carries a wide range of vegetation types ranging from tropical rain forest to alpine scrub. The flora of the massif has been described briefly by Meijers (1971).

At about 1400 m on Kinabalu, there is a serpentine outcrop at Bukit Hampuan where the normal forest is still of the dipterocarp type and on ultramafites is composed largely of *Agathis* spp., *Buxus rolfei*, and *Borneodendron aenigmaticum*. The latter is a common tree on serpentine and is related to species growing over ultramafites in New Caledonia. The forest in this zone is distinguishable from its small crowns which are readily identifiable from the air. Along the Marai-Parai trail, the ultramafic rocks form the best locality for the giant pitcher plant *Nepenthes rajah*.

The most dramatic change of vegetation on Kinabalu occurs at 2400 m where the dominant trees cease and are replaced by stenophyllic shrubs such as *Dacrydium gibbsiae*, *Rhododendron ericoides*, and *Leptospermum recurvum* accompanied by numerous small herbs such as *Elatostema bulbothrix*, *Didymocarpus* sp., *Schizaea fistulosa*, *Cyathea havilandii*, *Nepenthes villosa*, *Hedyotis macrostegia*, *Trachymene* sp., *Aletris foliata*, and *Euphrasia borneensis*. When the serpentine merges into granite or granodiorite, the trees can still reach 7 m at this altitude.

Only *Dacrydium gibbsiae* and *Schizaea fistulosa* are in fact serpentine endemics. The other plants of the community reappear at higher elevations and have a disjunct appearance on serpentine at these lower altitudes. They are quite common above 3000 m.

Although the serpentine vegetation at high altitude is distinct from "normal" vegetation, this is not the case in the tropical lowlands where Whitmore (1975) has pointed out that trees at sea level can reach up to 50 m in height, even over serpentine. In these localities there are, however, differences in species composition, if not of physiognomy. Typical components of the lowland serpentine forests of Sabah are the dipterocarps *Shorea andulensis*, *S. kunstleri*. *S. laxa*, *S. venulosa*, and *Dipterocarpus geniculatus* and *D. lowii*. Several serpentine-endemic plants from Sabah have been described and include *Dinochloa prunifera*, *D. obclavata* (Dransfield, 1982a), and two rattans, *Calamus laevigatus* var. *serpentinus* and *Daemonorops serpentina* (Dransfield 1982b).

18.2.6 Philippines

Surigao

As will be observed from Fig. 18.4, serpentine covers perhaps 5% of the total area of the Philippines including the island of Palawan where about one third of the area is covered by ultramafites. It is therefore surprising to find that until very recently, virtually no work had been done on the serpentine flora of this country. The island of Nonoc (see Fig. 18.4) is in Surigao Province and is an important source of nickel ore in the Philippines. The vegetation of this island has been described by Santos-Ynigo and Esguerra (1961). The island is covered with a typical dipterocarp rain forest (cf. lowland Sabah). In places where the original forest has been cleared or burnt, a more open, typically serpentinicolous secondary growth develops. This is composed largely of *Leptospermum annae* and a dwarf form of *Tristania decorticata*. The common ground cover species is *Pteridium aquilinum*, a well-known fern which grows very abundantly in the region and which grows on a variety of different substrates elsewhere. Several pitcher plants such as *Nepenthes alata* are also established in this serpentine community.

When the original forest is removed on Nonoc Island, there is intensive laterization of the terrain and it is unlikely that the original dipterocarp cover will ever be re-established. The boundary between ultramafic and other substrates is well marked by a carpet of the grass *Imperata exaltata* which will not grow over serpentine.

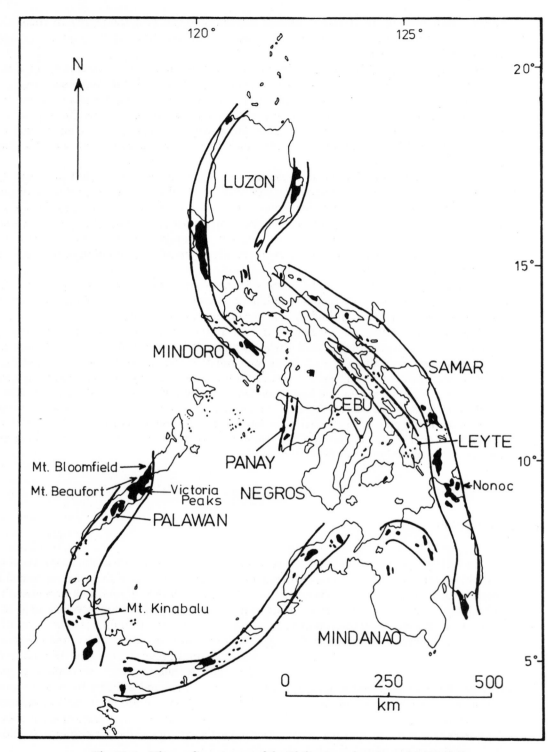

Fig. 18.4 Ultramafic outcrops of the Philippines showing ophiolitic belts.
Source: Bureau of Mines and Geosciences (Philippines) (1981).

Palawan

Among the serpentine floras of the Philippines, only that of the island of Palawan has been studied botanically to any measurable degree. An excellent report by Podzorski et al. (1985) describes the results of a 1984 expedition to this island during which 1870 botanical specimens were collected from 47 localities. Many of these were from ultramafites and raised the total of known species for the island, from 1519 to 1672, an increase of 10%.

Palawan has an area of 11,655 km² and has a central mountain chain with peaks in excess of 2000 m. The most important areas of serpentine vegetation are in the vicinity of Mts Bloomfield and Beaufort and further south at Victoria Peaks. The latter is the only recorded locality for the serpentine-endemic *Embolanthera* sp. and is also the home of striking serpentinophyte *Xanthostemon verdugonianus* (Plate 18.2c). One of the most striking examples of vegetation differentiation due to the presence of serpentine, is in the area of Mt Bloomfield and some attention will be given to this locality. Other sites will not be discussed because of space limitations and the reader is referred to Podzorski (1985) for more information.

On Mt Bloomfield (Plate 18.2d) there is a sharp transition at 100 m altitude from the 10–20 m high lowland rain forest to a sclerophyllous vegetation type averaging only 2–3 m in height and with typically serpentinicolous plants such as *Scaevola micrantha*, *Brackenridgea palustris* var. *foxworthyi* and *Exocarpus latifolius*, which occur at least 500 m below their normal distribution off serpentine. Also present are undescribed, probably serpentine-endemic, species of *Terminalia*, *Gymnostoma*, *Syzygium*, *Chionanthus* and *Guioa*. A checklist of species is given in Table 18.5. The taxa are unfortunately largely unidentified or undescribed and in many cases have only been identified at the generic rank.

A new botanical expedition to Palawan has just taken place and will surely provide much valuable new information on the fascinating serpentine flora of this island.

18.2.7 The Solomon Islands

Ultramafic rocks outcrop at several localities in the Solomon Islands (Fig. 18.1), principally on the islands of Choiseul, Santa Ysabel, San Jorge, Guadalcanal, and San Cristobal. The ultramafic soils have been described by Lee (1969) and by Thompson (1965). According to Whitmore (1969), the flora of the serpentine areas is poor in species and is dominated by *Casuarina papuana* (Plate 18.3) and *Dillenia crenata*. At present only 3 species have been identified as being serpentine endemic. These are *Gulubia hombronii* (a palm), *Pandanus lamprocephalus* (Plate 18.3) and *Xanthostemon* sp. When the forest is removed by burning, it is replaced by an open heath with a ground cover of *Gleichenia* spp. and *Lycopodium cernuum*.

18.2.8 New Guinea

Despite the wide occurrence of ultramafic rocks in New Guinea, very little work has been carried out on the serpentine flora of that territory. Royen (1963) has written a few brief notes on the serpentine flora of Waigeo Island (site #7 in Fig. 18.1) and the adjacent northwest coast of New Guinea. There is a belt of low shrubby vegetation, open in places and sharply contrasting with lowland rain forest off serpentine. This vegetation coincides exactly with ultramafic rocks and is composed of *Alphitonia* sp., *Dillenia alata*, *Myrtella beccari*, and *Styphelia abnormis*.

In most other parts of New Guinea, the physignomy of the serpentine vegetation is not noticeably different from other types and it includes large trees such as *Araucaria cunninghamii*.

328 SERPENTINE

TABLE 18.5 Serpentinicolous Vegetation of Mt Bloomfield, Palawan, Philippines

Adenia heterophylla (l)	Alchornia sp. (t)
Antidesma sp. (s)	Archidendron cf. parviflorum (t)
Ardisia sp. (t)	Artabotrys sp. (l)
Brackenridgea palustris var. foxworthyi (t)	Buchanania sp. (l)
Calamus microsphaerion (l)	Canthium sp. (t)
Canthium horridum (l)	Chionanthus sp. (s)
Dehaasia sp. (t)	Dendrobium sp. (h)
Dillenia sp.	Dinochloa spp. (h)
Dischidia sp. (l)	Eria sp. (h)
Exocarpus latifolius (t)	Gomphia serrata (s)
Grewia sp. (t)	Guettardella microphylla (t)
Guioa sp. (t)	Gymnostoma sp. (t)
Hemigraphis sp. (h)	Hydnophytum sp. (h)
Lecanopteris sinuosa (h)	Medinella sp. (s)
Morinda sp. (s)	Myrsine sp. (t)
Ochrosia glomerata (t)	Phyllanthus sp. (s)
Phyllanthus cf. emblica (s)	Pittosporum sp. (s)
Pittosporum cf. pentandrum (t)	Planchonella obovata (t)
Pouteria obovata (t)	Rothmanii sp. (t)
Scaevola micrantha (s)	Securidaca atroviolacea (l)
Suregada glomerulata (t)	Suregada sp. (t)
Syzygium punctulatum (t)	Syzygium spp. (4) (t)
Tabernaemontana sp. (s)	Terminalia sp. (t)
Urceola laevis (l)	Walsura monophylla (t)
Wikstroemia indica (t)	Wrightia hanleyi (t)
Zanthoxylon sp. (s)	

t = tree, h = herb, l = liana, s = shrub
Data after Pozorski (1985)

REFERENCES

Balgooy, M. M. J. van (Rijksherbarium, Leiden). 1985. Pers. commn.

Brooks, R. R. and Wither, E. D., 1977. Nickel accumulation by *Rinorea bengalensis* (Wall.) O. K. *J. Geochem. Explor.*, 7: 295–300.

Brooks, R. R., Wither, E. D. and Zepernick, B., 1977. Cobalt and nickel in *Rinorea* species. *Pl. Soil*, 47: 707–712.

Bureau of Mines and Geosciences, 1981. *Geology and Mineral Resources of the Philippines (Geology)*. Ministry Natural Resources, Manila.

Derry, D. R., 1980. *World Atlas of Geology and Mineral Deposits*. Mining Journal Books, London.

Dransfield, S., 1982a. The genus *Dinochloa* (Gramineae—Bambusiodeae) in Sabah. *Kew Bull.*, 36: 613–666.

Dransfield, J., 1982b. Notes on rattans (Palmae: Lepidocaryoideae) occurring in Sabah, Borneo. *Kew Bull.*, 36: 783–815.

Lam, H. J., 1927. En plantengeografisch Dorado. *Handlg. IV Nederl. Ind. Natuurw. Congr.*: 368–397.

Lam, H. J., 1945. Notes on the historical phytogeography of Celebes. *Blumea*, 5: 608–640.

Lee, K. E., 1969. Some soils of the British Solomon Islands Protectorate. *Phil. Trans. Roy. Soc.*, B255: 211–258.

Meijer, W., 1965. Forest types in North Borneo and their economic aspects. *Proc. Symp. Ecol. Res. Humid Tropics Veg.*, UNESCO, Kuching.

Plate 18.1 Serpentinicolous plants of the Soroako area, Celebes. (a) Above left: *Gymnostoma sumatrana* (large tree) and *Metrosideros petiolata*.
Photo by M. M. J. van Balgooy.
(b) Above right: *Mussaendopsis* sp.
Photo by E. F. De Vogel.
(c) Below left: *Deplanchea bancana*.
Photo by M. M. J. van Balgooy.
(d) Below right: *Xanthostemon confertiflorum*.
Photo by E. F. De Vogel.
Note: photos by Drs de Vogel and van Balgooy were taken during a Rijksherbarium field trip sponsored by the Netherlands Foundation for the Advancement of Tropical Research (WOTRO).

Plate 18.2. (a) Above: Almost pure stand of *Gymnostoma sumatrana* at Soroako, Celebes, with a foreground of *Kjellbergiodendron celebicum*.
Photo by E. F. De Vogel.
(b) Below: Small lake near Soroako, Celebes surrounded by Myrtaceae and with *Gluta papuana* in the background.
Photo by E. F. De Vogel

Plate 18.2 (c) Above: The serpentine-endemic *Xanthostemon verdugonianus* growing at Victoria Peaks, Palawan, Philippines.
Photo by J. Dransfield.
(d) Below: Ultramafic forest on Mt Bloomfield, Palawan, Philippines. The mountain in the background is St. Pauls Peak (limestone).
Photo by J. Dransfield.
Note: see caption for Plate 18.1 for acknowledgement of photos by Dr. de Vogel.

Plate 18.3 *Casuarina papuana* and *Pandanus lamprocephalus* growing over serpentine in the Solomon Islands.
Photo by R. B. Thompson.

Plate 19.1 Ligno-herbaceous scrub community on lateritic soils in New Caledonia.
Photo by T. Jaffré.

Meijer, W., 1971. Plant life in Kinabalu National Park. *Malay. Nat. J.*, 24: 184–189.

Meijer, W., 1984. Botanical exploration in Celebes and Bali. *Nat. Geogr. Soc. Res. Rep.* 1976 projects: 583–605.

Podzorski, A. C. et al., 1985. *The Palawan Botanical Expedition Final Paper.* Hilleshög Forestry AB, Landskrona, Sweden.

Proctor, J., Duff, G. K., Leakey, R., Munro, W. R. C. and Nelson, T. N., 1984. Report of the Stirling University expedition to Sabah, 1983. *Bull. Brit. Ecol. Soc.*, 15: 151–157.

Royen, P. van, 1963. *The Vegetation of the Island of New Guinea.* Dept. Forests, Lae.

Santos Ynigo, L. and Esguerra, F. B., 1961. *Geology and Geochemistry of the Nickeliferous Laterites of Nonoc and Adjacent Islands, Surigao Province, Philippines.* Philipp. Bur. Mines Spec. Proj. Ser., Pub. #18, 1–90.

Steenis, C. G. G. J. van, 1948-. *Flora Malesiana.* Noordhoft Pub. Co., Jakarta.

Thompson, R. B., 1965. Nickel-laterite cappings of ultrabasic rocks in the Solomons. *Brit. Sol. Is. Geol. Rec.*, 2: 147–161.

Vogel, E. F. de (Rijksherbarium, Leiden), 1985. Pers. commn.

Wallace, A. R., 1869. *Malay Archipelago.* Macmillan, London.

Whitmore, T. C., 1969. The vegetation of the Solomon Islands. *Phil. Trans. Roy. Soc.*, B225: 259–270.

Whitmore, T. C., 1975. *Tropical Rain Forests of the Far East.* Clarendon Press, Oxford.

Wither, E. D., 1977. *Biogeochemical Studies in Southeast Asia by use of Herbarium Material.* MSc Thesis, Massey University, Palmerston North, New Zealand.

Wither, E. D. and Brooks, R. R., 1977. Hyperaccumulation of nickel by some plants of Southeast Asia. *J. Geochem. Explor.*, 8: 579–583.

Woodman, D., 1955. *The Republic of Indonesia.* Cresset Press, London.

Chapter 19
NEW CALEDONIA

19.1 THE ENVIRONMENT

New Caledonia is a narrow island some 500 km in length and 50 km wide (Fig. 19.1) which extends between the latitudes of 20° and 23° just inside the Tropic of Capricorn. It has an area of about 19,000 km² and is very mountainous, plains being confined mainly to the west. The highest point (Mt Panié—1639 m) is close to the east coast. The whole island is surrounded by a coral reef enclosing a lagoon with an average width of 10 km.

Tectonically, New Caledonia belongs to the eastern extremity of the Malay Archipelago (see Chapter 18) as part of a line of islands extending from Sumatra in the west. The eastern and western parts of the archipelago have had quite different histories with the portion from Sumatra to Celebes having once been part of "Laurasia", the northern part of the grouping named "Pangaea" by Wegener (1924). The remainder of the chain from eastern Celebes, through Timor and New Guinea to New Caledonia was once part of "Gondwanaland". The whole chain, particularly in Indonesia, is still very active tectonically.

New Caledonia, along with New Guinea and Norfolk Island, is part of an island arc (Melanesian Arc) which underwent its first orogenic phase towards the end of the Palaeozoic era and led to its elevation from the oceans. This was followed by sedimentation in some of the basins during the Mesozoic followed by a period of metamorphism and partial elevation during the upper Jurassic. Sedimentation again occurred in the Cretaceous and Eocene after periods of vulcanism. The alpine orogeny began at the end of the Eocene and formed the central chain of the island. This orogeny occurred at the Eocene/Oligocene boundary and resulted in the emplacement of a large mass of ultramafic rocks derived from the upper mantle. After the Miocene, there was an episode of peneplanation alternating with orogenic thrusts. Perhaps one of the most useful English-language papers on the geology of New Caledonia is that of Lillie and Brothers (1970), who compared the geology of the island with that of other Pacific islands, including New Zealand.

The outcrops of ultramafic rocks in New Caledonia occupy about 5500 km² (nearly one third of the total surface) and have been described by Jaffré (1980) and Guillon (1978). The ultramafites represent fragments of a large peridotitic sheet emplaced 35–40 m.y. ago along the Melanesian Arc after deep folding caused by collision of the Pacific Plate with the Tasmano-Melanesian Sheet. The location of the ultramafic rocks of New Caledonia is shown in Fig. 19.1. These rocks are arranged partly in sills (several hundred metres in width and several kilometres long) corresponding to contact zones. They also exist as a number of large massifs distributed throughout the whole of the island. A very large massif (Grand Massif du Sud) occupies the southern third of the island. These massifs rest either on basalts or, less frequently, on sediments. The ultramafic sheet was probably once continuous but has now been broken up by the action of erosion.

The ultramafites of New Caledonia are composed primarily of harzburgites with poor representation of dunites or pyroxenites.

The mineralogy of the New Caledonian ultramafic rocks has been described by Lillie and Brothers (1970), Trescases (1975) and Guillon (1975). There has already been some discussion of the chemical composition of these rocks in Chapter 2, and it will suffice to say that they display the usual excess of magnesium, chromium, and nickel and deficiency of plant nutrients such as potassium, phosphorus and calcium.

Mention should be made of the important nickel mining industry on the island, an industry which provides over 90% of the exports of the territory. Nickel was discovered by

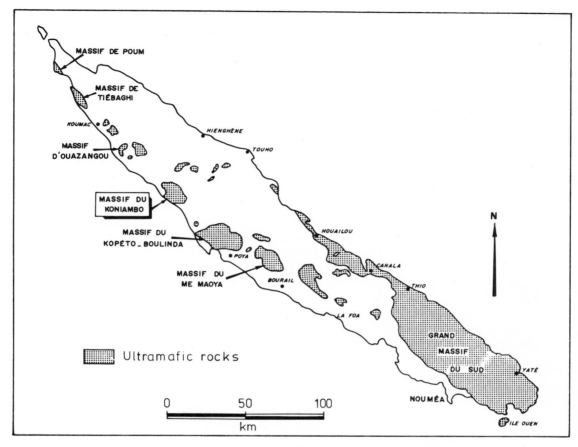

Fig. 19.1   Map of New Caledonia showing principal ultramafic massifs.
Source: Jaffré (1974).

the French engineer Garnier in the mid-1860s and production began in 1875. The nickel is present mainly as the mineral *garnierite* (hydrated nickel silicate). The principal mining centre is at Thio on the east coast (a centre also of the current unrest on the island). The ore is converted to a ferro-nickel matte at a large plant at Doniambo just north of the capital Nouméa. New Caledonia has about one third of the world's reserves of economic-grade nickel ores and can produce about 100,000 tonnes of nickel annually, either as the matte or as crude ore.

19.2 SOILS

The serpentine soils of New Caledonia have been exceptionally well studied by a number of workers such as Trescases (1969), Quantin (1969), and Latham (1975a, b, c). The chemical composition of two New Caledonian soils has also been given in Chapter 3.

Many of the soils of New Caledonia were formed as a result of pedogenesis beginning in the Miocene and resulting in a high degree of laterisation, hardening and reworking (Trescases, 1969; Latham, 1975).

There are two main types of serpentine soil found in New Caledonia. These are known respectively as brown eutrophic hypermagnesian and ferralitic ("sols férrallitiques"). Since the latter bear a strong resemblance to lateritic soils I will use the term "lateritic" rather than "ferralitic" though the French texts never use the term "sols latéritiques." The brown eutrophic soils are formed at the base of the ultramafic massifs when they rest on serpentinite or on more-or-less serpentinized peridotite. They represent a stage where there has been a recombination of silica, iron and magnesium. They have an argillaceous texture due to the presence of iron-rich magnesian smectites and have an elevated water retention capacity. The brown eutrophic soils have a fairly high silica, iron and magnesium content with relatively high concentrations of nickel and chromium and low levels of calcium, potassium and phosphorus. They have a strong cation-exchange capacity saturated with magnesium to the extent of 90%. In the slopes these soils are shallow and poorly developed. Their typical chemical composition is shown in Table 3.3 (column C).

The lateritic soils (sols férrallitiques) are by far the best represented on the ultramafic rocks of New Caledonia and have been described by Jaffré (1980). The chemical composition of one of these soils is given in Table 3.3 (column D). They are composed mainly of oxides and hydroxides of iron which is enriched due to removal of magnesium and silica. These soils typically contain 75% Fe_2O_3, 5% Cr_2O_3 and 1% NiO. The magnesium content is usually extremely low (<1% MgO). The pH averages 5.0 and is very low compared with the brown eutrophic soils (6.6). The lateritic soils have a very low cation-exchange capacity. The combination of high acidity, poor exchange capacity, high nickel and chromium, and low plant nutrient status of these soils renders them particularly unfavourable for plant growth. They have no counterpart in temperate areas though the brown eutrophic soils do have a strong affinity with the European and North American serpentine soils. The lack of magnesium in the lateritic soils has a pronounced effect on the infertility of them, since adverse edaphic factors do not include excess magnesium.

19.3 GENERAL OVERVIEW OF THE SERPENTINE VEGETATION OF NEW CALEDONIA

The flora of New Caledonia, serpentine or otherwise, is so rich and distinctive that it has been accorded its own floristic region—The New Caledonian Region (Good, 1974—see also Fig. 10.1). It contains about 2600 species and 600 genera of which about 80% of both are endemic to the island. Endemism among the serpentine vegetation is even higher and exceeds 90%. The flora has been greatly modified by human activity such as fire and mining activities, and much of the lowland is occupied by an anthropogenic savanna dominated by the fire resistant "niaouli" (*Melaleuca quinquenervia*). The true native vegetation persists at higher altitudes and is primarily forest. The ultramafic rocks support a somewhat xerophytic scrub (maquis). The genera richest in species are in descending order: *Psychotria* (70 species), *Phyllanthus*, *Ficus*, *Dendrobium*, *Parsonia*, *Xanthostemon*, *Tapeinosperma*, *Planchonella*, *Pittosporum*, *Hibbertia*, *Elaeocarpus*, *Syzygium*, *Eugenia*, and *Dysoxylon*. A surprising fact is that there are no native species in the families Poaceae, Asteraceae and Papilionaceae.

The New Caledonian genera with their many endemic species, fall into four equal groups (Good, 1974); widely-distributed genera occurring throughout the world; Asiatic-Australasian genera predominantly Asiatic in type; Asiatic-Australasian genera predominantly Australasian in type; other genera. The plants of Australian affinity occur primarily in the scrub.

Until fairly recently there was no definitive work on the serpentine flora of New Caledonia *per se*, and the relevant information had to be gleaned laboriously from widely dispersed sources in standard floras such as that of Guillaumin (1948), or from other authors (Table 19.1) who had considered only selected plants of this serpentine flora. Recently however a remarkable work by Jaffré (1980) has presented a complete overview of the serpentine flora of New Caledonia. T. Jaffré has done for New Caledonia what O. Rune did for the serpentine flora of Fennoscandia, W. Krause and K. H. Rechinger for the Balkans, R. Pichi-Sermolli for the serpentinophytes of Tuscany, and A. R. Kruckeberg for the serpentine plants of the western United States. Most of the material in this chapter has been gleaned

TABLE 19.1 Papers Which Describe the Serpentine Vegetation of New Caledonia

Baker et al. (1985)	Birrell and Wright (1945)
Brooks et al. (1974, 1977a, 1981)	Jaffré (1974, 1976, 1977a,b, 1979, 1980)
Jaffré and Latham (1974)	Jaffré and Schmidt (1974)
Jaffré et al. (1970, 1976, 1977, 1979a,b)	Kelly et al. (1975)
Kersten (1979)	Kersten et al. (1979)
Lee (1974, 1977)	Lee et al. (1977)
Morat et al. (1980)	Schmid (1980)

from Jaffré (1980) and from other works of this author. Jaffré's work seems to have appeared just in time since the current unrest on the island (cf. also Philippines—Chapter 18) has for the moment effectively terminated botanical exploration on the island, other than in the environs of Nouméa.

Although much of the original flora of New Caledonia has been destroyed by human activity, particularly mining and agriculture, the serpentine flora has been less affected because of its greater isolation in the mountains and partly because the infertility of the soils has rendered serpentine regions unattractive for agriculture. For these reasons, the serpentine vegetation of some areas (e.g., Kouakoué and Humboldt Massifs) has remained virtually in its original state.

Jaffré (1980) has assessed the serpentine vegetation of New Caledonia as having some 1500 species of which about 60% are confined to serpentine and almost all are confined to the island. The total of perhaps 900 serpentine-endemic species is a staggering number for such a small territory. Only Cuba has a degree of endemism even approaching this total.

The forested areas contain about as many serpentinicolous species (900) as non-serpentine plants (880) and the same pattern is repeated in the more open areas of serpentine scrub (maquis) where there are 835 serpentinicolous taxa compared with 690 on other substrates.

Jaffré (1980) has summarized the general characteristics of the serpentine flora of New Caledonia as follows:

1—The flora is significantly more endemic than that of other substrates. This is because the unfavourable edaphic factors have prevented colonisation by pantropical species.

2—The serpentinophytes are very diverse and include both primitive and advanced families such as the Gymnosperms, Winteraceae, Casuarinaceae, Cunoniaceae, Dillenaceae and Flacourtiaceae representing the former category and the Epacridaceae and Rubiaceae representing the advanced families.

3—The emplacement of peridotites at the Eocene/Oligocene boundary did not extinguish the ancient flora because it was a gradual process and hence allowed the flora to develop a certain genetic plasticity.

4—Some of the floral elements which colonised the peridotites adapted readily to a multiplicity of new environments within the ultramafic regions leading to a very active speciation among certain genera such as in *Araucaria*, *Phyllanthus*, *Alyxia*, *Xylosma*, *Exocarpus*, *Styphelia*, *Hibbertia*, *Homalium*, *Psychotria* and *Pancheria*.

5—The ultramafites have provided a refuge for many taxa which would otherwise have succumbed to competitive pressure on non-ultramafic substrates. This is probably the case for several gymnosperms such as *Decussocarpus minor*, *Dacrydium guillauminii*, and *Neocallitropsis pancheri*.

19.4 PLANT COMMUNITIES OVER SERPENTINE

19.4.1 Geological Contacts Involving Serpentine

The serpentine vegetation of New Caledonia differs very greatly from that of more temperate climates because of the frequent lack of physiognomic features distinguishing it from other neighbouring floras. To this extent it resembles the serpentine vegetation of other tropical areas such as Celebes (see chapter 18). This is particularly true of the forested areas of the highlands. For example, at Monts Koghis, there is no obvious transition at all between serpentine and sediments despite the sharp geological boundary, and the only way in which the boundary can be detected floristically is by plant mapping. For example, *Psychotria douarrei* and *Hybanthus austrocaledonicus* are abundant on the serpentine in this region but disappear completely once the geological boundary is crossed.

In areas in which geological contacts occur at low altitude, the physiognomic changes are much more obvious. In many cases, contacts at the base of the serpentine massifs involve a serpentine/basalt contact as, for example, at the base of the Massif du Boulinda (Jaffré and Latham, 1974). One reason for the sharper differentiation is the virtual absence of a poaceous ground cover on serpentines. Fires, frequent on the island during the dry season, devastate and degrade the non-serpentine vegetation to a much greater extent than that of ultramafic rocks because of the ready flammability of this grass cover.

Jaffré (1980) has emphasized the role of fire in controlling the vegetation at geological contacts. The serpentine scrub is usually denser and taller than that of the surrounding formations, which is the exact reverse of what would be expected in more temperate climates.

Changes in vegetation at a serpentine/micaschist geological boundary in the Ouegoa region of northeastern New Caledonia are illustrated in Fig. 19.2 (Jaffré, 1980). The niaouli (*Melaleuca quinquenervia*) grassland with its thick poaceous layer subject to frequent fires, grows on colluvial soils of mixed origin, giving way (right-hand side of the figure) to dense scrubland typical of serpentine soils of the brown eutrophic type. To the left on micaschist, a less dense scrub replaces the niaouli savanna.

In the south of New Caledonia, contact zones are barely perceptible except in the case of lower-lying regions on gabbro and granodiorite where hygrophile plants such as *Gahnia sieberana*, *Grevillea gillivrayi*, *Costularia comosa* and *Schoenus brevifolius* flourish on argillaceous soils with a good water retention capability.

19.4.2 Plants Communities on Serpentine

According to Jaffré (1980), the serpentine plant communities of New Caledonia can be divided into three main groups:

1—the evergreen rain forests at lower and middle altitudes;

2—the dense rain forest of higher altitudes;

3—the scrublands.

Each will be considered in turn.

1—*The evergreen rainforest of lower and middle altitudes.*

Jaffré (1980) has described the evergreen rainforest of lower and middle altitudes over serpentine in New Caledonia. They are found in the altitude range of 500–1000 m in regions receiving 1500–3500 mm of rain per annum. Below 500 m, the evergreen rainforests rarely cover the entire slopes, but are confined to talwegs along water courses (Plate 19.4c). They tend to be found on eroded lateritic soils rather than on deep soils of this type or over hypermagnesian eutrophic brown soils. This is perhaps only because the latter type of soil is seldom found at higher altitudes. As is the case for most of New Caledonia, the serpentine

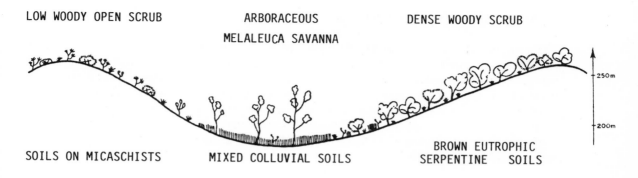

LOW WOODY OPEN SCRUB ARBORACEOUS MELALEUCA SAVANNA DENSE WOODY SCRUB SOILS ON MICASCHISTS MIXED COLLUVIAL SOILS BROWN EUTROPHIC SERPENTINE SOILS

DOMINANT SPECIES

Baeckia ericoides

Costularia arundinacea

Codia montana

Dracophyllum verticillatum

Styphelia cymbulae

Melaleuca quinquenervia

Austrobuxus carunculatus

Albigaardia ovata

Homalium deplanchei

Acacia spirorbis

Xanthostemon pubescens

Fig. 19.2 Section across micaschists and serpentine in the Ouegoa region, New Caledonia. The *Melaleuca* grassland on colluvial soils of mixed origin, gives way to dense serpentine scrub to the right of the figure. On the left the grassland is replaced by a less dense scrub.
Source: Jaffré (1980).

forest is not particularly tall and most trees are in the height range of 15–25 m. The forest is topped by gymnosperms such as *Agathis lanceolata* in the Grand Massif du Sud and in the Massif du Boulinda, and by different species of *Araucaria* (*A. montana. A. subulata, A. biramulata, A. bernieri, A. laubenfelsii*) on the so-called mining massifs (i.e., massifs such as Koniambo where extensive mining activity has been carried out). These forests are quite dense and have an understorey dominated by ferns such as *Lindsaea, Schizaea, Nephrolepis, Adiantum* and *Asplenium*. The shrubby component of the understorey is dominated by numerous palms (*Pandanus*) and by *Psychotria* species such as *P. douarrei*. Among the more common plants are: *Agathis lanceolata, Araucaria* spp., *Calophyllum caledonicum, Albizia granulusa, Montrouziera cauliflora* and various species of *Cryptocarya, Planchonella, Antholoma, Kermadecia* and *Syzygium*. It should be mentioned that many of the larger trees are bodenvag species not confined to serpentine.

The forest can be divided into 4 facies dependent on their dominant species. These are:

1—*Arillastrum gummiferum* (gum oak) facies, a more open community containing in places almost pure stands of the gum oak;

2—*Agathis ovata* facies found only in the south of the island and reduced now to isolated small stands in the altitude interval of 500–900 m on gravelly lateritic soils where the forest does not exceed 20 m in height and contains many heliophiles;

3—*Nothofagus* facies found as enclaves within the forest;

4—*Araucaria* facies occurring as almost pure stands amid the rainforest and with a more open texture permitting the growth of many heliophiles.

2—The high altitude evergreen rainforest

The high altitude evergreen rainforest over serpentine that occurs at altitudes about 1000 m on residual unsaturated lateritic soils, is found at sites bathed in cloud and mist and with an annual rainfall of about 3500 mm. Temperatures here can fall to 0°C. These are low trees (8–15 m) with trunks covered with numerous epiphytes (ferns, mosses and orchids). The leaves are often markedly sclerophyllic (*Metrosideros, Xylosma, Cunonia,* and all of the gymnosperms). Gymnosperms such as *Podocarpus sylvestris, Acmopyle pancheri, Decusso-carpus,* and *Callitris sulcata* are common. Endemic genera (*Phelline, Strasburgeria* and *Para-cryphia*) and the primitive genera (*Belliolum, Bubbia, Sphenostemon* and *Nemuaron*) are well represented in this community.

3—The serpentine scrub (maquis)

The serpentine scrub is really the most important community of the ultramafic outcrops of New Caledonia and occupies 80–90% of this type of terrain. The scrub extends from sea level to 1600 m and in areas with rainfall ranging from 900–4000 mm annually. It is composed of a shrubby sclerophyllous evergreen formation more or less thicketed. Sometimes it has the form of a shrubby grassland formation with a dense cyperaceous ground layer. This *maquis* has a physiognomy which is extremely variable and in its broadest definition can be described as any non-forested community or assemblage. The same type of formation is of course well known elsewhere in the world where it is variously referred to as *maquis* or *garique* (France and Corsica), *macchie* (Italy), *matorall* (Spain and Cuba), *chaparral* (California) and *xerovuni* (Greece).

19.4.3 The Serpentine Scrub of New Caledonia

Because of the vastness and complexity of the maquis of New Caledonia, it has been accorded a separate section in this book, which as usual is based on Jaffré (1980).

Different types of serpentine scrub

There are 3 main types of serpentine scrub in New Caledonia. The first of these is the woody scrubland (*maquis arbustif*). It is a formation of variable diversity and with a cyperaceous ground storey composed of low growths of *Fimbristylis, Scleria* and *Albigardia*. The woody stratum is composed of multi-branched nano- and micro-phanerophytes. It is found at the base of the serpentine massifs over eutrophic hypermagnesian brown soils.

The second type of *maquis* is a strongly bushy assemblage (*maquis buissonant*) with almost complete lack of lower ground cover. The formation consists largely of thickly-branched bushes which grow on gravelly lateritic soils or on hard-pan laterites on plateaus of about 200 m altitude.

The third type of scrub is known in French as the *maquis ligno-herbacé* (ligno-herbaceous scrub) consisting of a herbaceous cyperaceous layer (*Costularia, Lepidosperma* and *Schoenus*) interspersed with a discontinuous cover of woody bushes. This scrub association develops on lateritic soils reworked by erosion and colluvial action on slopes. It is illustrated in Plate 19.1.

The pioneer communities which establish themselves on previously-burnt terrain are characterised by a very open form with dominance of species such as the fern *Pteridium aquilinum*. The vegetation which replaces a burnt-out formation is usually identical to it. In contrast with the pioneer scrubland of burnt-out areas, there is a transitional forest formation which represents a climax vegetation not affected by human activity.

The life form spectra of serpentine scrub

The life form spectra of serpentine scrub have been described by Jaffré (1980) and are represented in Table 19.2 in comparison with those of other countries. The most remarkable feature of this table is the predominance of phanerophytes (comprising mainly nano- and micro-phanerophytes with mean heights of 0.3–2.5 m). The 8% of hemicryptophytes is represented primarily by the Cyperaceae, the 7% of chamaephytes are mainly woody in type, and the 6% of geophytes comprise mainly ferns. The small therophytic component is represented largely by *Mollugo nudicaulis*.

The predominance of phanerophytes in the serpentine maquis of New Caledonia is due partly to the great predominance of this class in the flora as a whole compared with its much lower abundance in floras of more temperate regions. Common plants of this class are: *Tristania guillainii*, *T. callobuxus*, *Codia discolor*, *C. montana*, *Alphitonia neocaledonica*, *Hibbertia lucens*, and *Styphelia pancheri*. Other important phanerophytes are represented in the genera *Alyxia*, *Parsonia*, *Artia*; *Coleospermum*, *Morinda*, *Ventilago*, *Flagelleria*, *Marsdenia*, *Ryssopteris*, *Oxera*, *Agatea* and *Nepenthes*.

TABLE 19.2 The Life Form Spectra of New Caledonian and Other Serpentine Floras

Locality	Ref	Percentage					Total No.
		P	C	H	G	T	
Siskiyou Mts, Oregon	Whittaker (1960)	20	19	44	15	3	116
Tuscany	Pichi-Sermolli (1948)	11	9	40	15	26	405
Washington	Kruckeberg (1969)	0	14	80	6	0	—
Scotland	Proctor and Woodell (1971)	0	7	77	4	12	58
Koniambo, New Caledonia	Jaffré (1980)	79	7	8	6	<1	291

P = phanerophytes, C = chamaephytes, H = hemicryptophytes, G = geophytes,
T = therophytes.
Source: Jaffré (1980)

A Phytosociological study of the serpentine scrub

Jaffré (1980) has attempted a phytosociological study of the vegetation of the serpentine regions of New Caledonia. The system used is not entirely that of the classical school of Braun-Blanquet (1932) and is more of a personalised approach. He has however divided the vegetation into 17 Associations among 5 Alliances and 3 Orders. No overall Class has been assigned to these units. The basic data are given in Fig. 19.3. The character species of each Association, Alliance and Order are shown in the appropriate lines or boxes. He has recognized eight main vegetation types as follows:

1—**The high elevation vegetation.** This is ordered within a single highly specialised Association which is very orophile (favouring a montane environment) and is found over ultramafic rocks at altitudes above 1200 m. This *Metrosideros tetrastichia*—*Quintinia oreophylla* community is found on the Humboldt and Kouakoué massifs.

2—**The vegetation of strongly hydromorphic soils.** This is found at low altitudes and is dominated by *Pancheria communis* and *Mooria buxifolia*.

3—**The vegetation of temporarily-hydromorphic environments.** This Association is found in the Plaine des Lacs and is characterised by *Homalium kanaliense* and *Costularia comosa*. It bears a resemblance to community #2 above, though only to the degree that hydromorphism extends over an appreciable part of the year.

4—**The vegetation of the hypermagnesian eutrophic brown soils.** These soils are the only ones in New Caledonia which have edaphic properties similar to "normal" serpentine soils in temperate regions. They are found below 500 m and occupy the driest and hottest parts of the massifs. In the Grand Massif du Sud, the vegetal grouping on this substrate is represented by the *Soulamea pancheri*—*Hibbertia lucida* Association. At the base of the Massif du Boulinda, it is represented by the *Atractocarpus deplanchei*—*Grevillea meisneri* Association. The vegetation of the Tiebaghi Massif also seems to belong to this latter grouping with the addition of *Pittosporum poumense*, *Phyllanthus montrouzieri* and *Storckiella pancheri*.

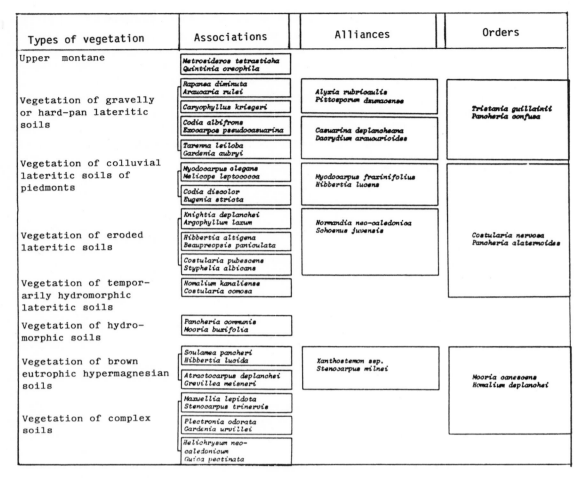

Types of vegetation	Associations	Alliances	Orders
Upper montane	*Metrosideros tetrasticha* *Quintinia oreophila*		
Vegetation of gravelly or hard-pan lateritic soils	*Rapanea diminuta* *Araucaria rulei*	*Alyxia rubricaulis* *Pittosporum drumacense*	*Tristania guillainii* *Pancheria confusa*
	Caryophyllus kriegeri		
	Codia albifrons *Exocarpos pseudocasuarina*	*Casuarina deplancheana* *Dacrydium araucarioides*	
	Tarenna leiloba *Gardenia aubryi*		
Vegetation of colluvial lateritic soils of piedmonts	*Myodocarpus elegans* *Melicope leptococca*	*Myodocarpus fraxinifolius* *Hibbertia lucens*	*Costularia nervosa* *Pancheria alaternoides*
	Codia discolor *Eugenia stricta*		
Vegetation of eroded lateritic soils	*Knightia deplanchei* *Argophyllum laxum*	*Normandia neo-caledonica* *Schoenus juvensis*	
	Hibbertia altigena *Beaupreopsis paniculata*		
	Costularia pubescens *Styphelia albicans*		
Vegetation of temporarily hydromorphic lateritic soils	*Homalium kanaliense* *Costularia comosa*		
Vegetation of hydromorphic soils	*Pancheria communis* *Mooria buxifolia*		
Vegetation of brown eutrophic hypermagnesian soils	*Soulamea pancheri* *Hibbertia lucida*	*Xanthostemon ssp.* *Stenocarpus milnei*	*Mooria canescens* *Homalium deplanchei*
	Atractocarpus deplanchei *Grevillea meisneri*		
Vegetation of complex soils	*Maxwellia lepidota* *Stenocarpus trinervis*		
	Plectronia odorata *Gardenia urvillei*		
	Helichrysum neo-caledonicum *Guioa pectinata*		

Fig. 19.3 Phytosociological classification of the serpentine vegetation of New Caledonia. Source: Jaffré (1980).

The plant Associations of the eutrophic brown soils may be considered to be part of the same Alliance characterised by magnesicolous plants with a wide geographic distribution such as *Xanthostemon flavum, Stenocarpus milnei, Tarenna microcarpa, Cleistanthus stipitatus, Fimbristylis neocaledonica, Gahnia aspera* and *Scleria brownii*. It is also noteworthy that a remarkable number of serpentinicolous species is represented in the genera *Xanthostemon* (Plate 19.2b), *Alyxia,* and *Phyllanthus. Alyxia* is noted for its large number of hyperaccumulators of manganese, and *Phyllanthus* for its hyperaccumulators of nickel.

5—**The vegetation of eroded lateritic soils.** This assemblage encompasses several Associations of somewhat homogeneous physiognomy. There are two Associations in the Grand Massif du Sud which are distinguished by altitude: the *Costularia pubescens— Styphelia albicans* (Plate 19.2a) below 600 m, and the *Hibbertia altigena—Beaupreopsis paniculata* between 600–1200 m.

A single Association linked to this type of soil is found in the Massif du Boulinda where the lateritic soils are seldom found below 500 m. This is known as the *Knightia deplanchei— Argophyllum laxum* community.

All three Associations mentioned above are linked to the same Alliance whose character species are *Normandia neocaledonica, Schoenus juvensis, Myrtus rufopunctata* and *Ficus asperula*.

6—**The vegetation of reworked, colluvial lateritic soils at piedmonts.** There are two distinct Associations within this vegetation type. There is a ligno-herbaceous scrub vegetation represented in the Grand Massif du Sud in the Plaine des Lacs and characterised by the *Codia discolor—Eugenia stricta* community. In the Massif du Boulinda, it is represented by the *Myodocarpus elegans—Melicope leptococca* Association. The first of these two Associations is not restricted to serpentine in the Plaine des Lacs.

The *Myodocarpus fraxinifolius—Hibbertia lucens* Alliance embraces a number of "plastic" taxa which attain their maximum abundance under these conditions. They include the two character species and also *Ixora collina*, *Styphelia cymbulae*, and *Alphitonia neocaledonica*. Also present are paraforestal species such as *Garcinia neglecta* and *Styphelia pancheri*.

7—**The vegetation of gravelly or hardened lateritic soils.** This assemblage is found at various altitudes in several of the massifs of New Caledonia. In the Grand Massif du Sud, the *Tarenna leiloba—Gardenia aubryi* Association is found below 550 m and the *Codia albifrons—Exocarpos pseudocasuarina* Association is found between 600–1200 m. At the Massif du Boulinda, the *Caryophyllus kriegeri* Association is found below 550 m and the *Rapanea diminuta—Araucaria rulei* at greater altitudes.

The two Associations of the Plaine des Lacs form part of the same Alliance characterised by *Casuarina deplancheana*, *Dacrydium araucarioides*, *Myrtopsis selingii*, *Dracophyllum involucratum* and *Beccariella baueri*.

The two Associations of the Massif du Boulinda form part of the *Alyxia rubricaulis* var. *boulindae—Pittosporum dzumacense* Alliance. Both Alliances are grouped with the *Tristania guillainii*, *Pancheria confusa*, *Styphelia veillonii* Order.

8—**The vegetation of complex soils.** This vegetation type is confined to the Massif du Boulinda and comprises 3 Associations of low altitude. The *Maxwellia lepidota—Stenocarpus trinervis* Association occupies steep slopes, whereas the *Plectronia odorata—Gardenia urvillei* community occupies level ground. The third Association, *Helichrysum neocaledonicum—Guioa pectinata* occupies a very limited area and has an impoverished flora, whereas the first two are found on more-or-less hydromorphic soils somewhat resembling the hypermagnesian eutrophic brown type.

General conclusions concerning the serpentine scrub of New Caledonia

A few general conclusions can now be made about the serpentine scrub vegetation of New Caledonia. These have been summarized in Fig. 19.4 for which the following comments are appropriate:

1—Three altitudinal stages are recognised; 0–600 m with heliophile plants, 600–1200 m with vegetal association of montane plants, above 1200 m with a truly semi-alpine montane flora.

2—The plants can be further subdivided into communities linked with the degree of drainage of the soils.

3—Further subdivision is possible into communities overlying hypermagnesian soils with a strong cation exchange capacity saturated with magnesium and consisting of:

    (a) vegetation units on brown eutrophic soils relatively deficient in iron.

    (b) As (a) above but with significantly higher iron, manganese and chromium levels.

4—The vegetation communities can finally be subdivided into units overlying more-or-less unsaturated lateritic soils with a very poor exchange capacity and covering 3 communities as follows:

    (a) Plants on eroded soils on crests and eroded slopes.

    (b) Plants on gravelly soils occupying gentle slopes.

    (c) Communities on reworked or colluvial lateritic soils occupying the piedmonts of the massifs.

Types of soil / Conditions of drainage	HYPERMAGNESIAN SOILS		LATERITIC SOILS			Altitude (m)
	Brown eutrophic	Mixed	Eroded	Colluvial	Gravelly & hard-pan	
WELL-DRAINED SOILS			*Metrosideros tetrasticha* *Quintinia oreophila*			>1200
WELL-DRAINED SOILS			*Hibbertia altigena* *Beaupreopsis paniculata* *Knightia deplanchei* *Argophyllum laxum*		*Codia albifrons* *Exocarpos pseudocasuarina* *Rapanea diminuta* *Araucaria rulei*	600-1200
WELL-DRAINED SOILS	*Soulamea pancheri* *Hibbertia lucida*			*Codia discolor* *Eugenia stricta*	*Tarenna leiloba* *Gardenia aubryi*	< 600
WELL-DRAINED SOILS	*Atractocarpus deplanchei* *Grevillea meisneri*	*Maxwellia lepidota* *Stenocarpus trinervis*	*Costularia pubescens* *Styphelia albicans*	*Myodocarpus elegans* *Melicope leptococca*	*Caryophyllus kriegeri*	< 600
WELL-DRAINED SOILS				*Helichrysum neo-caledonicum* *Guioa pectinata*		< 600
Average hydromorphic soils		*Plectronia odorata* *Gardenia urvillei*		*Homalium kanaliense* *Costularia Comosa*		< 600
Strongly-hydromorphic soils				*Pancheria communis* *Mooria buxifolia*		< 600

Fig. 19.4 Relationship between serpentine vegetation communities and ecological factors in New Caledonia.
Source: Jaffré (1980).

It will be noted from the above discussion that the scrub communities over serpentine in New Caledonia are extremely diverse and reflect conditions of their environment to a marked degree. Such a wide diversity and variety of vegetation associations on serpentine are found nowhere else on earth and this lends particular interest to the study of the vegetation of the island. The richness of the flora of these associations is quite varied. For example, the Associations of brown eutrophic hypermagnesian soils seem relatively rich as they contain about 100 species, compared with about 20 on the strongly hydromorphic soils, and 50 or so on the laterites.

The specificity of the flora of different associations is greater for the magnesicolous communities on soils with a high exchange capacity saturated with magnesium, than for those of the lateritic soils with low base saturation. In this sequence there is a change from a rich flora exclusive to the substrate to an impoverished, less specialised flora, rather resembling that of acid rocks. This is because the soils of these two types show a decreasing similarity with the parent rock in the sequence high to low exchange capacity (Jaffré and Latham, 1974).

19.4.4 The Serpentine Vegetation of the Massif du Koniambo

Although Morat et al. (1980) have produced a vegetation map of New Caledonia on a scale of 1:1,000,000, a comprehension of serpentine vegetation can better be achieved by considering in detail one particular representative area. Jaffré (1974) has carried out an extensive study of the serpentine vegetation of the Massif du Koniambo in the northern half of the island and his main findings are summarized below:

The Massif du Koniambo (Fig. 18.1) covers an area of about 200 km² and has a maximum elevation of 950 m. The eastern slopes are very steep but the western slopes stretch gently to the sea. The massif is criss-crossed with deep valleys through which turbulent streams (dry for half the year) rush to the sea.

Almost the entire massif is composed of serpentinite and peridotite. The soils at the base are of the usual eutrophic hypermagnesian brown type, whereas the flatter areas upslope carry alluvial and colluvial soils. The usual lateritic soils occur at altitudes above 300 m. The alluvial and colluvial soils are fairly homogeneous, are quite deep and have a pH around 7.0. They have a high exchange capacity (40 meq./100 g) and are saturated mainly with magnesium. The brown eutrophic soils are fairly shallow, have an appreciable clay content, and have a very high exchange capacity (50 meq/100 g). The iron content of the lateritic soils is around 70% Fe_2O_3, they are fairly acid (pH 3.5–6.5) and have the very low exchange capacity of only 10 meq/100 g.

All of the above soils are very deficient in calcium, nitrogen, potassium and phosphorus and contain 0.2–2.5% nickel, and 0.2–10% chromium. The annual rainfall of 1200 mm is low for serpentine massifs of New Caledonia.

Jaffré (1974) has recognised 12 vegetation groups on the massif and these are shown in Figs. 19.5 and 19.6. Fig. 19.5 shows a vegetation map and Fig. 19.6 gives a hypothetical floristic cross-section over the massif. Further details of the vegetation communities are given in Table 19.3. These are also illustrated in Plates 19.3 and 19.4.

The total number of species recorded on the Massif du Koniambo was 453 and represents 15% of the entire New Caledonian flora. If we remember that Koniambo covers only 1% of the total land area of the island, the richness of this flora becomes very obvious. Most of the species are endemic to New Caledonia and the majority is endemic to serpentine.

The ultramafic vegetation of Koniambo shows certain pecularities due both to its isolation and to its belonging to the New Caledonian floral domain. Because ultramafic rocks present a barrier to introduced species, this massif has been able to retain its original floristic composition despite the widespread damage caused by mining activities which ended about 30 years ago.

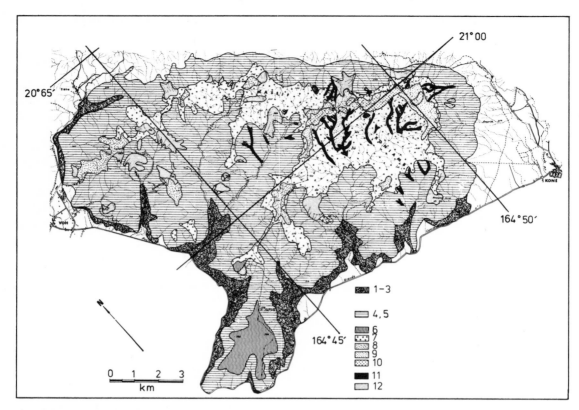

Fig. 19.5 Vegetation map of the Massif du Koniambo, New Caledonia. For key to vegetational units (1–12) see Table 19.3. See also Plates 19.3 and 19.4 for photographs of the communities.
Source: Jaffré (1974).

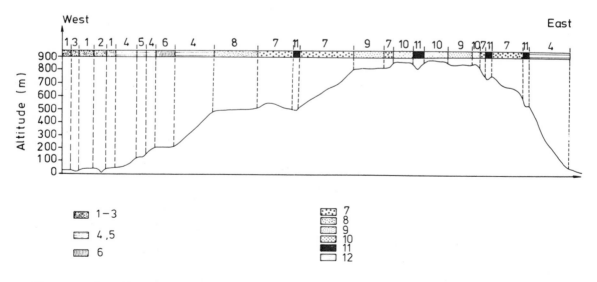

Fig. 19.6 Theoretical transverse section of vegetation communities of the Massif du Koniambo, New Caledonia. For key to vegetational units (1–12) see Table 19.3.
Source: Jaffré (1974).

TABLE 19.3 Vegetation Communities of the Massif du Koniambo, New Caledonia

Type of vegetation	Altitude (m)	Vegetation form	Constituent species
FORMATIONS ON LEVEL AREAS AND COLLUVIAL AND ALLUVIAL SOILS			
1. *Acacia-Alphitonia* savanna	0–50	Small trees (2–6 m)	*Acacia spirorbis*
		Herbaceous layer	*Fimbristylis neocaledonica*
		(magnesicolous Cyperaceae)	*Scleria brownii*
			Gahnia aspera
			Schoenus tendo
		Grasses	*Aristida novaecaledonicae*
			Themeda gigantea
		Fern	*Schizachyrium obliquiberbe*
2. Riverine forest (Plate 19.3a)	0–50	Trees (8–9 m)	*Calophyllum caledonicum*
			Sterculia sp.
		Herbaceous layer	*Schoenus tendo*
			Scleria papuana
3. *Melaleuca quinquenervia* transitional forest	0–50	Trees	*Melaleuca quinquenervia*
			Casuarina collina
			Alphitonia neocaledonica
FORMATIONS OF SLOPES OVER HYPERMAGNESIAN BROWN SOILS			
4. *Grevillea-Phyllanthus* ligno-herbaceous scrub	0–500	Bushes (0.5–3.5 m)	*Grevillea meisneri*
			Phyllanthus montrouzieri
			Psychotria calorhamnus
			Cerberiopsis comptonii
			Pittosporum poumense
			Terminalia gatopensis
			Ryssopteris angustifolia
			Oceanopapaver neocaledonica
			Boronia koniamboensis
5. *Gymnostoma chamaecyparis* forest (Plate 19.3b)	0–500	Trees (6–10 m)	*Gymnostoma chamaecyparis*
		Herbaceous layer	*Scleria papuana*
FORMATIONS ON SLOPES AND PLATEAUX ON LATERITIC SOILS			
6. *Acacia-Codia* thickets	500–600	Small trees (<2 m)	*Acacia spirorbis*
			Codia montana
		Herbaceous layer	*Lepidosperma laterale*

Type of vegetation	Altitude (m)	Vegetation form	Constituent species
7. *Hibbertia-Knightia* ligno-herbaceous scrub	500–800	Shrubs and herbs	*Hibbertia altigena* *Knightia deplanchei* *Costularia nervosa* *C. arundinacea* *Lepidosperma perteres* *Myodocarpus floribundus* *Schoenus neocaledonicus*
8. *Tristanea guillainii* open bushy scrub (Plate 19.4a)	500	Bushes (0.5–1.5 m) shrubs and herbs (<5% cover)	*Tristania guillainii* *Exocarpos baumannii* *Elaeocarpus castanaefolius* *Caryophyllus kriegeri*
9. *Tristanea guillainii* bushy scrub with montane species	900	Bushes (0.5–1.5 m), shrubs and herbs	*Tristanea guillainii* *Guioa koniamboensis* *Styphelia macrocarpa* *Metrosideros demonstrans* *Codia montana*
10. Open stands of *Araucaria montana* (Plate 19.4b)	>800	Trees (10–20 m)	*Araucaria montana*
11. Forest group of summits and talwegs (Plate 19.4c)	>800	Trees (20 m) Shrubs	*Nothofagus codonandra* *Cocconerion minor* *Dacrydium balansae* *Tristania guillainii* *T. callobuxus* *Cunonia balansae*
12. Pioneer communities on old mine workings (Plate 19.4d)	0–900		*Phyllanthus maytenifolius* and other adventive taxa

After: Jaffré (1974)

Plate 19.2 Some typical serpentine plants of New Caledonia.
(a) Above left: *Styphelia albicans*.
(b) Above right: *Xanthostemon rubrum*.
(c) Below left: *Geissois pruinosa*, a hyperaccumulator of nickel.
(d) Below right: *Bikkia campanulata*.
Photos by T. Jaffré.

Plate 19.3 Vegetation communities of the Koniambo ultramafic massif. (a) Left: Riverine community with *Pandanus viscidus*.
(b) Right: *Casuarina chamaecyparis* transitional forest.
Photos by T. Jaffré.

Plate 19.4 Vegetation of the Koniambo ultramafic massif. (a) Above: *Tristania guillainii* shrubby community on gravelly lateritic plateaux.

Plate 19.4   (b) Above: *Araucaria montana* summit forest.
(c) Middle: Talweg forest.
(d) Below: Pioneer plants on the site of an old mine. *Grevillea exul, Costularia comosa. Normandia neocaledonica,* and *Lepidosperma perteres.*
Photos by T. Jaffré.

Plate 19.5 (a) Above left: View of the Rivière Bleue in the Grand Massif du Sud. Photo by R. D. Reeves. (b) Above right: *Sebertia acuminata* (sève bleue). The sap contains up to 11.2% nickel as the citrate complex. This plant has easily the highest nickel content ever recorded in any plant. Photo by T. Jaffré. (c) Below left: View of the ligno-herbaceous scrub vegetation of the Plaine des Lacs. Photo by R. D. Reeves. (d) Below right: View of La Chute de la Madeleine, Plaine des Lacs. Photo by the author.

19.5 BIOGEOCHEMICAL INVESTIGATIONS ON THE SERPENTINE FLORA

19.5.1 Accumulation of Nickel by Serpentine Plants

There has already been some discussion in Chapter 8 of the so-called hyperaccumulators of nickel. The term was originally used by Brooks et al. (1977a) and refers to plants containing over 1000 μg/g nickel (0.1%) in dried leaves.

The history of the discovery of hyperaccumlators of nickel has already been given in Chapter 8 and will not be repeated. To date, 144 hyperaccumulators have been discovered of which 47 (one third) were found in New Caledonia (see Table 8.1). Table 19.4 lists the number of hyperaccumulators found in various parts of the world and relates these to the percentage of the total. A word of caution must be sounded here. Obviously a territory such as New Caledonia or Anatolia will feature high in the list because of the large areas of ultramafic rocks in both regions. A further factor is that the pace of discovery of hyperaccumulators has been largely related to the amount of effort expended. We might, for example, imagine that further work on the nickel content of Cuban or Celebes plants might turn up many more hyperaccumulators other than the total of 3 so far discovered in these territories. Nevertheless in a world-wide survey of the nickel content of the genera *Hybanthus* and *Homalium* and involving the anaysis of over 2000 specimens, Brooks et al. (1977a) found additional hyperaccumulators roughly in the proportion indicated by the data in Table 19.4. Jaffré and Schmidt (1974) have added a further category to the classification of plants which accumulate nickel. They used the term "hypernickelophores" to refer to plants containing over 10,000 μg/g (1%) in dried leaves. Using this more limited criterion, there are nine New Caledonian species which fall into this category: *Homalium guillainii*, *H. francii*, *Hybanthus austrocaledonicus*, *H. caledonicus* var. *linearifolius*, *Phyllanthus serpentinus*, *Geissois pruinosa* (Plate 19.2c), *G. intermedia*, *Psychotria douarrei* and *Sebertia acuminata*. The latter (Plate 19.5b), known as "sève bleue", is found in the Rivière Bleue area (Plate 19.5a), and is one of the most unusual of all plants since it contains a blue sap (hence the name) composed of nearly pure nickel citrate (Lee et al. 1977a) with 11.2% nickel in its fresh undried state. A more detailed description of phytochemical studies on this fascinating tree is given in Chapter 8. Of the 9 hypernickeliphores, 3 belong to the *maquis* communities and 6 are forest species.

New Caledonian hyperaccumulators of nickel are restricted to a very small number of subclasses, orders and families within the single class Magnoliatae. Table 19.5 shows that the Cunoniaceae, Euphorbiaceae, and Flacourtiaceae account for 30 of the 47 New Caledonian taxa known to have this unusual accumulatory character. To some extent this is a reflection

TABLE 19.4 Distribution of Hyperaccumulators of Nickel among various Countries and Regions

Country or Region	No. of species	% of total
New Caledonia	47	32.5
Anatolia and Cyprus	28	19.4
Balkan Peninsula and Aegean Islands	25	17.4
Central Europe, Italy and Corsica	17	11.8
Malay Archipelago	5	3.5
Syria and Iraq	4	2.8
United States	4	2.8
Zimbabwe	4	2.8
Iberian Peninsula	3	2.1
Western Australia	3	2.1
Cuba	2	1.4
Other	2	1.4

of the over-representation of these two families within the New Caledonan flora as a whole. The other hand, many families equally well represented, such as the Myrtaceae, Cyperaceae, and Proteaceae, do not include a single hyperaccumulator of nickel. All that can be said with certainty is that hyperaccumulation of nickel is a highly specialised character confined to a very few orders, families and genera.

Jaffré (1980) reported that about 4600 specimens of New Caledonian plants had been analysed for a number of elements in the course of biogeochemical work. To this must be added the very large number of specimens analysed in New Zealand as part of joint studies, so that it seems probable that the total number analysed is not far short of 10,000. In the course of these studies Jaffré (1980) showed that the most prevalent nickel content (geometric mean) of all serpentine plants was about 10–50 μg/g in dried leaves (42.5% of the plants had such levels) with only about 5.4% of the plants containing over 1000 μg/g nickel. The same author compared the mean nickel values in forest and scrub communities. These findings are summarized in Fig. 19.7 and show that very few species contained <10 μg/g. Nickel contents exceeding 100 μg/g were more common in the forest species (41%) than in the scrub associations (28.5%). Similarly a greater proportion of the forest species (9%) contained over 1000 μg/g nickel compared with 3.7% for the scrub plants. There was some evidence that the nickel content of plant species was dependent on the type of soil, with lateritic soils providing the highest values in foliar samples.

TABLE 19.5 Taxonomic Classification of New Caledonian Hyperaccumulators of Nickel within the Class Magnoliatae

Subclass	Order	Family	Genus	No. of species
Dilleniidae	Ebenales	Sapotaceae	*Sebertia*	1
	Theales	Oncothecaceae	*Oncotheca*	1
	Violales	Flacourtiaceae	*Casearia*	1
			Homalium	7
			Xylosma	11
		Violaceae	*Agatea*	1
			Hybanthus	3
Asteridae	Rubiales	Rubiaceae	*Psychotria*	1
Rosidae	Cunoniae	Cunoniaceae	*Geissois*	7
			Pancheria	1
	Rosales	Escalloniaceae	*Argophyllum*	2
	Euphorbiales	Euphorbiaceae	*Baloghia*	1
			Cleidion	1
			Phyllanthus	10

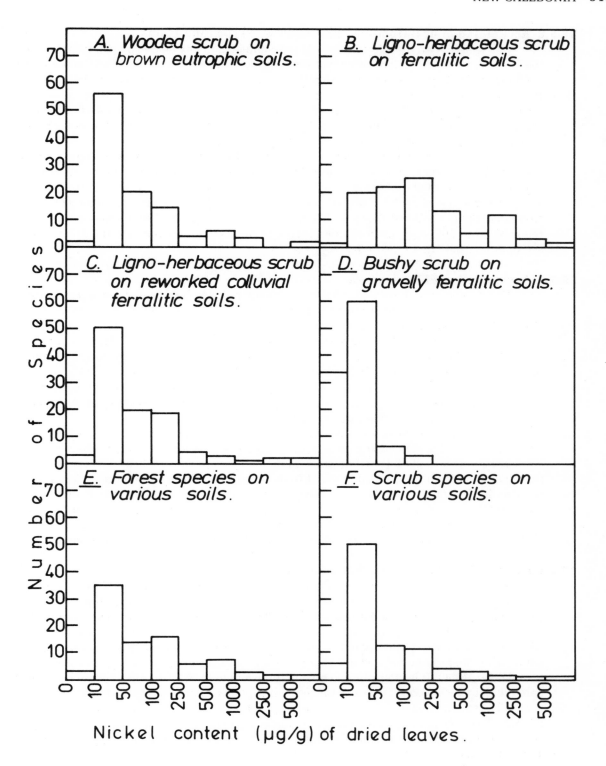

Fig. 19.7   Distribution of nickel (%) in various communities of the serpentine flora of New Caledonia. The y axis shows the number of species in each concentration class.
After: Jaffré (1980).

19.5.2 Accumulation of Chromium and Cobalt by Serpentine Plants

It is well known that chromium is not accumulated to any degree by plants and indeed there are no reliable data indicating that values above 100 μg/g can occur in uncontaminated samples. Jaffré (1980) has reported chromium values in 24 serpentine taxa from Boulinda and Plaine des Lacs. Despite one value of 430 μ/g in dried leaves of *Geissois pruinosa*, the maximum value was 120 μ/g in a specimen of *Agatea deplanchei* from Boulinda. Even in the vicinity of an old chrome mine (32% chromium in the soil) no value above 36 μg/g chromium was reported for any taxon.

Considerably higher values for cobalt might be expected in plants since hyperaccumulators of this element (>1000 μg/g in dried leaves) have been reported by Brooks and Malaisse (1985) and Brooks et al. (1980) for plants growing over cobalt deposits in southcentral Africa. Also the genus *Nyssa* contains several taxa able to concentrate several hundred μg/g of cobalt from soils not anomalously high in this element (Brooks et al. 1977b). Kersten et al. (1979) reported up to 796 μg/g cobalt in dried leaves of *Phyllanthus ngoyensis* and 270 μg/g in *P. serpentinus* from New Caledonia.

19.5.3 Accumulation of Manganese

The uptake of manganese by various serpentinophytes from New Caledonia has been studied by Jaffré (1977a, 1980) and by Brooks et al. (1981). Jaffré (1980) reported up to 55,200 μg/g (5.52%) manganese in dried leaves of *Macadamia neurophylla*, a member of the Proteaceae. The selectivity of this family in accumulating manganese was examined by Jaffré (1980) when he determined the manganese content of 40 of the 46 species of Protea in New Caledonia and found that 50% contained over 1000 μg/g manganese in dried leaves and that a further 7.5% contained over 10,000 μg/g (1%). The latter was defined as the threshold for *hypermanganésophores*. Unlike the case for nickel, hyperaccumulation of manganese is not restricted to plants growing over serpentine.

Jaffré (1980) has observed that the families with the greatest ability to accumulate manganese are (in descending order) the Proteaceae, Apocynaceae, Araliaceae, and Santalaceae. Brooks et al. (1981) determined the manganese content of 31 species of *Alyxia* (Apocynaceae) from New Caledonia and found a maximum of 1.15% in dried leaves of *A. rubricaulis*. Calcium, magnesium, potassium and nickel were also determined and it was established that manganese uptake was mainly at the expense of calcium rather than magnesium. It was suggested that manganese might have a physiological role in *Alyxia*, perhaps compensating for reduced uptake of the nutrients calcium and potassium.

19.5.4 Nutrient Balance in Serpentine Plants

Jaffré (1980) has carried out extensive studies on the nutrient status of New Caledonian serpentine plants. The work involved the determination of magnesium, sodium, nitrogen, phosphorus, calcium and potassium in nearly 300 species of serpentine plants from forested areas and a further 150 from serpentine scrub. For the sake of conciseness, all these data have been compressed into a single figure (Fig. 19.8). A few general observations may be made. The magnesium and sodium content of the plants is the same as for non-serpentine taxa (Heller, 1969). It is interesting to note that the magnesium levels are not very high compared with expected concentrations for serpentine plants outside New Caledonia. However, it must be remembered that the lateritic soils are actually deficient in this element. Although the most frequently encountered calcium content (1.10%) is at the lower end of the range for non-serpentinitic plants, the uptake of this element is not as low as is normally found in serpentine plants and the calcium/magnesium mole quotient of 1.74 is well above that normally found for other serpentine floras. For example, Brooks and Yang (1984) reported a mean value of 0.87 for the endemic flora of the Great Dyke in Zimbabwe.

In the course of a study on the elemental content of 156 specimens of 47 species of serpentinicolous Flacourtiaceae from New Caledonia, Yang et al. (1985) did not find any

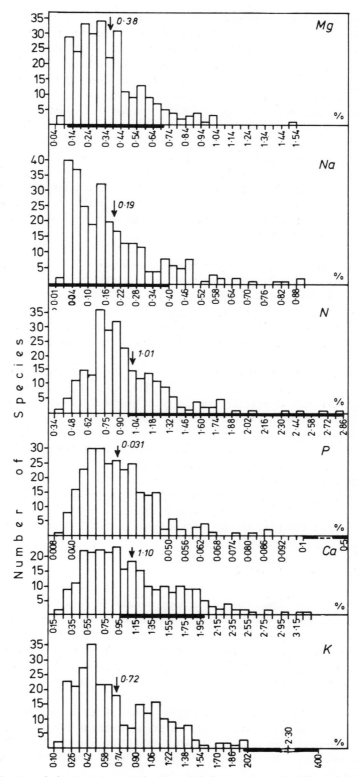

Fig. 19.8   Distribution of plant nutrients in the New Caledonian serpentine flora of the forests. Arrows indicate mean values.
After: Jaffré (1980).

inverse correlation between the magnesium content of the plants and the levels of nutrients such as phosphorus, whereas for the Zimbabwean situation, Brooks and Yang (1984) found a strong inverse correlation between magnesium and all of the following plant nutrients: aluminium, boron, iron, manganese, phosphorus and sulphur. The conclusion is clear. Most New Caledonian soils, except for the brown hypermagnesian eutrophic type, do not contain excessive amounts of magnesium and indeed in most cases are deficient in this element. The New Caledonian serpentine flora is therefore controlled by edaphic factors other than the magnesium content of the soils.

As shown in Fig. 19.8, the nitrogen content of the serpentine flora is well below normal and those of potassium and phosphorus are excessively so. The phosphorus content of the vegetation has a most probable (geometric mean) concentration of 0.03% compared with the lowest value of 0.10% for non-serpentine vegetation. The respective figures for nitrogen are 1.01 and 1.02%, and for potassium are 0.72 and 2.0%. It is likely therefore that the deficiencies of potassium and phosphorus in the soils are important edaphic factors controlling the New Caledonian serpentine flora.

19.5.5 Biogeochemical Prospecting in New Caledonia

Very little biogeochemical prospecting work has been carried out in New Caledonia, partly because of the ready accessibility of the soil for chemical analysis and partly because of the large volume of prospecting by other means carried out during the past century. Few tropical territories can have been as well explored by conventional means as has New Caledonia, and it is not suprising therefore that there has been little incentive to try other techniques.

The only biogeochemical prospecting work has been a study by Lee et al. (1977b) in which calcium, cobalt, chromium, copper, iron, magnesium, manganese, nickel, phosphorus and zinc were determined in plant leaves and associated soils at 147 sites in the southern part of New Caledonia (Monts Koghis and Plaine des Lacs—Plates 19.5c and d). The species studied were *Hybanthus austrocaledonicus* and *Homalium kanaliense*. Correlation analysis was carried out and highly significant plant/soil correlations (P <0.01) were obtained. These data are shown in Table 19.6.

In contrast with *H. kanaliense,* the nickel content of *H. austrocaledonicus* was related not only to extractable (ammonium oxalate) nickel in the soil, but also to the total nickel content. This species, therefore, shows a potential for biogeochemical prospecting for nickel. Both taxa gave a good correlation with the extractable fraction of the soils.

19.6 GENERAL CONCLUSIONS

Before leaving New Caledonia it is pertinent to summarize a few conclusions resulting from the many studies carried out on the fascinating serpentine flora of this island. These conclusions are as follows:

1—The serpentine flora of New Caledonia is extremely rich not only in absolute terms but also in comparison with its neighbouring non-serpentine floras, and contains several centres of speciation in the numerous ultramafic (massifs of the northern part of the island which are surrounded by non-serpentinitic vegetation.

2—Two thirds of the serpentine flora in over 30 genera and two monospecific families is endemic to serpentine, and nearly all are endemic to New Caledonia. The number of serpentinicolous species is so great (∼900 taxa) that it is not feasible to list them all. The reader is, however, referred to the appendix in Jaffré (1980) which lists about 500 of these plants.

3—Differentiation and speciation over the serpentine occurrences of New Caledonia has been very great due to a combination of favourable climatic factors and due to the

TABLE 19.6 Plant/soil Correlations for Various Elements in Soils and in Dried Leaves of *Homalium kanaliense* **(Plaine des Lacs) and** *Hybanthus austrocaledonicus* **(Monts Koghis).**

		SOILS											
		Ca	Co	Cr	Cu	Fe	K	Mg	Mn	Ni	P	Zn	XNi
Leaves of	Ca									+			
Homalium	Co	+		−				−					−
kanaliense	Cr	−						−				−	+
	Cu			+									
	Fe	−							−			−	
	K	−	−	+	+	+	−	−			−		
	Mg	+	+	−		−	+	+	−	+			
	Mn	−	−	+		+	−	−					
	Ni	−							+				+
	P			−		−							
Leaves of	Ca							+				−	
Hybanthus	Co		+										
austro-	Cr							−				+	
caledonicus	Mg							+				−	
	Mn					+			+				
	Ni							−		+	+	+	
	P											+	
	Zn											+	

XNi = extractable nickel (ammonium oxalate buffer)
+ = highly significant (P < 0.01) positive relationship
− = highly significant (P < 0.01) inverse relationship
Source: Lee et al. (1977b).

availability of a vast pool of floristic sources for speciation to occur. The serpentine vegetation bears some similarity with those of Japan (gymnosperms), Zimbabwe (Proteaceae) and New Zealand (Epacridaceae).

4—The serpentine vegetation of the scrub formations is usually more luxuriant than that of the surrounding non-serpentinitic substrates.

5—Discontinuities in the vegetation cover, so typical of serpentines of temperate climates, are very slight except over arid areas.

6—The serpentine scrub is more developed than that of other substrates because it lacks a poaceous layer which readily catches fires during dry spells and degrades the accompanying scrub vegetation.

7—The most characteristic serpentine floras are found over the least developed soils (i.e., brown eutrophic) of the piedmont areas. Lateritic soils carry a much less characteristic vegetation.

8—The serpentine floras carry a great deficiency of potassium and phosphorus though not of calcium, due perhaps to the low magnesium content of the lateritic soils which in excess would have been antagonistic to nutrient uptake, particularly calcium.

9—The serpentine flora carries a large number of hyperaccumulators of nickel (one third of the world total) and is therefore well adapted to the high nickel content of the soil. Hyperaccumulators of manganese have also been discovered and it is probable that this element also has a role in controlling the serpentine vegetation.

10—Although the serpentine vegetation of New Caledonia has certain physiognomic, floristic and biogeochemical similarities with serpentine areas elsewhere in the world, it also at the same time has a number of anomalous peculiarities and originalities. These have been able to develop over several million years because of favourable climatic and other reasons. Furthermore the evolution of the flora has not been hindered by such events as Ice Ages or subduction during the more recent geological periods. Perhaps it is not too much to say that this island carries the richest, most interesting, and most diverse serpentine vegetation anywhere on earth and it will long continue to excite the interest of botanists throughout the world.

REFERENCES

Baker, A. J. M., Brooks, R. R. and Kersten, W. J., 1985. Accumulation of nickel by *Psychotria* species from the Pacific Basin. *Taxon,* 34: 89–95.

Birrell, K. S. and Wright, A. C. S., 1945. A serpentine soil in New Caledonia. *N.Z. J. Sci. Technol.,* 27A: 72–76.

Braun-Blanquet, J., 1932. *Plant Sociology.* McGraw-Hill, New York.

Brooks, R. R., Lee, J. and Jaffré, T., 1974. Some New Zealand and New Caledonian plant accumulators of nickel. *J. Ecol.,* 62: 523–529.

Brooks, R. R., Lee, J., Reeves, R. D. and Jaffré, T., 1977a. Detection of nickeliferous rocks by analysis of herbarium specimens of indicator plants. *J. Geochem. Explor.,* 7: 49–57.

Brooks, R. R. and Malaisse, F., 1985. *The Heavy Metal Tolerant Flora of Southcentral Africa—A Multidisciplinary Approach.* Balkema, Rotterdam.

Brooks, R. R., McCleave, J. A. and Schofield, E. K., 1977b. Cobalt and nickel uptake by the Nyssaceae. *Taxon,* 26: 197–201.

Brooks, R. R., Reeves, R. D., Morrison, R. S. and Malaisse, F., 1980. Hyperaccumulation of copper and cobalt—a review. *Bull. Soc. Roy. Bot. Belg.,* 113: 166–172.

Brooks, R. R., Trow, J. M., Veillon, J.-M. and Jaffré, T., 1981. Studies on manganese accumulating *Alyxia* from New Caledonia. *Taxon,* 30: 420–423.

Brooks, R. R. and Yang, X. H., 1984. Elemental levels and relationships in the endemic serpentine flora of the Great Dyke, Zimbabwe and their significance as controlling factors for this flora. *Taxon,* 33: 392–399.

Good, R., 1974. *The Geography of the Flowering Plants.* Longman, London.

Guillaumin, A., 1948. *Flore Synoptique et Analytique de la Nouvelle-Calédonie. Phanérogames,* O.R.S.T.O.M., Paris.

Guillon, J. H., 1975. Les massifs péridotiques de Nouvelle-Calédonie. *Mém. O.R.S.T.O.M., Nouméa:* #76: 1–120.

Heller, R., 1969. *Biologie Végétale. II. Nutrition et Métabolisme.* Masson, Paris.

Jaffré, T., 1974. La végétation et la flore d'un massif de roches ultrabasiques de Nouvelle Calédonie, le Koniambo. *Candollea,* 29: 427–456.

Jaffré, T., 1976. Composition chimique et conditions de l'alimentation minérale des plantes sur roches ultrabasiques en Nouvelle-Calédonie. *Cah. O.R.S.T.O.M. Sér. Biol.,* 11: 53–63.

Jaffré, T., 1977a. Accumulation du manganèse par les espèces associées aux terrains ultrabasiques de Nouvelle Calédonie. *C. R. Acad. Sci. Paris Sér.D,* 284: 1573–1575.

Jaffré, T., 1977b. Composition chimique elementaire des tissus foliaires des espèces végétales colonisatrices des anciennes mines de nickel en Nouvelle Calédonie. *Cah. O.R.S.T.O.M. Sér. Biol.,* 12: 323–330.

Jaffré, T., 1979. Accumulation du manganèse par les Proteacées de Nouvelle Calédonie. *C. R. Acad. Sci. Paris Sér.D,* 289: 425–428.

Jaffré, T., 1980. *Etude Ecologique du Peuplement Végétal des Sols Dérivés de Roches Ultrabasiques en Nouvelle Calédonie.* O.R.S.T.O.M., Paris.

Jaffré, T., Brooks, R. R., Lee, J. and Reeves, R. D., 1976. *Sebertia acuminata* a hyperaccumulator of nickel from New Caledonia. *Science,* 193: 579–580.

Jaffré, T., Brooks, R. R. and Trow, J. M., 1979a. Hyperaccumulation of nickel by *Geissois* species. *Pl. Soil,* 51: 157–162.

Jaffré, T., Kersten, W. J., Brooks, R. R. and Reeves, R. D., 1979b. Nickel uptake by the Flacourtiaceae of New Caledonia. *Proc. Roy. Soc. Lond. Sec. B,* 205: 385–394.

Jaffré, T. and Latham, M., 1974. Contribution à l'étude des relations sol-végétation sur un massif de roches ultrabasiques de la côte ouest de la Nouvelle Calédonie; le Boulinda. *Adansonia,* 14: 311–336.

Jaffré, T., Latham, M. and Quantin, P., 1970. Les sols des massifs miniers de Nouvelle Calédonie et leur relation avec la végétation. *Rapp. O.R.S.T.O.M., Nouméa:* 1–20.

Jaffré, T., Latham, M. and Schmid, M., 1977. Aspects de l'influence de l'extraction du minérai de nickel sur la végétation et les sols en Nouvelle Calédcnie. *Cah. O.R.S.T.O.M. Sér. Biol.,* 12: 307–321.

Jaffré, T. and Schmid, M., 1974. Accumulation du nickel par une Rubiacée de Nouvelle Calédonie: *Psychotria douarrei* (G. Beauvisage) Däniker. *C. R. acad. Sci. Paris Sér.D,* 278: 1727–1730.

Kelly, P. C., Brooks, R. R., Dilli, S. and Jaffré, T., 1975. Preliminary observations on the ecology and plant chemistry of some nickel-accumulating plants from New Caledonia. *Proc. Roy. Soc. Lond. Sec.B.,* 189: 69–80.

Kersten, W. J., 1979. *Ecological and Phytochemical Studies on Nickel-accumulating Plants from the Pacific Basin Region.* MSc Thesis, Massey University, Palmerston North, New Zealand.

Kersten, W. J., Brooks, R. R. and Jaffré, T., 1979. Nickel uptake by New Caledonian species of *Phyllanthus. Taxon,* 28: 529–534.

Latham, M., 1975a. Géomorphologie d'un massif de roches ultrabasiques de la côte ouest de la Nouvelle Calédonie; le Boulinda. *Cah. O.R.S.T.O.M. Sér. Géol.,* 7: 17–37.

Latham, M., 1975b. Les sols d'un massif de roches ultrabasiques de la côte ouest de Nouvelle Calédonie: le Boulinda—généralités repartition des sols dans le massif. Les sols à l'accumulation humifère. *Cah. O.R.S.T.O.M. Sér. Pédol.,* 13: 27–35.

Latham, M., 1975c. Les sols d'un massif de roches ultrabasiques de Nouvelle Calédonie; le Boulinda. Les sols à l'accumulation férrugineuse relative. *Cah. O.R.S.T.O.M. Sér. Pédol.,* 13: 159–172.

Lee, J., 1974. *Biogeochemical Studies on some Nickel-accumulating Plants from New Zealand and New Caledonian Serpentine Areas.* MSc Thesis, Massey University, Palmerston North, New Zealand.

Lee, J., 1977. *Phytochemical and Biogeochemical Studies on Nickel Accumulation by some New Caledonian Plants.* PhD Thesis, Massey University, Palmerston North, New Zealand.

Lee, J., Reeves, R. D., Brooks, R. R. and Jaffré, T., 1977a. Isolation and identification of a citrato complex of nickel from nickel-accumulating plants. *Phytochemistry,* 16: 1503–1505.

Lee, J., Brooks, R. R., Reeves, R. D. and Jaffré, T., 1977b. Plant-soil relationships in a New Caledonian serpentine flora. *Pl. Soil,* 46: 675–680.

Lillie, A. R. and Brothers, R. N., 1970. The geology of New Caledonia. *N.Z. J. Geol. Geophys.,* 13: 145–183.

Morat, P., Jaffré, T., Veillon, J.-M. and McKee, H., 1980. Carte de la Végétation de la Nouvelle Calédonie au 1/10-ème. Notice Expliquative, *Atlas de Nouvelle Calédonie,* Paris.

Quantin, P., 1969. Note sur quelques sols en Nouvelle Calédonie. *Rapp. O.R.S.T.O.M. Nouméa:* 1–12.

Schmid, M., 1980. *Flore et Végétation de la Nouvelle Calédonie.* Hachette, Paris.

Trescases, J. J., 1969. Premières observations sur l'altération des péridotites de Nouvelle Calédonie. Pédologie, Géochimie, Géomorphologie. *Cah. O.R.S.T.O.M. Sér. Géol.,* 1: 27–57.

Trescases, J. J., 1975. L'évolution géochimique supergène des roches ultrabasiques en zone tropicale. *Mém. O.R.S.T.O.M.* #78: 1–259.

Wegener, A., 1924. *The Origin of Continents and Oceans.* Methuen, London.

Yang, X. H., Brooks, R. R., Jaffré, T. and Lee, J., 1985. Elemental levels and relationships in the Flacourtiaceae of New Caledonia. *Pl. Soil,* 87: 281–291.

Chapter 20

AUSTRALIA

20.1 GENERAL GEOLOGY AND TECTONICS

Australia has one of the largest areas of Archaean (> 2.6×10^9 yr.) rocks anywhere on earth. A large part of these rocks is concentrated in Western Australia in the Yilgarn and Pilbara cratons. The latter consists of narrow belts of closely-folded volcanic formations with subsidiary related sediments separated by wider areas of gneisses and granites. These are known as "Greenstone Belts" and are shown in Fig. 20.1. The belts underwent a major orogeny some 2600–3000 m.y. ago. Metallic deposits were formed at the same time and consist of gold-bearing veins in the greenstone belts and nickel deposits in ultramafic lava flows and sills in these same formations in the Kalgoorlie area. Although Fig. 20.1 shows large areas of greenstones in Western Australia designated as ultramafic (site #1), it must be remembered that ultramafites are widely disseminated in narrow sills within these greenstones and form only a small percentage of their total area. The same is true for the ultramafic/mafic occurrences at the borders of Western Australia, South Australia and Northern Territory (site #2 in Fig. 20.1).

There is a large belt of ophiolitic outcrops extending from Tasmania in the south and extending northwards through New South Wales and Queensland along the Great Divide and forming part of the Tasman Geosyncline which underwent a period of orogeny starting about 470 m.y. ago and lasting for about 370 m.y. It consisted of a series of surges of folding, broken by periods of quiescence and sedimentation.

Derry (1980) has suggested the following sequence of tectonic movements following the laying down of the east coast ophiolites. Some 130 m.y. ago, India parted from the western side of Australia and Antarctica; 80–69 m.y. ago, New Zealand parted from Australia; 53 m.y. ago, Australia parted from Antarctica; 32 m.y. ago, the Indian and Australian Plates which were both moving north, combined together again and converged on the Eurasian Plate, a process still continuing today.

20.2 THE GEOLOGY OF THE YILGARN CRATON

The serpentine vegetation of Western Australia is found almost entirely within the Yilgarn Craton, so a brief description of the geology of this block is appropriate. The craton consists of about 600,000 km² of Archaean granite and granite gneiss enclosing north-northwest trending belts of metavolcanics and metasediments. These "greenstone belts" have been studied by many workers such as Prider (1961) who has compared them with the Archaean rocks of Canada and Zimbabwe and noted the ubiquitous association of basic, often pillowed, lavas and serpentinized peridotites.

According to Severne (1972) the greenstone assemblages are metamorphosed usually to a greenschist facies, although higher metamorphic grades are observed in thin belts or towards the margins of larger belts (Prider, 1961)

More recent studies on the Yilmia greenstones between Spargoville and Kambalda (McCall and Doepel, 1969) led to the development of the following model to explain the association of layered ultramafic sills with pillowed metavolcanics. Submarine lava flows in a eugeosynclinal environment formed thick lenses and capped their conduits. Later magma pulses resulted in lateral intrusions along suitable horizontal parings to form penecon-temporaneous sills. These sills often display layered internal structure similar to the Stillwater Intrusion of Montana.

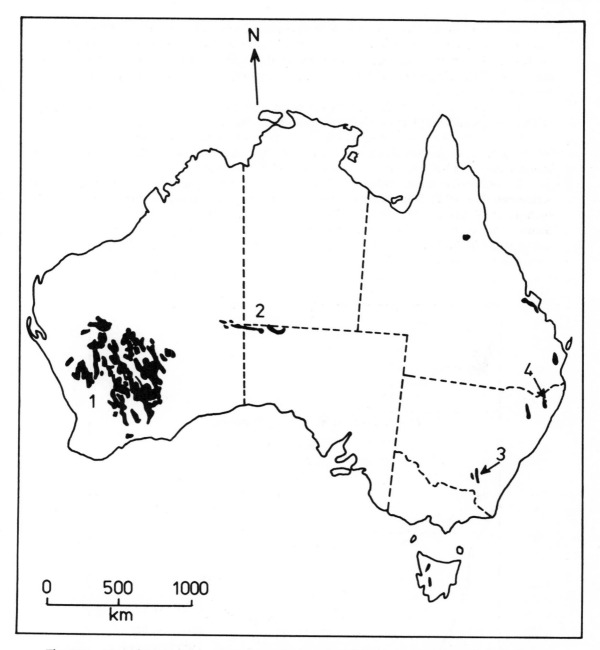

Fig. 20.1   Map of Australia showing ultramafic areas (solid black). 1 = Greenstone Belt of Western Australia, 2 = mafic/ultramafic rocks of the tristate boundaries of central Australia, 3 = Coolac Serpentinite Belt, 4 = Baryulgil. NB—The solid black areas at sites #1 and #2 are not entirely ultramafic as this rock type is present usually as thin belts within more extensive basic rocks.

The association of basic volcanics, differentiated sills and subordinate ultramafic rocks and pelitic metasediments is repeated several times throughout the stratigraphic sequence of the Kalgoorlie system and suggests an alternation of volcanic eruption with quiescent sedimentation. The recognition of layered structure within many sills in the premetamorphic eruptive site is recent.

The granitoid rocks have received scant attention. They are usually porphyritic microcline granites but become foliated adjacent to the greenstone belts.

Over much of the area the rocks bear remnants of ferrugineous and siliceous cappings inherited from a Tertiary (Pliocene) phase of deep weathering. Underlying or exposed bedrock may exhibit extensive kaolinisation and carbonation.

In 1966, high-grade nickel sulphide orebodies were discovered at Kambalda near Kalgoorlie (Fig. 20.2). This discovery was followed by many others in the greenstone belts such as at Widgiemooltha, Spargoville, Scotia, Nepean, Wildarra, Agnew and Mt Keith. Some of the orebodies are now producing nickel and have added to the prosperity of the "Eastern Goldfields" following the decline of gold in the 1960s, a decline which has now been halted and reversed.

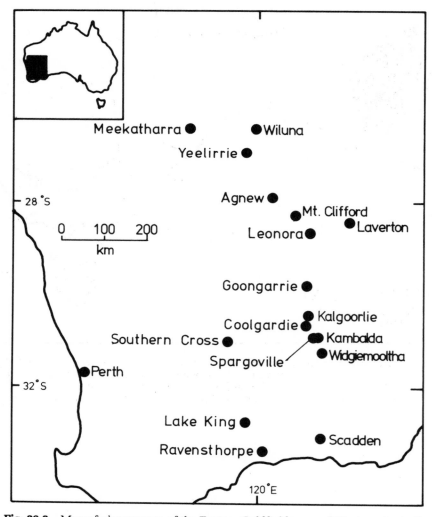

Fig. 20.2   Map of place names of the Eastern Goldfields area of Western Australia.

20.3 THE VEGETATION TYPES OF WESTERN AUSTRALIA

As is commonly the case with arid areas, the serpentine vegetation of Western Australia is not physiognomically very different from that of the surrounding non-ultramafic rocks. The serpentine vegetation of this region is part of the Eremean Botanical Province (Gardner, 1952) and has been studied by a number of workers (Table 20.1). The province is one of three in Western Australia and is delineated by areas in which the four consecutive wettest months have less than 180 mm rainfall. The Eremean Province has a typical semi-desert climate with very hot summers, cool winters and a rainfall averaging 200 mm in the "mulga" zone and 250–380 mm in the "eucalypt" zone, a rainfall which increases towards the south coast. July is the coldest month with an average daily maximum temperature of 17°C whereas January averages 40°C. The annual moisture evaporation is about 10 times that of the precipitation.

TABLE 20.1 Papers Which Describe the Serpentine Vegetation of Australia

Western Australia	New South Wales
Bennett (1969)	Lyons (1973)
Cole (1965, 1971, 1973)	Lyons et al. (1974)
Elkington (1969)	
Nielsen (1972)	
Nielsen et al. (1973)	
Severne (1972)	
Severne and Brooks (1972)	

The Eremean Province (Gr. eremikos = desert) contains 6 main vegetal formations (Fig. 20.3) of which the first 2 are the best represented over serpentines. A brief description of these formations follows.

1—The sclerophyllous woodland comprises trees about 25 m in height with a shrubby understorey averaging 1 m. It is found over loamy soils around the 225 mm isohyet. The woodland is never found over sand. These sand plains are usually covered with *Eucalyptus salmonophloia, E. salubris* and *E. longicornis*. In the lake country in the eastern part of the Eastern Goldfields, the number of species increases and includes *E. brockwayi, E. leptophylla, E. campaspe, E. flocktoniae* and *E. oleosa*.

2—The "mulga" bush is the most extensive vegetation formation in Australia. The demarcation zone is well defined in Western Australia. It commences just north of Kalgoorlie near Menzies (see Figs 20.2 and 20.3) where the eucalypt trees and shrubs become more and more scarce and the acacias become more dominant. The acacias form the tree or tall shrub layer while the low shrub storey is usually dominated by highly diversified species of *Eremophila* numbering about one hundred.

The genus *Cassia* also has great importance in the mulga scrub and forms part of the lower shrub layer. The development of an indumentum of felt enables these plants to endure extreme aridity.

The "mulga", *Acacia aneura* (Plate 20.1a) is by far the commonest tree in this zone. It is highly polymorphic and attains a height of about 5–10 m.

The ephemeral flora is extensive and the whole area is carpeted with herbs after modest rainfall. These consist mainly of Asteraceae. Summer rains can also bring an abundance of grasses such as *Aristida* and *Setaria*.

Outcropping hills bring a somewhat more varied flora including *Dodonaea filifolia, D. lobulata, Santalum* sp. and the green-leaved *Acacia quadrimarginea*.

3—The *Salsola* Shrub Steppe occurs in isolated areas particularly over limestones such as in the Nullarbor Plain which supports a vegetation averaging 50–100 cm composed chiefly of Chenopodiaceae.

4—The Halophytic Formations are found throughout the Eremean Province over dried lake beds and the remains of ancient river systems. They are characterised by a distinctive grey vegetation in which the Chenopodiaceae are dominant. Species of *Atriplex*, *Bassia* and *Kochia* are common.

5—The *Triodia* steppe is a grassy formation occurring on red sandy soils and is most common in areas receiving a summer rainfall. The dominant genus is *Triodia* (Poaceae) with about 12 species.

6—The desert formation is the true desert, occurring mainly in the centre of the region and having a very sparse vegetation cover.

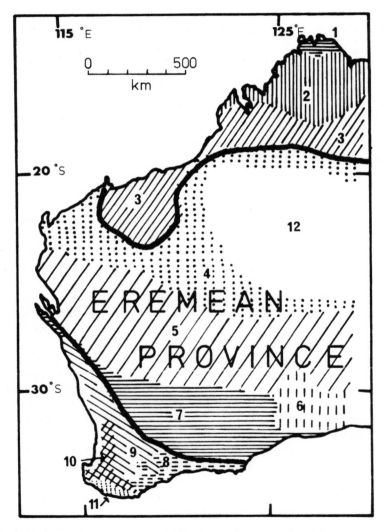

Fig. 20.3   The vegetation formations of Western Australia. 1—tropical sclerophyllous woodland, 2—monsoon, savanna and riverine woodland, 3—savanna and open savanna woodland, 4—*Triodia* steppe, 5—mulga bush, 6—salt bush steppe, 7—sclerophyllous woodland, 8—sand heath, 9—temperate savanna woodland, 10—sclerophyllous (jarrah) forest, 11—mesophytic (karri) forest, 12—desert.

20.4 THE SERPENTINE VEGETATION OF WESTERN AUSTRALIA

20.4.1 The Kambalda-Spargoville Area

The serpentine vegetation of Western Australia has been studied by several workers (Table 20.1) whose main aim was the use of geobotany in mineral exploration, but who nevertheless provided a good overview of the serpentine vegetation *per se*. One of the first of these studies was by Cole (1971) who described a close correlation between plant communities and geology in the Eastern Goldfields region near Kalgoorlie. She has reported that the savanna in the Kambalda-Widgiemooltha area is dominated by *Eucalyptus lesouefii* which grows over soils derived from mafic and ultramafic rocks. *E. torquata* is particularly common at ultramafic-mafic rock contacts, and *E. foecunda* and *E. campaspe* show some preference for serpentine soils. A number of geobotanical anomalies characterised by tree-less zones due to nickel toxicity, have been identified at Kambalda (Elkington, 1969).

In the Spargoville area (see Fig. 20.2), Nielsen (1972) and Nielsen et al. (1973) carried out extensive plant mapping over serpentine and amphibolite. They plotted the occurrence of 34 species of trees and shrubs and determined that two of these, *Cratystylis subspinescens* and *Pittosporum phillyraeoides* grew only over ultramafic rocks. *Dodonaea lobulata* was confined to ecotone areas at the ultramafic-amphibolite contacts. Using discriminant analysis, these workers were able to identify the nature of the bedrock (ultramafic, amphibolite, and intermediate between the two) on the basis of the distribution of the 34 taxa studied. These are listed in Table 20.2 and include the numbers of individuals per 30m × 15m quadrat of which 26 were on amphibolites, 11 on ultramafites and 7 were on the ecotones. The degree of discrimination was determined by use of the Mahalanobis D^2 statistic (Mahalanobis, 1936). The relevant discriminant data are shown in Table 20.3 and show that it was thereby possible to predict the geology of the bedrock for all of the amphibolitic and ultramafic quadrats and for 6 out of the 7 ecotone quadrats. The greater the value of D^2, the greater the degree of discrimination. This work shows the extraordinary degree to which vegetation patterns reflect the geology in the sclerophyllous eucalypt woodland of the Kambalda-Spargoville region.

One of the most extensive geobotanical studies of the eucalypt woodland has been by Elkington (1969). She reached the following conclusions:

1—There is remarkable degree of correlation between geology and vegetation in the region.

2—Plant associations are influenced to a significant degree by the chemical composition of the soil.

3—At the Kambalda nickel deposit, the zone with the highest nickel content is marked by discontinous distribution of several species.

4—At Jimberlana Dyke near Norseman (Fig. 20.2), a belt of *Eucalyptus* aff. *cylindrocarpus* woodland coincides with the nickel anomaly in the soil.

5—On the carbonated serpentinites at Mt Hunt, a high background concentration of nickel and chromium is accompanied by an extremely sparse vegetation cover with only *Melaleuca laterifolia* being widespread in the area.

6—A minimum area of ultramafic rocks is needed before characteristic vegetation communities will develop over the substrate.

7—Geobotanical relationships in one part of the Eastern Goldfields, may not occur elsewhere in the region. For example, communities of the Kalgoorlie area (mulga) are quite different from those over ultramafites at Norseman (sclerophyllous eucalypt woodland).

8—Biogeochemical methods of exploration are not particularly successful in the Eastern Goldfields due to the high pH of some soils rendering the nickel non-available to the plants.

Cole (1971) concluded that the serpentine vegetation of the Eremean Botanical Province was not particularly favourable for biological prospecting because of the following factors:

1—During the wet winter period, temperatures are too low for active plant growth and in summer the temperatures are too high and the moisture deficiency too great. The vegetation is therefore largely sclerophyllous and mainly restricted to ephemerals which do not penetrate the soil to any significant degree.

2—Nickel orebodies tend to be at ultramafic/mafic contacts where the soils support a similar type of vegetation.

3—The ubiquitous presence of laterites limits the extent to which the surface soil reflects bedrock.

4—Much of the landscape is covered by transported soils which do not reflect bedrock to any great extent.

TABLE 20.2 Mean Numbers of Species Found Over Each of Three Types of Quadrat at Spargoville, Western Australia

Species	Lithology of bedrock		
	Amphibolite	Serpentine	Contact zone
1. *Acacia acuminata*	0.57	0.17	2.86
2. *A. colletoides*	0.50	1.08	0.86
3. *A. aff. colletoides*	4.11	1.67	4.14
4. *A. erinacea*	0.46	1.33	0.86
5. *A. graffiana*	0.18	0.33	0.00
6. *Alyxia buxifolia*	0.11	0.25	0.57
7. *Cratystylis microphylla*	0.11	0.00	0.00
8. *C. subspinescens*	0.00	0.18	0.00
9. *Dodonaea filifolia*	0.54	0.00	0.29
10. *D. lobulata*	0.00	0.00	0.14
11. *D. microzyga*	0.04	0.00	0.29
12. *D. stenozyga*	0.68	6.08	2.86
13. *Eremophila caerulea*	0.00	0.08	0.86
14. *E. dempsteri*	12.93	1.92	10.14
15. *E. ionantha*	5.32	0.58	0.43
16. *E. oppositifolia*	4.36	5.83	5.14
17. *E. pachphylla*	2.43	3.83	14.86
18. *E. sp. I*	0.04	0.50	0.00
19. *E. sp. II*	1.46	0.25	0.14
20. *Eucalyptus calycogona*	0.89	1.58	1.86
21. *E. lesouefii*	49.93	39.67	43.86
22. *E. longicornis*	1.14	1.83	0.43
23. *E. salubris*	0.32	0.00	6.14
24. *E. torquata*	0.04	0.17	0.00
25. *Exocarpos aphyllus*	0.61	0.75	0.71
26. *Kochia pyramidata*	0.04	0.08	0.00
27. *Melaleuca sheathiana*	0.82	0.25	0.29
28. *Olearia muelleri*	3.43	3.67	2.29
29. *Pittosporum phillyraeoides*	0.00	0.17	0.00
30. *Rhagodia sp.*	0.04	0.00	0.14
31. *Santalum spicatum*	0.04	0.08	0.00
32. *Scaevola spinescens*	0.39	1.00	0.57
33. *Trymalium ledifolium*	0.00	0.17	0.14
34. *Westringia cephalantha*	0.07	0.33	1.29

Source: Nielsen (1972)

Plate 20.1   (a) Above: *Acacia aneura* growing near Leonora, Western Australia
(b) Middle: View south from the Marriott Prospect near Leonora, Western Australia showing a nearly monospecific community of *Acacia burkittii* on mafic and ultramafic rocks.
(c) Below: Gossanous zone at the Marriott Prospect, near Leonora, Western Australia showing *Acacia burkittii*. A juvenile *A. linophylla* can be seen on the left foreground.
Photos by B. C. Severne.

Plate 20.2 (a) Above left: *Eucalyptus lesouefii* over ultramafites at Spargoville, Western Australia. Photo by J. S. Nielsen.
(b) Above right: *Ricinocarpos bowmanii* on the Coolac Serpentinite Belt in New South Wales.
(c) Below left: *Casuarina stricta* on the Coolac Serpentinite Belt in New South Wales.
(d) Below right: The serpentinicolous grass tree *Xanthorrhoea australis* growing on the Coolac Serpentinite Belt, New South Wales. Last three photos by M. T. Lyons.

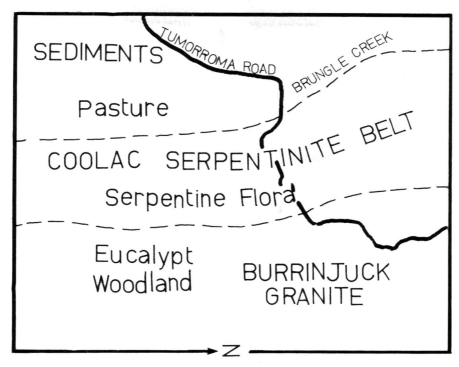

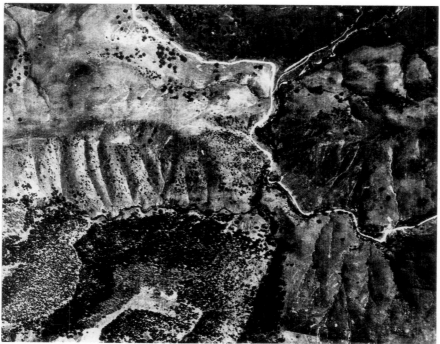

Plate 20.3 Aerial view of the Coolac serpentinite belt near Tumut, New South Wales. The serpentinite is shown in the middle of the photo and is characterised by prominent east-west trending drainage patterns. The Burrinjuck Granites on the eastern contact support a dense eucalypt woodland. the western contact with a sedimentary formation is obscured to some extent by clearing of the original vegetation for agriculture.
Source: Lyons (1973).

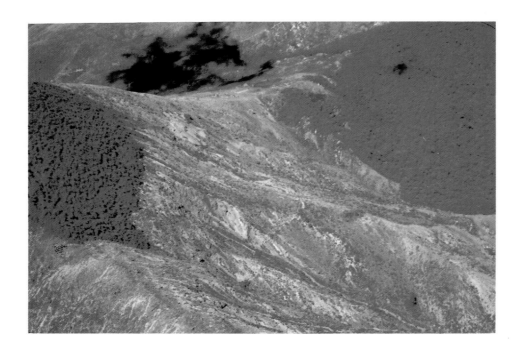

Plate 21.1 (a) Above: Infrared photo of the Dùn Mountain area. The darker red areas to the left, represent the beech forest on sediments of Wooded Peak which is higher in altitude than the serpentine saddle.
Photo by M. H. Timperley.
(b) Below: Serpentine scrub over ultramafites at North Cape.
Photo by P. Shepherd.

TABLE 20.3 Discriminant Analysis (D² statistic) Using the Distribution of Species on Three Types of Quadrat to Predict the Lithology

Plant species (numbers as in Table 20.2)	D²	Number of correct predictions		
		A(26)	UM(11)	A/UM(7)
21	0.5	11	6	0
21,23	6.2	10	6	1
2,21,23	8.3	21	7	1
2,4,14,21,23	21.1	19	9	1
2,4,14,15,16,21,23	29.1	22	11	2
2,4,14,15,16,21,23,25	29.4	20	10	2
2,4,14,15,16,21,23,24,27	42.2	22	10	4
1,2,4–6,12,14–16,21,23,24,27	51.8	24	10	3
1,2,4,7,8,12,14–17,21,23,24,27	67.8	24	10	4
1,2,4,5,7,8,12,14–17,19,21,23,24,27,29	81.3	23	9	5
1,2,4,5,7,8,12,14–17,19,21,23,24,31–33	137.5	25	10	6
1,2,4,5,7,8,11,12,14–17,19,21–24,31–33	140.2	24	10	6
1,2,4,5,7,8,12,14–17,19,21,23,24,30–33	173.9	26	10	5

A = amphibolite, UM = ultramafites, A/UM = contact zone. The total number of quadrats is shown in parentheses.
After: Nielsen (1972)

20.4.2 The Geology and Serpentine Vegetation of the Mulga Zone North of Kalgoorlie

Extensive studies have been carried out on the serpentine component of the mulga bush north of Kalgoorlie. The work was done by Severne (1972) who carried out much of it in the Mt Clifford area some 32 km north of Leonora on the main road to Agnew. The area is located by the presence of a gossanous zone which outcrops along a rocky ridge crest disappearing under an extensive blanket of colluvial soils in the east. This gossanous zone of oxidised mineralisation is seen as a pitted serpentinite with blebs of limonitic material which occasionally displays violet hues of violarite and a green bloom of zaratite. It outcrops discontinuously over a maximum width of 20 m and a strike of several hundred metres and appears to represent disseminated nickeliferous sulphides at depth.

The ground falls away gently to the north to a sediment band and to the south to a scarp which marks the footwall contact of the meta-ultramafite sequence with a basic gabbroic sill. The ground is relatively flat south of the gabbro serpentinite scarp, and laterite forms a thin capping over undifferentiated serpentinites at the southern edge of the area.

North of the main sediment band, amphibolites and serpentinized pyroxenites outcrop. The serpentinites which are host rocks for the mineralised zone are former dunites and peridotites. Outcrop is obscured to the south by laterite and to the east by solonised brown soils (up to 3 m in depth) but is otherwise excellent.

During the course of field work, Severne (1972) observed several plant associations controlled by lithology. These are shown in Fig. 20.4.

Acacia burkitti (Plate 20.1b) is restricted to serpentinized pyroxenites but does colonise serpentinized peridotites. *A. resinomarginea* (Plate 20.1c) displays an inverse relationship with *A. burkitti* and is confined to the basic gabbroic sill, albeit with some overlap on to serpentinized peridotites. *A. aneura* occurs on mafic and ultramafic lithologies but at a considerably lower density than the previous two species. *A. linophylla* is restricted to the high rocky areas which in this case coincide with a gossanous zone. Other species which are only occasionally seen include *Eremophila oldfieldii* and *Santalum spicatum*, and are usually found on low flat ground.

The genus *Eremophila* includes *E. exilifolia* which is restricted to rocky basic outcrops. *Dodonaea lobulata* is another shrub species which is restricted to serpentinites. *Cassia* species including *C. artemisioides* which grows on relatively calcareous soils, are found over sediment bands. *C. sturtii*, *C. desolata*, and *C. helmsii* also exhibit this preference for finely-powdered calcareous soils. *C. sturtii* forms a monospecific grouping near the base of the serpentinized peridotite-dunite unit which corresponds to a calcareous soil with high nickel levels (>1000 μg/g). *C. manicula* is strongly restricted to outcropping basic rocks, while *C. nemophila* is found only over serpentinites. The other shrub species, *Scaevola spinescens*, *Ptilotus obovatus*, *Calytrix* sp., *Acacia hilliana*, and *Prosthanthera* aff. *striatiflora* are of sparse distribution and the latter 3 species are usually found only on rocky basic outcrops.

The serpentinized peridotite units are flanked by metabasalts and metagabbros. These latter rock types with their neutral soils are characterised by the tree species *Acacia hilliana* and *A. resinomarginea* and by the shrubs *Eremophila exilifolia*, *Cassia manicula*, *Calytrix* sp. and by the mint *Prosthanthera* aff. *striatiflora*. The metaclinopyroxenites with their calcareous soils support *A. burkittii* which also grows over the sediment band.

To the east of the prospect, the metaclinopyroxenite hills are characterised by *A. burkittii*. The serpentinized peridotites usually only form low rocky outcrops separated by areas of solonised brown soils. *A. aneura* and *A. resinomarginea* characterise the serpentine islands and are joined occasionally by the mustard *Lepidium leptopetalum* and by *Eremophila platycalyx*.

The non-outcropping areas, occupied by the calcareous alkaline soils support *Hakea arida* and *H. leucoptera* with a shrub layer comprising *Cassia nemophila*, *C. artemisioides*, *C. sturtii* and *Eremophila pantoni*.

As a result of the investigations at Mt Clifford and elsewhere, Severne (1972) was able to formulate broad generalities about the relationship between lithology and plant species in the mulga zone of Eremean Botanical Province. These observations are summarized in Table 20.4. Considering first the tree layer, it was observed that the ubiquitous *Acacia aneura* has a virtually unlimited distribution whereas other *Acacia* species are restricted either to outcropping skeletal soil areas or to the relatively deep solonised brown soils. Specifically, *A. linophylla* prefers well-drained neutral to acid soils on higher ground. *A. resinomarginea* grows on ultramafic and mafic outcrops, whereas *A. burkittii* flourishes only on serpentinized clinopyroxenites. *A. grasbyi* occupies amphibole-chlorite soils which are usually intermediate in character between the skeletal and solonised brown soils.

Acacia quadrimarginea characterises the steep sedimentary and often silicified ridges, whilst *A. sowdenii* is restricted to the deep solonised brown soils together with various *Hakea* species. The drainage tracts are marked by a distinctive vegetation community comprising *Eucalyptus camuldensis*, *A. aneura*, and *A. dempsteri*.

The shrub layer also contains species which have restricted distributions over specific substrates. The basic metabasalts and metagabbros were characterised by *Calytrix* sp., *Cassia manicula*, *Eremophila exilifolia*, while the serpentine supports *Dodonaea lobulata*, *E. exilifolia* and 3 small species: *Hybanthus floribundus* (see below), *Trymalium ledifolium* and *Prosthanthera striatiflora*.

20.4.3 Phytosociology of the Serpentine Vegetation

Very few phytosociological studies of the serpentine vegetation of Western Australia have been carried out. However Ernst (1974) has defined the Hybanthion floribundii Alliance covering this vegetation. Details are given in Table 20.5. The Character species of the Alliance is *Hybanthus floribundus*, a well-known hyperaccumulator of nickel (see 20.4.4 below). There are 2 Associations within the Alliance and these are known respectively as Dodonaeo microzygae—Trymalietum myrtilli and Eremophiletum weldii. The former is found in the Widgiemooltha area where the phytotoxic soils show a complete absence of trees in sharp contrast with the surrounding *Eucalyptus oleosa—E. griffithsii—E. salmonophloia* woodland. Character species of the Alliance are *Hybanthus floribundus* and *Grevillea acuaria*. For the first of the above Associations, *Dodonaea microzyga* and

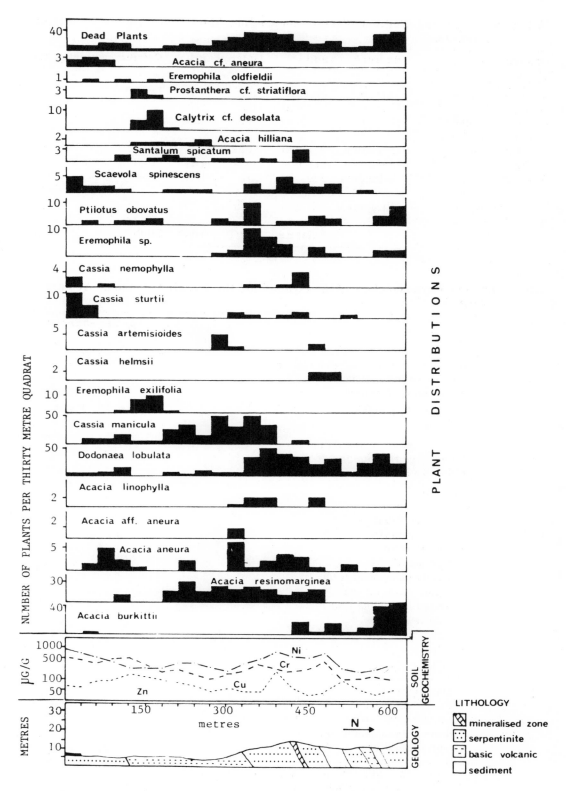

Fig. 20.4 Belt transect across a nickel prospect at Mt Clifford near Leonora.
Source: Severne (1972).

TABLE 20.4 Soil and Bedrock Factors Controlling Plant Communities in Western Australia

Dominant species	Bedrock	Soil	Outcrop	pH	Calcium content of soil
Acacia aneura/					
A. linophylla	Laterite	Laterite	High	Low	Low
A. burkittii	Ultramafic	Skeletal	High	Low	Low
A. coolgardiensis	Dolerite	Skeletal	High	Low	Low
A. dempsteri/Eremophila					
camuldensis	Unknown	Alluvial	None	—	—
A. grasbyi	Mafic	Skeletal	High	High	High
A. quadrimarginea	Sediments	Sed.	Low	Low	Low
A. resinomarginea/					
A. aneura	Ultramafic	Skeletal	High	Low	Low
A. sowdenii/Hakea					
leucoptera	—	Solonised	Low	High	High

After: Severne (1972)

TABLE 20.5 The Phytosociology of the Hybanthion floribundii Alliance of Western Australia

	Species abundance	
	A	B
Character species of the Associations		
Dodonaea microzyga	5	
Trymalium myrtillus	4	
Eremophila weldii		5
Westringia rigida		2
Character species of the Alliance		
Hybanthus floribundus	5	5
Grevillea acuaria	1	3
Companions		
Scaevola spinescens	4	4
Dodonaea lobulata	2	2
Acacia erinacea	1	2
Eucalyptus sp.	1	1
Alyxia buxifolia	4	
Eremophila oppositifolia	4	
Atriplex nummularia	4	
Eremophila elachantha	1	
Casuarina obesa		5
Eremophila oldfieldii		4
E. strongylophylla		3
Santalum spicatum		3
Kochia sedifolia		3
Cassia nemophila		3
Eucalyptus lesouefii		2
Acacia brachystachya		1
Sarcostemma tomentellum		1
Olearia muelleri		1

A = Dodonaeo microzygae—Trymalietum myrtilli Association:
B = Eremophiletum weldii Assocation.
Numbers 1–5 are relative abundances.
Source: Ernst (1974)

HYBANTHUS   FLORIBUNDUS

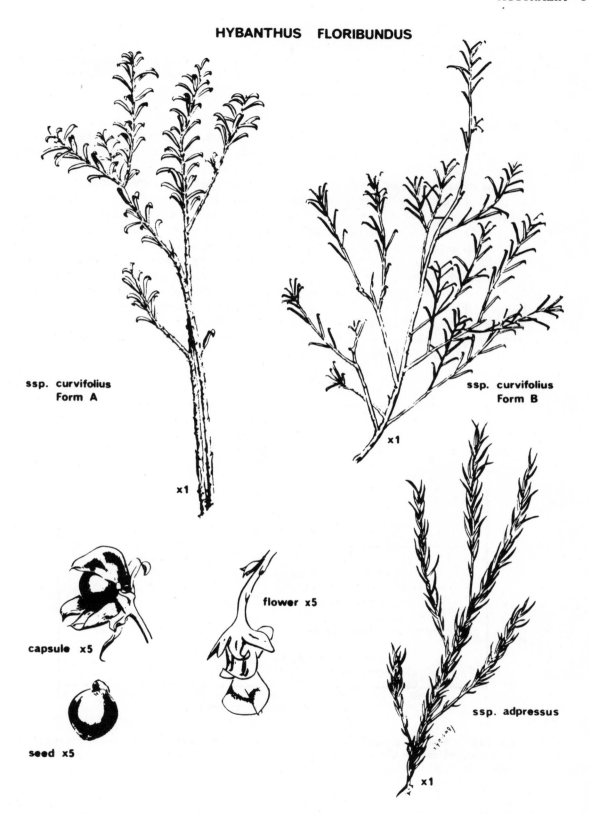

ssp. curvifolius
Form A

x1

ssp. curvifolius
Form B

x1

capsule x5

flower x5

seed x5

ssp. adpressus

x1

Fig. 20.5   Various morphological forms of *Hybanthus floribundus*. Sketch by G. Galloway.

Trymalium myrtillus are the character species. Companions of the Association include *Atriplex nummularia, Eremophila oppositifolia, Alyxia buxifolia* and *Scaevola spinescens.*

The Eremophiletum weldii Association is found over nickel-rich soils in the Kurnalpi region with *E. weldii* and *Westringia rigida* as character species. Companions include: *Casuarina obesa, Eremophila oldfieldii,* and *E. strongylophylla.*

20.4.4 Hybanthus floribundus

A special mention must be made of the nickel hyperaccumulator *Hybanthus floribundus* (Fig. 20.5) whose ecology and biogeochemistry have been described by Severne and Brooks (1972), Cole (1973), and Severne (1972, 1974).

The remarkable accumulation of nickel by *Hybanthus floribundus* was first reported in the open literature by Severne and Brooks (1972) though the original discovery was apparently made by M. M. Cole some years before, though it was not published until much later (Cole, 1973). Severne and Brooks (1972) reported 23% nickel in the plant ash (corresponding to about 1600 μg/g in dried leaves. The nickel and cobalt content of *H. floribundus* compared with other species and with soils and rocks from the area is shown in Fig. 20.6. It should be noted that the plant data are expressed on an ash weight basis and should by multiplied by 0.07 to convert to dry weight. It is interesting to record that other species of *Hybanthus* have an ability to hyperaccumulate nickel (see Chapter 8) as for example several species from New Caledonia (Jaffré, 1980). At the time of the discovery of its hyperaccumulating power, *H. floribundus* was only the third of such a type to be recorded (i.e., after *Alyssum bertolonii* and *A. murale*).

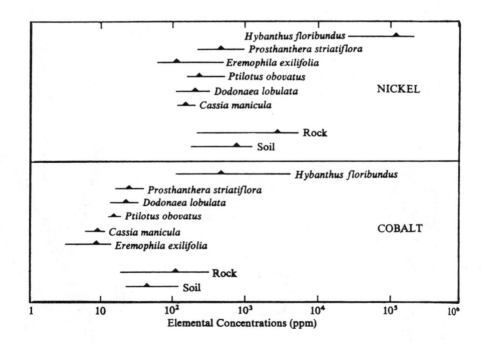

Fig. 20.6   Nickel and cobalt concentrations (μg/g ash weight) in *Hybanthus floribundus* and other serpentine plants from Western Australia. Values for associated rocks and soils are also shown. Source: Severne (1972).

The taxonomy of *Hybanthus* has been described by Bennett (1969) who has recognised several subspecies and forms of the original *H. floribundus* (see Fig. 20.5) such as subsp. *curvifolius* form A, subsp. *curvifolius* form B, subsp. *adpressus*. subsp. *floribundus* and *H. epacroides* subsp. *bilobus*. The levels of nickel and other elements in these taxa and in their associated soils are given in Table 20.6. It is noteworthy that uptake of nickel is extraordinarily high even when the content of this element in the soil is quite low. Even *H. epacroides* contains 200 μg/g nickel when growing over a soil which is not nickeliferous.

Severne (1972) studied the distribution of *H. floribundus* over a nickel deposit in the Kurrajong region of Western Australia. He counted the number of individuals growing on 179 quadrants (30 m × 30 m) and related the density to the nickel content of the soil (Fig. 20.7). He found a very good correlation between the 2 variables, particularly for quadrats containing over 880 μg/g nickel. As a result of his studies, Severne (1972) concluded that *Hybanthus floribundus* hyperaccumulates nickel and is restricted to laterised ultramafic outcrops and creek beds draining these areas.

In her studies of the biogeochemistry and ecology of *Hybanthus floribundus*, Cole (1973) decided that this taxon is restricted to soils with a high nickel content in the Widgiemooltha, Mt Thirsty, Mission Ridge and Kurnalpi regions. Four occurrences of this taxon were observed over outcropping serpentinite and at the contact of quartz felspar porphyry and hypersthenite dykes with serpentinite at Widgiemooltha and Dordie Rocks, and over alluvium and collovium at Kurrajong, Riverina and Coolgardie. Cole (1973) concluded that *H. floribundus* is an indicator of a nickeliferous environment though it does not necessarily delineate a nickel sulphide orebody within the ultramafites. The same author concluded that the nickel content of the plant bears some relation with the level of this element in the soil.

TABLE 20.6 The Nickel, Chromium and Cobalt Content (μg/g dry weight) of *Hybanthus* Species and their Associated Soils.

Species	Location	n	Nickel Plant	Nickel Soil	Cobalt Plant	Cobalt Soil	Chromium Plant	Chromium Soil
Hybanthus floribundus subsp. *curvifolius* form A	Marshall Pool	34	7025	800	63	70	1.7	840
	Kurrajong	22	3100	900	26	90	4.3	2000
form B	Kambalda	3	3000	900	7	—	3.5	700
	S. cross	6	4510	1400	129	250	1.5	2700
	Widgiemooltha	4	6010	2000	23	—	1.1	—
	Spargoville	4	740	970	7	85	.4.0	1070
subsp. *adpressus*	Ravensthorpe	12	1270	134	51	35	2.1	240
subsp. *floribundus*	Lake King	4	263	50	170	15	1.2	87
	S. Cross	2	1020	50	550	20	1.2	70
H. epacroides subsp. *bilobus*	Scadden	3	200	10	62	5	2.1	10

Source: Severne (1972)

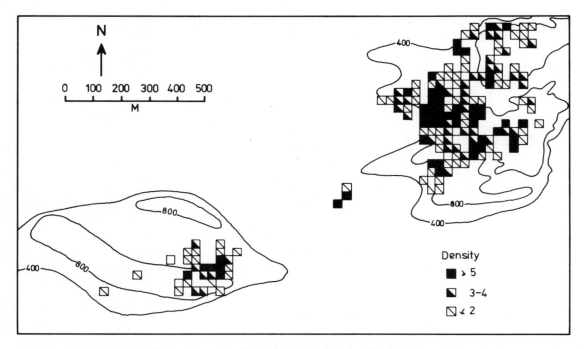

Fig. 20.7 The relationship between the abundance of *Hybanthus floribundus* and the nickel content of the soil in the Kurrajong area of Western Australia.
Source: Severne (1972).

20.5 BIOGEOCHEMICAL STUDIES IN WESTERN AUSTRALIA

Several biogeochemical investigations have been carried out on the serpentine vegetation of Western Australia. The original purpose of most of these studies was biogeochemical prospecting for minerals (Severne, 1972; Cole, 1971, 1973).

In the Murchison Region of the mulga bush north of Kalgoorlie, Severne (1972) used the leaves of the ubiquitous *Acacia aneura* (mulga) to delineate nickel anomalies in the bedrock. He found that this taxon could be used for biogeochemical prospecting even in the presence of a siliceous hardpan isolating the surface soil from the bedrock.

In the Kurrajong region, the same worker used the phylloides of *Acacia aneura* to determine nickel mineralization in the substrate. Coincident nickel and manganese anomalies in the plant material indicated a lateritic environment. The method successfully located nickel even with an overburden of up to 10 m of transported soil not related to bedrock. The effective depth of the method decreased with increasing laterisation.

Biogeochemical studies involving the use of *Melaleuca sheathiana* were carried out by Hall et al. (1973) in the sclerophyllous eucalypt woodland at Norseman. These workers found a relatively good correlation between the nickel content of the leaves of this taxon and that of the soil, as is illustrated in Fig. 20.8.

There has already been some mention of the work of Nielsen (1972) and Nielsen et al. (1973) in which discriminant analysis was used to predict the nature of the bedrock on the basis of the distribution of 34 plant species in the Spargoville area near Norseman. The same workers applied a biogeochemical method to the same problem. They determined 9 elements in bark samples of *Eucalyptus lesouefii* (Plate 20.2a) growing over 34 amphibolite and 29 ultramafic sites. The values are given in Table 20.7. Discriminant analysis of the data

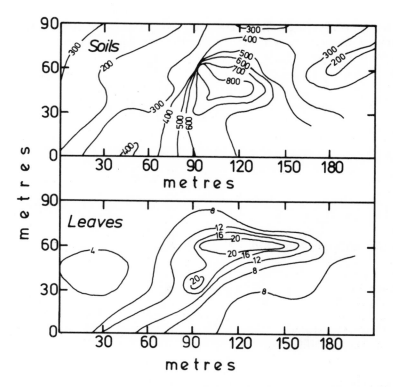

Fig. 20.8   Nickel concentrations in soils and dried leaves of *Melaleuca sheathiana* from the Norseman area, Western Australia.
Source: Hall et al. (1973).

TABLE 20.7   Mean Elemental Concentrations (μg/g ash weight) in Bark of *Eucalyptus lesouefii* from Spargoville, Western Australia.

Element	Lithology	
	Amphibolite	**Serpentine**
Calcium	12830	12526
Chromium	205	423
Cobalt	35	39
Copper	65	75
Lead	44	41
Magnesium	34930	38620
Manganese	334	353
Nickel	153	209
Zinc	68	77

Source: Nielsen (1972)

using the Mahalanobis D^2 statistic (Table 20.8) successfully predicted the nature of bedrock in 29 out of 34 amphibolite quadrats and in 19 of 29 ultramafic quadrats. The method is clearly not as effective as geobotany in predicting the nature of the substrate but has an obvious potential in the future with the development of newer methods of analysis such as plasma emission (ICP) spectrometry where up to 30 elements can be readily determined with great speed, precision and sensitivity. The technique presaged the work of Pape (1978) who used a modification of this procedure to predict the nature of the substrate in the Harz mountains of Germany (see Chapter 14).

TABLE 20.8 **Discriminant Analysis (D^2 statistic) Using the Elemental Composition of the Bark of *Eucalyptus lesouefii* to Predict the Lithology on Amphibolite and Ultramafic Sites**

Element	D^2	Number of correct predictions	
		A (34)	UM (29)
Ca	0.1	17	17
Co	1.7	23	15
Cr	9.4	24	14
Cu	2.2	24	14
Mg	0.8	24	15
Mn	0.2	21	10
Ni	3.1	24	14
Pb	1.2	20	13
Zn	3.8	26	14
Ca,Co,Cr,Cu,Mg,Mn,Ni,Pb,Zn	16.8	29	17
Cr,Ni	10.1	27	15
Co,Cr,Ni	13.5	26	16
Cr,Mg,Ni	13.9	25	18
Cr,Mg,Ni,Pb	14.2	25	19
Co,Cr,Mg,Ni,Pb	16.5	29	16
Ca,Cr,Cu,Mg,Mn,Ni	14.2	26	17
Cr,Cu,Mg,Mn,Ni,Zn	14.3	26	18

A = amphibolite, UM = ultramafic. The total number of quadrats is shown in parentheses.
After: Nielsen (1972)

20.6 STUDIES ON THE SERPENTINE VEGETATION OF EASTERN AUSTRALIA

Despite the occurrence of several fairly extensive ophiolitic serpentine belts in eastern Australia carrying an unusual serpentine flora, studies of the vegetation have only been carried out over the Coolac Serpentinite Belt of New South Wales (Lyons, 1973; Lyons et al. 1974). A brief description of this work will now be given.

20.6.1 The Geology of the Coolac Serpentinite Belt

The Coolac Serpentinite Belt (Site #3 in Fig. 20.1) is located in New South Wales about 450 km southwest of Sydney just north of the Snowy Mts near Tumut. The climate is cool-temperate with a mean maximum of 28°C in January and 10°C in July. The rainfall is an evenly-distributed 1000 mm. The Belt is a continuous outcrop of ultramafic and associated rocks extending over a distance of 55 km in a north-south direction. The geology of the region has been described by Golding (1969). The Belt is broadly divisible into 3 meridional physiographic zones which reflect lithological and structural discontinuities as well as the distribution of vegetation.

The eastern zone consists of a 915 m elevation dissected plateau underlain by Burrinjuck Granite. The central physiographic zone (Coolac Serpentinite Belt) is a zone of major tectonism which encloses all the ultramafic rocks. The western zone descends to 244 m at the Tumut River and is underlain by lower Palaeozoic sedimentary, volcanic and metamorphic rocks.

The Coolac Serpentinite Belt (Fig. 20.9) varies in width from 3.5 km at Red Hill to as little as 10 metres near the southern end. An aerial photograph (Plate 20.3) of part of the Belt in the Honeysuckle Range, shows 3 distinct zones: the Belt itself with strong east-west

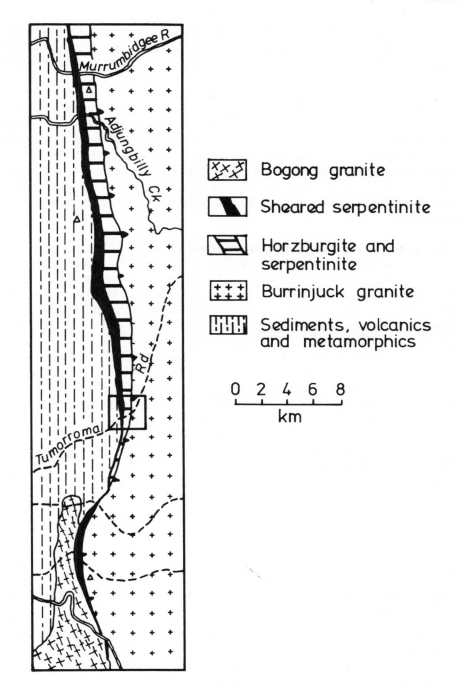

Fig. 20.9 The geology of the Coolac Serpentinite Belt. The square corresponds to the area in Plate 20.3.
Source: Golding (1969).

drainage patterns, sediments and volcanics to the west, and thickly-wooded Burrinjuck Granite in the east. The natural vegetation over sediments to the left of the scene has been cleared for pasture and does not show the vegetation gradation which would normally be expected.

The dominant rock types of the Coolac Serpentinite Belt are serpentinite and partly-serpentinized harzburgite. There are also widespread occurrences of small pockets of wehrlite, lherzolite, clinopyroxenite and chromite together with narrow discontinuous rodingite dykes. In addition there are numerous tectonic inclusions of variably deformed and metasomatised basic, intermediate, and acidic igneous and metamorphic rocks with minor sedimentary materials. The Burrinjuck Granite meets the ultramafites along the eastern contact. Along the western contact the Honeysuckle Beds is a discontinuous unit of low grade metabasaltic and spilitic rocks with quartzofeldspathic metasediments and porphyritic metadacite.

20.6.2 The Vegetation of the Coolac Serpentinite Belt

As is shown in Plate 20.3, the Burrinjuck Granite to the east of the contact supports a dense eucalypt woodland dominated by *Eucalyptus mellisiodora*. The boundary with the ultramafites is extremely sharp and apart from a few grasses there are no species common to both rock types. At the boundary the dense eucalypt woodland gives way to a typically xerophytic assemblage with paucity of numbers of species and a narrowing of leaf form, so typical of serpentine floras. Excluding grasses and herbs, the most typical plants of the serpentine are the small tree *Casuarina stricta* (Plate 20.2c), the shrub *Ricinocarpos bowmanii* (Plate 20.2b) and the unusual grass tree *Xanthorrhoea australis*. (Plate 20.2d). Other species found over serpentine are listed in Table 20.9. The boundary with the sediments to the west is not sharp because of the complete removal of the original vegetation cover to provide pasture.

The *Casuarina-Xanthorrhoea* association seems to be typical of the serpentine flora of New South Wales since it is also found elsewhere on the Coolac Serpentinite Belt and over ultramafites at Baryulgil in northern New South Wales (site #4 in Fig. 20.1). It must, however, be realised that both taxa are *bodenvag* and are not serpentine-endemic except locally.

TABLE 20.9   Major Species Encountered Over the Ultramafites of the Coolac Serpentinite Belt.

Species	Family	Relative abundance*
Acacia decora	Fabaceae	4
A. implexa	Fabaceae	2
Banksia marginata	Proteaceae	1
Casuarina stricta	Casuarinaceae	4
Clematis microphylla	Ranunculaceae	3
Exocarpus cupressiformis	Santalaceae	1
Ricinocarpos bowmanii	Euphorbiaceae	5
Stackhousia sp.	Stackhousiaceae	1
Xanthorrhoea australis	Xanthorrhoeaceae	4

* 5 = extremely abundant, 4 = abundant, 3 = fairly abundant, 2 = uncommon, 1 = rare.
Source: Lyons (1973).

20.6.3 Biogeochemical Investigations on the Coolac Serpentinite Belt

Lyons (1973) and Lyons et al. (1974) have carried out biogeochemical investigations over the serpentine of the Coolac Serpentinite Belt. The elemental data are shown in Table 20.10 for rocks, soils and plant material. The levels of calcium, magnesium, nickel, chromium and cobalt are as would be expected for serpentine soils developed in cool temperate climatic zones. The concentrations of the plant nutrients calcium and potassium in the soils are also predictably low.

Plant-soil correlation analysis did not show highly significant relationships involving "serpentine elements" such as nickel, chromium, cobalt and magnesium so that biogeochemical prospecting was not likely to be successful in this region. However discriminant analysis of the elemental composition of soils underlying each of the 3 main species showed that Casuarina stricta favoured sites with high potassium and nickel concentrations, whereas Xanthorrhoea australis favoured sites with the highest magnesium levels (8.15%) and lowest copper, nickel and potassium concentrations in the soils. The importance of magnesium in the metabolism of X. australis is further highlighted by the observation that the magnesium content of dry leaves of this taxon (1.4%) was far higher than for the other 2 species studied. X. australis also has a low calcium content so that its Ca/Mg mole quotient of 0.57 is three times lower than for the other 2 species. The Xanthorrhoea is apparently tolerant not only of high magnesium, but also of low calcium levels in the soils and is therefore well suited to ultramafic environments.

The paucity of work on the serpentine vegetation of the eastern seaboard of Australia is surprising, and it is certain that a rich field remains to be exploited here. There are extensive ultramafic occurrences in Queensland which will also repay investigation.

TABLE 20.10 The Mean (geometric) Elemental Content of Rocks (12), Soils (138) and Plants (42–46 of each species) from the Coolac Serpentinite Belt

Element	Rocks	Soils	Vegetation		
			C. stricta	R. bowmanii	X. australis
Cobalt (μg/g)	119	205	—	—	—
Chromium (μg/g)	1706	1496	4	5	3
Copper (μg/g)	19	22	7	15	8
Potassium (μg/g)	252	1582	5300	4600	6400
Manganese (μg/g)	913	1654	156	194	171
Nickel (μg/g)	2167	1984	47	75	27
Zinc (μg/g)	66	54	61	31	52
Calcium (%)	2.80	0.49	2.21	2.13	1.34
Iron (%)	6.56	10.27	0.05	0.07	0.02
Magnesium (%)	18.80	7.58	0.84	0.76	1.40
Ca/Mg*	0.09	0.04	1.58	1.68	0.57

C. = Casuarina, R. = Ricinocarpos, X. = Xanthorrhoea
* mole quotient
Source: Lyons (1973)

REFERENCES

Bennett, E. M., 1969. *The Genus Hybanthus Jacquin in Australia Including the Cytology and Anatomy of Western Australian Species.* MSc Thesis, Univ. Western Australia, Perth.

Cole, M. M., 1965. The use of vegetation in mineral exploration in Australia. *Proc. Commonw. Min. Metall. Congr.,* 6: 1429–1458.

Cole, M. M., 1971. The importance of environment in biogeographical/geobotanical and biogeochemical investigations. *Can. Inst. Min. Metall. Spec.* Vol. #11: 414–425.

Cole, M. M., 1973. Geobotanical and biogeochemical investigations in the sclerophyllous woodland and shrub associations of the Eastern Goldfields area of Western Australia with particular reference to the role of *Hybanthus floribundus* (Lindl.) F. Muell. as a nickel indicator and accumulator plant. *J. Appl. Ecol.,* 10: 269–320.

Derry, D. R., 1980. *A Concise Atlas of Geology and Mineral Deposits.* Mining Journal Books, London.

Elkington, J. E., 1969. *Vegetation Studies in the Eastern Goldfields of Western Australia with Particular Reference to their Role in Geological Reconnaissance and Mineral Exploration.* PhD Thesis, Univ. of London.

Ernst, W., 1974. *Schwermetallvegetation der Erde.* Fischer, Stuttgart.

Gardner, C. A., 1952. The vegetation of Western Australia. *J. Proc. Roy. Soc. W. Aust.,* 28: 11–37.

Golding, H. G., 1969. The Coolac-Goobarragandra ultramafic belt, New South Wales. *J. Proc. Roy. Soc. N.S.W.,* 102: 173–187.

Hall, J. S., Both, R. A. and Smith, F. A., 1973. A comparative study of rocks, soils and plant chemistry in relation to nickel mineralization in the Pioneer area, Western Australia. *Proc. Australas. Inst. Min. Metall.,* #247: 11–22.

Jaffré, T., 1980. *Etudes Ecologiques du Peuplement Végétal des Sols Dérivés de Roches Ultrabasiques en Nouvelle Calédonie.* O.R.S.T.O.M., Paris.

Lyons, M. T., 1973. *Soil Factors Controlling the Vegetation of the Coolac Serpentinite Belt in New South Wales.* MSc Thesis, Univ. N.S.W.

Lyons, M. T., Brooks, R. R. and Craig, D. C., 1974. The influence of soil composition on the vegetation of the Coolac Serpentinite Belt in New South Wales. *J. Proc. Roy. Soc. N.S.W.,* 107: 67–75.

Mahalanobis, P. C., 1936. On the generalized distance in statistics. *Proc. Nat. Inst. Sci.* (India) 12: 49–55.

McCall, G. J. H. and Doepel, J. J. G., 1969. Stratiform basic bodies within the Yilmia ophiolites, Western Australia. *Proc. Australas. Inst. Min. Metall.,* #231: 67–73.

Nielsen, J. S., 1972. *The Feasibility of Biogeochemical and Geobotanical Prospecting at Spargoville, Western Australia.* MSc Thesis, Massey University, Palmerston North, New Zealand.

Nielsen, J. S., Brooks, R. R. and Marshall, N. J., 1973. Statistical evaluation of geobotanical and biogeochemical data by discriminant analysis. *J. Appl. Ecol.,* 10: 251–258.

Pape, H., 1978. *Entwicklung einer Geochemischen Kartiermethode fur Lagerstättenprospektion, Umweltforschung, and Landesplanung auf der Grundlage von Multielementuntersuchungen an Pflanzenaschen.* Doct. Thesis, Tech. Univ., Clausthal.

Prider, R. T., 1961. The "greenstones" of southwestern Australia. *J. Proc. Roy. Soc. W. Aust.,* 44: 1–9.

Severne, B. C., 1972. *Botanical Methods for Mineral Exploration in Western Australia.* PhD Thesis, Massey University, Palmerston North, New Zealand.

Severne, B. C., 1974. Nickel accumulation by *Hybanthus floribundus. Nature,* 248: 807–808.

Severne, B. C. and Brooks, R. R., 1972. A nickel-accumulating plant from Western Australia. *Planta,* 103: 91–94.

Chapter 21

NEW ZEALAND

21.1 GEOLOGY AND TECTONICS

New Zealand is believed to have once been part of Australia until 80–60 m.y. ago and to have shared the same geological history as eastern Australia at least until the late Cretaceous, including the subsequent sedimentation in the great north-trending Tasman Geosyncline. These sediments and volcanics were involved in the great orogeny of 200–100 m.y. ago which affected eastern Australia as well as New Zealand, and was one of several which formed the Southern Alps of New Zealand (Derry, 1980). After the final orogeny the mountains of New Zealand were almost completely eroded. However a second major period of faulting and uplift occurred 10 m.y. ago and raised the Southern Alps for a second time to such an extent that the highest point (Mt Cook) is nearly 3800 m high.

A major feature of the geology of New Zealand is the spectacular Alpine Fault (Fig. 21.1) which represents a transcurrent movement of some 450 km along the junction of two plates. This lateral displacement has neatly bisected the previously-existing ophiolites and moved the two halves for the whole distance of 450 km. Hence, there is an extremely good match of the geology of the northern and southern parts of South Island in the vicinity, and at opposite sides of, the extremities of the fault.

The ophiolites of New Zealand were first described by Hochstetter (1864a,b) who then discovered and named the mineral dunite after its type locality at Dun Mountain near Nelson in the northern part of South Island. One of the best descriptions of the geology of the New Zealand ultramafites has been given by Coombs et al. (1976) who referred to the "Dun Mountain Ophiolitic Belt" stretching from Mossburn in the south of South Island to North Cape in the extreme north of North Island. The ultramafites in the northern part of South Island are sometimes referred to as the "Dun Mountain Belt" and have been described geologically by Lauder (1965).

As described by Coombs et al. (1976), the Dun Mountain Ophiolitic Belt extends for an observed and inferred length of over 1100 km. The belt is divided into a number of sections. In one of these, the Red Mountain segment, a relatively complete ophiolitic sequence is preserved. Elsewhere the ophiolites are commonly reduced to tectonic melanges. Geochemical and textural evidence suggests that the harzburgite peridotites of the belt represent residual mantle material and that some gabbro-diabase-spilite associations were formed in a zone of crustal accretion. The ophiolites are commonly overlain by breccias derived in part from the ophiolites themselves and in part from volcanic sources. These in turn are covered by thick sediments derived predominantly from a largely inactive volcanic arc without preservation of substantial pelagic deposits. Metamorphism and deformation include early events comparable to those occurring in spreading ocean ridges today, and later events including relatively high pressure metamorphism which also affected overlying Permian and younger strata. The geology of specific localities is discussed below in the appropriate sections.

21.2 AN OVERVIEW OF THE NEW ZEALAND SERPENTINE VEGETATION

21.2.1 Introduction

One of the first recorded observations of the serpentine vegetation of New Zealand was made over 200 years ago when Sir Joseph Banks (1770) travelling with Captain James Cook on one of his voyages of exploration along the west coast of South Island noted: ". . . much snow on the ridges of the high hills, two were, however seen on which was little or none. What ever the cause of it might be I could not guess. They were quite bare of trees and vegetables (sic) and seemed to consist of smouldering soft stone of the colour of bricks or light red ochre."

Banks was apparently describing the sparse vegetation of the Red Mountain ultramafic massif which is clearly visible from the sea. Over a century later, Park (1887) observed similar ultramafic terrain and described it as "extremely destitute of vegetation." A list of workers who have described the serpentine vegetation of New Zealand is given in Table 21.1. Among the first of these to give a check list of the ultramafic flora were Bell et al. (1911) who recorded a number of species growing in the Dun Mountain area near Nelson. They observed the xeromorphic nature of the vegetation as well as the occurrence of the serpentine-endemic *Pimelea suteri*. Other early work on the serpentine vegetation of New Zealand was carried out by Betts (1918), Cockayne (1910, 1922, 1928) and Scott Thomson (1935).

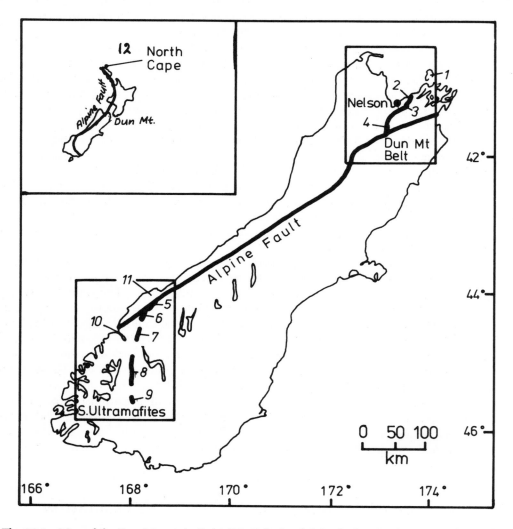

Fig. 21.1   Map of the Dun Mountain Ophiolitic Belt, South Island, showing important ultramafic outcrops. 1—D'Urville Island, 2—Saddle Hill, 3—Dun Mt, 4—Red Hill, 5—Martyr Hill, 6—Red Mt, 7—Fiery Peak, 8—Livingstone Mts, 9—Black Ridge (Mossburn), 10—Lake Ronald, 11—Cascade Plateau, 12—North Cape on North Island.

Plate 21.1 (c) Above: Summit plateau of Red Mountain, Westland, showing the very scanty vegetation over serpentine.
Photo by R. H. Wilde.
(d) Below: Stag Pass on the Livingstone Fault at the base of Little Red Mountain, Westland. There is a dramatic change of vegetation from the grassland of the schist at the left to the complete absence of vegetation on the harzburgites to the right.
Photo by D. Schultz-Ela.

Plate 21.2 (a) Above: Shrub grassland on serpentine at North Cape.
(b) Below: Gabbro community at North Cape.
Photos by T. Jaffré.

Plate 21.3 a) Left: Tall *Nothofagus* forest on sediments at Red Hill.
Photo by T. Jaffré.
(b) Right: *Pimelea suteri*, a serpentine-endemic plants from the Dun Mountain area. Note the extremely long root system of this typical serpentine plant.
Photo by the author.

Plate 21.4 Transitional forest between serpentine (downslope) and limestone (upslope) at Wooded Peak, Dun Mountain Belt. The stunted trees are *Nothofagus solandri* var. *cliffortioides*, a typical species of these transitional forests.
Photo by the author.

Plate 21.5 (a) Above: Shrub grassland community on ultramafic rocks at Dun Mt.
(b) Below: Scrub tussock on dunite at Dun Mountain.

Despite later work by Oliver (1944), Ogden (1970), Wardle et al. (1971) and Mark (1977), there was no definitive work embracing the whole of the serpentine vegetation of most of New Zealand until W. Lee (1980) described the serpentine flora of South Island. This is by far the most detailed treatment of this subject. In this Chapter references for Lee appear as either J. Lee or W. Lee because of potential confusion arising from two authors of the same surname who have studied serpentine vegetation.

The only ultramafic outcrop of any importance in North Island is situated at North Cape. Its flora has been the subject of numerous papers including one by Jaffré and Verlière (1973) who also covered South Island, and a thesis by Shepherd (1983).

Ultramafic rocks cover about 0.20% of the total surface of New Zealand and about 0.35% of South Island. They occupy sites ranging from lowland to alpine with climates varying from warm temperate to sub-Antarctic. In most cases the serpentine vegetation is strikingly different from that of the surrounding non-ultramafic rocks. Indeed in some parts of the country such as Dun Mountain or Red Mountain in southern Westland, the differences are as great or perhaps greater than anywhere else on earth.

In my description of the serpentine flora of New Zealand, I am particularly indebted to works by W. Lee (1980) and Jaffré and Verlière (1973) from which sources much of my material has been derived.

TABLE 21.1 Papers Which Describe the Serpentine Vegetation of New Zealand

Dun Mountain Belt	Southern Ultramafites	North Cape
Bell et al. (1911)	Jaffré and Verlière (1973)	Beever and Jane (1967)
Betts (1918)	W. Lee (1980)	Druce et al. (1979)
Cockayne (1910, 1922, 1928)	W. Lee et al. (1983a,b)	Gravatt (1966)
Jaffré and Verlière (1973)	W. Lee and Given (1984)	Jaffré and Verlière (1973)
J. Lee (1974)	W. Lee and Hewitt (1982)	Johnstone (1967, 1969)
W. Lee (1980)	Mark (1977)	Shepherd (1983)
W. Lee et al. (1983b)		Thompson et al. (1974)
Lyon (1969)		Wheeler (1963)
Lyon et al. (1968, 1970, 1971)		
Ogden (1970)		
Oliver (1944)		

21.2.2 Floristics of the New Zealand Serpentine Vegetation

According to W. Lee (1980), a total of 480 vascular plants has been recorded over the South Island ultramafites, including 53 pteridophytes, 15 gymnosperms, and 412 angiosperms. A further 100 or so vascular plants have been reported from the North Cape serpentines (Druce et al. 1979). The total of 480 for South Island is somewhat misleading because it includes sporadic occurrences. The total number of vascular plants is probably only in the region of 400 for the whole of the New Zealand ultramafites.

The representation of plant families in the ultramafic flora of New Zealand is given in Table 21.2 and the percentage of genera is shown in Table 21.3. It will be observed that the Podocarpaceae, Rubiaceae, Epacridaceae and Thymelaeaceae, which are predominantly woody families, have around 50% or more of their species growing over serpentine. At the generic level, Coprosma, Hymenanthera and Dracophyllum are exceptionally well represented. This is because they are common components of the grassy shrubland associations characteristic of the majority of ultramafic sites in New Zealand.

Very few exotic species have succeeded in colonising New Zealand ultramafites in spite of the presence of nearby agricultural land. The same observation has been made in New Caledonia (Chapter 19).

TABLE 21.2   Contribution of Major Plant Families to the ultramafic Flora of South Island, New Zealand.

Family	Total No. of species	Percentage on ultramafites
Asteraceae	189	24.8
Cyperaceae	120	34.2
Poaceae	101	35.6
Scrophulariaceae	97	22.6
Apiaceae	73	24.6
Orchidaceae	49	38.8
Rubiaceae	42	47.6
Ranunculaceae	41	14.6
Onagraceae	41	21.9
Fabaceae	37	2.7
Epacridaceae	32	53.3
Hymenophyllaceae	26	42.3
Boraginaceae	23	21.7
Rosaceae	23	34.7
Juncaceae	21	47.6
Gentianaceae	20	20.0
Caryophyllaceae	19	21.0
Thymelaeaceae	19	47.3
Brassicaceae	19	16.7
Blechnaceae	16	53.3
Podocarpaceae	15	73.3

Source: W. Lee (1980)

TABLE 21.3   Contribution of Major Plant Genera to the Ultramafic Flora of South Island, New Zealand

Genus	Total No. of species	Percentage on ultramafites
Hebe	56	23.2
Carex	54	22.2
Celmisia	46	36.9
Epilobium	40	22.5
Coprosma	35	54.2
Uncinia	27	33.3
Senecio	25	28.0
Scirpus	23	13.0
Myosotis	23	22.7
Aciphylla	20	20.0
Hymenophyllum	19	52.6
Raoulia	19	21.0
Dracophyllum	17	52.9
Olearia	17	35.2
Poa	16	25.0
Gentiana	14	21.4

Source: W. Lee (1980)

A comparison of growth forms between the flora of the Dun Mountain Belt and southern ultramafites of South Island has been given by W. Lee (1980) and is shown in Table 21.4. The northern group contains 174 taxa of which 13 are serpentine-endemic, whereas the southern group comprises only 104 species with only one serpentine-endemic taxon. This difference almost certainly arises from extensive Pleistocene glaciation in the south of South Island. Gymnosperms and dicotyledonous trees are less abundant in the north owing to the drier climate, and generally form a minor component of the ubiquitous *Leptospermum scoparium* scrubland. The serpentine endemic plants of New Zealand are listed in Table 21.5.

Another factor which has favoured the development of a richer serpentine flora in the north is the much lower degree of erosion of the terrain, which is by no means as steep and dissected as in the south.

It should be noted that the only serpentine-endemic plant of the Southern Ultramafites is *Celmisia spedenii* (Lee and Given, 1984) which formerly included a non-serpentinitic variant which has now been removed from this taxon and has been reclassified as *C. markii*.

TABLE 21.4 Comparison of Growth Forms for Serpentine Plants from the Dun Mountain Belt and the Southern Ultramafites.

Vegetation	Dun Mountain Belt		Southern Ultramafites		Species common to both
	No. species	% of flora	No. species	% of flora	
Gymnosperms	4	2.3	8	7.7	3
Dicotyledons					
Trees	6	3.5	9	8.6	5
Shrubs	41	23.5	26	25.0	22
Others	58	33.4	23	22.2	12
Monocotyledons	51	29.3	25	24.0	14
Pteridophytes	14	8.0	13	12.5	9
Total	174		104		65

Source: W. Lee (1980)

TABLE 21.5 Serpentine-endemic Plants of New Zealand

Location	Species
#1 D'Urville Island	*Hebe urvilleana*
#1–4 Dun Mt Belt	*Carex devia*
#2–4 Dun Mt Belt	*Carex traversii*
#3–4 Dun Mt and Red Hill	*Myosotis monroi, Pimelea suteri*
#4 Red Hill	*Myosotis laeta, Cotula pyrethrifolia* var. *linearifolia*
#9 Mossburn (West Dome)	*Celmisia spedenii*
#12 North Cape	*Cassinia leptophylla* var., *Coprosma* sp. aff. *obconica, C. rhamnoides* var., *C. spathulata, Corokia cotoneaster* var., *Cyathodes parviflora* var., *Geniostoma rupestre* var. *crassum, Haloragis erecta* subsp. *cartilaginea, Parsonia capsularis* var., *Phyllocladus trichomanoides* var., *Pittosporum crassifolium* var.

Sources: W. Lee (1980), Druce et al. (1979)

21.2.3 The Physiognomy of the New Zealand Serpentine Vegetation

Differences between serpentine and non-serpentine vegetation in New Zealand have been clearly shown by Brooks and McDonnell (1983) who used computer processing of LANDSAT digital data to achieve the most effective delineation of ultramafic rocks in New Zealand. This was achieved by histogram equalisation of bands MSS4, 5 and 6 (500–600, 600–700, and 700–800 nm) and the data were written in blue, red and green respectively on to positive colour film. Better delineation of the vegetation of ultramafic rocks was obtained with this procedure than with incorporation of the MSS7 infrared band (800–1100 nm) or by use of the more usual technique of band ratioing. The data clearly showed all of the major serpentine occurrences of New Zealand on the basis of vegetational changes across geological boundaries.

Serpentine areas show up quite well with aerial black-and-white or false colour infrared photography. This is illustrated in Plate 21.1a which is an infrared photograph of the Dun Mountain area near Nelson. The dark red areas represent beech (*Nothofagus*) forest over sedimentary formations. The boundaries are extremely sharp and are not due to the presence of a tree line since the areas of highest elevation are to the left of the plate over Wooded Peak sediments.

The vegetation boundary between ultramafic and other substrates is perhaps least sharp in the North Cape area of Northland, where the original coastal forest has in the main disappeared and the adjacent gabbros and ultramafites are covered with a low shrub grassland distinct in species but not in physiognomy.

W. Lee (1980) has discussed differences between serpentine and non-serpentine vegetation in South Island and has shown that below the normal tree line (1000 m), the tall podocarp and beech trees so typical of the mountainous regions of the island are absent on ultramafites, or at least play only a minor role. The forest gives way to shrubland communities of microphyllous species such as *Leptospermum scoparium*.

Above the tree line, the subalpine shrublands and snow tussock communities are replaced by a discontinuous dwarf grassland with intervening scree almost completely devoid of vegetation.

A summary of the serpentine plant communities of New Zealand is given in Table 21.6. The percentage of bare ground increases markedly with altitude over ultramafites and reaches about 55% in the alpine zone.

Gymnosperms, particularly small podocarps, are more abundant on serpentine soils than in the surrounding non-ultramafic soils. Although many New Zealand gymnosperms can tolerate serpentine to some extent, most broad-leaved plants cannot do so. This is probably because of the xeromorphic nature of serpentine communities where microphylls replace broad leaves.

Pteridophytes are also depleted over ultramafic soils in New Zealand. They are quite abundant in lowland and montane forests (5–10% of the cover), but decrease to about 1% in mixed forest over serpentine soils, and are virtually absent at higher elevations.

21.2.4 Anomalous Distributions in Serpentine Plants

Disjunctions and anomalous distributions are typical of serpentine floras in temperate climatic zones (e.g. Japan—see Chapter 16). Anomalous distributions are both latitudinal and altitudinal. In New Zealand there are relatively few latitudinal disjunctions, but a notable example is the occurrence of the grass *Chionochloa acicularis* on the Cascade Plateau in South Westland some 140 km from its nearest non-ultramafic population to the south. The more northerly serpentine location is probably a relic population surviving on ultramafites after climatic changes had altered the pattern of competition from other species. The two populations are not morphologically different.

There are several New Zealand species which have an anomalous altitudinal distribution. For example in the Southern Ultramafites, species typical of subalpine areas, such as

TABLE 21.6 Summary of Plant Communities over Ultramafic Rocks in New Zealand

Location	Communities
#1 D'Urville Island	1. Tall and dwarf *Leptospermum* shrubland with *Kunzea ericoides* and *L. scoparium*.
#3 Dun Mountain	1. Open *Leptospermum scoparium* shrubland. 2. Tall tussock (*Chionochloa rubra*) grassland.
#4 Red Hill	1. Open *Leptospermum scoparium* shrubland. 2. Tall tussock (*Chionochloa rubra*) grassland. 3. Fellfield.
#5 Martyr Hill	1. Low mixed forest on moraine including *Nothofagus solandri* var. *cliffortioides*, *Weinmannia racemosa*, *Dacrydium cupressinum*, and *Metrosideros umbellata*. 2. Low mixed forest on alluvium and ultramafic rocks including *N. solandri* var. *cliffortioides*, *D. intermedium* and *M. umbellata*. 3. Dwarf mixed open forest including *N. solandri* var. *cliffortioides*, *D. biforme*, *M. umbellata* and *Chionochloa rigida*.
#6 Red Mountain	1. Lowland-montane dwarf mixed forest with *N. solandri* var. *cliffortioides*, *D. intermedium*, *M. umbellata*, *L. scoparium*, *Phyllocladus alpinus*, *W. racemosa*. 2. Montane-subalpine open shrubland with *N. solandri* var. *cliffortioides*, *D. biforme*, *Dracophyllum uniflorum*, and *L. scoparium*. 3. Alpine tall tussock grassland with *C. rigida*.
#9 Mossburn	1. Open *L. scoparium* grassy shrubland.
#12 North Cape	1. Low tightly-closed *L. scoparium* scrub.

After: W. Lee (1980)

Chionochloa cf. *rigida*, *Dracophyllum uniflorum*, *D. longifolium* and *Coprosma pseudocuneata* descend to much lower altitudes on serpentine because of reduced competition. For similar reasons the lowland tree *Dacrydium colensoi* is found at 800 m on the upper slopes of Martyr Hill.

Another form of anomalous distribution in the serpentine flora of New Zealand is the colonisation of ultramafic sites by species requiring a moderate light requirement for seedling growth. For example *Nothofagus solandri* var. *cliffortioides* is the only southern beech species able to exploit ultramafic rocks. It is unable to compete in normal montane forest because the canopy is too closed to allow the seedlings to develop.

Leptospermum scoparium is a very successful coloniser of ultramafic habitats in New Zealand, and again is a species whose seedlings will not develop under a closed canopy. The same is true of southern rata (*Metrosideros umbellata*). The only tall-tussock grasses capable of colonising serpentine in New Zealand are *Chionochloa* cf. *rigida* and *C*. cf. *rubra*.

21.3 A DESCRIPTION OF THE VEGETATION OF SELECTED SERPENTINE SITES

The serpentine vegetation of New Zealand is found in 3 distinct regions. The most northerly of these is North Cape (site #12 in Fig. 21.1) in North Island, the second region is in the north of South Island in the Dun Mountain Belt which includes D'Urville Island, Dun Mountain and Red Hill. The third area is in the Southern Ultramafites and extends from Martyr Hill in southern Westland to Mossburn in Otago. Each of these 3 regions will now be described.

21.3.1 North Cape

Geology and Soils

The North Cape headland is a 6 km x 3 km raised formation consisting mainly of igneous rocks. Its geology has been described by Bennett (1967) and is illustrated in Fig. 21.2. On the northern edge of the headland the Surville Cliffs rise 200 m to a plateau covered by indurated lateritic soil. This plateau then falls away to the south over dissected hills down to the Waikuku flats which are only a few metres above sea level. The headland is divided into 2 roughly equal geological structures. The northern structure is an ultramafic complex known as the Kerr Pluton which is faulted against the southern half, the mainly Cretaceous basalts of the Whangakea volcanics.

The Kerr Pluton occupies about 8 km² and consists of 3 structures of roughly equal size. The first of these is serpentine which occupies the northern third of the pluton. These ultramafites occur mainly in the form of serpentinized harzburgite and lherzolite with subordinate wehrlite. The second structure consists of gabbro while the third most southerly section of the pluton is a sheet complex composed of gabbro and quartz diorite.

The soils of the Kerr Pluton are largely lateritic and this is the only ultramafic formation in New Zealand sufficiently far north to provide the climatic requirements for laterisation to occur, though it is thought that this laterisation took place during the Tertiary when the climate was more tropical than at present. The laterisation is not as advanced as in New Caledonia further north and the result is a soil intermediate in character between soils of that territory and of the serpentine soils of South Island. The laterisation process and its effect on the ultramafic soils of North Cape have been described by Thompson and Rodgers (1977).

Vegetation Communities

A number of different vegetation communities growing over North Cape have been identified by Thompson et al. (1974). They are shown in Fig. 21.3. A distinct serpentine flora is found on the northern part of the headland (Plate 21.1b). The serpentine flora of North Cape has been described by a number of workers including Jaffré and Verlière (1973), Druce et al. (1979) and Shepherd (1983).

The cliff communities merge quickly into a low scrub community (Plate 21.2a) composed of *Lepidosperma laterale, Schoenus brevifolius, Morelotia affinis, Carex* sp., *Phormium* sp., *Dianella intermedia, Astelia nervosa, Pteridium aquilinum* and *Gleichenia circinata.* There is an almost complete absence of grasses, a situation very similar to that of the New Caledonian serpentines (see Chapter 19).

The shrub layer does not exceed 120 cm and includes *Cyathodes juniperina, C. fasciculata, Hebe adamsii, Hebe speciosa, Corokia cotoneaster, Arthropodium sarmentosum, Coprosma parviflora, Geniostoma* sp., *Pseudopanax lessonii, Phyllocladus trichomanoides, Cassinia amoena* and *Leptospermum scoparium.*

In a few sheltered ravines there are tall shrubs of up to 4 m in height including *Knightia excelsa* and *Metrosideros excelsa*, which possibly represent a climax vegetation.

The serpentine scrub merges fairly abruptly into a cyperaceous formation on gabbro (Plate 21.2b) dominated by *Juncus gregiflorus, Schoenus brevifolius, Lepidosperma laterale, L. filiforme* and *Leptospermum scoparium* which is locally very abundant. The transition

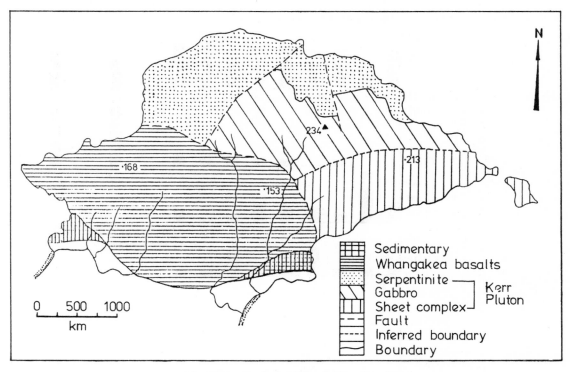

Fig. 21.2 Geology of North Cape Headland.
Source: Bennett (1967).

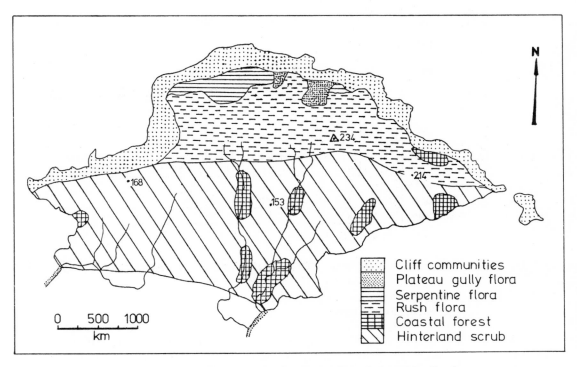

Fig. 21.3 Vegetation communities of North Cape Headland.
Source: Thompson et al. (1974).

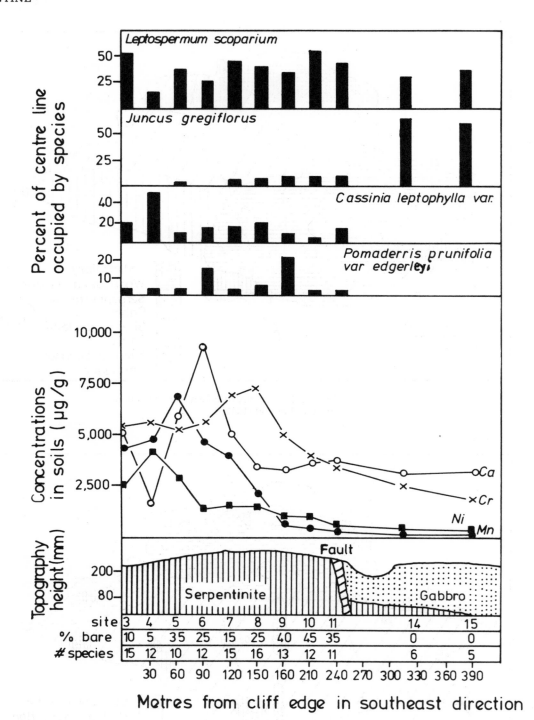

Fig. 21.4 Transect across serpentine and gabbro at North Cape.
Source: Shepherd (1980).

from serpentine to gabbro is represented in Fig. 21.4 which represents data from a botanical transect across the boundary area (Shepherd, 1983).

Fig. 21.4 shows the effect of soil composition upon the vegetation communities. The abundance of *Juncus gregiflorus* increases sharply in the transition from serpentine to gabbro whereas at the same time that of *Cassinia leptophylla* var. and *Pomaderris prunifolia* var. *edgerleyi* decreases to zero since both these taxa are restricted to ultramafites.

Endemic Plants and Disjunctions

A total of 11 serpentine-endemic plants has been listed in Table 21.5. None of these is distinct at specific rank, one is a subspecies and the others are distinct only at the varietal level, and only one of these has been properly described so far, due to a general lack of interest in this area by botanists. Most of the serpentine varieties are distinguished by a semi-lianoid habit with long flexible stems trailing down the cliffs among other species.

21.3.2 The Dun Mountain Belt

The Dun Mountain Belt is the most northerly section in South Island of the Dun Mountain Ophiolitic Belt. It extends southwards from D'Urville Island (site #1 in Fig. 21.1) through Saddle Hill (site #2), Dun Mountain (site #3), to Red Hill (site #4). The latter site must not be confused with Red Mountain in the Southern Ultramafites. Because of the 450 km displacement along the Great Alpine Fault, the next serpentine outcrop to the south is Martyr Hill. A map of the Dun Mountain Belt is given in Fig. 21.5.

D'Urville Island

D'Urville Island contains two bands of ultramafic rocks stretching almost continuously from Coppermine Bay in the south to Black Beach in the north where they are truncated by a fault (Coleman, 1966). The serpentinite is highly sheared and contains in many places inclusions of country rock or melange.

The serpentine vegetation of D'Urville Island has been described by Oliver (1944) and W. Lee (1980). A wide variety of vegetation types is found on serpentines throughout the island and depends largely on geological factors. For example, at Wells Peak, colluvial material derived from greywacke, overlies the serpentinite contact and broadens the ecotone to a distance of 50 m. On the greywacke, a tall (25 m) mixed podocarp forest with *Nothofagus menziesii*, *N. truncata*, and *Dacrydium cupressinum* gives way to a woodland in which *Metrosideros umbellata*, *N. truncata* and *Weinmannia racemosa* are codominant. Some 30 m from the geological boundary and into the ultramafites, the tree height is reduced to 8–10 m with dominance of *M. umbellata* and with a dense understorey of *Weinmannia racemosa* and sclerophyllous shrubs such as *Leptospermum scoparium*, *Dracophyllum filifolium* and *Cyathodes fasciculata*.

Over uncontaminated serpentinite, the typical *L. scoparium* scrub is evident. The herbaceous layer is poorly developed and open areas cover some 40% of the terrain.

Dun Mountain

The Dun Mountain Massif is situated some 13 km east of Nelson (site #3 in Fig. 21.5) and rises to an altitude of 1200 m. The ultramafites intrude the older surrounding sediments and volcanic rocks. The main rock types are dunite and harzburgite with a little pyroxenite. The ultramafic rocks have a concentric form with serpentinization at the contacts. Chrome and copper (mined at the turn of the century) are associated with a prominent fault near Wooded Peak. The surrounding rocks are predominantly spilites interspersed in a Permian sedimentary sequence composed of greywackes, argillites and calcareous rocks. The geology of the region has been described by Lauder (1965).

As described by W. Lee (1980), and Jaffré and Verlière (1973) the serpentine vegetation of the Dun Mountain area is perhaps the richest and best known in the whole of South

Island. The sedimentary rocks of Wooded Peak support a tall (23 m) mixed beech forest dominated by *Nothofagus fusca* (Plate 21.3a) with shrubs such as *Pseudowintera colorata* and *Coprosma* spp. in the understorey.

The southern beech forest of the sediments gives way to a transition forest (Plate 21.4), particularly where (as at Wooded Peak), the downslope movement of sediments has covered the ultramafic rocks and reduced the unfavourable edaphic factors of the bedrock. Here the major tree species is the mountain beech *Nothofagus solandri* var. *cliffortioides* with dwarf (2 m) forms of *Weinmannia racemosa*, *Metrosideros umbellata*, *Podocarpus hallii*, *Griselinia littoralis* and *Libocedrus bidwillii*. J. Lee (1974) has mapped plant distributions over this transitional zone and his data are shown in Fig. 21.6. There is a very sharp cutoff at the 24 m interval consistent with the first appearance of the serpentinicolous *Leptospermum scoparium* and the disappearance of *Nothofagus solandri* var. *cliffortioides*.

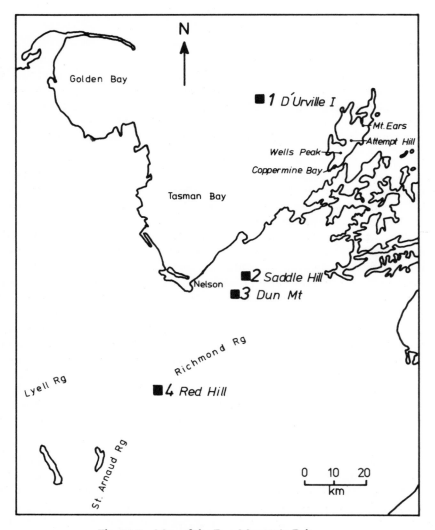

Fig. 21.5   Map of the Dun Mountain Belt.

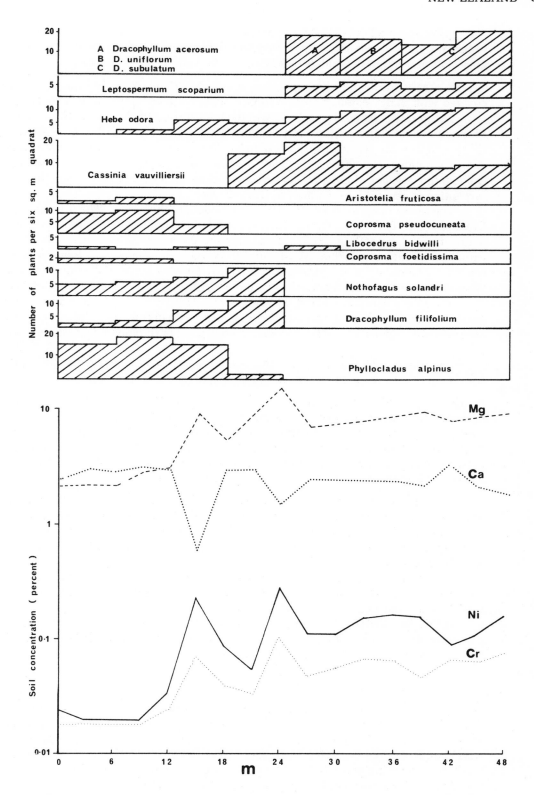

Fig. 21.6 Plant mapping across the sediment-serpentine boundary at Wooded Peak, Dun Mt

Source: J. Lee (1974).

Jaffré and Verlière (1973) have recognised 3 main vegetation communities in the Dun Mountain area. These are; 1—a grassy shrubland on serpentine, 2—a *Chionochloa rubra* grassland on serpentine, and 3—a scrub tussock community on dunite.

1—*The grassy shrubland community on serpentine* (Plate 21.5a) is found on steep slopes covered with shallow stony brown eutrophic soils. It includes 3 separate layers as follows:

The grassy layer covers up to 25% of the total surface of the terrain and is dominated by *Phormium cookianum*. Other components of this layer are (Jaffré and Verlière, 1974): *Chionochloa rubra, C. macra, Poa colensoi, Notodanthonia* sp., *Carex devia, Luzula* sp., *Astelia graminea, Helichrysum bellidioides, Notothlaspi australe* var. *stellatum* (Plate 21.6b), *Colobanthus wallei, Gentiana corymbifera, Senecio* sp., *Pteridium aquilinum* and the serpentine-endemic *Myosotis monroi* (Plate 21.6c).

The lower shrub layer (< 50 cm) covers 35–50% of the terrain. The principal species are *Dracophyllum filifolium, Cyathodes fasciculata. C. juniperina, Coprosma colensoi, C. microcarpa, C. parviflora, Hebe odora, Myrsine divaricata, Exocarpos bidwillii, Cassinia vauvilliersii* var. *serpentina, Aristotelia fruticosa, Pimelea suteri* (serpentine-endemic), *Corokia cotoneaster,* and *Hymenanthera alpina. Pimelea suteri* is illustrated in Plate 21.3b which clearly shows the macrorrhizous nature of this typical serpentine endemic plant.

The upper shrub layer (150–170 cm) covers 25–35% of the surface and its main components are: *Griselinia littoralis, Pseudopanax crassifolius, Leptospermum scoparium, Metrosideros umbellata, M. ericoides, Phyllocladus alpinus, Podocarpus hallii* and *Libocedrus* sp.

The grassy shrubland community bears some resemblance to the ligno-herbaceous community of New Caledonia on serpentinite and serpentinized peridotite.

2—*The Chionochloa rubra grassland* is found on gentle slopes where the soils are deeper and more argillaceous than under the shrubland community. The grasses frequently cover up to 90% of the terrain and are composed primarily of *Chionochloa rubra, Poa colensoi* and *Notodanthonia* sp. The shrub component does not exceed 8% of the total cover and is composed principally of *Dracophyllum filifolium, Cassinia vauvilliersii* var. *serpentina, Hebe odora, Leptospermum scoparium* and *Hymenanthera alpina.*

3—*The scrub tussock communities on dunites* are well represented on the summit of Dun Mountain (Plate 21.5b) and are found on steep slopes where rocky boulders cover about half the surface. The soil is ferrugineous with a fine texture. The grass layer which covers virtually all of the areas which have soil, is composed of *Chionochloa rubra, Poa* sp. and *Notodanthonia* sp.

The shrub layer (< 100 cm) covers 10–25% of the terrain and its principal components are: *Hebe odora, Myrsine divaricata, Leptospermum scoparium, Dracophyllum uniflorum, D. filifolium,* and *Cyathodes juniperina.*

Jaffré and Verlière (1973) have compared this formation with the New Caledonian grassy shrubland on reworked lateritic soils in New Caledonia. They noticed also the replacement of Cyperaceae by grasses in New Zealand.

Red Hill

Red Hill (site #4 in Fig. 21.5 is the most important isolated ultramafic massif in New Zealand. It has an area of 80 km^2 and an altitude of 2000 m, and forms a plateau cut off abruptly in the south by the Wairau Fault. The dominant rock is harzburgite interspersed with spilites. Unlike Dun Mountain, Red Hill is not in contact with calcareous rocks. The vegetation communities at Red Hill have been studied by Jaffré and Verlière (1973) and by W. Lee (1980). These workers have recognized three communities on ultramafic rocks: 1—an open grassy shrubland association which is not dominant on the massif; 2—a Chionochloa red tussock grassland; 3—fellfield vegetation on crests and ridges.

1—*The grassy shrubland community* is found at the base of Red Hill on steep slopes full of boulders. The scrub is found growing over poorly-developed soil between the boulders. It consists of an open formation with a maximum height of 2 m and a thin grassy layer occupying 10–15% of the surface. There is also a cover of the moss *Racomitrium lanuginosum*, a species well represented on serpentine throughout the world.

The grass layer is dominated by *Phormium cookianum* and several species of fern including *Pteridium aquilinum*.

The low shrub layer (<60 cm) is composed of a number of shrubs such as *Dracophyllum filifolium, Cyathodes juniperina, Coprosma parviflora, Aristotelia fruticosa, Myrsine divaricata, Hymenanthera alpina* and *Hebe* spp.

The tall shrub layer is very discontinuous and includes *Griselinia littoralis, Leptospermum scoparium, Kunzea ericoides, Phyllocladus alpinus, Podocarpus hallii,* and *Pseudopanax crassifolius.*

2—*The Chionochloa rubra grassland* occupies the major part of Red Hill, particularly on the plateau. This community is very homogeneous and comprises poaceous species such as *Chionochloa rubra, Notodanthonia setifolia, Agrostis tenuis,* and *Poa colensoi.* A light cover of Cyperaceae includes: *Carex* spp., *Carpha alpina, Schoenus pauciflorus,* and *Oreobolus strictus.* Cushion plants include *Pentachondra pumila, Cyathodes fraseri, Helichrysum filicaule* and *Racomitrium lanuginosum.* A number of rosette-type herbs include *Celmisia spectabilis* var. *angustifolia* and *Gentiana corymbifera.*

The shrub layer does not exceed 50 cm in height and includes principally *Hymenanthera alpina, Dracophyllum uniflorum, D. filifolium, Cassinia vauvilliersii* var. *serpentina, Coprosma cheesmanii* and *Hebe odora.*

Among the endemic species of Red Hill are *Myosotis monroi* and *M. laeta* which are found in both the scrub and grassland communities.

3—*The fellfield community* on ridges and on the crests of Red Hills Range includes bare areas amounting to 60% of the total, and which surround islets of *Chionochloa rubra* grassland. Weakly-weathered rocks usually support *Neopaxia australasica* and *Notothlaspi australe* var. *stellatum.*

21.3.3 The Southern Ultramafites

An extremely detailed description of the vegetation of the Southern Ultramafites has been given by W. Lee (1980). Space limitations preclude other than a brief description of Lee's work and discussion will be centred around only 3 of the localities covered by this author. These are: Martyr Hill and the Cascade Valley, Red Mountain, and Mossburn at the extreme southern limit of Great Alpine Fault. The Southern Ultramafites are illustrated in Fig. 21.7.

Martyr Hill and the Cascade Valley

Martyr Hill (site #5 in Fig. 21.7) is almost the most northerly of the Southern Ultramafites and unlike comparable areas further north in the Dun Mountain region, was heavily glaciated during the late Pleistocene. The Martyr Hill area is perhaps the most accessible of the outcrops of southern Westland. As described by W. Lee et al. (1983a), the area lies 19 km from the coast where the Cascade River flows northeast and occupies a narrow glaciated valley along the Alpine Fault. Geologically the area is diverse. Slopes west of the valley are formed of metagreywacke, and rocks of the extensive Haast schist predominate to the east on the Olivine Range. However a 3.5 km wide slice of ultramafites occurs between the two metamorphic rock groups and forms the eastern slopes of the valley, up to and including Martyr Hill. The ultramafic zone presents a conspicuous contrast to the other rock types, particularly the reddish rock, sparse stunted vegetation, large talus fans and rapidly eroding slopes. The valley floor is a complex of moraine talus, river terraces, and small flood plains. Moraines, perhaps laid down during the Otiran advance, and massive rock slide debris, form a mosaic of impoundments and gentle undulating hills in the northern part of the area.

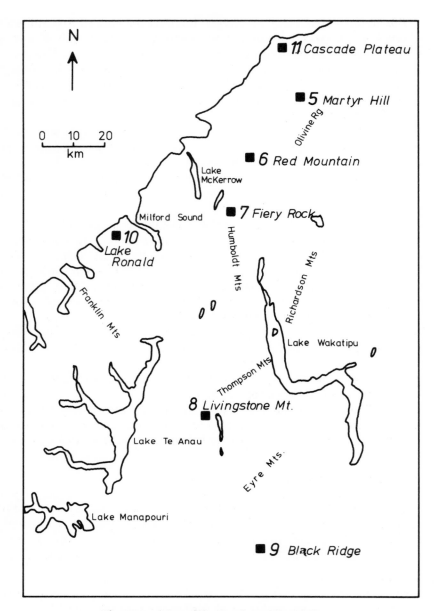

Fig. 21.7 Map of the Southern Ultramafites.

W. Lee et al. (1983a) have recorded a total of 82 vascular species on ultramafites compared with 404 on schists and greywackes. Their data (Table 21.7) clearly show the paucity of the ultramafic vegetation compared with the surrounding communities. In comparison with adjacent vegetation, the serpentine flora shows a pronounced over-representation of gymnosperms and deficiency of herbs. A representation of the different vegetation communities on and off serpentine in the area has been given by W. Lee et al. (1983a) and is shown in Fig. 21.8. Several of these communities will now be described.

The valley floor community consists of various vegetation types related to differences in soil type and composition. There are 4 terraces of which 3 are on non-ultramafic material. The fourth is of ultramafic origin and supports a low (< 8 m) heath forest of *Leptospermum scoparium. Dacrydium biforme, D. intermedium* and *Nothofagus solandri* var. *cliffortioides*

TABLE 21.7 Floristic Composition of Ultramafic Vegetation Compared with that of Schist and Greywacke in the Upper Cascade Valley, South Westland, New Zealand.

Vegetation	Number of species		% of total flora	
	Schist etc.	Ultramafites	Schist etc.	Ultramafites
Gymnosperms	8	11	2.0	13.4
Angiosperms				
Dicotyledons	228	37	56.4	45.1
Trees	18	6	4.5	7.3
Shrubs	70	21	17.3	25.6
Herbs	129	10	31.9	12.2
Lianes	11	0	2.7	0
Monocotyledons	109	19	27.0	23.2
Grasses	30	6	7.4	7.3
Sedges	38	3	9.4	3.7
Rushes	7	0	1.7	0
Orchids	13	5	3.2	6.1
Pteridophytes	59	15	14.6	18.3
Total vascular plants	404	82		

Source: W. Lee et al. (1983a)

over a shrub layer of *Phyllocladus* sp., *Coprosma parviflora*, and *Cyathodes juniperina*, and with the herbs *Libertia pulchella*, *Microlaena avenacea*, *Gleichenia circinata*, and *Gahnia procera*. Stones cover 40% of the surface. The non-ultramafic substrates on river terraces carry a community dominated by large *Nothofagus menziesii* with occasional *Weinmannia racemosa* and with the tree fern *Dicksonia squarrosa* in the understorey.

The vegetation of Mount Delta on the west of Cascade Creek is composed mainly of metagreywackes and supports a normal beech forest (mainly *Nothofagus fusca* and *N. menziesii*) with an understorey of the tree ferns *Cyathea smithii* and, *Dicksonia squarrosa*. Above 450 m the slopes are gentle and the tall southern beech forest gives way to a 2–4 m beech-podocarp-hardwood forest in which *Nothofagus solandri* var. *cliffortioides*, *Dacrydium intermedium*, *D. colensoi*, *D. biforme* and *Metrosideros umbellata* are dominant. The forest gradually decreases in height with altitude until at 750 m it merges into subalpine scrub which ceases at 1000 m, finally giving way to snow tussock grassland dominated by *Chionochloa rigida* and *C. crassiuscula*.

Martyr Hill on the eastern slopes of the Cascade Valley carries a talus debris on the lower slopes. The vegetation is mainly stunted *Dacrydium cupressinum* (rimu) with *Nothofagus solandri* var. *cliffortioides* (mountain beech), *D. biforme*, *D. intermedium*, *D. colensoi*, *Weinmannia racemosa* and a few specimens of *Metrosideros umbellata*. The forest gradually decreases in height with increasing altitude and at 600 m is less than 4 m tall. The top of Martyr Hill (600–1032 m) is a barren rock wasteland dotted with small stands of vegetation and scattered individual plants. The remnant forest patches are less than 2 ha and appear to owe their isolation to rapid degradation of the steep slopes. Mountain southern beech up to 6 m tall, grows along with *Cyathodes juniperina*, *Phormium cookianum* and subalpine species such as *Chionochloa rigida* and *Coprosma pseudocuneata*. It is interesting that there is a local sward of *Chionochloa rubra*, which does not otherwise occur in the region, and several bushes of *Dacrydium colensoi* at 760 m instead of in lowland swamps which are its normal habitat. Near the summit there are patches of the cushion plant *Donatia novae-zelandiae* and stunted specimens of *Dacrydium colensoi*.

The Olivine Range, despite its name, is composed mainly of schist near its contact with the Martyr Hill ultramafites. This contact occurs fortuitously nearly at the upper limit of the subalpine silver southern beech (Nothofagus menziesii) which is only 200 m wide, and at 1090 m gives way to a mixed tall tussock (Chionochloa rigida) scrub association, particularly on slopes. Two Dracophyllum species, D. uniflorum and D. menziesii, are the most abundant shrub species, with mountain flax (Phormium cookianum), Celmisia petriei and C. coriacea, the dominant large herbs. The summit area supports alpine fellfield. Chionochloa oreophila occupies sites of prolonged snow lie. Associated species include Poa colensoi, Celmisia sessiliflora, Drapetes lyallii, Phyllachne colensoi, and Raoulia subulata. Protected crevices support species such as Senecio scorzoneroides and Poa novae-zelandiae.

Red Mountain

Red Mountain (site #6 in Fig. 21.7 and Plate 1.1b) is the most impressive ultramafic massif in New Zealand. It is some 6 km across and with its rugged topography, barren surface, and reddish-coloured rocks amply justifies its name. It is not surprising that it drew the attention of Sir Joseph Banks over 200 years ago when he sailed past it in company with Captain James Cook.

W. Lee (1980) has recognised 3 vegetation communities on Red Mountain:

1—lowland—montane mountain beech—mixed pododarp forest;

2—montane mixed grassland; 3—subalpine tall tussock grassland—fellfield. The percentage cover of these 3 communities is given in Table 21.8.

There is a gradual change of species composition with increasing altitude and only 4 taxa (Schoenus pauciflorus, Poa colensoi, Phormium cookianum, and Helichrysum bellidioides) are common to all 3 communities.

1—The lowland—montaine mountain beech—mixed Podocarp forest is the tallest community on ultramafites (usually scree soils) and consists of numerous woody species such as Nothofagus solandri var. cliffortioides, Dacrydium intermedium, D. biforme, Metrosideros umbellata, Leptospermum scoparium, Phyllocladus alpinus and Weinmannia racemosa. The height of this forest is typically 3–8 m. A dense understorey is provided by Dracophyllum uniflorum, Cyathodes juniperina, Coprosma colensoi and C. foetidissima.

2—Montaine mixed grassy shrubland is found in the altitude range of 650–1000 m. Dacrydium biforme and the pygmy pine D. laxifolium increase in dominance with higher altitude, and together with Leptospermum scoparium form 24% of the vegetation cover. The trees are not much taller than the shrubs, of which Dracophyllum uniflorum is the most common. There is also a thin cover of alpine and subalpine grasses such a Chionochloa rigida, Poa colensoi and Rytidosperma setifolium. Dicotyledonous herbs are relatively rare and only Celmisia gracilenta, Wahlenbergia albomarginata and Senecio bidwilli represent this group of plants.

3—Subalpine-alpine tall tussock grassland—fellfield is found above 900 m. The vegetation cover is very sparse. The only woody species in the community are Dacrydium biforme, Phyllocladus alpinus (< 50 cm high) and Hymenanthera alpina, Myrsine nummularia, Muehlenbeckia axillaris, Dracophyllum uniflorum, Cyathodes juniperina and the ubiquitous serpentinicolous Hebe odora. Carpets of the moss Racomitrium lanuginosum occur in isolated pockets. The dominant grass is Chionochloa cf. rigida. Plate 21.1c shows the barren aspect of the summit zone of Red Mountain where the scree slopes are almost entirely devoid of vegetation.

The Red Mountain area provides a spectacular example of a sharp vegetation discontinuity between ultramafic and other rock types. This occurs in the Simonin Pass at the southern base of the mountain along the Livingstone Fault (Plate 21.6a). The subalpine Nothofagus menziesii, N. solandri var. cliffortioides, Dacrydium biforme, Hebe odora and tall tussock, Chionochloa rigida community on schist gives way to an almost completely bare boulder scree on ultramafites.

Plate 21.5   (c) Above: Shrub grassland on serpentine at Mossburn, South Island.
(d) Below: Shrub grassland on acid rocks at Denniston, in the northwest of South Island. The vegetation
has a "serpentine" physiognomy caused by heavy leaching of nutrients.
Photos by T. Jaffré.

Plate 21.6   (a) Above: Simonin Pass along the Livingstone Fault at the base of Red Mountain, Westland. The steep serpentine scree on the right is almost completely devoid of vegetation and contrasts very sharply with the vegetation on schist at the left. The schist community comprises subalpine *Nothofagus menziesii* and *N. solandri* var. *cliffortioides* with an understorey of the tall tussock grass *Chionochloa* cf. *rigida*.
Photo by L. F. Molloy.
(b) Below left: *Notothlaspi australe* var *stellatum* growing over serpentine at Dun Mountain. Though not strictly endemic to this rock type, this plant is widespread over ultramafites in the area.
Photo by R. D. Reeves.
(c) Below right: *Myosotis monroi,* a serpentine-endemic plant from the Dun Mountain area.
Photo by R. D. Reeves.

TABLE 21.8 Percentage Cover of Plants of Serpentine Communities on Red Mountain, New Zealand

Species	Percentage cover		
	A	B	C
Gymnosperms			
Podocarpus hallii	1.83		
Phyllocladus alpinus	3.96	0.47	0.25
Dacrydium laxifolium		6.00	3.44
D. intermedium	11.98	1.47	
D. biforme	5.08	7.54	0.38
Dicotyledonous trees			
Weinmannia racemosa	3.17		
Elaeocarpus hookerianus	0.42		
Nothofagus solandri var *cliffortioides*	13.62	0.71	
Metrosideros umbellata	5.63	0.41	
Pseudopanax linearis	0.42		
Dicotyledonous shrubs			
Myrsine divaricata	0.75		
Coprosma foetidissima	0.33		
C. colensoi	0.38		
Dracophyllum uniflorum	0.29	4.18	2.31
D. longifolium	1.04		
Myrsine nummularia		0.59	0.94
Leptospermum scoparium	4.38	11.18	
Cyathodes juniperina	1.92	0.71	
Pimelea oreophila		0.24	
Hymenanthera alpina		0.29	0.30
Muehlenbeckia axillaris			0.63
Hebe odora			0.33
Cyathodes fraseri			0.27
Dicotyledonous herbs			
Senecio bellidioides			0.29
Helichrysum bellidioides			0.31
Wahlenbergia albomarginata			0.28
Monocotyledonous grasses			
Chionochloa cf. rigida		3.18	6.10
Poa colensoi		0.53	3.95
Rytidosperma setifolium		1.47	3.06
Monocotyledonous herbs			
Phormium cookianum			0.44
Schoenus pauciflorus		4.12	3.20
Gahnia procera	3.29	3.06	
Pteridophyte			
Blechnum minus	0.88		

A = Lowland—montane *Nothofagus solandri* var. *cliffortioides*—mixed podocarp forest. B = Montane mixed grassy shrubland. C = subalpine tall tussock grassland—fellfield

Source: W. Lee (1980)

Another spectacular boundary can be seen along the same Livingston Fault near Stag Pass at the base of Little Red Hill. Here a grassy alpine fellfield on schist, gives way to a red harzburgite completely devoid of vegetation (Plate 21.1d).

Mossburn

The Mossburn region of Otago Province is the southern limit of the Dun Mountain Ophiolitic Belt along the Great Alpine Fault. Unlike the ultramafites of the Dun Mountain area, most of those at Mossburn are of shallow thickness and are heavily serpentinized.

The main ultramafic rock is harzburgite. The smaller ultramafic lenses in the extreme south of the area merge into bigger outcrops at West Dome (1400 m). Near Mossburn the ultramafites occupy a series of small plateaux inclined towards the south and are part of the so-called Livingstone Volcanics, a geosyncline of basalts, spilites, dolerites, andesites, tuff and agglomerate covered with Pleistocene moraine material.

The serpentine vegetation of the Mossburn area has been described by W. Lee (1980) and Jaffré and Verlière (1973). The latter observed that the ultramafites are covered with a mosaic of communities including a *Leptospermum scoparium* scrub, stands of *Nothofagus solandri* var. *cliffortioides*, a moss layer of *Racomitrium lanuginosum*, and a grassy shrubland. These communities are as much a result of anthropogenic disturbance as of edaphic factors. Where the serpentine has had the least disturbance, the natural vegetation appears to be an open grassy shrubland (Plate 21.5c) with *L. scoparium, Cassinia vauvilliersii* var. *serpentina, Cyathodes juniperina* and *Gaultheria antipoda* in the shrub layer. The grasses include *Chionochloa rubra* and *Notodanthonia setifolia*, and there are also a few Cyperaceae such as *Carex coriacea* and *Schoenus pauciflorus*. Other species are *Raoulia glabra, R. subsericea*, and the serpentine endemic *Celmisia spedenii* (W. Lee and Given, 1984).

Although the shrub-grassland community is usually associated with ultramafic substrates, vegetation of very similar physiognomy can sometimes develop over other types of rocks. This is illustrated in Plate 21.5d which shows a shrub grassland community developed over highly leached acid rocks in the Denniston area of Westland (northwest coast of South Island). The high rainfall together with the well-drained nature of the soil, has produced a deficiency of nutrients approaching that of serpentine soils.

21.4 BIOGEOCHEMICAL STUDIES ON THE SERPENTINE FLORA

The first biogeochemical investigations on the serpentine flora of New Zealand were carried out by Lyon (1969) and Lyon et al. (1968). They determined calcium, magnesium, cobalt, chromium, copper and nickel in 6 serpentinicolous taxa from the Dun Mountain area (*Myosotis monroi, Notothaspi australe* var. *stellatum, Pimelea suteri, Cassinia vauvilliersii* var. *serpentina, Hebe odora* and *Leptospermum scoparium*). Correlation analysis of the data showed highly significant (P < 0.01) plant-soil correlations for nickel, chromium and cobalt in *C. vauvilliersii* var. *serpentina, H. odora. P. suteri* and *L. scoparium*. It was concluded that all of these species could be used successfully for biogeochemical prospecting. The same workers noted the relatively high nickel content of *P. suteri*, an accumulation later confirmed by Lyon et al. (1971), and by J. Lee (1974) who found up to 450 μg/g nickel in dried leaves of this taxon. The data are shown in Fig. 21.8 and show that the other serpentine endemic, *Myosotis monroi*, contained up to 180 μg/g nickel. Neither species qualified for hyperaccumulator status (see Chapter 8) but the nickel levels were at least 3 times those normally encountered in non-endemic serpentine plants. It is also noteworthy (J. Lee et al. 1975—see also Chapter 4, Fig. 4.5) that both taxa colonised sites with the highest magnesium levels in the soils. A similar behaviour has been observed with *Xanthorrhoea australis* in Australia (see Chapter 20).

A detailed biogeochemical survey has also been carried out by W. Lee (1980) on a number of serpentinicolous plants from Red Mountain. The work was performed on vegeta-

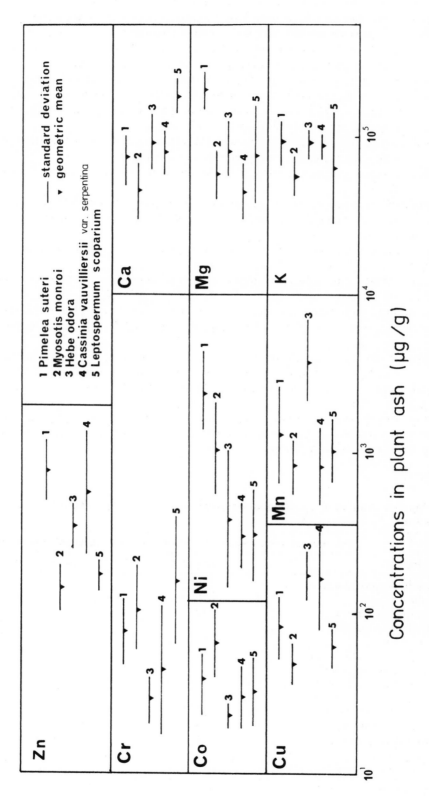

Concentrations in plant ash (μg /g)

Fig. 21.8 Range of elemental concentrations in serpentine plants from the Dun Mountain area.
Source: J. Lee (1974).

tion collected in the 880–1000 m altitude interval on the eastern slope of the mountain just below Simonin Pass (see above) on grey quartzofeldspathic schists as well as on talc-brucite serpentinite. The species analysed, and their relative abundance on ultramafites and schists are shown in Table 21.9. Leaves and terminal shoots were analysed for nitrogen, phosphorus, potassium, calcium, magnesium, nickel, copper, cobalt and chromium.

Several dominant patterns in the elemental data were observed as follows:

1—Species with high shoot levels of nickel, magnesium, nitrogen and phosphorus were *Hymenanthera alpina* and *Hebe odora*. It was proposed that nitrogen and magnesium were selectively absorbed to ameliorate damage from nickel.

2—The Ca/Mg mole quotient in plants (1.11) was more favourable than that of the soil (0.10) and 8 species, mainly trees, had quotients s exceeding 0.6.

3—The between-species variation ($\times 14$) for calcium was much higher than for other elements ($\times 2$–4).

4—Magnesium levels in shoots (ash weight basis) approximated to those of the soil but *Phormium cookianum*, *Poa colensoi*, and *Chionochloa* cf. *rigida* maintained the lowest shoot levels of magnesium.

5—Chromium levels were consistently low in plants. The highest value was about 15 μg/g in dried material from *Dacrydium biforme*.

6—The highest nickel value was found in *Hymenanthera alpina* which contained up to 110 μg/g in dried tissue.

7—Compared with plants growing over non-ultramafic soils, plants with the highest nickel levels over serpentine also had the highest chromium levels: e.g., *Hymenanthera alpina*.

8—None of the plants on ultramafites had a Ca/Mg quotient reaching even half of that found in conspecifics growing on schists. The biggest differences were for *Dacrydium biforme* and *Hymenanthera alpina*, where the Ca/Mg quotients were only 15% of those for the same taxa on schist.

In biogeochemical work at North Cape, Shepherd (1983) found highly significant (P < 0.01) plant-soil relationships involving nickel in *Juncus gregiflorus*, *Cyathodes parviflora*, *Phormium tenax* and *Baumea juncea*.

TABLE 21.9 Species Analysed in Biogeochemical Survey of Red Mountain, South Westland

Species	Number of sampling sites (out of 28) at which species occurred	
	Ultramafic	Schist
Dacrydium laxifolium	8	5
D. biforme	12	2
Phyllocladus alpinus	12	0
Hymenanthera alpina	8	1
Hebe odora	14	5
Dracophyllum uniflorum	11	5
Metrosideros umbellata	4	0
Nothofagus menziesii	11	5
N. solandri var. *cliffortioides*	15	0
Chionochloa cf. *rigida*	21	7
Phormium cookianum	15	5
Schoenus pauciflorus	11	4
Total sites	21	7

Source: W. Lee (1980)

With the existence today of techniques such as plasma emission spectrometry (ICP) by means of which some 24 elements can be determined simultaneously and at high sample throughputs, with good precision and sensitivity, and with the concomitant development of high-speed computers, there is no reason why future progress in biogeochemistry should not greatly exceed all the progress in the past. Such studies may be of use in helping to shed further light on the elusive solution to the "serpentine problem" (see Chapter 4).

21.5 ECOTYPIC DIFFERENTIATION IN THE NEW ZEALAND SERPENTINE FLORA

The presence of species such as *Leptospermum scoparium* and *Hebe odora* at virtually all of the serpentine sites in New Zealand has led to debate whether the plants on ultramafites are serpentine-tolerant ecotypes. Some putative ecotypes such as *Cassinia vauvilliersii* var. *serpentina* and *Olearia virgata* var. *serpentina* have been found to be present on non-ultramafic soils.

The first in-depth studies of ecotypic differentiation in New Zealand serpentine plants were carried out by W. Lee et al. (1983b) who investigated 15 species collected over ultramafic and non-ultramafic sites in New Zealand. The plants included naturalised species to determine whether these had been able to develop tolerance to serpentine over a period of about 200 years. All plants were grown on ultramafic soil and also on John Innes compost as a control. Their growth behaviour was measured by total yield (dry weight), shoot/root ratios, and relative growth rates. Some of the species showed evidence of ecotypes. These included 4 New Zealand indigenous species (*Luzula crinita* var. *petriana*, *Poa colensoi*, *Neopaxia australasica* and *Cotula pyrethrifolia*) and 3 naturalised grasses (*Agrostis tenuis*, *Anthoxanthemum odoratum* and *Lolium perenne*). No evidence of ecotypic differentiation was found in *Nothofagus solandri* var. *cliffortioides*, *Griselinia littoralis*, or *Leptospermum scoparium*.

The 2 varieties which were most clearly differentiated in their ability to grow on ultramafic soils were: *Cotula pyrethrifolia* var. *pyrethrifolia* (non-ultramafic) and var. *linearifolia* from Red Hill ultramafites.

The development of ecotypes of *Agrostis tenuis* shows that ultramafic tolerance can be developed in this plastic taxon in only 200 years or less, as has been shown for the same species producing "mine ecotypes" in Europe in an even shorter period of time (Antonovics et al. 1971). Since the highly successful serpentine coloniser *Leptospermum scoparium* has not produced a serpentine ecotype, it is probable that its success results from greater genetic plasticity (W. Lee et al. 1983b).

It is clear that a great deal of work remains to be done on the serpentine flora of New Zealand to determine the true status of serpentine-tolerant populations of certain species such as *Leptospermum scoparium*, *Hebe odora*, or *Cassinia vauvilliersii* which are so common on most ultramafic outcrops. At the same time there is a need for further studies on the taxonomy of a number of serpentinicolous plants which so far have not been properly described. Most of these are at North Cape where there are at least a dozen taxa of doubtful status, and it seems that studies similar to those carried out by W. Lee et al. (1983b) would greatly assist a proper evaluation of the serpentine vegetation of the North Cape area.

REFERENCES

Antonovics, J., Bradshaw, A. D. and Turner, R. G., 1971. Heavy metal tolerance in plants. *Adv. Ecol. Res.*, 7: 1–85.

Banks, J., 1770. *Endeavour Journal of Joseph Banks* V.1 (ed. J. C. Beaglehole). Angus Robertson, Sydney.

Beever, R. E. and Jane, G. T., 1967. Additional plant records from North Cape. *Tane*, 13: 147–148.

Bell, J. M., Clarke, E. de C. and Marshall, P., 1911. The geology of the Dun Mountain subdivision, Nelson. *N.Z. Geol. Surv. Bull.*, 12: 1–71.

Bennett, M. C., 1967. The ultramafic complex at North Cape, northernmost New Zealand. *Geol. Mag.*, 113: 61–76.

Betts, M. W., 1918. Notes on the autecology of certain plants of the peridotite belt, Nelson, Part 1—structures of some of the plants. *Trans. N.Z. Inst.*, 50: 230–242.

Brooks, R. R. and McDonnell, M. J., 1983. Delineation of New Zealand ultramafic rocks by computer processing of digital data from satellite imagery. *N.Z. J. Sci.*, 26: 65–71.

Caesalpino, A., 1583. *De Plantis Libri*, v16. Florentiae, p. 369.

Cockayne, L., 1910. *New Zealand Plants and their Story*. Government Printer, Wellington.

Cockayne, L., 1922. *The vegetation of a portion of the "Mineral Belt."* N.Z. Nature Notes, #39.

Cockayne, L., 1928. *The Vegetation of New Zealand*. Engelmann, Leipzig.

Coleman, R. G., 1966. New Zealand serpentinites and associated metasomatic rocks. *N.Z. Geol. Surv. Bull.* 76: 1–102.

Coombs, D. S., Landis, C. A., Norris, R. J., Sinton, J. M., Borns, D. J. and Craw, D., 1976. The Dun Mountain Ophiolitic Belt, its tectonic setting, constitution, and origin, with special reference to the southern portion. *Am. J. Sci.*, 276: 561–603.

Derry, D. R., 1980. *A Concise Atlas of Geology and Mineral Deposits*. Mining Journal Books, London.

Druce, A. P., Bartlett, J. K., Gardner, R. O., 1979. Indigenous vascular plants of the serpentine areas of Surville Cliffs and adjacent cliff tops northwest of North Cape, New Zealand. *Tane*, 25: 187–206.

Good, R., 1974. *The Geography of the Flowering Plants*. 4th ed. Longman, London.

Gravatt, D. J., 1966. Establishment of permanent quadrats on plateau scrub at North Cape. *Tane*, 12: 87–91.

Jaffré, T. and Verlière, G., 1973. *Rapport de mission en Nouvelle Zélande*. ORSTOM Rep., Nouméa.

Johnstone, I. M., 1967. A report on the permanent quadrats at North Cape. *Tane*, 13: 143–146.

Johnstone, I. M. (compiler), 1969. North Cape. A scientific case for conservation. *Tane*, 15: 5–11.

Lauder, W. R., 1965. The geology of Dun Mountain, Nelson, New Zealand. *N.Z. J. Geol. Geophys.*, 8: 475–504.

Lee, J., 1974. *Biogeochemical Studies on some Nickel-accumulating Plants from New Zealand and New Caledonia*. MSc Thesis, Massey University, Palmerston North, New Zealand.

Lee, J., Brooks, R. R., Reeves, R. D. and Boswell,. C. R., 1975. Soil factors controlling a New Zealand serpentine flora. *Pl. Soil*, 42: 153–160.

Lee, W. G., 1980. *Ultramafic Plant Ecology of the South Island, New Zealand*. PhD Thesis, University of Otago, Dunedin, New Zealand.

Lee, W. G. and Given, D. R., 1984. *Celmisia spedenii* G. Simpson, an ultramafic endemic and *Celmisia markii*, sp. nov., from southern New Zealand. *N.Z. J. Bot.*, 22: 585–592.

Lee, W. G. and Hewitt, A. E., 1982. Soil changes associated with development of vegetation on an ultramafic scree, Northwest Otago, New Zealand. *J. Roy. Soc. N.Z.*, 12: 229–242.

Lee, W. G., Johnson, P. N. and Wardle, P., 1983a. *Botanical notes on the upper Cascade River Valley, South Westland*. Rep. Botany Division. DSIR. Dunedin. New Zealand. 12 p.

Lee, W. G., Mark, A. F. and Wilson, J. B., 1983b. Ecotypic differentiation in the ultramafic flora of the South Island, New Zealand. *N.Z. J. Bot.,* 21: 141–156.

Lyon, G. L., 1969. *Trace Elements in New Zealand Plants.* PhD Thesis, Massey University, Palmerston North, New Zealand.

Lyon, G. L., Brooks, R. R., Peterson, P. J. and Butler, G. W., 1968. Trace elements in a New Zealand serpentine flora. *Pl. Soil,* 29: 225–240.

Lyon, G. L., Brooks, R. R., Peterson, P. J. and Butler, G. W., 1970. Some trace elements in plants from serpentine soils. *N. Z. J. Sci.,* 13: 133–139.

Lyon, G. L., Peterson, P. J., Brooks, R. R. and Butler, G. W. 1971. Calcium, magnesium, and trace elements in a New Zealand serpentine flora. *J. Ecol.,* 59: 421–429.

Mark, A. F., 1977. *Vegetation of Mount Aspiring National Park, New Zealand.* Natl. Parks Sci. Ser., #2: 1–79.

Ogden, J., 1970. Botany and entomology of the Red Hills. *Massif,* 3: 43–44.

Oliver, W. R. B., 1944. The vegetation and flora of D'Urville and Stephens Islands. *Rec. Dom. Mus.,* 1: 193–227.

Park, J., 1887. On the district between the Dart and Big Bay. In, *Geological Explorations 1885–1886.* 121–137.

Scott Thomson, J., 1935. Some aspects of the vegetation and flora of the South Island. *J. N.Z. Inst. Hort.,* 4: 1–18.

Thompson, R. C. and Rodgers, K. A., 1977. Laterisation of the ultramafic-gabbro associations at North Cape, northernmost New Zealand, *J. Roy. Soc. N.Z.,* 7: 347–377.

Thompson, R. C., Rogers, K. A. and Braggins, J. E., 1974. The relationship of serpentine and related floras to laterite and bedrock type at North Cape, northernmost New Zealand. *N.Z. J. Bot.,* 12: 275–282.

Wardle, J., Hayward, J. and Herbert, J., 1971. Forests and shrublands of northern Fiordland. *N.Z. J. For. Sci.,* 1: 80–115.

Wheeler, J. M., 1963. The vegetation of the North Cape area. *Tane,* 9: 63–84.

EPILOGUE

The previous chapter brought to a close a long journey of botanical exploration that began on the west coast of North America and extended through all the continents to finish in a small country "down under", separated by some 20,000 km from the European centres where study of serpentine vegetation began as early as the 16th Century. This isolation does not, however, lend unfamiliarity to the scene. If Caesalpino could have left his native Tuscany in 1583 when his first paper on serpentine plants appeared (Caesalpino, 1583), and travelled half a world away to New Zealand, he would have recognised in the scrub associations of Dun Mountain, his own Italian "macchie", and in the gleaming ochre mass of Red Mountain would have seen a reflection of his own Monterosso del Mare.

"Plus ça change plus c'est la même chose" was an apt saying of Voltaire, and is very appropriate to a description of the serpentine flora of the world. These floras are as diversified as their environments, but for one set of conditions in one part of the world, the same conditions in another part will almost certainly produce a similar serpentine vegetation provided that major catastrophes such as glaciation or subduction have not occurred.

The complex mosaic of endemisms, disjunctions, ecotypic differentiation, xeromorphic adaptations, and morphological changes that characterise serpentine floras seems to deny a unity of purpose, and yet there is such a unity. It lies in the triumph of the plant world over the hostility of its environment.

GLOSSARY OF TERMS

acidicolous – restricted to acid soils

alnoite – a lamprophre consisting of augite, biotite, melilite and olivine

alpine deserts – sparse alpine vegetation

amphibolite – a basic rock composed of amphibole and plagioclase

anatase – octahedrite, a mineral rich in titanium

Angiosperms – a class of plants in which the ovules are completely enclosed in an ovary

anorthite – plagioclase mineral

antigorite – serpentine mineral

apatite – calcium phosphate mineral

asbestos – fibrous form of amphibole

augite – pyroxene

azonal soils – soils whose formation is not related to climatic factors

basiphilous – restricted to base-rich soils

batholith – stock-shaped mass of igneous rock

berget (Swed.) – mountain

biogeochemical prospecting – prospecting by chemical analysis of vegetation

biomass index – ratio of the MSS7 and MSS5 bands in LANDSAT imagery

biotite – micaceous mineral

biotype depletion – process whereby formerly widespread taxa become restricted to specific environments

bodenstets taxa – plants restricted to a specific type of substrate

bodenvag taxa – plants not restricted to a specific type of substrate

bryophyte – moss or liverwort

calamine – a zinc-rich mineral, mainly hemimorphite

calcicolous – favouring soils rich in lime

calciphilous – more or less restricted to limestone soils

carbonatite – intrusive carbonate rock associated with alkaline igneous activity and formed from basic magmas

chamaephyte – a perennial plant with buds less than 0.4 m above the soil

chaparral – scrubland of the western United States

character species – in plant sociology, plants which characterize a specific sociological division or grouping

charrascales – serpentine scrub in Cuba

chernozem – black soil rich in humus

chlorite – hydrous silicate of Al, Fe and Mg, related to mica

chlorosis – yellowing of plant leaves due to iron deficiency often caused by excess of other elements

chromite – a chromium-rich mineral of the spinel group

chrysotile – highly-fibrous variety of serpentine

citric acid – a tricarboxylic organic acid

climax vegetation – the stable vegetation of a particular area

clinopyroxene – aluminosilicate rich in Mg and Fe

companions – in plant sociology, plants which accompany the character species in a sociological grouping, though these are not necessarily characteristic of that group

crassulescent – with fleshy leaves

craton – large immobile part of the earth's crust

cuabales – Cuban community of shrubby evergreen vegetation

cytoplasm – protoplasm of cell excepting that of the nucleus

depleted taxa – plants having undergone biotype depletion and now restricted to a specific substrate (often serpentine)

diabase – basaltic rock

diatreme – a volcanic pipe often associated with diamonds

differentials – in plant sociology, plants accompanying character species which are also typical of a particular plant sociological grouping

diopside – pyroxene-type mineral

diorite – sodic plutonic rock

disjunction – anomalous plant distribution involving a large distance from the nearest other occurrence

dolomite – calcium/magnesium carbonate

dunite – an ultramafic rock composed almost entirely of olivine

ecotone – a boundary between two plant communities of major rank

ecotypic differentiation – process of evolution whereby distinct morphological forms of species develop on a specific substrate

edaphic – related to some property of the soil

Eo-Europa – geological division of Europe

epiphytes – plants which grow on others but do not derive nutrients from them

eucalypt zone of Western Australia – zone within the Eremean Province and south of Kalgoorlie

eutrophic – pertaining to a lake or stagnant environment

facultative – concerning plants which grow on a specific substrate without having a specific requirement for it

fjäll (Swed.) – high mountain (cf. Eng. "fell")

flysch – sandstone, marl or shale

footwall – mass of rock beneath a fault plane, vein or lode

frost heave – lifting of ground surface by frost action

gabbro – basic plutonic rock

garique – Corsican term for scrubland

garnierite – nickel ore composed of hydrated magnesium/nickel silicates

genotypic specialization – specialization determined by genera

geobotanical prospecting – prospecting by the study of plant distributions and morphology

geophyte – a plant with subterranean buds

gibbsite – aluminium hydroxide mineral

glabrous – covered with fine hairs

glaucescent – covered with a dull waxy bloom

gley soils – bluish-grey soils developed under moist conditions

gneiss – coarse-grained granitic rock

goethite – iron mineral [FeO(OH)]

gossan – ferruginous deposit on surface of pyrite

granite – plutonic rock composed mainly of quartz and biotite

granodiorite – plutonic rock composed mainly of quartz, calcic oligoclase, or andesine

greenstone – altered mafic or ultramafic igneous rock

greywacke – type of sandstone

gymnosperms – plants which produce ovules or seeds on surface of fertile leaf

harzburgite – a peridotite composed of olivine and subordinate orthopyroxene

heliophile – sun loving

hematite – principal ore of iron (Fe_2O_3)

hemicryptophyte – a plant with buds just above or just below the soil surface

herbarium – an institute where dried plants are stored for scientific study

heterotrophic – depending on live or dead organisms for nutrients

hornblende – form of amphibole

horst – raised mass of earth's crust limited by faults

hyperaccumulator – a plant containing inordinate concentrations of a particular element. In the case of nickel, >1000 μg/g (0.1%) in dried tissue

hypermanganésiphore – a plant containing >10,000 μg/g (1%) manganese in dried tissue

hypernickéliphore – a plant containing >10,000 μg/g (1%) nickel in dried tissue

hypersthenite – a magnesium-rich ultramafic rock

insular – see under palaeoendemic

jaure (Lapp.) – lake

kaolinite – common clay mineral

kimberlite – variety of micaceous peridotite

Krummholz growth habit – crooked habit typical of many trees on serpentine

LANDSAT imagery – the use of LANDSAT satellites for sensing the earth's surface

Laurasia – hypothetical part of the supercontinent Pangaea which broke up at the end of the Carboniferous

lherzolite – ultramafic rock with type

locality at Lac Lherz, Pyrenees

lichen – lower plant consisting of an alga and fungus in intimate association

life form spectrum – classification of plants in accordance with the position of resting buds in relation to the soil surface

limonite – brown hydrous iron oxide, mainly goethite

lithosol – azonal soil composed mainly of freshly-weathered fragments on steep hillsides

lizardite – ultramafic rock type

loessic soils – aeolian (wind blown) deposits

lopolith – large-floored intrusion centrally sunken in form of basin

lucency – transparency

macchie (Ital.) – scrubland

macrorrhizism – the property of having large root systems

magnesite – magnesium mineral composed mainly of magnesium carbonate

Mahalanobis D² statistic – a form of discriminant analysis in which the degree of discrimination is indicated by the magnitude of D^2

malic acid – a dicarboxylic acid

malonic acid – a dicarboxylic acid

maquis (Fr.) – scrubland

maquis arbustif (Fr.) – woody scrubland

maquis buissonant (Fr.) – shrubby scrubland

maquis ligno-herbacée (Fr.) – scrubland composed mainly of woody herbs

mesic – with adequate water supply

Meso-Europa – geological division of Europe

molasse – soft green sandstone

monotypic – a genus containing only one species

mulga zone of Western Australia – part of Eremean Province north of Kalgoorlie dominated by the mulga (*Acacia aneura*)

multiband scanner – scanner used on LANDSAT satellites to sense the earth's surface at four different wavelengths.

mycobiont – fungus supporting a plant

nanism – dwarfism

necrosis – death of live tissue

Neo-Europa – geological division of Europe

neoendemic – a plant evolved from surrounding taxa which will not grow on the substrate supporting the neoendemic

nepheline syenite – alkalic plutonic rock

nephelite – alkalic plutonic rock

nickel plant – see hyperaccumulator of nickel

norite – a form of gabbro in which orthopyroxene is dominant over clinopyroxene

obduction – the sliding of one tectonic plate under another

obligate – refers to plants which have a specific requirement for a given substrate

olivine – mineral composed mainly of ferrous magnesium silicate

ordination analysis – a form of statistical analysis in which components of a system are classified into groups of similar properties

orthopyroxene – ultramafic mineral found in most ultramafic rocks

oviposition – deposition of eggs (mainly by insects)

Palaeo-Europa – a geological division of Europe

palaeoendemic – a relic plant which has survived over substrates hostile to competitors and which is not surrounded by possible parent species

paludification – the forming of marshlands

Pangaea – theoretical great continent which fragmented to produce the present continents

pelitic –argillaceous

penecontemporaneous – applies to sediments formed at the same time as the material of their surrounding rocks

peneplanation – the subaerial degradation of a region to base level forming a peneplain

peridotite – general name for ultramafic rock

perovskite – mineral found in kimberlites and rich in niobium and titanium

phanerogam – flowering plant

phanerophyte – plants with resting buds carried over 0.4 m above the soil surface

phloem – the vascular tissue which carries nutrients in plants

phosphatase – an enzyme which hydrolyses orthophosphoric esters to phosphoric acid and alcohol

phyllite – argillaceous rock

phytosociological Alliance – third highest division of a plant sociological system comes below Class and Order.

phytosociological Association – fourth highest division of a plant sociological system. Comes below Alliance.

phytosociological Class – highest division of a plant sociological system

phytosociological Order – the second highest division of a plant sociological system. Comes after Class.

pinares – pine-savanna community in Cuba dominated by *Pinus caribaea*

pioneer species – species which are the first to colonize a newly-created environment

pixel – picture element (LANDSAT) representing approximately 0.6 ha on the ground

plagiotropic – orientated at a constant angle to light stimulation

plasma emission spectrometry (ICP) – a multielement form of analysis using a plasma source to excite emission spectra

plasmalemma – plasma membrane

plasmolytic resistance – degree of resistance to plasmolysis (shrinking of tissue)

pluviosilva de montana – Cuban rainforest

podzol – highly-bleached soil low in Fe and Ca and formed under cool moist conditions

principal components analysis – a statistical technique in which several variables are studied and their relative importance in controlling a given process is evaluated

pteridophyte – fern

pyrope – garnet

pyroxenite – a medium or coarse-grained rock consisting mainly of pyroxene

quadrat – a plot set out for measuring plant distributions

quartz – a mineral composed mainly of silica

residual biotypes – plants which survive on a given substrate having died out elsewhere

schist and micaschist – medium or coarse-grained metamorphic rocks

sclerenchyma – tissue composed of cells with thick lignified walls and little or no living contents

sclerophyllous – with hard stiff leaves

serpentine – mineral composed of antigorite and chrysotile

serpentine superphosphate – superphosphate fertilizer with added serpentine to provide magnesium

serpentinimorphosis – the formation of morphologically-different strains of a taxon under the edaphic stress of an ultramafic substrate

serpentinite – a rock formed principally from serpentine minerals

serpentinophyte – a plant which favours ultramafic substrates

siderophile elements – elements of the iron family (Fe, Co, Ni, Cr, V)

sjön (Swed.) – lake

smectite – green clay

sol férralitique – lateritic soil

spilite – basaltic rocks

steatitization – formation of talc-rich rocks

stenophyllous – having narrow leaves

talus – fully-disintegrated rocky material forming a slope at foot of steeper declivity

taxon – a living organism irrespective of taxonomic rank

tectonic suture – a line marking the fusion of two tectonic plates. E.g. Urals

thallus – plant body not differentiated into root and shoot

therophyte – ephemeral annual

tjärn (Swed.) – tarn

tonoplast – cytoplasmic membrane surrounding vacuole in protoplast

ultrabasic rock – igneous rock with <45% silica

ultrabasicosaxicolous taxa – term used by Japanese botanists to describe plants confined to ultramafic substrates

ultramafic rock – igneous rock with <45% silica and composed principally of ferromagnesian minerals

ultramafite – ultramafic rock

vacuole – a fluid-filled space within a cell

vare (Lapp.) – high mountain

vascular plants – plants which convey liquids within their systems

vermiculite – platy hydrous luminosilicate related to chlorite and montmorillonite

vicariousness – degree to which a given taxon is found in the same environment elsewhere

Wisconsin Glaciation – fourth Pleistocene glaciation in North America

xeric – dry

xeromorphic – concerning plants whose morphology has adapted to dry conditions

xerovuni – Greek scrubland

xylem – woody material suporting plants and through which liquids circulate

zonal soils – soils whose formation is due to climatic factors

BOTANICAL INDEX

GEOGRAPHICAL INDEX

SUBJECT INDEX